Index of Applications

(Continued on inside back cover)

SPECIAL EIGHTH EDITION

SELECTED MATERIAL

BASIC COLLEGE MATHEMATICS

AN APPLIED APPROACH

RICHARD N. AUFMANN
PALOMAR COLLEGE, CALIFORNIA

VERNON C. BARKER
PALOMAR COLLEGE, CALIFORNIA

JOANNE S. LOCKWOOD
PLYMOUTH STATE UNIVERSITY, NEW HAMPSHIRE

HOUGHTON MIFFLIN COMPANY   BOSTON   NEW YORK

Editor-in-Chief: Jack Shira
Senior Sponsoring Editor: Lynn Cox
Associate Editor: Melissa Parkin
Editorial Assistant: Noel Kamm
Senior Project Editor: Carol Merrigan
Editorial Assistant: Eric Moore
Manufacturing Manager: Karen Banks
Senior Marketing Manager: Ben Rivera
Marketing Assistant: Lisa Lawler

Cover Design: Althea Chen
Cover Image: PhotoDisc

Custom Publishing Editor: Todd Corbin
Custom Publishing Production Manager: Tina Kozik
Project Coordinator: Janell Sims

This book contains select works from existing Houghton Mifflin Company resources and was produced by Houghton Mifflin Custom Publishing for collegiate use. As such, those adopting and/or contributing to this work are responsible for editorial content, accuracy, continuity and completeness.

Printed in the United States of America.

ISBN-13: 978-0-618-78931-3
ISBN-10: 0-618-78931-6
N-06421

1 2 3 4 5 6 7 8 9 – CCI – 08 07 06

Houghton Mifflin
Custom Publishing

222 Berkeley Street • Boston, MA 02116

Address all correspondence and order information to the above address.

Contents

4   Ratio and Proportion   173

5   Percents   201

12   Geometry   513

Eduspace Student Registration and Enrollment Guide

Preface

The eighth edition of *Basic College Mathematics: An Applied Approach* provides mathematically sound and comprehensive coverage of the topics considered essential in a basic college mathematics course. The text has been designed not only to meet the needs of the traditional college student but also to serve the needs of returning students whose mathematical proficiency may have declined during years away from formal education.

In this new edition of *Basic College Mathematics: An Applied Approach*, we have continued to integrate approaches suggested by AMATYC. Each chapter opens by illustrating and referencing a mathematical application within the chapter. At the end of each section there are Applying the Concepts exercises, that include writing, synthesis, critical thinking, and challenge problems. At the end of each chapter there is a "Focus on Problem Solving" that introduces students to various problem-solving strategies. This is followed by "Projects and Group Activities" that can be used for cooperative learning activities.

One of the main challenges for students is the ability to translate verbal phrases into mathematical expressions. One reason for this difficulty is that students are not exposed to verbal phrases until later in most texts. In *Basic College Mathematics: An Applied Approach*, we introduce verbal phrases for operations as we introduce the operation. For instance, after addition concepts have been presented, we provide exercises which say "Find the sum of . . ." or "What is 6 more than 7?" In this way, students are constantly confronted with verbal phrases and must make a mathematical connection between the phrase and a mathematical operation.

NEW! Changes to This Edition

In this textbook, as always, students are provided with ample practice in solving application problems requiring addition, subtraction, multiplication, or division. In this edition, however, we have increased the number of application problems that require a student first to determine which operation is required to solve the problem. See, for example, the Applying the Concept exercises on pages 44 and 45. Here is an opportunity for students to apply their understanding of the four basic operations and the words in an application problem that indicate each. This "mixed practice" will improve their ability to determine what operation to use to solve an application problem, a skill that is vital to their becoming good problem solvers. For further examples, see also the Applying the Concept exercises on pages 108 and 109 of Chapter 2 and pages 158 and 159 of Chapter 3.

We have updated the material in Chapter 1 on estimation. And to emphasize the importance of using estimation to check the result of a calculation performed on a calculator, exercises now ask students first to perform the operation on a calculator and then to use estimation to determine if that answer is reasonable. See, for example, the calculator exercises on pages 14, 23, 31, and 43. In this text, estimation is presented as a problem-solving tool; see, for example, the exercises on page 223 of Chapter 5.

In Chapter 2, we choose to present addition and subtraction of fractions prior to multiplication and division of fractions. For instructors who prefer to teach multiplication first, an alternative sequencing of the sections in the chapter is provided on page 77.

The exposition in Section 1 of Chapter 3 includes more instruction on the relationship between decimals and fractions, and the corresponding exercise set includes problems asking students to convert fractions to decimals and decimals to fractions.

Chapter 8 now has a section on converting units of time, and Chapter 11 now includes an objective in which students use a formula to convert degrees Fahrenheit to degrees Celsius.

The in-text examples are now highlighted by a prominent HOW TO bar. Students looking for a worked-out example can easily locate one of these problems.

Throughout the text, data problems have been updated to reflect current data and trends. Also, titles have been added to the application exercises in the exercise sets. These changes emphasize the relevance of mathematics and the variety of problems in real life that require mathematical analysis.

The Chapter Summaries have been remodeled and expanded. Students are provided with definitions, rules, and procedures, along with examples of each. An objective reference and a page reference accompany each entry. We are confident that these will be valuable aids as students review material and study for exams.

Margin notes entitled Integrating Technology provide suggestions for using a scientific calculator. An annotated illustration of a scientific calculator appears on the inside back cover of this text.

chapter

1 Whole Numbers

How much would it cost to take a vacation that looks as relaxing as this one? What would you have to pay for travel, accommodations, and food? Do you have enough money in the bank, or would you need to earn and save more money? If you are considering taking a vacation, you will need to know the answers to these and other questions. The **Focus on Problem Solving on page 54** illustrates how we use operations on whole numbers to determine costs associated with planning a vacation.

Need help? For online student resources, such as section quizzes, visit this textbook's website at **math.college.hmco.com/students**.

OBJECTIVES

Section 1.1
A To identify the order relation between two numbers
B To write whole numbers in words and in standard form
C To write whole numbers in expanded form
D To round a whole number to a given place value

Section 1.2
A To add whole numbers
B To solve application problems

Section 1.3
A To subtract whole numbers without borrowing
B To subtract whole numbers with borrowing
C To solve application problems

Section 1.4
A To multiply a number by a single digit
B To multiply larger whole numbers
C To solve application problems

Section 1.5
A To divide by a single digit with no remainder in the quotient
B To divide by a single digit with a remainder in the quotient
C To divide by larger whole numbers
D To solve application problems

Section 1.6
A To simplify expressions that contain exponents
B To use the Order of Operations Agreement to simplify expressions

Section 1.7
A To factor numbe[rs]
B To find the prime [factorization of] a number

Page 1

Chapter Opening Features

NEW! Chapter Opener
New, motivating chapter opener photos and captions have been added, illustrating and referencing a specific application from the chapter.

The 🌐 at the bottom of the page lets students know of additional online resources at math.college.hmco.com/students.

Objective-Specific Approach
Each chapter begins with a list of learning objectives that form the framework for a complete learning system. The objectives are woven throughout the text (i.e., Exercises, Prep Tests, Chapter Review Exercises, Chapter Tests, Cumulative Review Exercises) as well as through the print and multimedia ancillaries. This results in a seamless learning system delivered in one consistent voice.

Page 2

Prep Test and Go Figure

Prep Tests occur at the beginning of each chapter and test students on previously covered concepts that are required in the coming chapter. Answers are provided in the Answer Section. Objective references are also provided if a student needs to review specific concepts.

The **Go Figure** problem that follows the *Prep Test* is a playful puzzle problem designed to engage students in problem solving.

PREP TEST

Do these exercises to prepare for Chapter 1.

1. Name the number of ♦s shown below.

   ♦ ♦ ♦ ♦ ♦ ♦ ♦ ♦

2. Write the numbers from 1 to 10.

   1 __ __ __ __ __ __ __ __ 10

3. Match the number with its word form.
   a. 4   A. five
   b. 2   B. one
   c. 5   C. zero
   d. 1   D. four
   e. 3   E. two
   f. 0   F. three

GO FIGURE

Five adults and two children want to cross a river in a canoe. The canoe can hold one adult or two children or one child. Everyone is able to paddle the canoe. What is the minimum number of trips that will be necessary for everyone to get to the other side?

Aufmann Interactive Approach (AIM)

An Interactive Approach

Basic College Mathematics: An Applied Approach uses an interactive style that provides a student with an opportunity to try a skill as it is presented. Each section is divided into objectives, and every objective contains one or more sets of matched-pair examples. The first example in each set is worked out; the second example, called "You Try It," is for the student to work. By solving this problem, the student actively practices concepts as they are presented in the text.

There are complete worked-out solutions to these examples in an appendix. By comparing their solution to the solution in the appendix, students obtain immediate feedback on, and reinforcement of, the concept.

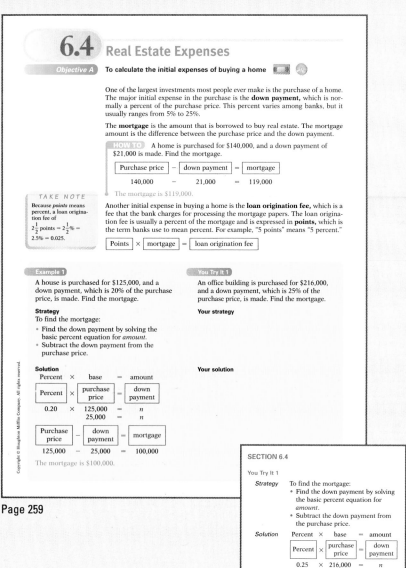

Page 259

Page S17

Page xxv

AIM for Success Student Preface

This student 'how to use this book' preface explains what is required of a student to be successful and how this text has been designed to foster student success, including the Aufmann Interactive Method (AIM). *AIM for Success* can be used as a lesson on the first day of class or as a project for students to complete to strengthen their study skills. There are suggestions for teaching this lesson in the *Instructor's Resource Manual*.

AIM for Success

Welcome to *Basic College Mathematics: An Applied Approach*. As you begin this course, we know two important facts: (1) We want you to succeed. (2) You want to succeed. To do that requires an effort from each of us. For the next few pages, we are going to show you what is required of you to achieve that success and how you can use the features of this text to be successful.

Motivation   One of the most important keys to success is motivation. We can try to motivate you by offering interesting or important ways mathematics can benefit you. But, in the end, the motivation must come from you. On the first day of class, it is easy

Problem Solving

Focus on Problem Solving

At the end of each chapter is a Focus on Problem Solving feature which introduces the student to various successful problem-solving strategies. Strategies such as drawing a diagram, applying solutions to other problems, working backwards, inductive reasoning, and trial and error are some of the techniques that are demonstrated.

Page 88

Focus on Problem Solving

Common Knowledge An application problem may not provide all the information that is needed to solve the problem. Sometimes, however, the necessary information is common knowledge.

HOW TO You are traveling by bus from Boston to New York. The trip is 4 hours long. If the bus leaves Boston at 10 A.M., what time should you arrive in New York?

What other information do you need to solve this problem?

You need to know that, using a 12-hour clock, the hours run

10 A.M.
11 A.M.
12 P.M.
1 P.M.
2 P.M.

Four hours after 10 A.M. is 2 P.M.

You should arrive in New York at 2 P.M.

HOW TO You purchase a 37¢ stamp at the Post Office and hand the clerk a one-dollar bill. How much change do you receive?

What information do you need to solve this problem?

You need to know that there are 100¢ in one dollar.

Your change is 100¢ − 37¢.

$100 - 37 = 63$

You receive 63¢ in change.

What information do you need to know to solve each of the following problems?

1. You sell a dozen tickets to a fundraiser. Each ticket costs $10. How much money do you collect?

2. The weekly lab period for your science course is 1 hour and 20 minutes long. Find the length of the science lab period in minutes.

3. An employee's monthly salary is $3750. Find the employee's annual salary.

4. A survey revealed that eighth graders spend an average of 3 hours each day watching television. Find the total time an eighth grader spends watching TV each week.

5. You want to buy a carpet for a room that is 15 feet wide ... the amount of carpet that you need.

Page 114

Problem-Solving Strategies

The text features a carefully developed approach to problem solving that emphasizes the importance of *strategy* when solving problems. Students are encouraged to develop their own strategies—to draw diagrams, to write out the solution steps in words—as part of their solution to a problem. In each case, model strategies are presented as guides for students to follow as they attempt the "You Try It" problem. Having students provide strategies is a natural way to incorporate writing into the math curriculum.

Example 6

A $2\frac{2}{3}$-inch piece is cut from a $6\frac{5}{8}$-inch board. How much of the board is left?

Strategy
To find the length remaining, subtract the length of the piece cut from the total length of the board.

Solution

$$6\frac{5}{8} = 6\frac{15}{24} = 5\frac{39}{24}$$
$$-2\frac{2}{3} = 2\frac{16}{24} = 2\frac{16}{24}$$
$$3\frac{23}{24}$$

$3\frac{23}{24}$ inches of the board are left.

You Try It 6

A flight from New York to Los Angeles takes $5\frac{1}{2}$ hours. After the plane has been in the air for $2\frac{3}{4}$ hours, how much flight time remains?

Your strategy

Your solution

Example 7

Two painters are staining a house. In 1 day one painter stained $\frac{1}{3}$ of the house, and the other stained $\frac{1}{4}$ of the house. How much of the job remains to be done?

Strategy
To find how much of the job remains:
- Find the total amount of the house already stained $\left(\frac{1}{3} + \frac{1}{4}\right)$.
- Subtract the amount already stained from 1, which represents the complete job.

Solution

$$\frac{1}{3} = \frac{4}{12} \qquad 1 = \frac{12}{12}$$
$$+\frac{1}{4} = \frac{3}{12} \qquad -\frac{7}{12} = \frac{7}{12}$$
$$\frac{7}{12} \qquad \qquad \frac{5}{12}$$

$\frac{5}{12}$ of the house remains to be stained.

You Try It 7

A patient is put on a diet to lose 24 pounds in 3 months. The patient lost $7\frac{1}{2}$ pounds the first month and $5\frac{3}{4}$ pounds the second month. How much weight must be lost the third month to achieve the goal?

Your strategy

Your solution

Solutions on p. S6

Real Data and Applications

Applications

One way to motivate an interest in mathematics is through applications. Wherever appropriate, the last objective of a section presents applications that require the student to use problem-solving strategies, along with the skills covered in that section, to solve practical problems. This carefully integrated applied approach generates student awareness of the value of algebra as a real-life tool.

Applications are taken from many disciplines including agriculture, business, carpentry, chemistry, construction, education, finance, nutrition, real estate, sports, and weather.

Page 222

 Objective B   To solve application problems

To solve an application problem, first read the problem carefully. The **strategy** involves identifying the quantity to be found and planning the steps that are necessary to find that quantity. The **solution of an application problem** involves performing each operation stated in the strategy and writing the answer.

The table below displays the Wal-Mart store counts as reported in the Wal-Mart 2003 Annual Report.

	Discount Stores	Supercenters	SAM'S CLUBS	Neighborhood Markets
Within the United States	1568	1258	525	49
Outside the United States	942	238	71	37

HOW TO   Find the total number of Wal-Mart stores in the United States.

Strategy   To find the total number of Wal-Mart stores in the United States, read the table to find the number of each type of store in the United States. Then add these numbers.

Solution
```
   1568
   1258
    525
 +   49
   3400
```
Wal-Mart has a total of 3400 stores in the United States.

Example 4

According to the table above, how many discount stores does Wal-Mart have worldwide?

Strategy
To determine the number of discount stores worldwide, read the table to find the number of discount stores within the United States and the number of discount stores outside the United States. Then add the two numbers.

Solution
```
   1568
 +  942
   2510
```
Wal-Mart has 2510 discount stores worldwide.

You Try It 4

Use the table above to determine the total number of Wal-Mart stores that are outside the United States.

Your strategy

Your solution

Real Data

Real data examples and exercises, identified by , ask students to analyze and solve problems taken from actual situations. Students are often required to work with tables, graphs, and charts drawn from a variety of disciplines.

---

27.   Lodging   The graph at the right shows the breakdown of the locations of the 53,500 hotels throughout the United States. How many hotels in the United States are located along highways?

28.   Poultry   In a recent year, North Carolina produced 1,300,000,000 pounds of turkey. This was 18.6% of the U.S. total in that year. Calculate the U.S. total turkey production for that year. Round to the nearest billion.

29.   Mining   During 1 year, approximately 2,240,000 ounces of gold went into the manufacturing of electronic equipment in the United States. This is 16% of all the gold mined in the United States that year. How many ounces of gold were mined in the United States that year?

30.   Demography   The table at the right shows the predicted increase in population from 2000 to 2040 for each of four counties in the Central Valley of California.
a. What percent of the 2000 population of Sacramento County is the increase in population?
b. What percent of the 2000 population of Kern County is the increase in population? Round to the nearest tenth of a percent.

31.   Police Officers   The graph at the right shows the causes of death for all police officers killed in the line of duty during a recent year. What percent of the deaths were due to traffic accidents? Round to the nearest tenth of a percent.

32.   Demography   According to a 25-city survey of the status of hunger and homelessness by the U.S. Conference of Mayors, 41% of the homeless in the United States are single men, 41% are families with children, 13% are single women, and 5% are unaccompanied minors. How many homeless people in the United States are single men?

APPLYING THE CONCEPTS

33.   The Federal Government   In the 108th Senate, there were 51 Republicans, 48 Democrats, and 1 Independent. In the 108th House of Representatives, there were 229 Republicans, 205 Democrats, and 1 Independent. Which had the larger percent of Republicans, the 108th Senate or the 108th House of Representatives?

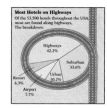

Most Hotels on Highways
Of the 53,500 hotels throughout the USA, most are found along highways. The breakdown:
Highways 42.2%
Suburban 33.6%
Urban 10.2%
Airport 7.7%
Resort 6.3%

Source: American Hotel and Lodging Association

County	2000 Population	Projected Increase
Sacramento	1,200,000	900,000
Kern	651,700	948,300
Fresno	794,200	705,800
San Joaquin	562,000	737,400

Source: California Department of Finance

Job-related illness 19
Other 6
Violent attacks 58
Traffic accidents 73

Causes of Death for Police Officers Killed in the Line of Duty
Source: International Union of Police Associations

Student Pedagogy

Icons

The   at each objective head remind students that both a video and a tutorial lesson are available for that objective.

Study Tips

These margin notes remind students of study skills presented in the *AIM for Success;* some notes provide page references to the original descriptions. They also provide students with reminders of how to practice good study habits.

Take Note

These margin notes alert students to a point requiring special attention or are used to amplify the concept under discussion.

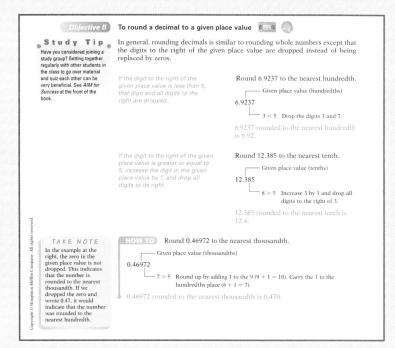

Page 129

Page 260

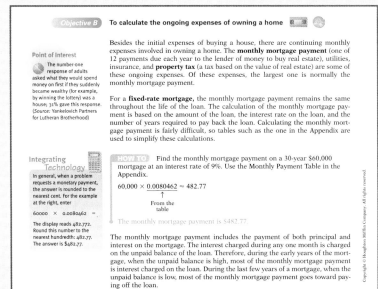

Page 111

The Order of Operations Agreement

Step 1. Do all the operations inside parentheses.
Step 2. Simplify any number expressions containing exponents.
Step 3. Do multiplications and divisions as they occur from left to right.
Step 4. Do additions and subtractions as they occur from left to right.

Point of Interest

These margin notes contain interesting sidelights about mathematics, its history, or its application.

Integrating Technology

These margin notes provide suggestions for using a scientific calculator.

HOW TO Examples

HOW TO examples use annotations to explain what is happening in key steps of the complete, worked-out solutions.

Key Terms and Concepts

Key terms, in bold, emphasize important terms. The key terms are also provided in a **Glossary** at the back of the text.

Key Concepts are presented in orange boxes in order to highlight these important concepts and to provide for easy reference.

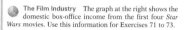 For Exercises 61 to 64, use a calculator to add. Then round the numbers to the nearest ten-thousand, and use estimation to determine whether the sum is reasonable.

61. 67,421
82,984
66,361
10,792
+ 34,037

62. 21,896
4,235
62,544
21,892
+ 1,334

63. 281,421
9,874
34,394
526,398
+ 94,631

64. 542,698
97,327
7,235
73,667
+ 173,201

For Exercises 65 to 68, use a calculator to add. Then round the numbers to the nearest million, and use estimation to determine whether the sum is reasonable.

65. 28,627,052
983,073
+ 3,081,496

66. 1,792,085
29,919,301
+ 3,406,882

67. 12,377,491
3,409,723
7,928,026
+ 10,705,682

68. 46,751,070
6,095,832
280,011
+ 1,563,897

Objective B **To solve application problems**

69. **Demographics** In a recent year, according to the U.S. Department of Health and Human Services, there were 110,670 twin births in this country, 6919 triplet births, 627 quadruplet deliveries, and 79 quintuplet and other higher-order multiple births. Find the total number of multiple births during the year.

70. **Demographics** The Census Bureau estimates that the U.S. population will grow by 296 million people from 2000 to 2100. Given that the U.S. population in 2000 was 281 million, find the Census Bureau's estimate of the U.S. population in 2100.

The Film Industry The graph at the right shows the domestic box-office income from the first four *Star Wars* movies. Use this information for Exercises 71 to 73.

71. Estimate the total income from the first four *Star Wars* movies.

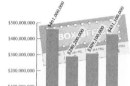

72. Find the total income from the first four *Star Wars* movies.

73. a. Find the total income f
the lowest box-office in
b. Does the total income
the lowest box-office in
from the 1977 *Star Wa*

Page 15

APPLYING THE CONCEPTS

80. a. How many two-digit numbers are there? **b.** How many three-digit numbers are there?

81. If you roll two ordinary six-sided dice and add the two numbers that appear on top, how many different sums are possible?

82. If you add two *different* whole numbers, is the sum always greater than either one of the numbers? If not, give an example.

83. If you add two whole numbers, is the sum always greater than either one of the numbers? If not, give an example. (Compare this with the previous exercise.)

84. Make up a word problem for which the answer is the sum of 34 and 28.

85. Call a number "lucky" if it ends in a 7. How many lucky numbers are less than 100?

Page 16

Exercises and Projects

Exercises

The exercise sets of *Basic College Mathematics: An Applied Approach* emphasize skill building, skill maintenance, and applications. Concept-based writing or developmental exercises have been integrated with the exercise sets. Icons identify appropriate writing , data analysis , and calculator exercises.

Included in each exercise set are **Applying the Concepts** that present extensions of topics, require analysis, or offer challenge problems. The writing exercises ask students to explain answers, write about a topic in the section, or research and report on a related topic.

Page 192

Projects and Group Activities

The Projects and Group Activities featured at the end of each chapter can be used as extra credit or for cooperative learning activities. The projects cover various aspects of mathematics, including the use of calculators, collecting data from the Internet, data analysis, and extended applications.

Projects and Group Activities

The Golden Ratio There are certain designs that have been repeated over and over in both art and architecture. One of these involves the **golden rectangle**.

A golden rectangle is drawn at the right. Begin with a square that measures, say, 2 inches on a side. Let *A* be the midpoint of a side (halfway between two corners). Now measure the distance from *A* to *B*. Place this length along the bottom of the square, starting at *A*. The resulting rectangle is a golden rectangle.

The **golden ratio** is the ratio of the length of the golden rectangle to its width. If you have drawn the rectangle following the procedure above, you will find that the golden ratio is approximately 1.6 to 1.

The golden ratio appears in many different situations. Some historians claim that some of the great pyramids of Egypt are based on the golden ratio. The drawing at the right shows the Pyramid of Giza, which dates from approximately 2600 B.C. The ratio of the height to a side of the base is approximately 1.6 to 1.

1. There are instances of the golden rectangle in the Mona Lisa painted by Leonardo da Vinci. Do some research on this painting and write a few paragraphs summarizing your findings.

2. What do 3 × 5 and 5 × 8 index cards have to do with the golden rectangle?

3. What does the United Nations Building in New York City have to do with the golden rectangle?

4. When was the Parthenon in Athens, Greece, built? What does the front of that building have to do with the golden rectangle?

End of Chapter

Chapter 3 Summary

Key Words	Examples
A number written in *decimal notation* has three parts: a *whole-number part*, a *decimal point*, and a *decimal part*. The decimal part of a number represents a number less than 1. A number written in decimal notation is often simply called a *decimal*. [3.1A, p. 127]	For the decimal 31.25, 31 is the whole-number part and 25 is the decimal part.

Essential Rules and Procedures	Examples
To write a decimal in words, write the decimal part as if it were a whole number. Then name the place value of the last digit. The decimal point is read as "and." [3.1A, p. 127]	The decimal 12.875 is written in words as twelve and eight hundred seventy-five thousandths.
To write a decimal in standard form when it is written in words, write the whole-number part, replace the word *and* with a decimal point, and write the decimal part so that the last digit is in the given place-value position. [3.1A, p. 128]	The decimal forty-nine and sixty-three thousandths is written in standard form as 49.063.
To round a decimal to a given place value, use the same rules used with whole numbers, except drop the digits to the right of the given place value instead of replacing them with zeros. [3.1B, p. 129]	2.7134 rounded to the nearest tenth is 2.7. 0.4687 rounded to the nearest hundredth is 0.47.

Page 165

Chapter Summary

At the end of each chapter there is a Chapter Summary that includes Key Words, Essential Rules and Procedures, and an example of each. Each entry includes an objective reference and a page reference indicating where the concept is introduced. These chapter summaries provide a single point of reference as the student prepares for a test.

Chapter Review Exercises

Chapter Review Exercises are found at the end of each chapter. These exercises are selected to help the student integrate all of the topics presented in the chapter.

Page 167

Chapter 3 Review Exercises

Chapter 3 Review Exercises **167**

1. Find the quotient of 3.6515 and 0.067.

2. Find the sum of 369.41, 88.3, 9.774, and 366.474.

3. Place the correct symbol, < or >, between the two numbers.
0.055   0.1

4. Write 22.0092 in words.

Chapter Test

Each Chapter Test is designed to simulate a possible test of the material in the chapter.

Page 169

Chapter 3 Test

Chapter 3 Test **169**

1. Place the correct symbol, < or >, between the two numbers.
0.66   0.666

2. Subtract: 13.027
− 8.94

3. Write 45.0302 in words.

4. Convert $\frac{9}{13}$ to a decimal. Round to the nearest thousandth.

Cumulative Review Exercises

Cumulative Review Exercises, which appear at the end of each chapter (beginning with Chapter 2), help students maintain skills learned in previous chapters.

The answers to all Chapter Review Exercises, all Chapter Test exercises, and all Cumulative Review Exercises are given in the Answer Section. Along with the answer, there is a reference to the objective that pertains to each exercise.

Page 171

Cumulative Review Exercises

Cumulative Review Exercises **171**

1. Divide: 89)20,932

2. Simplify: $2^3 \cdot 4^2$

3. Simplify: $2^2 − (7 − 3) \div 2 + 1$

4. Find the LCM of 9, 12, and 24.

Page A8

CUMULATIVE REVIEW EXERCISES

1. 235 r17 [1.5C]   **2.** 128 [1.6A]   **3.** 3 [1.6B]   **4.** 72 [2.1A]   **5.** $4\frac{2}{5}$ [2.2B]   **6.** $\frac{37}{8}$ [2.2B]

Instructor Resources

Basic College Mathematics: An Applied Approach has a complete set of support materials for the instructor.

Instructor's Annotated Edition This edition contains a replica of the student text and additional resources just for the instructor. These include: *Instructor Notes, New Vocabulary/Symbols, etc., Vocabulary/Symbols, etc. to Review, In-Class Examples, Discuss the Concepts, Concept Checks, Optional Student Activities, Suggested Assignments, Quick Quizzes, Answers to Writing Exercises/Focus on Problem Solving/Projects and Group Activities,* and *PowerPoints.* Answers to all exercises are also provided.

Instructor's Solutions Manual The *Instructor's Solutions Manual* contains worked-out solutions for all exercises in the text.

Instructor's Resource Manual with Testing This resource includes eight ready-to-use printed *Chapter Tests* per chapter, suggested *Course Sequences,* and a printout of the *AIM for Success* PowerPoint slide show. All resources are also available on the Instructor website and *Class Prep CD.*

HM ClassPrep with HM Testing CD-ROM *HM ClassPrep* contains a multitude of text-specific resources for instructors to use to enhance the classroom experience. These resources can be easily accessed by chapter or resource type and can also link you to the text's website. *HM Testing* is our computerized test generator and contains a database of algorithmic test items as well as providing **online testing** and **gradebook** functions.

Instructor Text-Specific Website The resources available on the *Class Prep CD* are also available on the instructor website at math.college.hmco.com/instructors. Appropriate items are password protected. Instructors also have access to the student part of the text's website.

WebCT ePacks *WebCT ePacks* provide instructors with a flexible, Internet-based education platform providing multiple ways to present learning materials. The *WebCT ePacks* come with a full array of features to enrich the online learning experience.

Blackboard Cartridges The *Houghton Mifflin Blackboard cartridge* allows flexible, efficient, and creative ways to present learning materials and opportunities. In addition to course management benefits, instructors may make use of an electronic grade book, receive papers from students enrolled in the course via the Internet, and track student use of the communication and collaboration functions.

NEW! **HM Eduspace®** is a powerful course management system powered by Blackboard that makes preparing, presenting, and managing courses easier. You can use this distance-learning platform to customize, create, and deliver course materials and tests online, and easily maintain student portfolios using the grade book, where grades for all assignments are automatically scored, averaged, and saved.

Student Resources

Student Solutions Manual The *Student Solutions Manual* contains complete solutions to all odd-numbered exercises in the text.

Math Study Skills Workbook by Paul D. Nolting This workbook is designed to reinforce skills and minimize frustration for students in any math class, lab, or study skills course. It offers a wealth of study tips and sound advice on note taking, time management, and reducing math anxiety. In addition, numerous opportunities for self-assessment enable students to track their own progress.

HM Eduspace® Online Learning Environment *Eduspace* is a text-specific, web-based learning environment which combines an algorithmic tutorial program with homework capabilities. Specific content is available 24 hours a day to help you further understand your textbook.

HM mathSpace® Tutorial CD-ROM This tutorial CD-ROM allows students to practice skills and review concepts as many times as necessary by providing algorithmically-generated exercises and step-by-step solutions for practice.

SMARTHINKING™ Live, Online Tutoring Houghton Mifflin has partnered with SMARTHINKING to provide an easy-to-use and effective online tutorial service. **Whiteboard Simulations** and **Practice Area** promote real-time visual interaction.

Three levels of service are offered.

- **Text-specific Tutoring** provides real-time, one-on-one instruction with a specially qualified "e-structor."
- **Questions Any Time** allows students to submit questions to the tutor outside the scheduled hours and receive a reply within 24 hours.
- **Independent Study Resources** connect students with around-the-clock access to additional educational services, including interactive websites, diagnostic tests, and Frequently Asked Questions posed to SMARTHINKING e-structors.

Houghton Mifflin Instructional Videos and DVDs Text-specific videos and DVDs, hosted by Dana Mosely, cover all sections of the text and provide a valuable resource for further instruction and review.

Student Text-Specific Website Online student resources can be found at this text's website at math.college.hmco.com/students.

Acknowledgments

The authors would like to thank the people who have reviewed this manuscript and provided many valuable suggestions.

Dorothy A. Brown, *Camden County College, NJ*
Kim Doyle, *Monroe Community College, NY*
Kimberly A. Gregor, *Delaware Technical and Community College, DE*
Allen Grommet, *East Arkansas Community College, AR*
Anne Haney
Rose M. Kaniper, *Burlington County College, NJ*
Mary Ann Klicka, *Bucks County Community College, PA*
Helen Medley
Dr. James R. Perry, *Owens Community College, OH*
Susan Wessner, *Tallahassee Community College, FL*

With special thanks to Dawn Nuttall for her contributions in the developmental editing of three editions of this textbook series.

AIM for Success

Welcome to *Basic College Mathematics: An Applied Approach*. As you begin this course, we know two important facts: (1) We want you to succeed. (2) You want to succeed. To do that requires an effort from each of us. For the next few pages, we are going to show you what is required of you to achieve that success and how you can use the features of this text to be successful.

Motivation

One of the most important keys to success is motivation. We can try to motivate you by offering interesting or important ways mathematics can benefit you. But, in the end, the motivation must come from you. On the first day of class, it is easy to be motivated. Eight weeks into the term, it is harder to keep that motivation.

To stay motivated, there must be outcomes from this course that are worth your time, money, and energy.

List some reasons you are taking this course.

_____

_____

_____

Although we hope that one of the reasons you listed was an interest in mathematics, we know that many of you are taking this course because it is required to graduate, it is a prerequisite for a course you must take, or because it is required for your major. Although you may not agree that this course is necessary, it is! If you are motivated to graduate or complete the requirements for your major, then use that motivation to succeed in this course. Do not become distracted from your goal to complete your education!

Commitment

To be successful, you must make a commitment to succeed. This means devoting time to math so that you achieve a better understanding of the subject.

List some activities (sports, hobbies, talents such as dance, art, or music) that you enjoy and at which you would like to become better.

ACTIVITY	TIME SPENT	TIME WISHED SPENT

Thinking about these activities, put the number of hours that you spend each week practicing these activities next to the activity. Next to that number, indicate the number of hours per week you would like to spend on these activities.

Whether you listed surfing or sailing, aerobics or restoring cars, or any other activity you enjoy, note how many hours a week you spend doing it. To succeed in math, you must be willing to commit the same amount of time. Success requires some sacrifice.

The "I Can't Do Math" Syndrome

There may be things you cannot do, such as lift a two-ton boulder. You can, however, do math. It is much easier than lifting the two-ton boulder. When you first learned the activities you listed above, you probably could not do them well. With practice, you got better. With practice, you will be better at math. Stay focused, motivated, and committed to success.

It is difficult for us to emphasize how important it is to overcome the "I Can't Do Math" Syndrome. If you listen to interviews of very successful atheletes after a particularly bad performance, you will note that they focus on the positive aspect of what they did, not the negative. Sports psychologists encourage athletes to always be positive—to have a "Can Do" attitude. Develop this attitude toward math.

Strategies for Success

Textbook Review   Right now, do a 15-minute "textbook review" of this book. Here's how:

First, read the table of contents. Do it in three minutes or less. Next, look through the entire book, page by page. Move quickly. Scan titles, look at pictures, notice diagrams.

A textbook review shows you where a course is going. It gives you the big picture. That's useful because brains work best when going from the general to the specific. Getting the big picture before you start makes details easier to recall and understand later on.

Your textbook review will work even better if, as you scan, you look for ideas or topics that are interesting to you. List three facts, topics, or problems that you found interesting during your textbook review.

_____

_____

_____

The idea behind this technique is simple: It's easier to work at learning material if you know it's going to be useful to you.

Not all the topics in this book will be "interesting" to you. But that is true of any subject. Surfers find that on some days the waves are better than others, musicians find some music more appealing than other music, computer gamers find some computer games more interesting than others, car enthusiasts find some cars more exciting than others. Some car enthusiasts would rather have a completely restored 1957 Chevrolet than a new Ferrari.

Know the Course Requirements   To do your best in this course, you must know exactly what your instructor requires. Course requirements may be stated in a *syllabus*, which is a printed outline of the main topics of the course, or they may be presented orally. When they are listed in a syllabus or on other printed pages, keep them in a safe place. When they are presented orally, make sure to take complete notes. In either case, it is important that you understand them completely and follow them exactly. Be sure you know the answer to each of the following questions.

1. What is your instructor's name?
2. Where is your instructor's office?
3. At what times does your instructor hold office hours?
4. Besides the textbook, what other materials does your instructor require?
5. What is your instructor's attendance policy?
6. If you must be absent from a class meeting, what should you do before returning to class? What should you do when you return to class?

7. What is the instructor's policy regarding collection or grading of homework assignments?

8. What options are available if you are having difficulty with an assignment? Is there a math tutoring center?

9. If there is a math lab at your school, where is it located? What hours is it open?

10. What is the instructor's policy if you miss a quiz?

11. What is the instructor's policy if you miss an exam?

12. Where can you get help when studying for an exam?

Remember: Your instructor wants to see you succeed. If you need help, ask! Do not fall behind. If you are running a race and fall behind by 100 yards, you may be able to catch up but it will require more effort than had you not fallen behind.

Time Management We know that there are demands on your time. Family, work, friends, and entertainment all compete for your time. We do not want to see you receive poor job evaluations because you are studying math. However, it is also true that we do not want to see you receive poor math test scores because you devoted too much time to work. When several competing and important tasks require your time and energy, the only way to manage the stress of being successful at both is to manage your time efficiently.

Instructors often advise students to spend twice the amount of time outside of class studying as they spend in the classroom. Time management is important if you are to accomplish this goal and succeed in school. The following activity is intended to help you structure your time more efficiently.

List the name of each course you are taking this term, the number of class hours each course meets, and the number of hours you should spend studying each subject outside of class. Then fill in a weekly schedule like the one printed below. Begin by writing in the hours spent in your classes, the hours spent at work (if you have a job), and any other commitments that are not flexible with respect to the time that you do them. Then begin to write down commitments that are more flexible, including hours spent studying. Remember to reserve time for activities such as meals and exercise. You should also schedule free time.

	Monday	Tuesday	Wednesday	Thursday	Friday	Saturday	Sunday
7–8 a.m.							
8–9 a.m.							
9–10 a.m.							
10–11 a.m.							
11–12 p.m.							
12–1 p.m.							
1–2 p.m.							
2–3 p.m.							
3–4 p.m.							
4–5 p.m.							
5–6 p.m.							
6–7 p.m.							
7–8 p.m.							
8–9 p.m.							
9–10 p.m.							
10–11 p.m.							
11–12 a.m.							

We know that many of you must work. If that is the case, realize that working 10 hours a week at a part-time job is equivalent to taking a three-unit class. If you must work, consider letting your education progress at a slower rate to allow you to be successful at both work and school. There is no rule that says you must finish school in a certain time frame.

Schedule Study Time As we encouraged you to do by filling out the time management form above, schedule a certain time to study. You should think of this time the way you would the time for work or class—that is, reasons for missing study time should be as compelling as reasons for missing work or class. "I just didn't feel like it" is not a good reason to miss your scheduled study time.

Although this may seem like an obvious exercise, list a few reasons you might want to study.

_____

_____

_____

Of course we have no way of knowing the reasons you listed, but from our experience one reason given quite frequently is "To pass the course." There is nothing wrong with that reason. If that is the most important reason for you to study, then use it to stay focused.

One method of keeping to a study schedule is to form a ***study group***. Look for people who are committed to learning, who pay attention in class, and who are punctual. Ask them to join your group. Choose people with similar educational goals but different methods of learning. You can gain insight from seeing the material from a new perspective. Limit groups to four or five people; larger groups are unwieldy.

There are many ways to conduct a study group. Begin with the following suggestions and see what works best for your group.

1. Test each other by asking questions. Each group member might bring two or three sample test questions to each meeting.
2. Practice teaching each other. Many of us who are teachers learned a lot about our subject when we had to explain it to someone else.
3. Compare class notes. You might ask other students about material in your notes that is difficult for you to understand.
4. Brainstorm test questions.
5. Set an agenda for each meeting. Set approximate time limits for each agenda item and determine a quitting time.

And now, probably the most important aspect of studying is that it should be done in relatively small chunks. If you can only study three hours a week for this course (probably not enough for most people), do it in blocks of one hour on three separate days, preferably after class. Three hours of studying on a Sunday is not as productive as three hours of paced study.

Text Features That Promote Success

There are 12 chapters in this text. Each chapter is divided into sections, and each section is subdivided into learning objectives. Each learning objective is labeled with a letter from A to D.

Preparing for a Chapter Before you begin a new chapter, you should take some time to review previously learned skills. There are two ways to do this. The first is to complete the ***Cumulative Review Exercises,*** which occurs after every chapter (except Chapter 1). For instance, turn to page 231. The questions in this review are taken from the previous chapters. The answers for all these exercises can be found on page A11. Turn to that page now and locate the answers for the Chapter 5 Cumulative Review Exercises. After the answer to the first exercise, which is 4, you will see the objective reference [1.6B]. This means that this question was taken from Chapter 1, Section 6, Objective B. If you missed this question, you should return to that objective and restudy the material.

A second way of preparing for a new chapter is to complete the ***Prep Test***. This test focuses on the particular skills that will be required for the new chapter. Turn to page 202 to see a Prep Test. The answers for the Prep Test are the first set of answers in the answer section for a chapter. Turn to page A10 to see the answers for the Prep Test for Chapter 5. Note that an objective reference is given for each question. If you answer a question incorrectly, restudy the objective from which the question was taken.

Before the class meeting in which your professor begins a new section, you should read each objective statement. Next, browse through the objective material, being sure to note each word in bold type. These words indicate important concepts that you must know in order to learn the material. Do not worry about trying to understand all the material. Your professor is there to assist you with that endeavor. The purpose of browsing through the material is that when it is presented to you, your brain will be prepared to accept and organize the new information.

Turn to page 3. Write down the title of the first objective in Section 1.1. Under the title of the objective, write down the words on that page that are in bold print. It is not necessary for you to understand the meaning of these words. You are in this class to learn their meaning.

_____ _____ _____ _____

_____ _____ _____ _____

_____ _____ _____ _____

Math Is Not a Spectator Sport To learn mathematics you must be an active participant. Listening and watching your professor do mathematics is not enough. Mathematics requires that you interact with the lesson you are studying. If you filled in the blanks above, you were being interactive. There are other ways this textbook has been designed to help you be an active learner.

Annotated Examples The HOW TO feature indicates an example with explanatory remarks to the right of the work. Using paper and pencil, you should work along as you go through the example.

When you complete the example, get a clean sheet of paper. Write down the problem and then try to complete the solution without referring to your notes or the book. When you can do that, move on to the next part of the objective.

Leaf through the book now and write down the page numbers of two other occurrences of a HOW TO feature.

$$\frac{5}{6} = \frac{10}{12}$$

$$-\frac{1}{4} = \frac{3}{12}$$

$$\frac{7}{12}$$

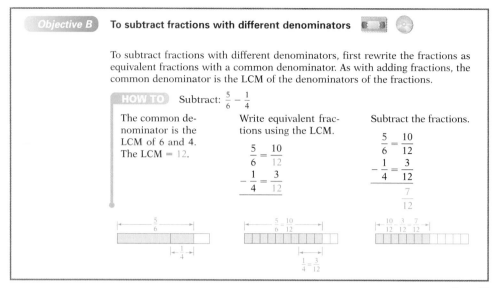

Page 85

You Try Its   One of the key instructional features of this text is the paired examples. Notice that in each example box, the example on the left is completely worked out and the "You Try It" example on the right is not. Study the worked-out example carefully by working through each step. Then work the You Try It. If you get stuck, refer to the page number at the end of the example which directs you to the page on which the You Try It is solved—a complete worked-out solution is provided. Try to use the given solution to get a hint for the step you are stuck on. Then try to complete your solution.

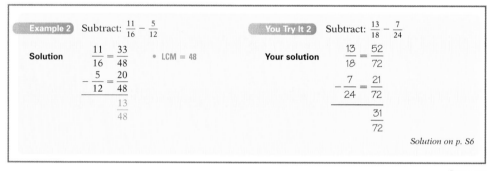

Page 86

When you have completed your solution, check your work against the solution we provided. (Turn to page S6 to see the solution of You Try It 2.) Be aware that frequently there is more than one way to solve a problem. Your answer, however, should be the same as the given answer. If you have any question as to whether your method will "always work," check with your instructor or with someone in the math center.

Browse through the textbook and write down the page numbers of two other occurrences of the paired example feature.

Remember: Be an active participant in your learning process. When you are sitting in class watching and listening to an explanation, you may think that you understand. However, until you actually try to do it, you will have no confirmation of the new knowledge or skill. Most of us have had the experience of sitting in class thinking we knew how to do something only to get home and realize that we didn't.

Word Problems   Word Problems are difficult because we must read the problem, determine the quantity we must find, think of a method to do that, and then

T A K E   N O T E

There is a strong connection between reading and being a successful student in math or any other subject. If you have difficulty reading, consider taking a reading course. Reading is much like other skills. There are certain things you can learn that will make you a better reader.

actually solve the problem. A short summary of this process is to formulate a *strategy* to solve the problem and then devise a *solution*.

Note in the paired example below that part of every word problem is a strategy and a solution. The strategy is a written description of how we will solve the problem. In the corresponding You Try It, you are asked to formulate a strategy. Do not skip this step and be sure to write it out.

Example 6

A $2\frac{2}{3}$-inch piece is cut from a $6\frac{5}{8}$-inch board. How much of the board is left?

Strategy
To find the length remaining, subtract the length of the piece cut from the total length of the board.

Solution

$$6\frac{5}{8} = 6\frac{15}{24} = 5\frac{39}{24}$$
$$-2\frac{2}{3} = 2\frac{16}{24} = 2\frac{16}{24}$$
$$\overline{3\frac{23}{24}}$$

$3\frac{23}{24}$ inches of the board are left.

You Try It 6

A flight from New York to Los Angeles takes $5\frac{1}{2}$ hours. After the plane has been in the air for $2\frac{3}{4}$ hours, how much flight time remains?

Your strategy
To find how much flight time remains, subtract the amount of time the plane has been in the air $\left(2\frac{3}{4}\right)$ from the total time for the trip $\left(5\frac{1}{2}\right)$.

Your solution

$$5\frac{1}{2} = 5\frac{2}{4} = 4\frac{6}{4}$$
$$-2\frac{3}{4} = 2\frac{3}{4} = 2\frac{3}{4}$$
$$\overline{2\frac{3}{4}}$$

$2\frac{3}{4}$ hours of flight time remains.

Page 88

Rule Boxes Pay special attention to rules placed in boxes. These rules give you the reasons certain types of problems are solved the way they are. When you see a rule, try to rewrite the rule in your own words.

Objective B   **To use the Order of Operations Agreement to simplify expressions**

More than one operation may occur in a numerical expression. The answer may be different, depending on the order in which the operations are performed. For example, consider $3 + 4 \times 5$.

Multiply first, then add.

$$3 + \underbrace{4 \times 5}$$
$$\underbrace{3 + 20}$$
$$23$$

Add first, then multiply.

$$\underbrace{3 + 4} \times 5$$
$$\underbrace{7 \times 5}$$
$$35$$

An Order of Operations Agreement is used so that only one answer is possible.

The Order of Operations Agreement

Step 1. Do all the operations inside parentheses.

Step 2. Simplify any number expressions containing exponents.

Step 3. Do multiplication and division as they occur from left to right.

Step 4. Do addition and subtraction as they occur from left to right.

Parentheses
Exponents
Multiplication and division
Addition and subtraction

TAKE NOTE

If you are working at home and need assistance, there is online help available at math.college.hmco.com/students, at this text's website.

Chapter Exercises   When you have completed studying an objective, do the exercises in the exercise set that correspond with that objective. The exercises are labeled with the same letter as the objective. Math is a subject that needs to be learned in small sections and practiced continually in order to be mastered. Doing all of the exercises in each exercise set will help you master the problem-solving techniques necessary for success. As you work through the exercises for an objective, check your answers to the odd-numbered exercises with those in the back of the book.

Preparing for a Test   There are important features of this text that can be used to prepare for a test.

- Chapter Summary
- Chapter Review Exercises
- Chapter Test

After completing a chapter, read the Chapter Summary. (See pages 116–118 for the Chapter 2 Summary.) This summary highlights the important topics covered in the chapter. The page number following each topic refers you to the page in the text on which you can find more information about the concept.

Following the Chapter Summary are Chapter Review Exercises (see page 119) and a Chapter Test (see page 121). Doing the review exercises is an important way of testing your understanding of the chapter. The answer to each review exercise is given at the back of the book along with its objective reference. After checking your answers, restudy any objective from which a question you missed was taken. It may be helpful to retry some of the exercises for that objective to reinforce your problem-solving techniques.

The Chapter Test should be used to prepare for an exam. We suggest that you try the Chapter Test a few days before your actual exam. Take the test in a quiet place and try to complete the test in the same amount of time you will be allowed for your exam. When taking the Chapter Test, practice the strategies of successful test takers: 1) scan the entire test to get a feel for the questions; 2) read the directions carefully; 3) work the problems that are easiest for you first; and perhaps most importantly, 4) try to stay calm.

When you have completed the Chapter Test, check your answers. If you missed a question, review the material in that objective and rework some of the exercises from that objective. This will strengthen your ability to perform the skills in that objective.

Is it difficult to be successful? YES! Successful music groups, artists, professional athletes, chefs, and <u>Write your major here</u> have to work very hard to achieve their goals. They focus on their goals and ignored distractions. The things we ask you to do to achieve success take time and commitment. We are confident that if you follow our suggestions, you will succeed.

How much would it cost to take a vacation that looks as relaxing as this one? What would you have to pay for travel, accommodations, and food? Do you have enough money in the bank, or would you need to earn and save more money? If you are considering taking a vacation, you will need to know the answers to these and other questions. The **Focus on Problem Solving on page 54** illustrates how we use operations on whole numbers to determine costs associated with planning a vacation.

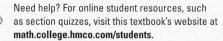

Need help? For online student resources, such as section quizzes, visit this textbook's website at **math.college.hmco.com/students.**

OBJECTIVES

Section 1.1

A To identify the order relation between two numbers

B To write whole numbers in words and in standard form

C To write whole numbers in expanded form

D To round a whole number to a given place value

Section 1.2

A To add whole numbers

B To solve application problems

Section 1.3

A To subtract whole numbers without borrowing

B To subtract whole numbers with borrowing

C To solve application problems

Section 1.4

A To multiply a number by a single digit

B To multiply larger whole numbers

C To solve application problems

Section 1.5

A To divide by a single digit with no remainder in the quotient

B To divide by a single digit with a remainder in the quotient

C To divide by larger whole numbers

D To solve application problems

Section 1.6

A To simplify expressions that contain exponents

B To use the Order of Operations Agreement to simplify expressions

Section 1.7

A To factor numbers

B To find the prime factorization of a number

PREP TEST · · ·

Do these exercises to prepare for Chapter 1.

1. Name the number of ♦s shown below.

♦ ♦ ♦ ♦ ♦ ♦ ♦ ♦

2. Write the numbers from 1 to 10.

1 ___ ___ ___ ___ ___ ___ ___ ___ 10

3. Match the number with its word form.
   a. 4   **A.** five
   b. 2   **B.** one
   c. 5   **C.** zero
   d. 1   **D.** four
   e. 3   **E.** two
   f. 0   **F.** three

GO FIGURE · · ·

Five adults and two children want to cross a river in a canoe. The canoe can hold one adult or two children or one child. Everyone is able to paddle the canoe. What is the minimum number of trips that will be necessary for everyone to get to the other side?

1.1 Introduction to Whole Numbers

Objective A   **To identify the order relation between two numbers**

The **whole numbers** are 0, 1, 2, 3, 4, 5, 6, 7, 8, 9, 10, 11, 12, 13, 14, ...

The three dots mean that the list continues on and on and that there is no largest whole number.

Just as distances are associated with the markings on the edge of a ruler, the whole numbers can be associated with points on a line. This line is called the **number line.** The arrow on the number line below indicates that there is no largest whole number.

The **graph of a whole number** is shown by placing a heavy dot directly above that number on the number line. Here is the graph of 7 on the number line:

The number line can be used to show the order of whole numbers. A number that appears to the left of a given number **is less than (<)** the given number. A number that appears to the right of a given number **is greater than (>)** the given number.

Four is less than seven.
4 < 7

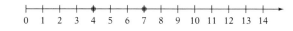

Twelve is greater than seven.
12 > 7

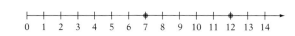

Example 1 Graph 11 on the number line.

Solution 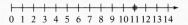

You Try It 1 Graph 6 on the number line.

Your solution 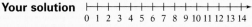

Example 2 Place the correct symbol, < or >, between the two numbers.
  a. 39   24
  b. 0   51

Solution **a.** 39 > 24
        b. 0 < 51

You Try It 2 Place the correct symbol, < or >, between the two numbers.
  a. 45   29
  b. 27   0

Your solution **a.**
             b.

Solutions on p. S1

Objective B   To write whole numbers in words and in standard form

Point of Interest

The Babylonians had a place-value system based on 60. Its influence is still with us in angle measurement and time: 60 seconds in 1 minute, 60 minutes in 1 hour. It appears that the earliest record of a base-10 place-value system for natural numbers dates from the 8th century.

When a whole number is written using the digits 0, 1, 2, 3, 4, 5, 6, 7, 8, and 9, it is said to be in **standard form.** The position of each digit in the number determines the digit's **place value.** The diagram below shows a **place-value chart** naming the first 12 place values. The number 37,462 is in standard form and has been entered in the chart.

In the number 37,462, the position of the digit 3 determines that its place value is ten-thousands.

When a number is written in standard form, each group of digits separated from the digits by a comma (or commas) is called a **period.** The number 3,786,451,294 has four periods. The period names are shown in red in the place-value chart above.

To write a number in words, start from the left. Name the number in each period. Then write the period name in place of the comma.

3,786,451,294 is read "three billion seven hundred eighty-six million four hundred fifty-one thousand two hundred ninety-four."

To write a whole number in standard form, write the number named in each period, and replace each period name with a comma.

Four million sixty-two thousand five hundred eighty-four is written 4,062,584. The zero is used as a place holder for the hundred-thousands place.

Example 3   Write 25,478,083 in words.

Solution   Twenty-five million four hundred seventy-eight thousand eighty-three

You Try It 3   Write 36,462,075 in words.

Your solution

Example 4   Write three hundred three thousand three in standard form.

Solution   303,003

You Try It 4   Write four hundred fifty-two thousand seven in standard form.

Your solution

Solutions on p. S1

Objective C   To write whole numbers in expanded form

The whole number 26,429 can be written in **expanded form** as

20,000 + 6000 + 400 + 20 + 9.

The place-value chart can be used to find the expanded form of a number.

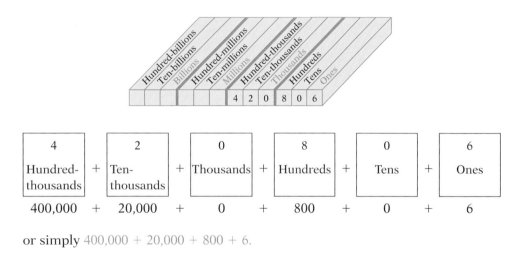

2 Ten-thousands	+	6 Thousands	+	4 Hundreds	+	2 Tens	+	9 Ones
20,000	+	6000	+	400	+	20	+	9

The number 420,806 is written in expanded form below. Note the effect of having zeros in the number.

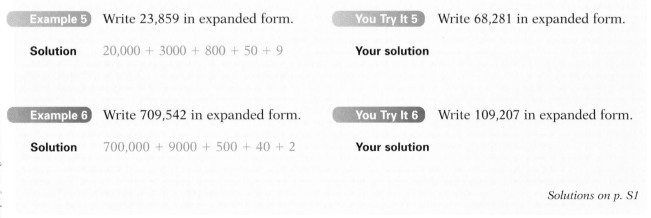

4 Hundred-thousands	+	2 Ten-thousands	+	0 Thousands	+	8 Hundreds	+	0 Tens	+	6 Ones
400,000	+	20,000	+	0	+	800	+	0	+	6

or simply 400,000 + 20,000 + 800 + 6.

Example 5   Write 23,859 in expanded form.

Solution   20,000 + 3000 + 800 + 50 + 9

You Try It 5   Write 68,281 in expanded form.

Your solution

Example 6   Write 709,542 in expanded form.

Solution   700,000 + 9000 + 500 + 40 + 2

You Try It 6   Write 109,207 in expanded form.

Your solution

Solutions on p. S1

Objective D   **To round a whole number to a given place value**

When the distance to the moon is given as 240,000 miles, the number represents an approximation to the true distance. Taking an approximate value for an exact number is called **rounding.** A rounded number is always rounded to a given place value.

37 is closer to 40 than it is to 30. 37 rounded to the nearest ten is 40.

673 rounded to the nearest ten is 670. 673 rounded to the nearest hundred is 700.

A whole number is rounded to a given place value without using the number line by looking at the first digit to the right of the given place value.

If the digit to the right of the given place value is less than 5, that digit and all digits to the right are replaced by zeros.

HOW TO   Round 13,834 to the nearest hundred.

┌──── Given place value
13,834
    └──── 3 < 5

13,834 rounded to the nearest hundred is 13,800.

If the digit to the right of the given place value is greater than or equal to 5, increase the digit in the given place value by 1, and replace all other digits to the right by zeros.

HOW TO   Round 386,217 to the nearest ten-thousand.

┌──── Given place value
386,217
     └──── 6 > 5

386,217 rounded to the nearest ten-thousand is 390,000.

Example 7   Round 525,453 to the nearest ten-thousand.

Solution

┌──── Given place value
525,453
    └──── 5 = 5

525,453 rounded to the nearest ten-thousand is 530,000.

You Try It 7   Round 368,492 to the nearest ten-thousand.

Your solution

Example 8   Round 1972 to the nearest hundred.

Solution

┌──── Given place value
1972
   └──── 7 > 5

1972 rounded to the nearest hundred is 2000.

You Try It 8   Round 3962 to the nearest hundred.

Your solution

Solutions on p. S1

1.1 Exercises

Objective A   **To identify the order relation between two numbers**

For Exercises 1 to 4, graph the number on the number line.

1. 3

2. 5

3. 9

4. 0

For Exercises 5 to 13, place the correct symbol, < or >, between the two numbers.

5. 37   49

6. 58   21

7. 101   87

8. 16   5

9. 245   158

10. 2701   2071

11. 0   45

12. 107   0

13. 815   928

Objective B   **To write whole numbers in words and in standard form**

For Exercises 14 to 17, name the place value of the digit 3.

14. 83,479

15. 3,491,507

16. 2,634,958

17. 76,319,204

For Exercises 18 to 25, write the number in words.

18. 2675

19. 3790

20. 42,928

21. 58,473

22. 356,943

23. 498,512

24. 3,697,483

25. 6,842,715

For Exercises 26 to 31, write the number in standard form.

26. Eighty-five

27. Three hundred fifty-seven

28. Three thousand four hundred fifty-six

29. Sixty-three thousand seven hundred eighty

30. Six hundred nine thousand nine hundred forty-eight

31. Seven million twenty-four thousand seven hundred nine

Objective C   **To write whole numbers in expanded form**

For Exercises 32 to 39, write the number in expanded form.

32. 5287

33. 6295

34. 58,943

35. 453,921

36. 200,583

37. 301,809

38. 403,705

39. 3,000,642

Objective D   **To round a whole number to a given place value**

For Exercises 40 to 51, round the number to the given place value.

40. 926   Tens

41. 845   Tens

42. 1439   Hundreds

43. 3973   Hundreds

44. 43,607   Thousands

45. 52,715   Thousands

46. 389,702   Thousands

47. 629,513   Thousands

48. 647,989   Ten-thousands

49. 253,678   Ten-thousands

50. 36,702,599   Millions

51. 71,834,250   Millions

APPLYING THE CONCEPTS

Answer true or false for Exercise 52a and 52b. If the answer is false, give an example to show that it is false.

52. **a.** If you are given two distinct whole numbers, then one of the numbers is always greater than the other number.
   b. A rounded-off number is always less than its exact value.

53. What is the largest three-digit whole number? What is the smallest five-digit whole number?

54. If 3846 is rounded to the nearest ten and then that number is rounded to the nearest hundred, is the result the same as what you get when you round 3846 to the nearest hundred? If not, which of the two methods is correct for rounding to the nearest hundred?

1.2 Addition of Whole Numbers

Objective A **To add whole numbers**

Addition is the process of finding the total of two or more numbers.

> **TAKE NOTE**
> The numbers being added are called **addends.** The result is the **sum.**

By counting, we see that the total of $3 and $4 is $7.

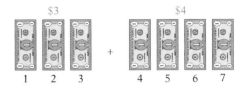

$3   + $4   = $7

Addend   Addend   Sum

Addition can be illustrated on the number line by using arrows to represent the addends. The size, or magnitude, of a number can be represented on the number line by an arrow.

The number 3 can be represented anywhere on the number line by an arrow that is 3 units in length.

> **Point of Interest**
> The first use of the plus sign appeared in 1489 in *Mercantile Arithmetic.* It was used to indicate a surplus, not as the symbol for addition. That use did not appear until about 1515.

To add on the number line, place the arrows representing the addends head to tail, with the first arrow starting at zero. The sum is represented by an arrow starting at zero and stopping at the tip of the last arrow.

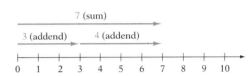

$$3 + 4 = 7$$

More than two numbers can be added on the number line.

$$3 + 2 + 4 = 9$$

Some special properties of addition that are used frequently are given below.

Addition Property of Zero

Zero added to a number does not change the number.

$$4 + 0 = 4$$
$$0 + 7 = 7$$

Commutative Property of Addition

Two numbers can be added in either order; the sum will be the same.

$$4 + 8 = 8 + 4$$
$$12 = 12$$

Associative Property of Addition

> **TAKE NOTE**
> This is the same addition problem shown on the number line above.

Grouping the addition in any order gives the same result. The parentheses are grouping symbols and have the meaning "Do the operations inside the parentheses first."

$$(3 + 2) + 4 = 3 + (2 + 4)$$
$$5 \quad + 4 = 3 + \quad 6$$
$$9 = 9$$

The number line is not useful for adding large numbers. The basic addition facts for adding one digit to one digit should be memorized. Addition of larger numbers requires the repeated use of the basic addition facts.

To add large numbers, begin by arranging the numbers vertically, keeping the digits of the same place value in the same column.

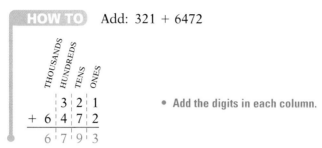

HOW TO Add: 321 + 6472

$$\begin{array}{r} 3\;2\;1 \\ +\;6\;4\;7\;2 \\ \hline 6\;7\;9\;3 \end{array}$$

THOUSANDS HUNDREDS TENS ONES

• Add the digits in each column.

There are several words or phrases in English that indicate the operation of addition. Here are some examples:

added to	3 added to 5	5 + 3
more than	7 more than 5	5 + 7
the sum of	the sum of 3 and 9	3 + 9
increased by	4 increased by 6	4 + 6
the total of	the total of 8 and 3	8 + 3
plus	5 plus 10	5 + 10

Integrating Technology

Most scientific calculators use *algebraic logic:* the add (+), subtract (−), multiply (×), and divide (÷) keys perform the indicated operation on the number in the display and the next number keyed in. For instance, for the example at the right, enter 24 + 71 = . The display reads 95.

HOW TO What is the sum of 24 and 71?

$$\begin{array}{r} 24 \\ +\;71 \\ \hline 95 \end{array}$$

• The phrase *the sum of* means to add.

The sum of 24 and 71 is 95.

When the sum of the digits in a column exceeds 9, the addition will involve **carrying.**

HOW TO Add: 487 + 369

$$\begin{array}{r} {\scriptstyle 1} \\ 4\;8\;7 \\ +\;3\;6\;9 \\ \hline 6 \end{array}$$

HUNDREDS TENS ONES

• Add the ones column.
7 + 9 = 16 (1 ten + 6 ones).
Write the 6 in the ones column and carry the 1 ten to the tens column.

$$\begin{array}{r} {\scriptstyle 1\;1} \\ 4\;8\;7 \\ +\;3\;6\;9 \\ \hline 5\;6 \end{array}$$

• Add the tens column.
1 + 8 + 6 = 15 (1 hundred + 5 tens).
Write the 5 in the tens column and carry the 1 hundred to the hundreds column.

$$\begin{array}{r} {\scriptstyle 1\;1} \\ 4\;8\;7 \\ +\;3\;6\;9 \\ \hline 8\;5\;6 \end{array}$$

• Add the hundreds column.
1 + 4 + 3 = 8 (8 hundreds).
Write the 8 in the hundreds column.

Example 1 Find the total of 17, 103, and 8.

Solution

$$
\begin{array}{r}
\overset{1}{17} \\
103 \\
+\ \ 8 \\
\hline
128
\end{array}
$$

• $7 + 3 + 8 = 18$
Write the 8 in the ones column. Carry the 1 to the tens column.

You Try It 1 What is 347 increased by 12,453?

Your solution

Example 2 Add: $89 + 36 + 98$

Solution

$$
\begin{array}{r}
\overset{2}{89} \\
36 \\
+\ 98 \\
\hline
223
\end{array}
$$

• $9 + 6 + 8 = 23$
Write the 3 in the ones column. Carry the 2 to the tens column.

You Try It 2 Add: $95 + 88 + 67$

Your solution

Example 3 Add:

$$
\begin{array}{r}
41{,}395 \\
4{,}327 \\
497{,}625 \\
+\ 32{,}991
\end{array}
$$

Solution

$$
\begin{array}{r}
\overset{1\,1\,2\ \,2\,1}{41{,}395} \\
4{,}327 \\
497{,}625 \\
+\ 32{,}991 \\
\hline
576{,}338
\end{array}
$$

You Try It 3 Add:

$$
\begin{array}{r}
392 \\
4{,}079 \\
89{,}035 \\
+\ 4{,}992
\end{array}
$$

Your solution

Solutions on p. S1

● E S T I M A T I O N ●

Estimation and Calculators

At some places in the text, you will be asked to use your calculator. Effective use of a calculator requires that you estimate the answer to the problem. This helps ensure that you have entered the numbers correctly and pressed the correct keys.

Integrating
Technology
This example illustrates that estimation is important when one is using a calculator.

For example, if you use your calculator to find $22{,}347 + 5896$ and the answer in the calculator's display is 131,757,912, you should realize that you have entered some part of the calculation incorrectly. In this case, you pressed $\times$ instead of $+$. By estimating the answer to a problem, you can help ensure the accuracy of your calculations. We have a special symbol for **approximately equal to ($\approx$).**

For example, to estimate the answer to $22{,}347 + 5896$, round each number to the same place value. In this case, we will round to the nearest thousand. Then add.

$$
\begin{array}{r}
22{,}347 \approx\ \ 22{,}000 \\
+\ \ 5{,}896 \approx +\ \ 6{,}000 \\
\hline
28{,}000
\end{array}
$$

The sum $22{,}347 + 5896$ is approximately 28,000. Knowing this, you would know that 131,757,912 is much too large and is therefore incorrect.

To estimate the sum of two numbers, first round each whole number to the same place value and then add. Compare this answer with the calculator's answer.

To solve application problems

To solve an application problem, first read the problem carefully. The **strategy** involves identifying the quantity to be found and planning the steps that are necessary to find that quantity. The **solution of an application problem** involves performing each operation stated in the strategy and writing the answer.

The table below displays the Wal-Mart store counts as reported in the Wal-Mart 2003 Annual Report.

	Discount Stores	Supercenters	SAM'S CLUBS	Neighborhood Markets
Within the United States	1568	1258	525	49
Outside the United States	942	238	71	37

HOW TO Find the total number of Wal-Mart stores in the United States.

Strategy To find the total number of Wal-Mart stores in the United States, read the table to find the number of each type of store in the United States. Then add these numbers.

Solution

$$
\begin{array}{r}
1568 \\
1258 \\
525 \\
+\ \ \ 49 \\
\hline
3400
\end{array}
$$

Wal-Mart has a total of 3400 stores in the United States.

Example 4

According to the table above, how many discount stores does Wal-Mart have worldwide?

Strategy
To determine the number of discount stores worldwide, read the table to find the number of discount stores within the United States and the number of discount stores outside the United States. Then add the two numbers.

Solution

$$
\begin{array}{r}
1568 \\
+\ 942 \\
\hline
2510
\end{array}
$$

Wal-Mart has 2510 discount stores worldwide.

You Try It 4

Use the table above to determine the total number of Wal-Mart stores that are outside the United States.

Your strategy

Your solution

Solution on p. S1

1.2 Exercises

Objective A   **To add whole numbers**

For Exercises 1 to 32, add.

1.   17
        + 11

2.   25
        + 63

3.   83
        + 42

4.   63
        + 94

5.   77
        + 25

6.   63
        + 49

7.   56
        + 98

8.   86
        + 68

9.   658
        + 831

10.   842
         + 936

11.   735
         + 93

12.   189
         + 50

13.   859
         + 725

14.   637
         + 829

15.   470
         + 749

16.   427
         + 690

17.   36,925
         + 65,392

18.   56,772
         + 51,239

19.   50,873
         + 28,453

20.   34,872
         + 46,079

21.   878
          737
        + 189

22.   768
          461
        + 669

23.   319
          348
        + 912

24.   292
          579
        + 315

25.   9409
          3253
        + 7078

26.   8188
          8020
        + 7104

27.   2038
          2243
        + 3139

28.   4252
          6882
        + 5235

29.   67,428
          32,171
        + 20,971

30.   52,801
          11,664
        + 89,638

31.   76,290
          43,761
        + 87,402

32.   43,901
          98,301
        + 67,943

For Exercises 33 to 40, add.

33. 20,958 + 3218 + 42

34. 80,973 + 5168 + 29

35. 392 + 37 + 10,924 + 621

36. 694 + 62 + 70,129 + 217

37. 294 + 1029 + 7935 + 65

38. 692 + 2107 + 3196 + 92

39. 97 + 7234 + 69,532 + 276

40. 87 + 1698 + 27,317 + 727

41. What is 9874 plus 4509?

42. What is 7988 plus 5678?

43. What is 3487 increased by 5986?

44. What is 99,567 added to 126,863?

45. What is 23,569 more than 9678?

46. What is 7894 more than 45,872?

47. What is 479 added to 4579?

48. What is 23,902 added to 23,885?

49. Find the total of 659, 55, and 1278.

50. Find the total of 4561, 56, and 2309.

51. Find the sum of 34, 329, 8, and 67,892.

52. Find the sum of 45, 1289, 7, and 32,876.

 For Exercises 53 to 56, use a calculator to add. Then round the numbers to the nearest hundred, and use estimation to determine whether the sum is reasonable.

53. 1234 + 9780 + 6740

54. 919 + 3642 + 8796

55. 241 + 569 + 390 + 1672

56. 107 + 984 + 1035 + 2904

 For Exercises 57 to 60, use a calculator to add. Then round the numbers to the nearest thousand, and use estimation to determine whether the sum is reasonable.

57.
```
   32,461
    9,844
+  59,407
```

58.
```
   29,036
   22,904
+   7,903
```

59.
```
   25,432
   62,941
+  70,390
```

60.
```
   66,541
   29,365
+  98,742
```

For Exercises 61 to 64, use a calculator to add. Then round the numbers to the nearest ten-thousand, and use estimation to determine whether the sum is reasonable.

61.
67,421
82,984
66,361
10,792
+ 34,037

62.
21,896
4,235
62,544
21,892
+ 1,334

63.
281,421
9,874
34,394
526,398
+ 94,631

64.
542,698
97,327
7,235
73,667
+ 173,201

 For Exercises 65 to 68, use a calculator to add. Then round the numbers to the nearest million, and use estimation to determine whether the sum is reasonable.

65.
28,627,052
983,073
+ 3,081,496

66.
1,792,085
29,919,301
+ 3,406,882

67.
12,377,491
3,409,723
7,928,026
+ 10,705,682

68.
46,751,070
6,095,832
280,011
+ 1,563,897

Objective B   **To solve application problems**

69. **Demographics**   In a recent year, according to the U.S. Department of Health and Human Services, there were 110,670 twin births in this country, 6919 triplet births, 627 quadruplet deliveries, and 79 quintuplet and other higher-order multiple births. Find the total number of multiple births during the year.

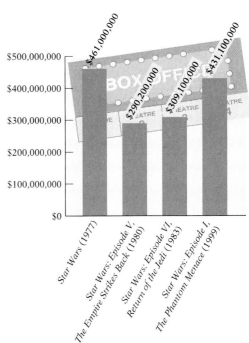

70. **Demographics**   The Census Bureau estimates that the U.S. population will grow by 296 million people from 2000 to 2100. Given that the U.S. population in 2000 was 281 million, find the Census Bureau's estimate of the U.S. population in 2100.

The Film Industry   The graph at the right shows the domestic box-office income from the first four *Star Wars* movies. Use this information for Exercises 71 to 73.

71. Estimate the total income from the first four *Star Wars* movies.

72. Find the total income from the first four *Star Wars* movies.

73. **a.** Find the total income from the two movies with the lowest box-office incomes.
b. Does the total income from the two movies with the lowest box-office incomes exceed the income from the 1977 *Star Wars* production?

Source: **www.worldwideboxoffice.com**

74. Geometry   The perimeter of a triangle is the sum of the lengths of the three sides of the triangle. Find the perimeter of a triangle that has sides that measure 12 inches, 14 inches, and 17 inches.

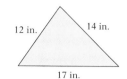

12 in. 14 in.

17 in.

75. Travel   The odometer on a moving van reads 68,692. The driver plans to drive 515 miles the first day, 492 miles the second day, and 278 miles the third day.
a. How many miles will be driven during the three days?
b. What will the odometer reading be at the end of the trip?

Investments   The table below shows the average amounts of money that all Americans have invested in selected assets and the average amounts invested for Americans between the ages of 16 and 34. Use this table for Exercises 76 to 79.

76. What is the total average amount for all Americans in checking accounts, savings accounts, and U.S. Savings Bonds?

77. What is the total average amount for Americans aged 16 to 34 in checking accounts, savings accounts, and U.S. Savings Bonds?

	All Americans	*Ages 16 to 34*
Checking accounts	$487	$375
Savings accounts	$3,494	$1,155
U.S. Savings Bonds	$546	$266
Money market	$10,911	$4,427
Stock/mutual funds	$4,510	$1,615
Home equity	$43,070	$17,184
Retirement	$9,016	$4,298

78. What is the total average amount for Americans aged 16 to 34 in all categories except home equity and retirement?

79. Is the sum of the average amounts invested in home equity and retirement for all Americans greater than or less than the sum of all categories for Americans between the ages of 16 and 34?

APPLYING THE CONCEPTS

80. a. How many two-digit numbers are there? **b.** How many three-digit numbers are there?

81. If you roll two ordinary six-sided dice and add the two numbers that appear on top, how many different sums are possible?

82. If you add two *different* whole numbers, is the sum always greater than either one of the numbers? If not, give an example.

83. If you add two whole numbers, is the sum always greater than either one of the numbers? If not, give an example. (Compare this with the previous exercise.)

84. ✎   Make up a word problem for which the answer is the sum of 34 and 28.

85. Call a number "lucky" if it ends in a 7. How many lucky numbers are less than 100?

1.3 Subtraction of Whole Numbers

Objective A   **To subtract whole numbers without borrowing**

Subtraction is the process of finding the difference between two numbers.

By counting, we see that the difference between $8 and $5 is $3.

$$\underset{\textbf{Minuend}}{\$8} \quad - \quad \underset{\textbf{Subtrahend}}{\$5} \quad = \quad \underset{\textbf{Difference}}{\$3}$$

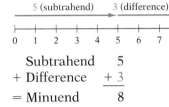

The difference $8 - 5$ can be shown on the number line.

Note from the number line that addition and subtraction are related.

$$
\begin{array}{ll}
& \text{Subtrahend} \quad 5 \\
+ & \text{Difference} \quad + \ 3 \\
\hline
= & \text{Minuend} \quad \ \ 8
\end{array}
$$

Point of Interest

The use of the minus sign dates from the same period as the plus sign, around 1515.

The fact that the sum of the subtrahend and the difference equals the minuend can be used to check subtraction.

To subtract large numbers, begin by arranging the numbers vertically, keeping the digits that have the same place value in the same column. Then subtract the digits in each column.

HOW TO   Subtract $8955 - 2432$ and check.

$$
\begin{array}{r}
\overset{\text{THOUSANDS} \ \text{HUNDREDS} \ \text{TENS} \ \text{ONES}}{} \\
8 \ 9 \ 5 \ 5 \\
- \ 2 \ 4 \ 3 \ 2 \\
\hline
6 \ 5 \ 2 \ 3
\end{array}
$$

Check:
$$
\begin{array}{ll}
\text{Subtrahend} & 2432 \\
+ \text{Difference} & + 6523 \\
\hline
= \text{Minuend} & 8955
\end{array}
$$

Example 1   Subtract $6594 - 3271$ and check.

Solution
$$
\begin{array}{r}
6594 \\
- 3271 \\
\hline
3323
\end{array}
\qquad
\textit{Check:}
\begin{array}{r}
3271 \\
+ 3323 \\
\hline
6594
\end{array}
$$

You Try It 1   Subtract $8925 - 6413$ and check.

Your solution

Example 2   Subtract $15{,}762 - 7541$ and check.

Solution
$$
\begin{array}{r}
15{,}762 \\
- \ 7{,}541 \\
\hline
8{,}221
\end{array}
\qquad
\textit{Check:}
\begin{array}{r}
7{,}541 \\
+ 8{,}221 \\
\hline
15{,}762
\end{array}
$$

You Try It 2   Subtract $17{,}504 - 9302$ and check.

Your solution

Solutions on p. S1

Objective B To subtract whole numbers with borrowing

In all the subtraction problems in the previous objective, for each place value the lower digit was not larger than the upper digit. When the lower digit *is* larger than the upper digit, subtraction will involve **borrowing.**

HOW TO Subtract: 692 − 378

HUNDREDS	TENS	ONES
	8+1	
6	9̷	2
− 3	7	8

Because 8 > 2, borrowing is necessary.
9 tens = 8 tens + 1 ten.

HUNDREDS	TENS	ONES
	8+①	10
6	9̷	2
− 3	7	8

Borrow 1 ten from the tens column and write 10 in the ones column.

HUNDREDS	TENS	ONES
	8	12
6	9̷	2̷
− 3	7	8

Add the borrowed 10 to 2.

HUNDREDS	TENS	ONES
	8	12
6	9̷	2̷
− 3	7	8
3	1	4

Subtract the digits in each column.

The phrases below are used to indicate the operation of subtraction. An example is shown at the right of each phrase.

minus	8 minus 5	8 − 5
less	9 less 3	9 − 3
less than	2 less than 7	7 − 2
the difference between	the difference between 8 and 2	8 − 2
decreased by	5 decreased by 1	5 − 1

HOW TO Find the difference between 1234 and 485, and check.

"The difference between 1234 and 485" means 1234 − 485.

$$
\begin{array}{r}
\;\;2\;\;14 \\
1\;\;2\;\;\cancel{3}\;\;\cancel{4} \\
-\;\;\;\;4\;\;8\;\;5 \\
\hline
9
\end{array}
\qquad
\begin{array}{r}
\;1\;\;12\;\;14 \\
1\;\;\cancel{2}\;\;\cancel{3}\;\;\cancel{4} \\
-\;\;\;\;4\;\;8\;\;5 \\
\hline
4\;\;9
\end{array}
\qquad
\begin{array}{r}
0\;\;11\;\;12\;\;14 \\
\cancel{1}\;\;\cancel{2}\;\;\cancel{3}\;\;\cancel{4} \\
-\;\;\;\;4\;\;8\;\;5 \\
\hline
7\;\;4\;\;9
\end{array}
\qquad
Check:\;
\begin{array}{r}
1\;1 \\
485 \\
+\;749 \\
\hline
1234
\end{array}
$$

Subtraction with a zero in the minuend involves repeated borrowing.

HOW TO Subtract: 3904 − 1775

$$
\begin{array}{r}
\;\;8\;\;10 \\
3\;\;\cancel{9}\;\;\cancel{0}\;\;4 \\
-\;1\;\;7\;\;7\;\;5
\end{array}
\qquad
\begin{array}{r}
\;\;\;\;\;9 \\
\;\;8\;\;10\;\;14 \\
3\;\;\cancel{9}\;\;\cancel{0}\;\;\cancel{4} \\
-\;1\;\;7\;\;7\;\;5
\end{array}
\qquad
\begin{array}{r}
\;\;\;\;\;9 \\
\;\;8\;\;10\;\;14 \\
3\;\;\cancel{9}\;\;\cancel{0}\;\;\cancel{4} \\
-\;1\;\;7\;\;7\;\;5 \\
\hline
2\;\;1\;\;2\;\;9
\end{array}
$$

5 > 4
There is a 0 in the tens column. Borrow 1 hundred (= 10 tens) from the hundreds column and write 10 in the tens column.

Borrow 1 ten from the tens column and add 10 to the 4 in the ones column.

Subtract the digits in each column.

Example 3   Subtract 4392 − 678 and check.

Solution

$$
\begin{array}{r}
\overset{3}{\cancel{4}}\ \overset{13}{\cancel{3}}\ \overset{8}{\cancel{9}}\ \overset{12}{\cancel{2}} \\
-\ \ 6\ \ 7\ \ 8 \\
\hline
3\ \ 7\ \ 1\ \ 4
\end{array}
$$

Check:
$$
\begin{array}{r}
678 \\
+\ 3714 \\
\hline
4392
\end{array}
$$

You Try It 3   Subtract 3481 − 865 and check.

Your solution

Example 4   Find 23,954 less than 63,221 and check.

Solution

$$
\begin{array}{r}
\overset{5}{\cancel{6}}\ \overset{12}{\cancel{3}},\overset{11}{\cancel{2}}\ \overset{11}{\cancel{2}}\ \overset{11}{\cancel{1}} \\
-\ 2\ 3\ ,9\ 5\ 4 \\
\hline
3\ 9\ ,2\ 6\ 7
\end{array}
$$

Check:
$$
\begin{array}{r}
23,954 \\
+39,267 \\
\hline
63,221
\end{array}
$$

You Try It 4   Find 54,562 decreased by 14,485 and check.

Your solution

Example 5   Subtract 46,005 − 32,167 and check.

Solution

$$
\begin{array}{r}
4\ \overset{5}{\cancel{6}},\overset{10}{\cancel{0}}\ 0\ 5 \\
-3\ 2\ ,1\ 6\ 7
\end{array}
$$

- There are two zeros in the minuend. Borrow 1 thousand from the thousands column and write 10 in the hundreds column.

$$
\begin{array}{r}
4\ \overset{5}{\cancel{6}},\overset{10}{\cancel{0}}\ \overset{10}{\cancel{0}}\ 5 \\
-3\ 2\ ,1\ 6\ 7
\end{array}
$$

- Borrow 1 hundred from the hundreds column and write 10 in the tens column.

$$
\begin{array}{r}
4\ \overset{5}{\cancel{6}},\overset{\overset{9}{10}}{\cancel{0}}\ \overset{10}{\cancel{0}}\ \overset{15}{\cancel{5}} \\
-3\ 2\ ,1\ 6\ 7 \\
\hline
1\ 3\ ,8\ 3\ 8
\end{array}
$$

- Borrow 1 ten from the tens column and add 10 to the 5 in the ones column.

Check:
$$
\begin{array}{r}
32,167 \\
+13,838 \\
\hline
46,005
\end{array}
$$

You Try It 5   Subtract 64,003 − 54,936 and check.

Your solution

Solutions on pp. S1–S2

● E S T I M A T I O N ●

Estimating the Difference Between Two Whole Numbers

Calculate 323,502 − 28,912. Then use estimation to determine whether the difference is reasonable.

Subtract to find the exact difference. To estimate the difference, round each number to the same place value. Here we have rounded to the nearest ten-thousand. Then subtract. The estimated answer is 290,000, which is very close to the exact difference 294,590.

$$
\begin{array}{rcr}
323,502 & \approx & 320,000 \\
-\ 28,912 & \approx & -\ 30,000 \\
\hline
294,590 & & 290,000
\end{array}
$$

Objective C   **To solve application problems**

The table at the right shows the number of personnel on active duty in the branches of the U.S. military in 1940 and 1945. Use this table for Example 6 and You Try It 6.

Branch	1940	1945
U.S. Army	267,767	8,266,373
U.S. Navy	160,997	3,380,817
U.S. Air Force	51,165	2,282,259
U.S. Marine Corps	28,345	474,680

Source: Dept. of the Army, Dept. of the Navy, Air Force Dept., Dept. of the Marines, U.S. Dept. of Defense

---

Example 6

Find the difference between the number of U.S. Army personnel on active duty in 1945 and the number in 1940.

Strategy

To find the difference, subtract the number of U.S. Army personnel on active duty in 1940 (267,767) from the number on active duty in 1945 (8,266,373).

Solution

$$\begin{array}{r} 8{,}266{,}373 \\ -\quad 267{,}767 \\ \hline 7{,}998{,}606 \end{array}$$

There were 7,998,606 more personnel on active duty in the U.S. Army in 1945 than in 1940.

You Try It 6

Find the difference between the number of personnel on active duty in the Navy and the number in the Air Force in 1945.

Your strategy

Your solution

Example 7

You had a balance of $415 on your student debit card. You then used the card, deducting $197 for books, $48 for art supplies, and $24 for theater tickets. What is your new student debit card balance?

Strategy

To find your new debit card balance:

• Add to find the total of the three deductions (197 + 48 + 24).
• Subtract the total of the three deductions from the old balance (415).

Solution

$$\begin{array}{r} 197 \\ 48 \\ +\ 24 \\ \hline 269 \end{array} \text{ total deductions} \qquad \begin{array}{r} 415 \\ -269 \\ \hline 146 \end{array}$$

Your new debit card balance is $146.

You Try It 7

Your total weekly salary is $638. Deductions of $127 for taxes, $18 for insurance, and $35 for savings are taken from your pay. Find your weekly take-home pay.

Your strategy

Your solution

Solutions on p. S2

1.3 Exercises

To subtract whole numbers without borrowing

For Exercises 1 to 35, subtract.

1. $\begin{array}{r} 9 \\ -\ 5 \\ \hline \end{array}$
2. $\begin{array}{r} 8 \\ -\ 7 \\ \hline \end{array}$
3. $\begin{array}{r} 8 \\ -\ 4 \\ \hline \end{array}$
4. $\begin{array}{r} 7 \\ -\ 3 \\ \hline \end{array}$
5. $\begin{array}{r} 10 \\ -\ 0 \\ \hline \end{array}$

6. $\begin{array}{r} 11 \\ -\ 4 \\ \hline \end{array}$
7. $\begin{array}{r} 12 \\ -\ 8 \\ \hline \end{array}$
8. $\begin{array}{r} 19 \\ -\ 8 \\ \hline \end{array}$
9. $\begin{array}{r} 15 \\ -\ 6 \\ \hline \end{array}$
10. $\begin{array}{r} 16 \\ -\ 7 \\ \hline \end{array}$

11. $\begin{array}{r} 25 \\ -\ 3 \\ \hline \end{array}$
12. $\begin{array}{r} 55 \\ -\ 4 \\ \hline \end{array}$
13. $\begin{array}{r} 68 \\ -\ 8 \\ \hline \end{array}$
14. $\begin{array}{r} 77 \\ -\ 3 \\ \hline \end{array}$
15. $\begin{array}{r} 89 \\ -23 \\ \hline \end{array}$

16. $\begin{array}{r} 54 \\ -21 \\ \hline \end{array}$
17. $\begin{array}{r} 88 \\ -57 \\ \hline \end{array}$
18. $\begin{array}{r} 1202 \\ -\ 701 \\ \hline \end{array}$
19. $\begin{array}{r} 1305 \\ -\ 404 \\ \hline \end{array}$
20. $\begin{array}{r} 1763 \\ -\ 801 \\ \hline \end{array}$

21. $\begin{array}{r} 1497 \\ -\ 706 \\ \hline \end{array}$
22. $\begin{array}{r} 8974 \\ -3972 \\ \hline \end{array}$
23. $\begin{array}{r} 2836 \\ -1711 \\ \hline \end{array}$
24. $\begin{array}{r} 8976 \\ -7463 \\ \hline \end{array}$
25. $\begin{array}{r} 9273 \\ -6142 \\ \hline \end{array}$

26. $77 - 36$
27. $129 - 82$
28. $132 - 61$
29. $969 - 44$
30. $1347 - 103$

31. $4865 - 304$
32. $1525 - 702$
33. $9999 - 6794$
34. $7806 - 3405$
35. $8843 - 7621$

36. What is 3795 minus 1092?

37. What is 9071 minus 6050?

38. Find the difference between 9763 and 541.

39. Find the difference between 6094 and 3072.

40. What is 3701 less than 6932?

41. What is 2031 less than 5071?

42. Find 6509 decreased by 3102.

43. Find 7994 decreased by 7782.

44. Find 23,907 less 12,705.

45. Find 65,986 less 5741.

Objective B **To subtract whole numbers with borrowing**

For Exercises 46 to 89, subtract.

46. $\begin{array}{r} 71 \\ -\,18 \\ \hline \end{array}$ 47. $\begin{array}{r} 93 \\ -\,28 \\ \hline \end{array}$ 48. $\begin{array}{r} 47 \\ -\,18 \\ \hline \end{array}$ 49. $\begin{array}{r} 44 \\ -\,27 \\ \hline \end{array}$

50. $\begin{array}{r} 37 \\ -\,29 \\ \hline \end{array}$ 51. $\begin{array}{r} 50 \\ -\,27 \\ \hline \end{array}$ 52. $\begin{array}{r} 70 \\ -\,33 \\ \hline \end{array}$ 53. $\begin{array}{r} 993 \\ -\,537 \\ \hline \end{array}$

54. $\begin{array}{r} 250 \\ -\,192 \\ \hline \end{array}$ 55. $\begin{array}{r} 840 \\ -\,783 \\ \hline \end{array}$ 56. $\begin{array}{r} 768 \\ -\,194 \\ \hline \end{array}$ 57. $\begin{array}{r} 770 \\ -\,395 \\ \hline \end{array}$

58. $674 - 337$ 59. $3526 - 387$ 60. $1712 - 289$ 61. $4350 - 729$

62. $1702 - 948$ 63. $1607 - 869$ 64. $5933 - 3754$ 65. $7293 - 3748$

66. $9407 - 2918$ 67. $3706 - 2957$ 68. $8605 - 7716$ 69. $8052 - 2709$

70. $80,305 - 9176$ 71. $70,702 - 4239$ 72. $10,004 - 9306$ 73. $80,009 - 63,419$

74. $70,618 - 41,213$ 75. $80,053 - 27,649$ 76. $70,700 - 21,076$ 77. $80,800 - 42,023$

78. $\begin{array}{r} 2600 \\ -\,1972 \\ \hline \end{array}$ 79. $\begin{array}{r} 8400 \\ -\,3762 \\ \hline \end{array}$ 80. $\begin{array}{r} 9003 \\ -\,2471 \\ \hline \end{array}$ 81. $\begin{array}{r} 6004 \\ -\,2392 \\ \hline \end{array}$

82. $\begin{array}{r} 8202 \\ -\,3916 \\ \hline \end{array}$ 83. $\begin{array}{r} 7050 \\ -\,4137 \\ \hline \end{array}$ 84. $\begin{array}{r} 7015 \\ -\,2973 \\ \hline \end{array}$ 85. $\begin{array}{r} 4207 \\ -\,1624 \\ \hline \end{array}$

86. $\begin{array}{r} 7005 \\ -\,1796 \\ \hline \end{array}$ 87. $\begin{array}{r} 8003 \\ -\,2735 \\ \hline \end{array}$ 88. $\begin{array}{r} 20,005 \\ -\,9,627 \\ \hline \end{array}$ 89. $\begin{array}{r} 80,004 \\ -\,8,237 \\ \hline \end{array}$

90. Find 10,051 less 9027.

91. Find 17,031 less 5792.

92. Find the difference between 1003 and 447.

93. What is 29,874 minus 21,392?

94. What is 29,797 less than 68,005?

95. What is 69,379 less than 70,004?

96. What is 25,432 decreased by 7994?

97. What is 86,701 decreased by 9976?

For Exercises 98 to 101, use the relationship between addition and subtraction to complete the statement.

98. ___ + 39 = 104   **99.** 67 + ___ = 90   **100.** ___ + 497 = 862   **101.** 253 + ___ = 4901

For Exercises 102 to 107, use a calculator to subtract. Then round the numbers to the nearest ten-thousand and use estimation to determine whether the difference is reasonable.

102.   80,032
           − 19,605

103.   90,765
           − 60,928

104.   32,574
           − 10,961

105.   96,430
           − 59,762

106.   567,423
           − 208,444

107.   300,712
           − 198,714

Objective C   **To solve application problems**

108. Banking   You have $304 in your checking account. If you write a check for $139, how much is left in your checking account?

109. **Identity Theft**   Use the graph at the right to determine the increase in the number of identity theft complaints from 2001 to 2002.

110. Consumerism   The tennis coach at a high school purchased a video camera that costs $1079 and made a down payment of $180. Find the amount that remains to be paid.

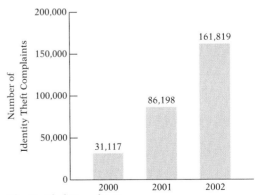

Identity Theft Complaints

Source: Federal Trade Commission

111. Consumerism   Rod Guerra, an engineer, purchased a used car that cost $11,225 and made a down payment of $950. Find the amount that remains to be paid.

112. 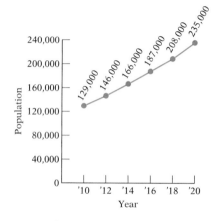 **Earth Science**   Use the graph at the right to find the difference between the maximum height to which Great Fountain geyser erupts and the maximum height to which Valentine erupts.

113. **Earth Science**   According to the graph at the right, how much higher is the eruption of the Giant than that of Old Faithful?

114. **Education**   The National Center for Education Statistics estimates that 850,000 women and 587,000 men will earn a bachelor's degree in 2012. How many more women than men are expected to earn a bachelor's degree in 2012?

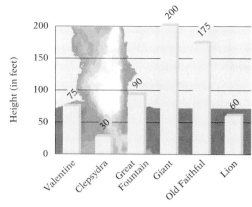

The Maximum Heights of the Eruptions of Six Geysers at Yellowstone National Park

Demographics   The graph at the right shows the expected U.S. population aged 100 and over, every 2 years from 2010 to 2020. Use this information for Exercises 115 and 116.

115.   What is the expected growth in the population aged 100 and over during the 10-year period?

116. a. Which 2-year period has the smallest expected increase in the number of people aged 100 and over?
   b. Which 2-year period has the greatest expected increase?

Expected U.S. Population Aged 100 and Over

Source: Census Bureau

117. Expense Accounts   A sales executive has a monthly expense account of $1500. This month the executive has already spent $479 for transportation, $268 for food, and $317 for lodging. Find the amount remaining in this month's expense account.

118. Finances   You had a credit card balance of $409 before you used the card to purchase books for $168, CDs for $36, and a pair of shoes for $97. You then made a payment to the credit card company of $350. Find your new credit card balance.

APPLYING THE CONCEPTS

119.   Answer true or false.
   a. The phrases "the difference between 9 and 5" and "5 less than 9" mean the same thing.
   b. $9 - (5 - 3) = (9 - 5) - 3$.
   c. Subtraction is an associative operation. *Hint:* See part b of this exercise.

120. Make up a word problem for which the difference between 15 and 8 is the answer.

1.4 Multiplication of Whole Numbers

Objective A   **To multiply a number by a single digit**

Six boxes of toasters are ordered. Each box contains eight toasters. How many toasters are ordered?

This problem can be worked by adding 6 eights.

$8 + 8 + 8 + 8 + 8 + 8 = 48$

This problem involves repeated addition of the same number and can be worked by a shorter process called **multiplication.** Multiplication is the repeated addition of the same number.

$8 + 8 + 8 + 8 + 8 + 8 = 48$

The numbers that are multiplied are called **factors.** The result is called the **product.**

or
$$6 \times 8 = 48$$
Factor Factor   Product

The product of 6×8 can be represented on the number line. The arrow representing the whole number 8 is repeated 6 times. The result is the arrow representing 48.

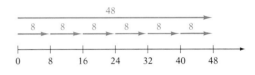

The times sign "$\times$" is only one symbol that is used to indicate multiplication. Each of the expressions that follow represent multiplication.

$$7 \times 8 \qquad 7 \cdot 8 \qquad 7(8) \qquad (7)(8) \qquad (7)8$$

As with addition, there are some useful properties of multiplication.

Multiplication Property of Zero
The product of a number and zero is zero.

$0 \times 4 = 0$
$7 \times 0 = 0$

Multiplication Property of One
The product of a number and one is the number.

$1 \times 6 = 6$
$8 \times 1 = 8$

Commutative Property of Multiplication
Two numbers can be multiplied in either order. The product will be the same.

$4 \times 3 = 3 \times 4$
$12 = 12$

Associative Property of Multiplication
Grouping the numbers to be multiplied in any order gives the same result. Do the multiplication inside the parentheses first.

$(4 \times 2) \times 3 = 4 \times (2 \times 3)$
$8 \times 3 = 4 \times 6$
$24 = 24$

The basic facts for multiplying one-digit numbers should be memorized. Multiplication of larger numbers requires the repeated use of the basic multiplication facts.

HOW TO Multiply: 37×4

$$
\begin{array}{r}
\overset{2}{3}\ 7 \\
\times\quad 4 \\
\hline
8
\end{array}
$$

- $4 \times 7 = 28$ (2 tens + 8 ones).
  Write the 8 in the ones column and
  carry the 2 to the tens column.

$$
\begin{array}{r}
\overset{2}{3}\ 7 \\
\times\quad 4 \\
\hline
14\ \ 8
\end{array}
$$

- The 3 in 37 is 3 tens.
  $$
  \begin{array}{r}
  4 \times 3 \text{ tens} = 12 \text{ tens} \\
  \text{Add the carry digit.} \quad + 2 \text{ tens} \\
  \hline
  14 \text{ tens}
  \end{array}
  $$

- Write the 14.

The phrases below are used to indicate the operation of multiplication. An example is shown at the right of each phrase.

times	7 times 3	$7 \cdot 3$
the product of	the product of 6 and 9	$6 \cdot 9$
multiplied by	8 multiplied by 2	$2 \cdot 8$

Example 1 Multiply: 735×9

Solution

$$
\begin{array}{r}
\overset{3\ 4}{735} \\
\times\quad 9 \\
\hline
6615
\end{array}
$$

- $9 \times 5 = 45$
  Write the 5 in the ones
  column. Carry the 4 to the
  tens column.
  $9 \times 3 = 27, 27 + 4 = 31$
  $9 \times 7 = 63, 63 + 3 = 66$

You Try It 1 Multiply: 648×7

Your solution

Solution on p. S2

Objective B **To multiply larger whole numbers**

Note the pattern when the following numbers are multiplied.

Multiply the nonzero part of the factors.

Now attach the same number of zeros to the product as the total number of zeros in the factors.

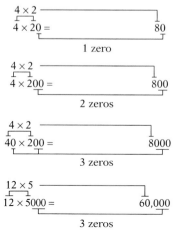

4×2
$4 \times 20 = 80$
1 zero

4×2
$4 \times 200 = 800$
2 zeros

4×2
$40 \times 200 = 8000$
3 zeros

12×5
$12 \times 5000 = 60,000$
3 zeros

HOW TO   Find the product of 47 and 23.

Multiply by the ones digit.	Multiply by the tens digit.	Add.

$$\begin{array}{r} 47 \\ \times\ 23 \\ \hline 141 \end{array} (= 47 \times 3)$$

$$\begin{array}{r} 47 \\ \times\ 23 \\ \hline 141 \\ 940 \end{array} (= 47 \times 20)$$

$$\begin{array}{r} 47 \\ \times\ 23 \\ \hline 141 \\ 940 \\ \hline 1081 \end{array}$$

Writing the 0 is optional.

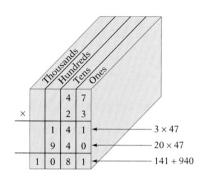

3 × 47
20 × 47
141 + 940

The place-value chart illustrates the placement of the products.

Note the placement of the products when we are multiplying by a factor that contains a zero.

HOW TO   Multiply: 439 × 206

$$\begin{array}{r} 439 \\ \times\ 206 \\ \hline 2634 \\ 000 \\ 878 \\ \hline 90{,}434 \end{array}$$

0 × 439

When working the problem, we usually write only one zero. Writing this zero ensures the proper placement of the products.

$$\begin{array}{r} 439 \\ \times\ 206 \\ \hline 2634 \\ 8780 \\ \hline 90{,}434 \end{array}$$

Example 2   Find 829 multiplied by 603.

Solution

$$\begin{array}{r} 829 \\ \times\ 603 \\ \hline 2487 \\ 49740 \\ \hline 499{,}887 \end{array}$$

- **3 × 829 = 2487**
- **Write a zero in the tens column for 0 × 829.**
- **6 × 829 = 4974**

You Try It 2   Multiply: 756 × 305

Your solution

Solution on p. S2

● E S T I M A T I O N ●

Estimating the Product of Two Whole Numbers

Calculate 3267 × 389. Then use estimation to determine whether the product is reasonble.

Multiply to find the exact product.   3267 × 389 = 1,270,863

To estimate the product, round each number so there is one nonzero digit. Then multiply. The estimated answer is 1,200,000, which is very close to the exact product 1,270,863.

$$\begin{array}{r} 3267 \approx\quad 3000 \\ \times\ 389 \approx\ \times\ 400 \\ \hline 1{,}200{,}000 \end{array}$$

To solve application problems

Example 3

An auto mechanic receives a salary of $1050 each week. How much does the auto mechanic earn in 4 weeks?

Strategy

To find the mechanic's earnings for 4 weeks, multiply the weekly salary (1050) by the number of weeks (4).

Solution

```
  1050
×    4
  4200
```

The mechanic earns $4200 in 4 weeks.

You Try It 3

A new-car dealer receives a shipment of 37 cars each month. Find the number of cars the dealer will receive in 12 months.

Your strategy

Your solution

Example 4

A press operator earns $640 for working a 40-hour week. This week the press operator also worked 7 hours of overtime at $26 an hour. Find the press operator's total pay for the week.

Strategy

To find the press operator's total pay for the week:

- Find the overtime pay by multiplying the hours of overtime (7) by the overtime rate of pay (26).
- Add the weekly salary (640) to the overtime pay.

Solution

```
      26              640
×      7            +182
  182 overtime pay   822
```

The press operator earned $822 this week.

You Try It 4

The buyer for Ross Department Store can buy 80 men's suits for $4800. Each sports jacket will cost the store $23. The manager orders 80 men's suits and 25 sports jackets. What is the total cost of the order?

Your strategy

Your solution

Solutions on p. S2

1.4 Exercises

Objective A   **To multiply a number by a single digit**

For Exercises 1 to 4, write the expression as a product.

1. $2 + 2 + 2 + 2 + 2 + 2$ **2.** $4 + 4 + 4 + 4 + 4$ **3.** $7 + 7 + 7 + 7$ **4.** $18 + 18 + 18$

For Exercises 5 to 39, multiply.

5. $\begin{array}{r} 3 \\ \times\, 4 \\ \hline \end{array}$ **6.** $\begin{array}{r} 2 \\ \times\, 8 \\ \hline \end{array}$ **7.** $\begin{array}{r} 5 \\ \times\, 7 \\ \hline \end{array}$ **8.** $\begin{array}{r} 6 \\ \times\, 4 \\ \hline \end{array}$ **9.** $\begin{array}{r} 5 \\ \times\, 5 \\ \hline \end{array}$

10. $\begin{array}{r} 7 \\ \times\, 7 \\ \hline \end{array}$ **11.** $\begin{array}{r} 0 \\ \times\, 7 \\ \hline \end{array}$ **12.** $\begin{array}{r} 8 \\ \times\, 0 \\ \hline \end{array}$ **13.** $\begin{array}{r} 8 \\ \times\, 9 \\ \hline \end{array}$ **14.** $\begin{array}{r} 7 \\ \times\, 6 \\ \hline \end{array}$

15. $\begin{array}{r} 66 \\ \times\, 3 \\ \hline \end{array}$ **16.** $\begin{array}{r} 70 \\ \times\, 4 \\ \hline \end{array}$ **17.** $\begin{array}{r} 67 \\ \times\, 5 \\ \hline \end{array}$ **18.** $\begin{array}{r} 127 \\ \times\, 9 \\ \hline \end{array}$ **19.** $\begin{array}{r} 623 \\ \times\, 4 \\ \hline \end{array}$

20. $\begin{array}{r} 802 \\ \times\, 5 \\ \hline \end{array}$ **21.** $\begin{array}{r} 607 \\ \times\, 9 \\ \hline \end{array}$ **22.** $\begin{array}{r} 300 \\ \times\, 5 \\ \hline \end{array}$ **23.** $\begin{array}{r} 600 \\ \times\, 7 \\ \hline \end{array}$ **24.** $\begin{array}{r} 906 \\ \times\, 8 \\ \hline \end{array}$

25. $\begin{array}{r} 703 \\ \times\, 9 \\ \hline \end{array}$ **26.** $\begin{array}{r} 127 \\ \times\, 5 \\ \hline \end{array}$ **27.** $\begin{array}{r} 632 \\ \times\, 3 \\ \hline \end{array}$ **28.** $\begin{array}{r} 559 \\ \times\, 4 \\ \hline \end{array}$ **29.** $\begin{array}{r} 632 \\ \times\, 8 \\ \hline \end{array}$

30. $\begin{array}{r} 524 \\ \times\, 4 \\ \hline \end{array}$ **31.** $\begin{array}{r} 337 \\ \times\, 5 \\ \hline \end{array}$ **32.** $\begin{array}{r} 841 \\ \times\, 6 \\ \hline \end{array}$ **33.** $\begin{array}{r} 6709 \\ \times\, 7 \\ \hline \end{array}$ **34.** $\begin{array}{r} 3608 \\ \times\, 5 \\ \hline \end{array}$

35. $\begin{array}{r} 8568 \\ \times\, 7 \\ \hline \end{array}$ **36.** $\begin{array}{r} 5495 \\ \times\, 4 \\ \hline \end{array}$ **37.** $\begin{array}{r} 4780 \\ \times\, 4 \\ \hline \end{array}$ **38.** $\begin{array}{r} 3690 \\ \times\, 5 \\ \hline \end{array}$ **39.** $\begin{array}{r} 9895 \\ \times\, 2 \\ \hline \end{array}$

40. Find the product of 5, 7, and 4.   **41.** Find the product of 6, 2, and 9.

42. Find the product of 5304 and 9.   **43.** Find the product of 458 and 8.

44. What is 3208 multiplied by 7?

45. What is 5009 multiplied by 4?

46. What is 3105 times 6?

47. What is 8957 times 8?

Objective B   **To multiply larger whole numbers**

For Exercises 48 to 79, multiply.

48.   16
      × 21

49.   18
      × 24

50.   35
      × 26

51.   27
      × 72

52.   693
      × 91

53.   581
      × 72

54.   419
      × 80

55.   727
      × 60

56.   8279
      × 46

57.   9577
      × 35

58.   6938
      × 78

59.   8875
      × 67

60.   7035
      × 57

61.   6702
      × 48

62.   3009
      × 35

63.   6003
      × 57

64.   809
      × 530

65.   607
      × 460

66.   800
      × 325

67.   700
      × 274

68.   987
      × 349

69.   688
      × 674

70.   312
      × 134

71.   423
      × 427

72.   379
      × 500

73.   684
      × 700

74.   985
      × 408

75.   758
      × 209

76.   3407
      × 309

77.   5207
      × 902

78.   4258
      × 986

79.   6327
      × 876

80. What is 5763 times 45?

81. What is 7349 times 27?

82. Find the product of 2, 19, and 34.

83. Find the product of 6, 73, and 43.

84. What is 376 multiplied by 402?

85. What is 842 multiplied by 309?

86. Find the product of 3005 and 233,489.

87. Find the product of 9007 and 34,985.

 For Exercises 88 to 95, use a calculator to multiply. Then use estimation to determine whether the product is reasonable.

88.	**89.**	**90.**	**91.**
8745	4732	2937	8941
× 63	× 93	× 206	× 726

92.	**93.**	**94.**	**95.**
3097	6379	32,508	62,504
× 1025	× 2936	× 591	× 923

Objective C   **To solve application problems**

96. **Fuel Efficiency**   Rob Hill owns a compact car that averages 43 miles on 1 gallon of gas. How many miles could the car travel on 12 gallons of gas?

97. **Fuel Efficiency**   A plane flying from Los Angeles to Boston uses 865 gallons of jet fuel each hour. How many gallons of jet fuel were used on a 6-hour flight?

98. **Geometry**   The perimeter of a square is equal to four times the length of a side of the square. Find the perimeter of a square whose side measures 16 miles.

16 mi

99. **Geometry**   To find the area of a square, multiply the length of one side of the square times itself. What is the area of a square whose side measures 16 miles? The area of the square will be in square miles.

100. **Geometry**   The area of a rectangle is equal to the product of the length of the rectangle times its width. Find the area of a rectangle that has a length of 24 meters and a width of 15 meters. The area will be in square meters.

15 m

24 m

Interior Design   A lighting consultant to a bank suggests that the bank lobby contain 43 can lights, 15 high-intensity lights, 20 fire safety lights, and one chandelier. The table at the right gives the costs for each type of light from two companies. Use this table for Exercises 101 and 102.

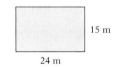

	Company A	*Company B*
Can lights	$2 each	$3 each
High-intensity	$6 each	$4 each
Fire safety	$12 each	$11 each
Chandelier	$998 each	$1089 each

101. Which company offers the lights for the lower total price?

102. How much can the lighting consultant save by purchasing the lights from the company that offers the lower total price?

Construction   The table at the right shows the hourly wages of four different job classifications at a small construction company. Use this table for Exercises 103 to 105.

Type of Work	Wage per Hour
Electrician	$34
Plumber	$30
Clerk	$16
Bookkeeper	$20

103. The owner of this company wants to provide the electrical installation for a new house. On the basis of the architectural plans for the house, it is estimated that it will require 3 electricians, each working 50 hours, to complete the job. What is the estimated cost for the electricians' labor?

104. Carlos Vasquez, a plumbing contractor, hires 4 plumbers from this company at the hourly wage given in the table. If each plumber works 23 hours, what are the total wages paid by Carlos?

105. The owner of this company estimates that remodeling a kitchen will require 1 electrician working 30 hours and 1 plumber working 33 hours. This project also requires 3 hours of clerical work and 4 hours of bookkeeping. What is the total cost for these four components of this remodeling?

APPLYING THE CONCEPTS

106. Determine whether each of the following statements is always true, sometimes true, or never true.
   a. A whole number times zero is zero.
   b. A whole number times one is the whole number.
   c. The product of two whole numbers is greater than either one of the whole numbers.

107.   **Safety**   According to the National Safety Council, in a recent year a death resulting from an accident occurred at the rate of 1 every 5 minutes. At this rate, how many accidental deaths occurred each hour? Each day? Throughout the year? Explain how you arrived at your answers.

108.   **Demographics**   According to the Population Reference Bureau, in the world today, 261 people are born every minute and 101 people die every minute. Using this statistic, what is the increase in the world's population every hour? Every day? Every week? Every year? Use a 365-day year. Explain how you arrived at your answers.

109.   Pick your favorite number between 1 and 9. Multiply the number by 3. Multiply that product by 37,037. How is the product related to your favorite number? Explain why this works. (*Suggestion:* Multiply 3 and 37,037 first.)

110. There are quite a few tricks based on whole numbers. Here's one about birthdays. Write down the month in which you were born. Multiply by 5. Add 7. Multiply by 20. Subtract 100. Add the day of the month on which you were born. Multiply by 4. Subtract 100. Multiply by 25. Add the year you were born. Subtract 3400. The answer is the month/day/year of your birthday.

1.5 Division of Whole Numbers

Objective A   **To divide by a single digit with no remainder in the quotient**

Division is used to separate objects into equal groups.

A store manager wants to display 24 new objects equally on 4 shelves. From the diagram, we see that the manager would place 6 objects on each shelf.

The manager's division problem can be written as follows:

> **TAKE NOTE**
> The **divisor** is the number that is divided into another number. The **dividend** is the number into which the divisor is divided. The result is the **quotient.**

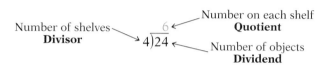

Note that the quotient multiplied by the divisor equals the dividend.

$$4\overline{)24} \quad \text{because} \quad \boxed{\begin{array}{c}6\\ \text{Quotient}\end{array}} \times \boxed{\begin{array}{c}4\\ \text{Divisor}\end{array}} = \boxed{\begin{array}{c}24\\ \text{Dividend}\end{array}}$$

$$9\overline{)54} \quad \text{because} \quad 6 \quad \times \quad 9 \quad = \quad 54$$

$$8\overline{)40} \quad \text{because} \quad 5 \quad \times \quad 8 \quad = \quad 40$$

Here are some important quotients and the properties of zero in division:

Properties of One in Division

Any whole number, except zero, divided by itself is 1.

$$8\overline{)8} \qquad 14\overline{)14} \qquad 10\overline{)10}$$

Any whole number divided by 1 is the whole number.

$$1\overline{)9} \qquad 1\overline{)27} \qquad 1\overline{)10}$$

Properties of Zero in Division

Zero divided by any other whole number is zero.

$$7\overline{)0} \qquad 13\overline{)0} \qquad 10\overline{)0}$$

Division by zero is not allowed.

$$0\overline{)8}$$

There is no number whose product with 0 is 8.

Integrating Technology

Enter 8 ÷ 0 = on your calculator. An error message is displayed because division by zero is not allowed.

When the dividend is a larger whole number, the digits in the quotient are found in steps.

HOW TO   Divide $4\overline{)3192}$ and check.

$$
\begin{array}{r}
7 \\
4\overline{)\,3192} \\
-28 \\
\hline
39
\end{array}
$$

- Think $4\overline{)31}$.
- Subtract 7×4.
- Bring down the 9.

$$
\begin{array}{r}
79 \\
4\overline{)\,3192} \\
-28 \\
\hline
39 \\
-36 \\
\hline
32
\end{array}
$$

- Think $4\overline{)39}$.
- Subtract 9×4.
- Bring down the 2.

$$
\begin{array}{r}
798 \\
4\overline{)\,3192} \\
-28 \\
\hline
39 \\
-36 \\
\hline
32 \\
-32 \\
\hline
0
\end{array}
$$

- Think $4\overline{)32}$.
- Subtract 8×4.

Check:

$$
\begin{array}{r}
798 \\
\times\quad 4 \\
\hline
3192
\end{array}
$$

The place-value chart can be used to show why this method works.

$$
\begin{array}{r}
7\ 9\ 8 \\
4\overline{)\,3\ 1\ 9\ 2} \\
-2\ 8\ 0\ 0 \quad \text{7 hundreds} \times 4 \\
\hline
3\ 9\ 2 \\
-3\ 6\ 0 \quad \text{9 tens} \times 4 \\
\hline
3\ 2 \\
-3\ 2 \quad \text{8 ones} \times 4 \\
\hline
0
\end{array}
$$

(HUNDREDS, TENS, ONES)

There are other ways of expressing division.

54 divided by 9 equals 6.

54 ÷ 9 equals 6.

$\dfrac{54}{9}$ equals 6.

Example 1   Divide 7)56 and check.

Solution $\dfrac{8}{7)56}$

Check: 8 × 7 = 56

You Try It 1   Divide 9)63 and check.

Your solution

Example 2   Divide 2808 ÷ 8 and check.

Solution

$$
\begin{array}{r}
351 \\
8)\overline{2808} \\
-24 \\
\hline
40 \\
-40 \\
\hline
08 \\
-\ 8 \\
\hline
0
\end{array}
$$

Check: 351 × 8 = 2808

You Try It 2   Divide 4077 ÷ 9 and check.

Your solution

Example 3   Divide 7)2856 and check.

Solution

$$
\begin{array}{r}
408 \\
7)\overline{2856} \\
-28 \\
\hline
05 \\
-0 \\
\hline
56 \\
-56 \\
\hline
0
\end{array}
$$

- Think 7)5. Place 0 in quotient.
- Subtract 0 × 7.
- Bring down the 6.

Check: 408 × 7 = 2856

You Try It 3   Divide 9)6345 and check.

Your solution

Solutions on pp. S2–S3

Objective B   **To divide by a single digit with a remainder in the quotient**

Sometimes it is not possible to separate objects into a whole number of equal groups.

A baker has 14 muffins to pack into 3 boxes. Each box holds 4 muffins. From the diagram, we see that after the baker places 4 muffins in each box, there are 2 left over. The 2 is called the **remainder.**

The clerk's division problem could be written

$$
\begin{array}{r}
\textbf{Quotient} \\
4 \swarrow \text{(Number in each box)}
\end{array}
$$

$$
\begin{array}{r}
\textbf{Divisor} \quad \longrightarrow 3)\overline{\,14\,} \longleftarrow \quad \textbf{Dividend} \\
\text{(Number of boxes)} \qquad \underline{-12} \quad \text{(Total number of objects)} \\
2 \longleftarrow \quad \text{Remainder} \\
\text{(Number left over)}
\end{array}
$$

The answer to a division problem with a remainder is frequently written

$$
\begin{array}{r}
4 \text{ r2} \\
3)\overline{14}
\end{array}
$$

Note that $\boxed{\begin{array}{c} 4 \\ \text{Quotient} \end{array} \times \begin{array}{c} 3 \\ \text{Divisor} \end{array}} + \boxed{\begin{array}{c} 2 \\ \text{Remainder} \end{array}} = \boxed{\begin{array}{c} 14 \\ \text{Dividend} \end{array}}$.

Example 4 Divide $4)\overline{2522}$ and check.

Solution

$$
\begin{array}{r}
630 \text{ r2} \\
4)\overline{2522} \\
\underline{-24} \\
12 \\
\underline{-12} \\
02 \\
\underline{-\ 0} \\
2
\end{array}
$$

     • Think $4)\overline{2}$. Place 0 in quotient.

     • Subtract 0 × 4.

Check: $(630 \times 4) + 2 =$
$\qquad 2520 \ + 2 = 2522$

You Try It 4 Divide $6)\overline{5225}$ and check.

Your solution

Example 5 Divide $9)\overline{27,438}$ and check.

Solution

$$
\begin{array}{r}
3,048 \text{ r6} \\
9)\overline{27,438} \\
\underline{-27} \\
04 \\
\underline{-\ 0} \\
43 \\
\underline{-36} \\
78 \\
\underline{-72} \\
6
\end{array}
$$

     • Think $9)\overline{4}$.

     • Subtract 0 × 9.

Check: $(3048 \times 9) + 6 =$
$\qquad 27,432 \ + 6 = 27,438$

You Try It 5 Divide $7)\overline{21,409}$ and check.

Your solution

Solutions on p. S3

Objective C   **To divide by larger whole numbers**

When the divisor has more than one digit, estimate at each step by using the first digit of the divisor. If that product is too large, lower the guess by 1 and try again.

HOW TO   Divide 34)$\overline{1598}$ and check.

$$\begin{array}{r} 5 \\ 34)\overline{1598} \\ -170 \end{array}$$
• Think 3)$\overline{15}$.
• Subtract 5 × 34.

$$\begin{array}{r} 4 \\ 34)\overline{1598} \\ -136 \\ \hline 238 \end{array}$$
• Subtract 4 × 34.

170 is too large. Lower the guess by 1 and try again.

$$\begin{array}{r} 47 \\ 34)\overline{1598} \\ -136 \\ \hline 238 \\ -238 \\ \hline 0 \end{array}$$
• Think 3)$\overline{23}$.
• Subtract 7 × 34.

Check:
$$\begin{array}{r} 47 \\ \times 34 \\ \hline 188 \\ 141 \\ \hline 1598 \end{array}$$

The phrases below are used to indicate the operation of division. An example is shown at the right of each phrase.

| the quotient of | the quotient of 9 and 3 | 9 ÷ 3 |
| divided by | 6 divided by 2 | 6 ÷ 2 |

Example 6   Find 7077 divided by 34 and check.

Solution

$$\begin{array}{r} 208 \text{ r5} \\ 34)\overline{7077} \\ -68 \\ \hline 27 \\ -0 \\ \hline 277 \\ -272 \\ \hline 5 \end{array}$$
• Think 34)$\overline{27}$.
• Place 0 in the quotient.
• Subtract 0 × 34.

Check: (208 × 34) + 5 =
7072 + 5 = 7077

You Try It 6   Divide 4578 ÷ 42 and check.

Your solution

Solution on p. S3

Example 7 Find the quotient of 21,312 and 56 and check.

Solution

$$
\begin{array}{r}
380 \text{ r}32 \\
56\overline{)21,312} \\
-16\ 8 \\
\hline
4\ 51 \\
-4\ 48 \\
\hline
32 \\
-\ 0 \\
\hline
32
\end{array}
$$

• Think 5)21.
4 × 56 is too large. Try 3.

Check: $(380 \times 56) + 32 =$
21,280 + 32 = 21,312

You Try It 7 Divide 18,359 ÷ 39 and check.

Your solution

Example 8 Divide 427)24,782 and check.

Solution

$$
\begin{array}{r}
58 \text{ r}16 \\
427\overline{)24,782} \\
-21\ 35 \\
\hline
3\ 432 \\
-3\ 416 \\
\hline
16
\end{array}
$$

Check: $(58 \times 427) + 16 =$
24,766 + 16 = 24,782

You Try It 8 Divide 534)33,219 and check.

Your solution

Example 9 Divide 386)206,149 and check.

Solution

$$
\begin{array}{r}
534 \text{ r}25 \\
386\overline{)206,149} \\
-193\ 0 \\
\hline
13\ 14 \\
-11\ 58 \\
\hline
1\ 569 \\
-1\ 544 \\
\hline
25
\end{array}
$$

Check: $(534 \times 386) + 25 =$
206,124 + 25 = 206,149

You Try It 9 Divide 515)216,848 and check.

Your solution

Solutions on p. S3

ESTIMATION

Estimating the Quotient of Two Whole Numbers

Calculate 36,936 ÷ 54. Then use estimation to determine whether the quotient is reasonable.

Divide to find the exact quotient.   36,936 ÷ 54 = 684

To estimate the quotient, round each number   36,936 ÷ 54 ≈
so there is one nonzero digit. Then divide.   40,000 ÷ 50 = 800
The estimated answer is 800, which is close to
the exact quotient 684.

Objective D   **To solve application problems**

The **average** of several numbers is the sum of all the numbers divided by the number of those numbers.

$$\text{Average test score} = \frac{81 + 87 + 80 + 85 + 79 + 86}{6} = \frac{498}{6} = 83$$

HOW TO   The table at the right shows what an upper-income family can expect to spend to raise a child to the age of 17 years. Find the average amount spent each year. Round to the nearest dollar.

Strategy
To find the average amount spent each year:

* Add all the numbers in the table to find the total amount spent during the 17 years.
* Divide the sum by 17.

Expenses to Raise a Child	
Housing	$89,580
Food	$35,670
Transportation	$32,760
Child care/education	$26,520
Clothing	$13,770
Health care	$13,380
Other	$30,090

Source: Department of Agriculture,
Expenditures on Children by Families

Solution

```
   89,580            14,221
   35,670        17) 241,770
   32,760            -17
   26,520             71
   13,770            -68
   13,380             3 7
 + 30,090            -3 4
  -------             37
  241,770            -34
                     30
Sum of all          -17
the costs            13
```

* When rounding to the nearest whole number, compare twice the remainder to the divisor. If twice the remainder is less than the divisor, drop the remainder. If twice the remainder is greater than or equal to the divisor, add 1 to the units digit of the quotient.

* Twice the remainder is 2 × 13 = 26. Because 26 > 17, add 1 to the units digit of the quotient.

The average amount spent each year to raise a child to the age of 17 is $14,222.

Example 10

Ngan Hui, a freight supervisor, shipped 192,600 bushels of wheat in 9 railroad cars. Find the amount of wheat shipped in each car.

Strategy

To find the amount of wheat shipped in each car, divide the number of bushels (192,600) by the number of cars (9).

Solution

$$
\begin{array}{r}
21{,}400 \\
9)\overline{\,192{,}600\,} \\
-18 \\
\hline
12 \\
-9 \\
\hline
36 \\
-36 \\
\hline
0
\end{array}
$$

Each car carried 21,400 bushels of wheat.

You Try It 10

Suppose a Michelin retail outlet can store 270 tires on 15 shelves. How many tires can be stored on each shelf?

Your strategy

Your solution

Example 11

The used car you are buying costs $11,216. A down payment of $2000 is required. The remaining balance is paid in 48 equal monthly payments. What is the monthly payment?

Strategy

To find the monthly payment:

• Find the remaining balance by subtracting the down payment (2000) from the total cost of the car (11,216).

• Divide the remaining balance by the number of equal monthly payments (48).

Solution

$$
\begin{array}{r}
11{,}216 \\
-\ 2{,}000 \\
\hline
9{,}216
\end{array}
$$

Remaining balance

$$
\begin{array}{r}
192 \\
48)\overline{\,9216\,} \\
-48 \\
\hline
441 \\
-432 \\
\hline
96 \\
-96 \\
\hline
0
\end{array}
$$

The monthly payment is $192.

You Try It 11

A soft-drink manufacturer produces 12,600 cans of soft drink each hour. Cans are packed 24 to a case. How many cases of soft drink are produced in 8 hours?

Your strategy

Your solution

Solutions on pp. S3–S4

1.5 Exercises

Objective A   **To divide by a single digit with no remainder in the quotient**

For Exercises 1 to 20, divide.

1. $4\overline{)8}$

2. $3\overline{)9}$

3. $6\overline{)36}$

4. $9\overline{)81}$

5. $7\overline{)49}$

6. $5\overline{)80}$

7. $6\overline{)96}$

8. $6\overline{)480}$

9. $4\overline{)840}$

10. $3\overline{)690}$

11. $7\overline{)308}$

12. $7\overline{)203}$

13. $9\overline{)6327}$

14. $4\overline{)2120}$

15. $8\overline{)7280}$

16. $9\overline{)8118}$

17. $3\overline{)64,680}$

18. $4\overline{)50,760}$

19. $6\overline{)21,480}$

20. $5\overline{)18,050}$

21. Find the quotient of 1446 and 3.

22. Find the quotient of 4123 and 7.

23. What is 7525 divided by 7?

24. What is 32,364 divided by 4?

For Exercises 25 to 28, use the relationship between multiplication and division to complete the multiplication problem.

25. ___ × 7 = 364

26. 8 × ___ = 376

27. 5 × ___ = 170

28. ___ × 4 = 92

Objective B   **To divide by a single digit with a remainder in the quotient**

For Exercises 29 to 51, divide.

29. $4\overline{)9}$

30. $2\overline{)7}$

31. $5\overline{)27}$

32. $9\overline{)88}$

33. $3\overline{)40}$

34. $6\overline{)97}$

35. $8\overline{)83}$

36. $5\overline{)54}$

37. $7\overline{)632}$

38. $4\overline{)363}$

39. $4\overline{)921}$ **40.** $7\overline{)845}$ **41.** $8\overline{)1635}$ **42.** $5\overline{)1548}$ **43.** $7\overline{)9432}$

44. $7\overline{)8124}$ **45.** $3\overline{)5162}$ **46.** $5\overline{)3542}$ **47.** $8\overline{)3274}$

48. $4\overline{)15,301}$ **49.** $7\overline{)43,500}$ **50.** $8\overline{)72,354}$ **51.** $5\overline{)43,542}$

52. Find the quotient of 3107 and 8.

53. Find the quotient of 8642 and 8.

54. What is 45,738 divided by 4? Round to the nearest ten.

55. What is 37,896 divided by 9? Round to the nearest hundred.

56. What is 3572 divided by 7? Round to the nearest ten.

57. What is 78,345 divided by 4? Round to the nearest hundred.

Objective C   **To divide by larger whole numbers**

For Exercises 58 to 85, divide.

58. $27\overline{)96}$ **59.** $44\overline{)82}$ **60.** $42\overline{)87}$ **61.** $67\overline{)93}$

62. $41\overline{)897}$ **63.** $32\overline{)693}$ **64.** $23\overline{)784}$ **65.** $25\overline{)772}$

66. $74\overline{)600}$ **67.** $92\overline{)500}$ **68.** $70\overline{)329}$ **69.** $50\overline{)467}$

70. $36\overline{)7225}$ **71.** $44\overline{)8821}$ **72.** $19\overline{)3859}$ **73.** $32\overline{)9697}$

74. $88\overline{)3127}$ **75.** $92\overline{)6177}$ **76.** $33\overline{)8943}$ **77.** $27\overline{)4765}$

78. $22\overline{)98,654}$ **79.** $77\overline{)83,629}$ **80.** $64\overline{)38,912}$ **81.** $78\overline{)31,434}$

82. $206\overline{)3097}$ **83.** $504\overline{)6504}$ **84.** $654\overline{)1217}$ **85.** $546\overline{)2344}$

86. Find the quotient of 5432 and 21.   **87.** Find the quotient of 8507 and 53.

88. What is 37,294 divided by 72?   **89.** What is 76,788 divided by 46?

90. Find 23,457 divided by 43. Round to the nearest hundred.   **91.** Find 341,781 divided by 43. Round to the nearest ten.

For Exercises 92 to 103, use a calculator to divide. Then use estimation to determine whether the quotient is reasonable.

92. $76\overline{)389,804}$ **93.** $53\overline{)117,925}$ **94.** $29\overline{)637,072}$ **95.** $67\overline{)738,072}$

96. $38\overline{)934,648}$ **97.** $34\overline{)906,304}$ **98.** $309\overline{)876,324}$ **99.** $642\overline{)323,568}$

100. $209\overline{)632,016}$ **101.** $614\overline{)332,174}$ **102.** $179\overline{)5,734,444}$ **103.** $374\overline{)7,712,254}$

Objective D   **To solve application problems**

Finance   The graph at the right shows the annual expenditures, in a recent year, of the average household in the United States. Use this information for Exercises 104 to 106. Round answers to the nearest whole number.

104. What is the total amount spent annually by the average household in the United States?

105. What is the average monthly expense for housing?

106. What is the difference between the average monthly expense for food and the average monthly expense for health care?

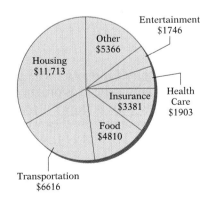

Entertainment $1746

Other $5366

Housing $11,713

Insurance $3381

Health Care $1903

Food $4810

Transportation $6616

Average Annual Household Expenses

Source: Bureau of Labor Statistics Consumer Expenditure Survey

Insurance The table at the right shows the sources of insurance claims for losses of laptop computers in a recent year. Claims have been rounded to the nearest ten thousand dollars. Use this information for Exercises 107 and 108.

107. What was the average monthly claim for theft?

108. For all sources combined, find the average claims per month.

Source	Claims
Accidents	$560,000
Theft	$300,000
Power surge	$80,000
Lightning	$50,000
Transit	$20,000
Water/flood	$20,000
Other	$110,000

Source: Safeware, The Insurance Company

Work Hours The table at the right shows, for different countries, the average number of hours per year that employees work. Use this information for Exercises 109 and 110. Use a 50-week year. Round answers to the nearest whole number.

109. What is the average number of hours worked per week by employees in Britain?

110. On average, how many more hours per week do employees in the United States work than employees in France?

Country	Annual Number of Hours Worked
Britain	1731
France	1656
Japan	1889
Norway	1399
United States	1966

Source: International Labor Organization

111. **Coins** The U.S. Mint estimates that about 114,000,000,000 of the 312,000,000,000 pennies it has minted over the last 30 years are in active circulation. That works out to how many pennies in circulation for each of the 300,000,000 people living in the United States?

APPLYING THE CONCEPTS

112. **Payroll Deductions** Your paycheck shows deductions of $225 for savings, $98 for taxes, and $27 for insurance. Find the total of the three deductions.

Dairy Products The topic of the graph at the right is the eggs produced in the United States in a recent year. It shows where the eggs that were produced went or how they were used. Use this table for Exercises 113 and 114.

113. Use the graph to determine the total number of cases of eggs produced during the year.

114. How many more cases of eggs were sold by retail stores than were used for non-shell products?

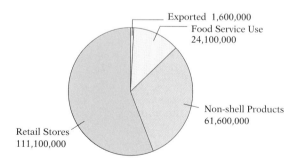

Exported 1,600,000
Food Service Use 24,100,000
Non-shell Products 61,600,000
Retail Stores 111,100,000

Eggs Produced in the United States (in cases)
Source: American Egg Board

115. **Fuel Consumption**   The Energy Information Administration projects that in 2020, the average U.S. household will spend $1562 annually on gasoline. Use this estimate to determine how much the average U.S. household will spend on gasoline each month in 2020. Round to the nearest dollar.

Salaries   The table at the right lists average starting salaries for students graduating with one of six different bachelor's degree. Use this table for Exercises 116 and 117.

Degree	Average Starting Salary
Accounting	$40,546
Biology	$29,554
Business	$37,122
Computer Sciences	$47,419
History	$32,108
Psychology	$27,454

Source: National Association of Colleges

116. Find the difference between the average starting salary of a computer sciences major and that of a biology major.

117. How much greater is the average starting salary of an accounting major than that of a psychology major?

The Military   The graph at the right shows the basic monthly pay for Army commissioned officers with 20 years of service. Use this graph for Exercises 118 and 119.

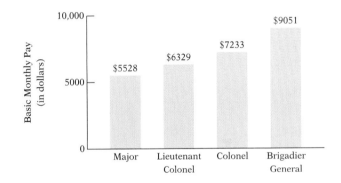

Basic Monthly Pay for Army Officers
Source: Department of Defense

118. What is a major's annual pay?

119. What is the difference between a colonel's annual pay and a lieutenant colonel's annual pay?

120. **Farming**   A farmer harvested 48,290 pounds of avocados from one grove and 23,710 pounds of avocados from another grove. The avocados were packed in shipping boxes with 24 pounds in each box. How many boxes were needed to pack the avocados?

121. **Wages**   A sales associate earns $374 for working a 40-hour week. Last week the associate worked an additional 9 hours at $13 an hour. Find the sales associate's total pay for last week's work.

122. **Finances**   You purchase a used car with a down payment of $2500 and monthly payments of $195 for 48 months. Find the total amount paid for the car.

123. A palindromic number is a whole number that remains unchanged when its digits are written in reverse order. For instance, 292 is a palindromic number. Find the smallest three-digit palindromic number that is divisible by 4.

1.6 Exponential Notation and the Order of Operations Agreement

Objective A   **To simplify expressions that contain exponents**

Repeated multiplication of the same factor can be written in two ways:

$$3 \cdot 3 \cdot 3 \cdot 3 \cdot 3 \qquad \text{or} \qquad 3^5 \leftarrow \textbf{Exponent}$$

The **exponent** indicates how many times the factor occurs in the multiplication. The expression 3^5 is in **exponential notation.**

It is important to be able to read numbers written in exponential notation.

$6 = 6^1$ is read "six to the first **power**" or just "six." Usually the exponent 1 is not written.

$6 \cdot 6 = 6^2$ is read "six squared" or "six to the second power."

$6 \cdot 6 \cdot 6 = 6^3$ is read "six cubed" or "six to the third power."

$6 \cdot 6 \cdot 6 \cdot 6 = 6^4$ is read "six to the fourth power."

$6 \cdot 6 \cdot 6 \cdot 6 \cdot 6 = 6^5$ is read "six to the fifth power."

Each place value in the place-value chart can be expressed as a power of 10.

$$
\begin{aligned}
\text{Ten} &= 10 &=& \quad 10 &=& \ 10^1 \\
\text{Hundred} &= 100 &=& \quad 10 \cdot 10 &=& \ 10^2 \\
\text{Thousand} &= 1000 &=& \quad 10 \cdot 10 \cdot 10 &=& \ 10^3 \\
\text{Ten-thousand} &= 10{,}000 &=& \quad 10 \cdot 10 \cdot 10 \cdot 10 &=& \ 10^4 \\
\text{Hundred-thousand} &= 100{,}000 &=& \quad 10 \cdot 10 \cdot 10 \cdot 10 \cdot 10 &=& \ 10^5 \\
\text{Million} &= 1{,}000{,}000 &=& \ 10 \cdot 10 \cdot 10 \cdot 10 \cdot 10 \cdot 10 &=& \ 10^6
\end{aligned}
$$

Integrating Technology

A calculator can be used to evaluate an exponential expression. The y^x key (or, on some calculators, a x^y or $\wedge$ key) is used to enter the exponent. For instance, for the example at the right, enter 4 y^x 3 = . The display reads 64.

To simplify a numerical expression containing exponents, write each factor as many times as indicated by the exponent and carry out the indicated multiplication.

$$4^3 = 4 \cdot 4 \cdot 4 = 64$$
$$2^2 \cdot 3^4 = (2 \cdot 2) \cdot (3 \cdot 3 \cdot 3 \cdot 3) = 4 \cdot 81 = 324$$

Example 1 Write $3 \cdot 3 \cdot 3 \cdot 5 \cdot 5$ in exponential notation.

Solution $3 \cdot 3 \cdot 3 \cdot 5 \cdot 5 = 3^3 \cdot 5^2$

You Try It 1 Write $2 \cdot 2 \cdot 2 \cdot 2 \cdot 3 \cdot 3 \cdot 3$ in exponential notation.

Your solution

Example 2 Write as a power of 10: $10 \cdot 10 \cdot 10 \cdot 10$

Solution $10 \cdot 10 \cdot 10 \cdot 10 = 10^4$

You Try It 2 Write as a power of 10: $10 \cdot 10 \cdot 10 \cdot 10 \cdot 10 \cdot 10 \cdot 10$

Your solution

Example 3 Simplify $3^2 \cdot 5^3$.

Solution $3^2 \cdot 5^3 = (3 \cdot 3) \cdot (5 \cdot 5 \cdot 5)$
            $= 9 \cdot 125 = 1125$

You Try It 3 Simplify $2^3 \cdot 5^2$.

Your solution

Solutions on p. S4

Objective B   **To use the Order of Operations Agreement to simplify expressions**

More than one operation may occur in a numerical expression. The answer may be different, depending on the order in which the operations are performed. For example, consider $3 + 4 \times 5$.

Multiply first, then add.

$$3 + \underbrace{4 \times 5}$$
$$\underbrace{3 + 20}$$
$$23$$

Add first, then multiply.

$$\underbrace{3 + 4} \times 5$$
$$\underbrace{7 \times 5}$$
$$35$$

An Order of Operations Agreement is used so that only one answer is possible.

The Order of Operations Agreement

Step 1. Do all the operations inside parentheses.

Step 2. Simplify any number expressions containing exponents.

Step 3. Do multiplication and division as they occur from left to right.

Step 4. Do addition and subtraction as they occur from left to right.

Integrating Technology

Many scientific calculators have an x^2 key. This key is used to square the displayed number. For example, after the user presses 2 x^2 = , the display reads 4.

HOW TO   Simplify $3 \times (2 + 1) - 2^2 + 4 \div 2$ by using the Order of Operations Agreement.

$$3 \times \underbrace{(2 + 1)} - 2^2 + 4 \div 2$$
$$\underbrace{3 \times 3} - 2^2 + 4 \div 2$$
$$3 \times 3 - \underbrace{4} + 4 \div 2$$
$$\underbrace{9} - 4 + \underbrace{4 \div 2}$$
$$9 - \underbrace{4 + 2}$$
$$\underbrace{5 + 2}$$
$$7$$

1. Perform operations in parentheses.

2. Simplify expressions with exponents.

3. Do multiplication and division as they occur from left to right.

4. Do addition and subtraction as they occur from left to right.

One or more of the foregoing steps may not be needed to simplify an expression. In that case, proceed to the next step in the Order of Operations Agreement.

HOW TO   Simplify $5 + 8 \div 2$.   There are no parentheses or exponents. Proceed to Step 3 of the agreement.

$$5 + \underbrace{8 \div 2}$$
$$\underbrace{5 + 4}$$
$$9$$

3. Do multiplication or division.

4. Do addition or subtraction.

Example 4   Simplify: $64 \div (8 - 4)^2 \cdot 9 - 5^2$

Solution

$$64 \div (8 - 4)^2 \cdot 9 - 5^2$$
$$= 64 \div 4^2 \cdot 9 - 5^2 \quad \bullet \text{ Parentheses}$$
$$= 64 \div 16 \cdot 9 - 25 \quad \bullet \text{ Exponents}$$
$$= 4 \cdot 9 - 25 \qquad\qquad \bullet \text{ Division and}$$
$$= 36 - 25 \qquad\qquad\quad \text{ multiplicaton}$$
$$= 11 \qquad\qquad\qquad\quad \bullet \text{ Subtraction}$$

You Try It 4   Simplify: $5 \cdot (8 - 4)^2 \div 4 - 2$

Your solution

Solution on p. S4

1.6 Exercises

Objective A To simplify expressions that contain exponents

For Exercises 1 to 12, write the number in exponential notation.

1. $2 \cdot 2 \cdot 2$

2. $7 \cdot 7 \cdot 7 \cdot 7 \cdot 7$

3. $6 \cdot 6 \cdot 6 \cdot 7 \cdot 7 \cdot 7 \cdot 7$

4. $6 \cdot 6 \cdot 9 \cdot 9 \cdot 9 \cdot 9$

5. $2 \cdot 2 \cdot 2 \cdot 3 \cdot 3 \cdot 3$

6. $3 \cdot 3 \cdot 10 \cdot 10$

7. $5 \cdot 7 \cdot 7 \cdot 7 \cdot 7 \cdot 7$

8. $4 \cdot 4 \cdot 4 \cdot 5 \cdot 5 \cdot 5$

9. $3 \cdot 3 \cdot 3 \cdot 6 \cdot 6 \cdot 6 \cdot 6$

10. $2 \cdot 2 \cdot 5 \cdot 5 \cdot 5 \cdot 8$

11. $3 \cdot 3 \cdot 3 \cdot 5 \cdot 9 \cdot 9 \cdot 9$

12. $2 \cdot 2 \cdot 2 \cdot 4 \cdot 7 \cdot 7 \cdot 7$

For Exercises 13 to 37, simplify.

13. 2^3

14. 2^6

15. $2^4 \cdot 5^2$

16. $2^6 \cdot 3^2$

17. $3^2 \cdot 10^2$

18. $2^3 \cdot 10^4$

19. $6^2 \cdot 3^3$

20. $4^3 \cdot 5^2$

21. $5 \cdot 2^3 \cdot 3$

22. $6 \cdot 3^2 \cdot 4$

23. $2^2 \cdot 3^2 \cdot 10$

24. $3^2 \cdot 5^2 \cdot 10$

25. $0^2 \cdot 4^3$

26. $6^2 \cdot 0^3$

27. $3^2 \cdot 10^4$

28. $5^3 \cdot 10^3$

29. $2^2 \cdot 3^3 \cdot 5$

30. $5^2 \cdot 7^3 \cdot 2$

31. $2 \cdot 3^4 \cdot 5^2$

32. $6 \cdot 2^6 \cdot 7^2$

33. $5^2 \cdot 3^2 \cdot 7^2$

34. $4^2 \cdot 9^2 \cdot 6^2$

35. $3^4 \cdot 2^6 \cdot 5$

36. $4^3 \cdot 6^3 \cdot 7$

37. $4^2 \cdot 3^3 \cdot 10^4$

Objective B To use the Order of Operations Agreement to simplify expressions

For Exercises 38 to 76, simplify by using the Order of Operations Agreement.

38. $4 - 2 + 3$

39. $6 - 3 + 2$

40. $6 \div 3 + 2$

41. $8 \div 4 + 8$

42. $6 \cdot 3 + 5$

43. $5 \cdot 9 + 2$

44. $3^2 - 4$

45. $5^2 - 17$

46. $4 \cdot (5 - 3) + 2$ **47.** $3 + (4 + 2) \div 3$ **48.** $5 + (8 + 4) \div 6$ **49.** $8 - 2^2 + 4$

50. $16 \cdot (3 + 2) \div 10$ **51.** $12 \cdot (1 + 5) \div 12$ **52.** $10 - 2^3 + 4$ **53.** $5 \cdot 3^2 + 8$

54. $16 + 4 \cdot 3^2$ **55.** $12 + 4 \cdot 2^3$ **56.** $16 + (8 - 3) \cdot 2$ **57.** $7 + (9 - 5) \cdot 3$

58. $2^2 + 3 \cdot (6 - 2)^2$ **59.** $3^3 + 5 \cdot (8 - 6)^3$ **60.** $2^2 \cdot 3^2 + 2 \cdot 3$ **61.** $4 \cdot 6 + 3^2 \cdot 4^2$

62. $16 - 2 \cdot 4$ **63.** $12 + 3 \cdot 5$ **64.** $3 \cdot (6 - 2) + 4$

65. $5 \cdot (8 - 4) - 6$ **66.** $8 - (8 - 2) \div 3$ **67.** $12 - (12 - 4) \div 4$

68. $8 + 2 - 3 \cdot 2 \div 3$ **69.** $10 + 1 - 5 \cdot 2 \div 5$ **70.** $3 \cdot (4 + 2) \div 6$

71. $(7 - 3)^2 \div 2 - 4 + 8$ **72.** $20 - 4 \div 2 \cdot (3 - 1)^3$ **73.** $12 \div 3 \cdot 2^2 + (7 - 3)^2$

74. $(4 - 2) \cdot 6 \div 3 + (5 - 2)^2$ **75.** $18 - 2 \cdot 3 + (4 - 1)^3$ **76.** $100 \div (2 + 3)^2 - 8 \div 2$

APPLYING THE CONCEPTS

77. **Computers**   Memory in computers is measured in bytes. One kilobyte (1 K) is 2^{10} bytes. Write this number in standard form.

78. Explain the difference that the order of operations makes between **a.** $(14 - 2) \div 2 \cdot 3$ and **b.** $(14 - 2) \div (2 \cdot 3)$. Work the two problems. What is the difference between the larger answer and the smaller answer?

1.7 Prime Numbers and Factoring

Objective A **To factor numbers**

Whole-number **factors of a number** divide that number evenly (there is no remainder).

1, 2, 3, and 6 are whole-number factors of 6 because they divide 6 evenly.

$$\overset{6}{1)6} \quad \overset{3}{2)6} \quad \overset{2}{3)6} \quad \overset{1}{6)6}$$

Note that both the divisor and the quotient are factors of the dividend.

To find the factors of a number, try dividing the number by 1, 2, 3, 4, 5, ... Those numbers that divide the number evenly are its factors. Continue this process until the factors start to repeat.

> **HOW TO** Find all the factors of 42.
>
> $42 \div 1 = 42$ 1 and 42 are factors.
> $42 \div 2 = 21$ 2 and 21 are factors.
> $42 \div 3 = 14$ 3 and 14 are factors.
> $42 \div 4$ Will not divide evenly
> $42 \div 5$ Will not divide evenly
> $42 \div 6 = 7$ 6 and 7 are factors. ⎤ Factors are repeating; all the
> $42 \div 7 = 6$ 7 and 6 are factors. ⎦ factors of 42 have been found.
>
> 1, 2, 3, 6, 7, 14, 21, and 42 are factors of 42.

The following rules are helpful in finding the factors of a number.

2 is a factor of a number if the last digit of the number is 0, 2, 4, 6, or 8.

436 ends in 6; therefore, 2 is a factor of 436. (436 ÷ 2 = 218)

3 is a factor of a number if the sum of the digits of the number is divisible by 3.

The sum of the digits of 489 is 4 + 8 + 9 = 21. 21 is divisible by 3. Therefore, 3 is a factor of 489. (489 ÷ 3 = 163)

5 is a factor of a number if the last digit of the number is 0 or 5.

520 ends in 0; therefore, 5 is a factor of 520. (520 ÷ 5 = 104)

Example 1 Find all the factors of 30.

Solution
$30 \div 1 = 30$
$30 \div 2 = 15$
$30 \div 3 = 10$
$30 \div 4$ Will not divide
          evenly
$30 \div 5 = 6$
$30 \div 6 = 5$

1 2, 3, 5, 6, 10, 15, and 30 are factors of 30.

You Try It 1 Find all the factors of 40.

Your solution

Solution on p. S4

Objective B   **To find the prime factorization of a number**

Point of Interest

Prime numbers are an important part of cryptology, the study of secret codes. To make it less likely that codes can be broken, cryptologists use prime numbers that have hundreds of digits.

A number is a **prime number** if its only whole-number factors are 1 and itself. 7 is prime because its only factors are 1 and 7. If a number is not prime, it is called a **composite number.** Because 6 has factors of 2 and 3, 6 is a composite number. The number 1 is not considered a prime number; therefore, it is not included in the following list of prime numbers less than 50.

$$2, 3, 5, 7, 11, 13, 17, 19, 23, 29, 31, 37, 41, 43, 47$$

The **prime factorization** of a number is the expression of the number as a product of its prime factors. We use a "T-diagram" to find the prime factors of 60. Begin with the smallest prime number as a trial divisor, and continue with prime numbers as trial divisors until the final quotient is 1.

$$
\begin{array}{r|r}
\multicolumn{2}{c}{60} \\
\hline
2 & 30 \\
2 & 15 \\
3 & 5 \\
5 & 1 \\
\end{array}
\qquad
\begin{array}{l}
60 \div 2 = 30 \\
30 \div 2 = 15 \\
15 \div 3 = 5 \\
5 \div 5 = 1 \\
\end{array}
$$

The prime factorization of 60 is $2 \cdot 2 \cdot 3 \cdot 5$.

Finding the prime factorization of larger numbers can be more difficult. Try each prime number as a trial divisor. Stop when the square of the trial divisor is greater than the number being factored.

HOW TO Find the prime factorization of 106.

$$
\begin{array}{r|r}
\multicolumn{2}{c}{106} \\
\hline
2 & 53 \\
53 & 1 \\
\end{array}
$$

• 53 cannot be divided evenly by 2, 3, 5, 7, or 11. Prime numbers greater than 11 need not be tested because 11^2 is greater than 53.

The prime factorization of 106 is $2 \cdot 53$.

Example 2 Find the prime factorization of 315.

Solution

$$
\begin{array}{r|r}
\multicolumn{2}{c}{315} \\
\hline
3 & 105 \\
3 & 35 \\
5 & 7 \\
7 & 1 \\
\end{array}
$$

• $315 \div 3 = 105$
• $105 \div 3 = 35$
• $35 \div 5 = 7$
• $7 \div 7 = 1$

$315 = 3 \cdot 3 \cdot 5 \cdot 7$

You Try It 2 Find the prime factorization of 44.

Your solution

Example 3 Find the prime factorization of 201.

Solution

$$
\begin{array}{r|r}
\multicolumn{2}{c}{201} \\
\hline
3 & 67 \\
67 & 1 \\
\end{array}
$$

• Try only 2, 3, 5, 7, and 11 because $11^2 > 67$.

$201 = 3 \cdot 67$

You Try It 3 Find the prime factorization of 177.

Your solution

Solutions on p. S4

1.7 Exercises

Objective A **To factor numbers**

For Exercises 1 to 40, find all the factors of the number.

1. 4   **2.** 6   **3.** 10   **4.** 20

5. 7   **6.** 12   **7.** 9   **8.** 8

9. 13   **10.** 17   **11.** 18   **12.** 24

13. 56   **14.** 36   **15.** 45   **16.** 28

17. 29   **18.** 33   **19.** 22   **20.** 26

21. 52   **22.** 49   **23.** 82   **24.** 37

25. 57   **26.** 69   **27.** 48   **28.** 64

29. 95   **30.** 46   **31.** 54   **32.** 50

33. 66   **34.** 77   **35.** 80   **36.** 100

37. 96   **38.** 85   **39.** 90   **40.** 101

Objective B **To find the prime factorization of a number**

For Exercises 41 to 84, find the prime factorization.

41. 6   **42.** 14   **43.** 17   **44.** 83

45. 24   **46.** 12   **47.** 27   **48.** 9

49. 36   **50.** 40   **51.** 19   **52.** 37

53. 90   **54.** 65   **55.** 115   **56.** 80

57. 18   **58.** 26   **59.** 28   **60.** 49

61. 31   **62.** 42   **63.** 62   **64.** 81

65. 22   **66.** 39   **67.** 101   **68.** 89

69. 66   **70.** 86   **71.** 74   **72.** 95

73. 67   **74.** 78   **75.** 55   **76.** 46

77. 120   **78.** 144   **79.** 160   **80.** 175

81. 216   **82.** 400   **83.** 625   **84.** 225

APPLYING THE CONCEPTS

85. Twin primes are two prime numbers that differ by 2. For instance, 17 and 19 are twin primes. Find three sets of twin primes, not including 17 and 19.

86. In 1742, Christian Goldbach conjectured that every even number greater than 2 could be expressed as the sum of two prime numbers. Show that this conjecture is true for 8, 24, and 72. (*Note:* Mathematicians have not yet been able to determine whether Goldbach's conjecture is true or false.)

87. Explain why 2 is the only even prime number.

88. If a number is divisible by 6 and 10, is the number divisible by 30? If so, explain why. If not, give an example.

Focus on Problem Solving

Questions to Ask

You encounter problem-solving situations every day. Some problems are easy to solve, and you may mentally solve these problems without considering the steps you are taking in order to draw a conclusion. Others may be more challenging and may require more thought and consideration.

Suppose a friend suggests that you both take a trip over spring break. You'd like to go. What questions go through your mind? You might ask yourself some of the following questions:

How much will the trip cost? What will be the cost for travel, hotel rooms, meals, and so on?

Are some costs going to be shared by both me and my friend?

Can I afford it?

How much money do I have in the bank?

How much more money than I have now do I need?

How much time is there to earn that much money?

How much can I earn in that amount of time?

How much money must I keep in the bank in order to pay the next tuition bill (or some other expense)?

These questions require different mathematical skills. Determining the cost of the trip requires **estimation;** for example, you must use your knowledge of air fares or the cost of gasoline to arrive at an estimate of these costs. If some of the costs are going to be shared, you need to **divide** those costs by 2 in order to determine your share of the expense. The question regarding how much more money you need requires **subtraction:** the amount needed minus the amount currently in the bank. To determine how much money you can earn in the given amount of time requires **multiplication**—for example, the amount you earn per week times the number of weeks to be worked. To determine if the amount you can earn in the given amount of time is sufficient, you need to use your knowledge of **order relations** to compare the amount you can earn with the amount needed.

Facing the problem-solving situation described above may not seem difficult to you. The reason may be that you have faced similar situations before and, therefore, know how to work through this one. You may feel better prepared to deal with a circumstance such as this one because you know what questions to ask. An important aspect of learning to solve problems is learning what questions to ask. As you work through application problems in this text, try to become more conscious of the mental process you are going through. You might begin the process by asking yourself the following questions whenever you are solving an application problem.

1. Have I read the problem enough times to be able to understand the situation being described?

2. Will restating the problem in different words help me to understand the problem situation better?

3. What facts are given? (You might make a list of the information contained in the problem.)

4. What information is being asked for?

5. What relationship exists among the given facts? What relationship exists between the given facts and the solution?

6. What mathematical operations are needed in order to solve the problem?

Try to focus on the problem-solving situation, not on the computation or on getting the answer quickly. And remember, the more problems you solve, the better able you will be to solve other problems in the future, partly because you are learning what questions to ask.

Projects and Group Activities

Order of Operations

Does your calculator use the Order of Operations Agreement? To find out, try this problem:

$$2 + 4 \cdot 7$$

If your answer is 30, then the calculator uses the Order of Operations Agreement. If your answer is 42, it does not use that agreement.

Even if your calculator does not use the Order of Operations Agreement, you can still correctly evaluate numerical expressions. The parentheses keys, (and) , are used for this purpose.

Remember that $2 + 4 \cdot 7$ means $2 + (4 \cdot 7)$ because the multiplication must be completed before the addition. To evaluate this expression, enter the following:

Enter: 2   +   (4   ×   7   )   =

Display: 2   2   (4   4   7   28   30

When using your calculator to evaluate numerical expressions, insert parentheses around multiplications and around divisions. This has the effect of forcing the calculator to do the operations in the order you want.

For Exercises 1 to 10, evaluate.

1. $3 \cdot 8 - 5$

2. $6 + 8 \div 2$

3. $3 \cdot (8 - 2)^2$

4. $24 - (4 - 2)^2 \div 4$

5. $3 + (6 \div 2 + 4)^2 - 2$

6. $16 \div 2 + 4 \cdot (8 - 12 \div 4)^2 - 50$

7. $3 \cdot (15 - 2 \cdot 3) - 36 \div 3$

8. $4 \cdot 2^2 - (12 + 24 \div 6) + 5$

9. $16 \div 4 \cdot 3 + (3 \cdot 4 - 5) + 2$

10. $15 \cdot 3 \div 9 + (2 \cdot 6 - 3) + 4$

Patterns in Mathematics

For the circle at the left, use a straight line to connect each dot on the circle with every other dot on the circle. How many different straight lines are there?

Follow the same procedure for each of the circles shown below. How many different straight lines are there in each?

Find a pattern to describe the number of dots on a circle and the corresponding number of different lines drawn. Use the pattern to determine the number of different lines that would be drawn in a circle with 7 dots and in a circle with 8 dots.

Now use the pattern to answer the following question. You are arranging a tennis tournament with 9 players. How many singles matches will be played among the 9 players if each player plays each of the other players only once?

Search the World Wide Web

Go to **www.census.gov** on the Internet.

1. Find a projection for the total U.S. population 10 years from now and a projection for the total population 20 years from now. Record the two numbers.

2. Use the data from Exercise 1 to determine the expected growth in the population over the next 10 years.

3. Use the answer from Exercise 2 to find the average increase in the U.S. population per year over the next 10 years. Round to the nearest million.

4. Use data in the population table you found to write two word problems. Then state whether addition, subtraction, multiplication, or division is required to solve each of the problems.

Chapter 1 Summary

Key Words	Examples
The *whole numbers* are 0, 1, 2, 3, 4, 5, 6, 7, 8, 9, 10, ... [1.1A, p. 3]	
The *graph of a whole number* is shown by placing a heavy dot directly above that number on the number line. [1.1A, p. 3]	This is the graph of 4 on the number line. 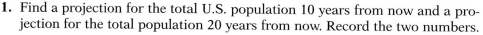 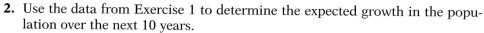
The symbol for *is less than* is <. The symbol for *is greater than* is >. These symbols are used to show the order relation between two numbers. [1.1A, p. 3]	3 < 7 9 > 2

When a whole number is written using the digits 0, 1, 2, 3, 4, 5, 6, 7, 8, and 9, it is said to be in *standard form*. The position of each digit in the number determines the digit's *place value*. The place values are used to write the expanded form of a number. [1.1B, p. 4]

The number 598,317 is in standard form. The digit 8 is in the thousands place. The number 598,317 is written in expanded form as 500,000 + 90,000 + 8000 + 300 + 10 + 7.

Addition is the process of finding the total of two or more numbers. The numbers being added are called *addends*. The result is the *sum*. [1.2A, p. 9]

$$\begin{array}{r} \overset{1\ \ 11}{8,762} \\ +\ 1,359 \\ \hline 10,121 \end{array}$$

Subtraction is the process of finding the difference between two numbers. The *minuend* minus the *subtrahend* equals the *difference*. [1.3A, p. 17]

$$\begin{array}{r} \overset{4}{\cancel{5}}\ \overset{11}{\cancel{2}},\overset{11}{\cancel{1}}\ \overset{6}{7}\ \overset{13}{\cancel{3}} \\ -3\ 4\,,9\ 6\ 8 \\ \hline 1\ 7\,,2\ 0\ 5 \end{array}$$

Multiplication is the repeated addition of the same number. The numbers that are multiplied are called *factors*. The result is the *product*. [1.4A, p. 25]

$$\begin{array}{r} \overset{4\ \ 5}{3\ 5\ 8} \\ \times\ \ \ \ \ \ \ 7 \\ \hline 2\ 5\ 0\ 6 \end{array}$$

Division is used to separate objects into equal groups. The *dividend* divided by the *divisor* equals the *quotient*. [1.5A, p. 33]

For any division problem,
(*quotient · divisor*) + *remainder* = *dividend*. [1.5B, p. 36]

$$\begin{array}{r} 93\ \text{r}3 \\ 7)\overline{654} \\ -63\ \ \ \\ \hline 24 \\ -21 \\ \hline 3 \end{array}$$

Check: $(7 \cdot 93) + 3 = 651 + 3 = 654$

The expression 4^3 is in *exponential notation*. The *exponent*, 3, indicates how many times 4 occurs as a factor in the multiplication. [1.6A, p. 46]

$5^4 = 5 \cdot 5 \cdot 5 \cdot 5 = 625$

Whole-number *factors of a number* divide that number evenly (there is no remainder). [1.7A, p. 50]

$18 \div 1 = 18$
$18 \div 2 = 9$
$18 \div 3 = 6$
$18 \div 4$ 4 does not divide 18 evenly.
$18 \div 5$ 5 does not divide 18 evenly.
$18 \div 6 = 3$ The factors are repeating.
The factors of 18 are 1, 2, 3, 6, 9, and 18.

A number greater than 1 is a *prime number* if its only whole-number factors are 1 and itself. If a number is not prime, it is a *composite number*. [1.7B, p. 51]

The prime numbers less than 20 are 2, 3, 5, 7, 11, 13, 17, and 19. The composite numbers less than 20 are 4, 6, 8, 9, 10, 12, 14, 15, 16, and 18.

The *prime factorization* of a number is the expression of the number as a product of its prime factors. [1.7B, p. 51]

$$\begin{array}{r} 42 \\ \hline 2\ |\ 21 \\ 3\ |\ \ 7 \\ 7\ |\ \ 1 \end{array}$$

The prime factorization of 42 is $2 \cdot 3 \cdot 7$.

Essential Rules and Procedures	**Examples**
To round a number to a given place value: If the digit to the right of the given place value is less than 5, replace that digit and all digits to the right by zeros. If the digit to the right of the given place value is greater than or equal to 5, increase the digit in the given place value by 1, and replace all other digits to the right by zeros. [1.1D, p. 6]	36,178 rounded to the nearest thousand is 36,000. 4592 rounded to the nearest thousand is 5000.

Properties of Addition [1.2A, p. 9]

Addition Property of Zero
Zero added to a number does not change the number.

$7 + 0 = 7$

Commutative Property of Addition
Two numbers can be added in either order; the sum will be the same.

$8 + 3 = 3 + 8$

Associative Property of Addition
Numbers to be added can be grouped in any order; the sum will be the same.

$(2 + 4) + 6 = 2 + (4 + 6)$

| **To estimate the answer to a calculation:** Round each number to the same place value. Perform the calculation using the rounded numbers. [1.2A, p. 11] | $\begin{array}{r} 39{,}471 \\ 12{,}586 \end{array}$ $\begin{array}{r} 40{,}000 \\ +10{,}000 \\ \hline 50{,}000 \end{array}$ |

50,000 is an estimate of the sum of 39,471 and 12,586.

Properties of Multiplication [1.4A, p. 25]

Multiplication Property of Zero
The product of a number and zero is zero.

$3 \cdot 0 = 0$

Multiplication Property of One
The product of a number and one is the number.

$6 \cdot 1 = 6$

Commutative Property of Multiplication
Two numbers can be multiplied in either order; the product will be the same.

$2 \cdot 8 = 8 \cdot 2$

Associative Property of Multiplication
Grouping numbers to be multiplied in any order gives the same result.

$(2 \cdot 4) \cdot 6 = 2 \cdot (4 \cdot 6)$

Division Properties of Zero and One [1.5A, p. 33]
Any whole number, except zero, divided by itself is 1.
Any whole number divided by 1 is the whole number.
Zero divided by any other whole number is zero.
Division by zero is not allowed.

$3 \div 3 = 1$
$3 \div 1 = 3$
$0 \div 3 = 0$
$3 \div 0$ is not allowed.

Order of Operations Agreement [1.6B, p. 47]

Step 1 Do all the operations inside parentheses.

Step 2 Simplify any number expressions containing exponents.

Step 3 Do multiplications and divisions as they occur from left to right.

Step 4 Do addition and subtraction as they occur from left to right.

$5^2 - 3(2 + 4) = 5^2 - 3(6)$
$= 25 - 3(6)$
$= 25 - 18$
$= 7$

Chapter 1 Review Exercises

1. Simplify: $3 \cdot 2^3 \cdot 5^2$

2. Write 10,327 in expanded form.

3. Find all the factors of 18.

4. Find the sum of 5894, 6301, and 298.

5. Subtract: $\begin{array}{r} 4926 \\ -\ 3177 \\ \hline \end{array}$

6. Divide: $7\overline{)14{,}945}$

7. Place the correct symbol, $<$ or $>$, between the two numbers: 101   87

8. Write $5 \cdot 5 \cdot 7 \cdot 7 \cdot 7 \cdot 7 \cdot 7$ in exponential notation.

9. What is 2019 multiplied by 307?

10. What is 10,134 decreased by 4725?

11. Add: $\begin{array}{r} 298 \\ 461 \\ +\ 322 \\ \hline \end{array}$

12. Simplify: $2^3 - 3 \cdot 2$

13. Round 45,672 to the nearest hundred.

14. Write 276,057 in words.

15. Find the quotient of 109,763 and 84.

16. Write two million eleven thousand forty-four in standard form.

17. What is 3906 divided by 8?

18. Simplify: $3^2 + 2^2 \cdot (5 - 3)$

19. Simplify: $8 \cdot (6 - 2)^2 \div 4$

20. Find the prime factorization of 72.

21. What is 3895 minus 1762?

22. Multiply: 843
$$\times \ 27$$

23. Wages Vincent Meyers, a sales assistant, earns $480 for working a 40-hour week. Last week Vincent worked an additional 12 hours at $24 an hour. Find Vincent's total pay for last week's work.

24. Fuel Efficiency Louis Reyes, a sales executive, drove a car 351 miles on 13 gallons of gas. Find the number of miles driven per gallon of gasoline.

25. Consumerism A car is purchased for $17,880, with a down payment of $3000. The balance is paid in 48 equal monthly payments. Find the monthly car payment.

26. Compensation An insurance account executive received commissions of $723, $544, $812, and $488 during a 4-week period. Find the total income from commissions for the 4 weeks.

27. Banking You had a balance of $516 in your checking account before making deposits of $88 and $213. Find the total amount deposited, and determine your new account balance.

28. Compensation You have a car payment of $246 per month. What is the total of the car payments over a 12-month period?

Athletics The table at the right shows the athletic participation by males and females at U.S. colleges in 1972 and 2001. Use this information for Exercises 29 to 32.

29. In which year, 1972 or 2001, were there more males involved in sports at U.S. colleges?

Year	Male Athletes	Female Athletes
1972	170,384	29,977
2001	208,866	150,916

Source: U.S. Department of Education commission report

30. What is the difference between the number of males involved in sports and the number of females involved in sports at U.S. colleges in 1972?

31. Find the increase in the number of females involved in sports in U.S. colleges from 1972 to 2001.

32. How many more U.S. college students were involved in athletics in 2001 than in 1972?

Chapter 1 Test

1. Simplify: $3^3 \cdot 4^2$

2. Write 207,068 in words.

3. Subtract: 17,495
  $-$ 8,162

4. Find all the factors of 20.

5. Multiply: 9736
  $\times$ 704

6. Simplify: $4^2 \cdot (4 - 2) \div 8 + 5$

7. Write 906,378 in expanded form.

8. Round 74,965 to the nearest hundred.

9. Divide: $97\overline{)108,764}$

10. Write $3 \cdot 3 \cdot 3 \cdot 7 \cdot 7$ in exponential form.

11. Find the sum of 8756, 9094, and 37,065.

12. Find the prime factorization of 84.

13. Simplify: $16 \div 4 \cdot 2 - (7 - 5)^2$

14. Find the product of 8 and 90,763.

15. Write one million two hundred four thousand six in standard form.

16. Divide: $7\overline{)60,972}$

17. Place the correct symbol, < or >, between the two numbers: 21   19

18. Find the quotient of 5624 and 8.

19. Add: 25,492
          +71,306

20. Find the difference between 29,736 and 9814.

Education The table at the right shows the projected enrollment in public and private elementary and secondary schools in the fall of 2009 and the fall of 2012. Use this information for Exercises 21 and 22.

Year	Kindergarten through Grade 8	Grades 9 through 12
2009	37,726,000	15,812,000
2012	38,258,000	15,434,000

Source: The National Center for Education Statistics

21. Find the difference between the total enrollment in 2012 and that in 2009.

22. Find the average enrollment in each of grades 9 through 12 in 2012.

23. **Farming** A farmer harvested 48,290 pounds of lemons from one grove and 23,710 pounds of lemons from another grove. The lemons were packed in boxes with 24 pounds of lemons in each box. How many boxes were needed to pack the lemons?

24. **Investments** An investor receives $237 each month from a corporate bond fund. How much will the investor receive over a 12-month period?

25. **Travel** A family drives 425 miles the first day, 187 miles the second day, and 243 miles the third day of their vacation. The odometer read 47,626 miles at the start of the vacation.
a. How many miles were driven during the 3 days?
b. What is the odometer reading at the end of the 3 days?

2 Fractions

Members of the Los Angeles Philharmonic follow conductor Esa-Pekka Salonen's movements to guarantee synchronized playing. By paying attention to both Salonen and the time signature for each musical piece, the musicians play in time with each other. The time signature appears as a fraction at the beginning of a piece of music and tells them how many beats to play per measure. The **project on page 115** demonstrates how to interpret the time signature.

Need help? For online student resources, such as section quizzes, visit this textbook's website at **math.college.hmco.com/students**.

OBJECTIVES

Section 2.1

A To find the least common multiple (LCM)
B To find the greatest common factor (GCF)

Section 2.2

A To write a fraction that represents part of a whole
B To write an improper fraction as a mixed number or a whole number, and a mixed number as an improper fraction

Section 2.3

A To find equivalent fractions by raising to higher terms
B To write a fraction in simplest form

Section 2.4

A To add fractions with the same denominator
B To add fractions with different denominators
C To add whole numbers, mixed numbers, and fractions
D To solve application problems

Section 2.5

A To subtract fractions with the same denominator
B To subtract fractions with different denominators
C To subtract whole numbers, mixed numbers, and fractions
D To solve application problems

Section 2.6

A To multiply fractions
B To multiply whole numbers, mixed numbers, and fractions
C To solve application problems

Section 2.7

A To divide fractions
B To divide whole numbers, mixed numbers, and fractions
C To solve application problems

Section 2.8

A To identify the order relation between two fractions
B To simplify expressions containing exponents
C To use the Order of Operations Agreement to simplify expressions

PREP TEST • • •

Do these exercises to prepare for Chapter 2.

For Exercises 1 to 6, add, subtract, multiply, or divide.

1. 4×5

2. $2 \cdot 2 \cdot 2 \cdot 3 \cdot 5$

3. 9×1

4. $6 + 4$

5. $10 - 3$

6. $63 \div 30$

7. Which of the following numbers divide evenly into 12?
1 2 3 4 5 6 7 8 9 10 11 12

8. Simplify: $8 \times 7 + 3$

9. Complete: $8 = ? + 1$

10. Place the correct symbol, $<$ or $>$, between the two numbers.
44   48

GO FIGURE • • •

You and a friend are swimming laps in a pool. You swim one lap every 4 minutes. Your friend swims one lap every 5 minutes. If you start at the same time from the same end of the pool, in how many minutes will both of you be at the starting point again? How many times will you have passed each other in the pool prior to that time?

2.1 The Least Common Multiple and Greatest Common Factor

Objective A   **To find the least common multiple (LCM)**

The **multiples of a number** are the products of that number and the numbers 1, 2, 3, 4, 5, ...

$3 \times 1 = 3$
$3 \times 2 = 6$
$3 \times 3 = 9$
$3 \times 4 = 12$ The multiples of 3 are 3, 6, 9, 12, 15, ...
$3 \times 5 = 15$

A number that is a multiple of two or more numbers is a **common multiple** of those numbers.

The multiples of 4 are 4, 8, 12, 16, 20, 24, 28, 32, 36, ...
The multiples of 6 are 6, 12, 18, 24, 30, 36, 42, ...
Some common multiples of 4 and 6 are 12, 24, and 36.

The **least common multiple (LCM)** is the smallest common multiple of two or more numbers.

The least common multiple of 4 and 6 is 12.

Listing the multiples of each number is one way to find the LCM. Another way to find the LCM uses the prime factorization of each number.

To find the LCM of 450 and 600, find the prime factorization of each number and write the factorization of each number in a table. Circle the greatest product in each column. The LCM is the product of the circled numbers.

	2	3	5
450 =	2	(3 · 3)	(5 · 5)
600 =	(2 · 2 · 2)	3	5 · 5

In the column headed by 5, the products are equal. Circle just one product.

The LCM is the product of the circled numbers.
The LCM = $2 \cdot 2 \cdot 2 \cdot 3 \cdot 3 \cdot 5 \cdot 5 = 1800$.

Example 1   Find the LCM of 24, 36, and 50.

Solution

	2	3	5
24 =	(2 · 2 · 2)	3	
36 =	2 · 2	(3 · 3)	
50 =	2		(5 · 5)

The LCM = $2 \cdot 2 \cdot 2 \cdot 3 \cdot 3 \cdot 5 \cdot 5$
= 1800.

You Try It 1   Find the LCM of 12, 27, and 50.

Your solution

Solution on p. S4

Objective B   **To find the greatest common factor (GCF)**

Recall that a number that divides another number evenly is a factor of that number. The number 64 can be evenly divided by 1, 2, 4, 8, 16, 32, and 64, so the numbers 1, 2, 4, 8, 16, 32, and 64 are factors of 64.

A number that is a factor of two or more numbers is a **common factor** of those numbers.

The factors of 30 are 1, 2, 3, 5, 6, 10, 15, and 30.
The factors of 105 are 1, 3, 5, 7, 15, 21, 35, and 105.
The common factors of 30 and 105 are 1, 3, 5, and 15.

The **greatest common factor (GCF)** is the largest common factor of two or more numbers.

The greatest common factor of 30 and 105 is 15.

Listing the factors of each number is one way of finding the GCF. Another way to find the GCF uses the prime factorization of each number.

To find the GCF of 126 and 180, find the prime factorization of each number and write the factorization of each number in a table. Circle the least product in each column that does not have a blank. The GCF is the product of the circled numbers.

	2	3	5	7
126 =	②	③·③		7
180 =	2·2	3·3	5	

In the column headed by 3, the products are equal. Circle just one product.
Columns 5 and 7 have a blank, so 5 and 7 are not common factors of 126 and 180. Do not circle any number in these columns.

The GCF is the product of the circled numbers.
The GCF = 2 · 3 · 3 = 18.

Example 2   Find the GCF of 90, 168, and 420.

Solution

	2	3	5	7
90 =	②	3·3	5	
168 =	2·2·2	③		7
420 =	2·2	3	5	7

The GCF = 2 · 3 = 6.

You Try It 2   Find the GCF of 36, 60, and 72.

Your solution

Example 3   Find the GCF of 7, 12, and 20.

Solution

	2	3	5	7
7 =				7
12 =	2·2	3		
20 =	2·2		5	

Because no numbers are circled, the GCF = 1.

You Try It 3   Find the GCF of 11, 24, and 30.

Your solution

Solutions on p. S4

2.1 Exercises

Objective A   **To find the least common multiple (LCM)**

For Exercises 1 to 34, find the LCM.

1. 5, 8   **2.** 3, 6   **3.** 3, 8   **4.** 2, 5   **5.** 5, 6

6. 5, 7   **7.** 4, 6   **8.** 6, 8   **9.** 8, 12   **10.** 12, 16

11. 5, 12   **12.** 3, 16   **13.** 8, 14   **14.** 6, 18   **15.** 3, 9

16. 4, 10   **17.** 8, 32   **18.** 7, 21   **19.** 9, 36   **20.** 14, 42

21. 44, 60   **22.** 120, 160   **23.** 102, 184   **24.** 123, 234   **25.** 4, 8, 12

26. 5, 10, 15   **27.** 3, 5, 10   **28.** 2, 5, 8   **29.** 3, 8, 12   **30.** 5, 12, 18

31. 9, 36, 64   **32.** 18, 54, 63   **33.** 16, 30, 84   **34.** 9, 12, 15

Objective B   **To find the greatest common factor (GCF)**

For Exercises 35 to 68, find the GCF.

35. 3, 5   **36.** 5, 7   **37.** 6, 9   **38.** 18, 24   **39.** 15, 25

40. 14, 49   **41.** 25, 100   **42.** 16, 80   **43.** 32, 51   **44.** 21, 44

45. 12, 80   **46.** 8, 36   **47.** 16, 140   **48.** 12, 76

49. 24, 30   **50.** 48, 144   **51.** 44, 96   **52.** 18, 32

53. 3, 5, 11   **54.** 6, 8, 10   **55.** 7, 14, 49   **56.** 6, 15, 36

57. 10, 15, 20   **58.** 12, 18, 20   **59.** 24, 40, 72   **60.** 3, 17, 51

61. 17, 31, 81   **62.** 14, 42, 84   **63.** 25, 125, 625   **64.** 12, 68, 92

65. 28, 35, 70   **66.** 1, 49, 153   **67.** 32, 56, 72   **68.** 24, 36, 48

APPLYING THE CONCEPTS

69. Define the phrase *relatively prime numbers*. List three pairs of relatively prime numbers.

70. **Work Schedules**   Joe Salvo, a lifeguard, works 3 days and then has a day off. A friend works 5 days and then has a day off. How many days after Joe and his friend have a day off together will they have another day off together?

71. Find the LCM of each of the following pairs of numbers: 2 and 3, 5 and 7, and 11 and 19. Can you draw a conclusion about the LCM of two prime numbers? Suggest a way of finding the LCM of three distinct prime numbers.

72. Find the GCF of each of the following pairs of numbers: 3 and 5, 7 and 11, and 29 and 43. Can you draw a conclusion about the GCF of two prime numbers? What is the GCF of three prime distinct numbers?

73. Is the LCM of two numbers always divisible by the GCF of the two numbers? If so, explain why. If not, give an example.

74. Using the pattern for the first two triangles at the right, determine the center number of the last triangle.

2.2 Introduction to Fractions

Objective A   To write a fraction that represents part of a whole

TAKE NOTE

The **fraction bar** separates the numerator from the denominator. The **numerator** is the part of the fraction that appears above the fraction bar. The **denominator** is the part of the fraction that appears below the fraction bar.

A **fraction** can represent the number of equal parts of a whole.

The shaded portion of the circle is represented by the fraction $\frac{4}{7}$. Four of the seven equal parts of the circle (that is, four-sevenths of it) are shaded.

Each part of a fraction has a name.

$$\text{Fraction bar} \rightarrow \frac{4 \leftarrow \textbf{Numerator}}{7 \leftarrow \textbf{Denominator}}$$

Point of Interest

The fraction bar was first used in 1050 by al-Hassar. It is also called a vinculum.

A **proper fraction** is a fraction less than 1. The numerator of a proper fraction is smaller than the denominator. The shaded portion of the circle can be represented by the proper fraction $\frac{3}{4}$.

A **mixed number** is a number greater than 1 with a whole-number part and a fractional part. The shaded portion of the circles can be represented by the mixed number $2\frac{1}{4}$.

An **improper fraction** is a fraction greater than or equal to 1. The numerator of an improper fraction is greater than or equal to the denominator. The shaded portion of the circles can be represented by the improper fraction $\frac{9}{4}$. The shaded portion of the square can be represented by $\frac{4}{4}$.

Example 1   Express the shaded portion of the circles as a mixed number.

Solution $3\frac{2}{5}$

You Try It 1   Express the shaded portion of the circles as a mixed number.

Your solution

Example 2   Express the shaded portion of the circles as an improper fraction.

Solution $\frac{17}{5}$

You Try It 2   Express the shaded portion of the circles as an improper fraction.

Your solution

Solutions on pp. S4–S5

Objective B   **To write an improper fraction as a mixed number or a whole number, and a mixed number as an improper fraction**

Note from the diagram that the mixed number $2\frac{3}{5}$ and the improper fraction $\frac{13}{5}$ both represent the shaded portion of the circles.

$$2\frac{3}{5} = \frac{13}{5}$$

An improper fraction can be written as a mixed number or a whole number.

HOW TO   Write $\frac{13}{5}$ as a mixed number.

Divide the numerator by the denominator.	To write the fractional part of the mixed number, write the remainder over the divisor.	Write the answer.
$$\begin{array}{r} 2 \\ 5\overline{)\,13} \\ -10 \\ \hline 3 \end{array}$$	$$\begin{array}{r} 2\frac{3}{5} \\ 5\overline{)\,13} \\ -10 \\ \hline 3 \end{array}$$	$$\frac{13}{5} = 2\frac{3}{5}$$

Point of Interest

Archimedes (c. 287–212 B.C.) is the person who calculated that $\pi \approx 3\frac{1}{7}$. He actually showed that $3\frac{10}{71} < \pi < 3\frac{1}{7}$. The approximation $3\frac{10}{71}$ is more accurate but more difficult to use.

To write a mixed number as an improper fraction, multiply the denominator of the fractional part by the whole-number part. The sum of this product and the numerator of the fractional part is the numerator of the improper fraction. The denominator remains the same.

HOW TO   Write $7\frac{3}{8}$ as an improper fraction.

$$7\frac{3}{8} = \frac{(8 \times 7) + 3}{8} = \frac{56 + 3}{8} = \frac{59}{8} \qquad 7\frac{3}{8} = \frac{59}{8}$$

Example 3   Write $\frac{21}{4}$ as a mixed number.

Solution
$$\begin{array}{r} 5 \\ 4\overline{)\,21} \\ -20 \\ \hline 1 \end{array} \qquad \frac{21}{4} = 5\frac{1}{4}$$

You Try It 3   Write $\frac{22}{5}$ as a mixed number.

Your solution

Example 4   Write $\frac{18}{6}$ as a whole number.

Solution
$$\begin{array}{r} 3 \\ 6\overline{)\,18} \\ -18 \\ \hline 0 \end{array} \qquad \frac{18}{6} = 3$$

Note: The remainder is zero.

You Try It 4   Write $\frac{28}{7}$ as a whole number.

Your solution

Example 5   Write $21\frac{3}{4}$ as an improper fraction.

Solution $21\frac{3}{4} = \frac{84 + 3}{4} = \frac{87}{4}$

You Try It 5   Write $14\frac{5}{8}$ as an improper fraction.

Your solution

Solutions on pp. S4–S5

2.2 Exercises

Objective A **To write a fraction that represents part of a whole**

For Exercises 1 to 4, identify the fraction as a proper fraction, an improper fraction, or a mixed number.

1. $\dfrac{12}{7}$

2. $5\dfrac{2}{11}$

3. $\dfrac{29}{40}$

4. $\dfrac{19}{13}$

For Exercises 5 to 8, express the shaded portion of the circle as a fraction.

5.

6.

7.

8.

For Exercises 9 to 14, express the shaded portion of the circles as a mixed number.

9.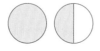

10.

11.

12.

13.

14.

For Exercises 15 to 20, express the shaded portion of the circles as an improper fraction.

15.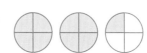

16.

17.

18.

19.

20.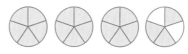

21. Shade $\dfrac{5}{6}$ of

22. Shade $\dfrac{3}{8}$ of

23. Shade $1\dfrac{2}{5}$ of

24. Shade $1\dfrac{3}{4}$ of

25. Shade $\frac{6}{5}$ of

26. Shade $\frac{7}{3}$ of

Objective B To write an improper fraction as a mixed number or a whole number, and a mixed number as an improper fraction

For Exercises 27 to 50, write the improper fraction as a mixed number or a whole number.

27. $\frac{11}{4}$ **28.** $\frac{16}{3}$ **29.** $\frac{20}{4}$ **30.** $\frac{18}{9}$ **31.** $\frac{9}{8}$ **32.** $\frac{13}{4}$

33. $\frac{23}{10}$ **34.** $\frac{29}{2}$ **35.** $\frac{48}{16}$ **36.** $\frac{51}{3}$ **37.** $\frac{8}{7}$ **38.** $\frac{16}{9}$

39. $\frac{7}{3}$ **40.** $\frac{9}{5}$ **41.** $\frac{16}{1}$ **42.** $\frac{23}{1}$ **43.** $\frac{17}{8}$ **44.** $\frac{31}{16}$

45. $\frac{12}{5}$ **46.** $\frac{19}{3}$ **47.** $\frac{9}{9}$ **48.** $\frac{40}{8}$ **49.** $\frac{72}{8}$ **50.** $\frac{3}{3}$

For Exercises 51 to 74, write the mixed number as an improper fraction.

51. $2\frac{1}{3}$ **52.** $4\frac{2}{3}$ **53.** $6\frac{1}{2}$ **54.** $8\frac{2}{3}$ **55.** $6\frac{5}{6}$ **56.** $7\frac{3}{8}$

57. $9\frac{1}{4}$ **58.** $6\frac{1}{4}$ **59.** $10\frac{1}{2}$ **60.** $15\frac{1}{8}$ **61.** $8\frac{1}{9}$ **62.** $3\frac{5}{12}$

63. $5\frac{3}{11}$ **64.** $3\frac{7}{9}$ **65.** $2\frac{5}{8}$ **66.** $12\frac{2}{3}$ **67.** $1\frac{5}{8}$ **68.** $5\frac{3}{7}$

69. $11\frac{1}{9}$ **70.** $12\frac{3}{5}$ **71.** $3\frac{3}{8}$ **72.** $4\frac{5}{9}$ **73.** $6\frac{7}{13}$ **74.** $8\frac{5}{14}$

APPLYING THE CONCEPTS

75. Name three situations in which fractions are used. Provide an example of a fraction that is used in each situation.

2.3 Writing Equivalent Fractions

Objective A **To find equivalent fractions by raising to higher terms**

Equal fractions with different denominators are called **equivalent fractions.**

$\frac{4}{6}$ is equivalent to $\frac{2}{3}$.

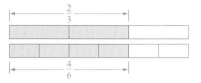

Remember that the Multiplication Property of One states that the product of a number and one is the number. This is true for fractions as well as whole numbers. This property can be used to write equivalent fractions.

$$\frac{2}{3} \times 1 = \frac{2}{3} \times \frac{1}{1} = \frac{2 \cdot 1}{3 \cdot 1} = \frac{2}{3}$$

$$\frac{2}{3} \times 1 = \frac{2}{3} \times \boxed{\frac{2}{2}} = \frac{2 \cdot 2}{3 \cdot 2} = \frac{4}{6} \qquad \frac{4}{6} \text{ is equivalent to } \frac{2}{3}.$$

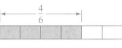

$$\frac{2}{3} \times 1 = \frac{2}{3} \times \boxed{\frac{4}{4}} = \frac{2 \cdot 4}{3 \cdot 4} = \frac{8}{12} \qquad \frac{8}{12} \text{ is equivalent to } \frac{2}{3}.$$

$\frac{2}{3}$ was rewritten as the equivalent fractions $\frac{4}{6}$ and $\frac{8}{12}$.

HOW TO Write a fraction that is equivalent to $\frac{5}{8}$ and has a denominator of 32.

$32 \div 8 = 4$

$\dfrac{5}{8} = \dfrac{5 \cdot 4}{8 \cdot 4} = \dfrac{20}{32}$

- Divide the larger denominator by the smaller.
- Multiply the numerator and denominator of the given fraction by the quotient (4).

$\frac{20}{32}$ is equivalent to $\frac{5}{8}$.

Example 1 Write $\frac{2}{3}$ as an equivalent fraction that has a denominator of 42.

Solution $42 \div 3 = 14$ $\dfrac{2}{3} = \dfrac{2 \cdot 14}{3 \cdot 14} = \dfrac{28}{42}$

$\frac{28}{42}$ is equivalent to $\frac{2}{3}$.

You Try It 1 Write $\frac{3}{5}$ as an equivalent fraction that has a denominator of 45.

Your solution

Example 2 Write 4 as a fraction that has a denominator of 12.

Solution Write 4 as $\frac{4}{1}$.

$12 \div 1 = 12 \qquad 4 = \dfrac{4 \cdot 12}{1 \cdot 12} = \dfrac{48}{12}$

$\frac{48}{12}$ is equivalent to 4.

You Try It 2 Write 6 as a fraction that has a denominator of 18.

Your solution

Solutions on p. S5

To write a fraction in simplest form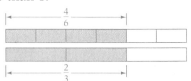

Writing the **simplest form of a fraction** means writing it so that the numerator and denominator have no common factors other than 1.

The fractions $\frac{4}{6}$ and $\frac{2}{3}$ are equivalent fractions.

$\frac{4}{6}$ has been written in simplest form as $\frac{2}{3}$.

The Multiplication Property of One can be used to write fractions in simplest form. Write the numerator and denominator of the given fraction as a product of factors. Write factors common to both the numerator and denominator as an improper fraction equivalent to 1.

$$\frac{4}{6} = \frac{2 \cdot 2}{2 \cdot 3} = \boxed{\frac{2}{2}} \cdot \frac{2}{3} = \boxed{\frac{2}{2}} \cdot \frac{2}{3} = 1 \cdot \frac{2}{3} = \frac{2}{3}$$

The process of eliminating common factors is displayed with slashes through the common factors as shown at the right.

To write a fraction in simplest form, eliminate the common factors.

An improper fraction can be changed to a mixed number.

$$\frac{4}{6} = \frac{\cancel{2} \cdot 2}{\cancel{2} \cdot 3} = \frac{2}{3}$$

$$\frac{18}{30} = \frac{\cancel{2} \cdot \cancel{3} \cdot 3}{\cancel{2} \cdot \cancel{3} \cdot 5} = \frac{3}{5}$$

$$\frac{22}{6} = \frac{\cancel{2} \cdot 11}{\cancel{2} \cdot 3} = \frac{11}{3} = 3\frac{2}{3}$$

Example 3 Write $\frac{15}{40}$ in simplest form.

Solution $\frac{15}{40} = \frac{3 \cdot \cancel{5}}{2 \cdot 2 \cdot 2 \cdot \cancel{5}} = \frac{3}{8}$

You Try It 3 Write $\frac{16}{24}$ in simplest form.

Your solution

Example 4 Write $\frac{6}{42}$ in simplest form.

Solution $\frac{6}{42} = \frac{\cancel{2} \cdot \cancel{3}}{\cancel{2} \cdot \cancel{3} \cdot 7} = \frac{1}{7}$

You Try It 4 Write $\frac{8}{56}$ in simplest form.

Your solution

Example 5 Write $\frac{8}{9}$ in simplest form.

Solution $\frac{8}{9} = \frac{2 \cdot 2 \cdot 2}{3 \cdot 3} = \frac{8}{9}$

$\frac{8}{9}$ is already in simplest form because there are no common factors in the numerator and denominator.

You Try It 5 Write $\frac{15}{32}$ in simplest form.

Your solution

Example 6 Write $\frac{30}{12}$ in simplest form.

Solution $\frac{30}{12} = \frac{\cancel{2} \cdot \cancel{3} \cdot 5}{\cancel{2} \cdot 2 \cdot \cancel{3}} = \frac{5}{2} = 2\frac{1}{2}$

You Try It 6 Write $\frac{48}{36}$ in simplest form.

Your solution

Solutions on p. S5

2.3 Exercises

Objective A   To find equivalent fractions by raising to higher terms

For Exercises 1 to 40, write an equivalent fraction with the given denominator.

1. $\dfrac{1}{2} = \dfrac{}{10}$

2. $\dfrac{1}{4} = \dfrac{}{16}$

3. $\dfrac{3}{16} = \dfrac{}{48}$

4. $\dfrac{5}{9} = \dfrac{}{81}$

5. $\dfrac{3}{8} = \dfrac{}{32}$

6. $\dfrac{7}{11} = \dfrac{}{33}$

7. $\dfrac{3}{17} = \dfrac{}{51}$

8. $\dfrac{7}{10} = \dfrac{}{90}$

9. $\dfrac{3}{4} = \dfrac{}{16}$

10. $\dfrac{5}{8} = \dfrac{}{32}$

11. $3 = \dfrac{}{9}$

12. $5 = \dfrac{}{25}$

13. $\dfrac{1}{3} = \dfrac{}{60}$

14. $\dfrac{1}{16} = \dfrac{}{48}$

15. $\dfrac{11}{15} = \dfrac{}{60}$

16. $\dfrac{3}{50} = \dfrac{}{300}$

17. $\dfrac{2}{3} = \dfrac{}{18}$

18. $\dfrac{5}{9} = \dfrac{}{36}$

19. $\dfrac{5}{7} = \dfrac{}{49}$

20. $\dfrac{7}{8} = \dfrac{}{32}$

21. $\dfrac{5}{9} = \dfrac{}{18}$

22. $\dfrac{11}{12} = \dfrac{}{36}$

23. $7 = \dfrac{}{3}$

24. $9 = \dfrac{}{4}$

25. $\dfrac{7}{9} = \dfrac{}{45}$

26. $\dfrac{5}{6} = \dfrac{}{42}$

27. $\dfrac{15}{16} = \dfrac{}{64}$

28. $\dfrac{11}{18} = \dfrac{}{54}$

29. $\dfrac{3}{14} = \dfrac{}{98}$

30. $\dfrac{5}{6} = \dfrac{}{144}$

31. $\dfrac{5}{8} = \dfrac{}{48}$

32. $\dfrac{7}{12} = \dfrac{}{96}$

33. $\dfrac{5}{14} = \dfrac{}{42}$

34. $\dfrac{2}{3} = \dfrac{}{42}$

35. $\dfrac{17}{24} = \dfrac{}{144}$

36. $\dfrac{5}{13} = \dfrac{}{169}$

37. $\dfrac{3}{8} = \dfrac{}{408}$

38. $\dfrac{9}{16} = \dfrac{}{272}$

39. $\dfrac{17}{40} = \dfrac{}{800}$

40. $\dfrac{9}{25} = \dfrac{}{1000}$

Objective B   To write a fraction in simplest form

For Exercises 41 to 75, write the fraction in simplest form.

41. $\dfrac{4}{12}$

42. $\dfrac{8}{22}$

43. $\dfrac{22}{44}$

44. $\dfrac{2}{14}$

45. $\dfrac{2}{12}$

46. $\dfrac{50}{75}$ **47.** $\dfrac{40}{36}$ **48.** $\dfrac{12}{8}$ **49.** $\dfrac{0}{30}$ **50.** $\dfrac{10}{10}$

51. $\dfrac{9}{22}$ **52.** $\dfrac{14}{35}$ **53.** $\dfrac{75}{25}$ **54.** $\dfrac{8}{60}$ **55.** $\dfrac{16}{84}$

56. $\dfrac{20}{44}$ **57.** $\dfrac{12}{35}$ **58.** $\dfrac{8}{36}$ **59.** $\dfrac{28}{44}$ **60.** $\dfrac{12}{16}$

61. $\dfrac{16}{12}$ **62.** $\dfrac{24}{18}$ **63.** $\dfrac{24}{40}$ **64.** $\dfrac{44}{60}$ **65.** $\dfrac{8}{88}$

66. $\dfrac{9}{90}$ **67.** $\dfrac{144}{36}$ **68.** $\dfrac{140}{297}$ **69.** $\dfrac{48}{144}$ **70.** $\dfrac{32}{120}$

71. $\dfrac{60}{100}$ **72.** $\dfrac{33}{110}$ **73.** $\dfrac{36}{16}$ **74.** $\dfrac{80}{45}$ **75.** $\dfrac{32}{160}$

APPLYING THE CONCEPTS

76. Make a list of five different fractions that are equivalent to $\frac{2}{3}$.

77. Make a list of five different fractions that are equivalent to 3.

78. Show that $\frac{15}{24} = \frac{5}{8}$ by using a diagram.

79. a. Geography What fraction of the states in the United States of America have names that begin with the letter M?
 b. What fraction of the states have names that begin and end with a vowel?

2.4 Addition of Fractions and Mixed Numbers

Objective A   **To add fractions with the same denominator**

Fractions with the same denominator are added by adding the numerators and placing the sum over the common denominator. After adding, write the sum in simplest form.

HOW TO   Add: $\frac{2}{7} + \frac{4}{7}$

$$\begin{array}{r} \frac{2}{7} \\ +\frac{4}{7} \\ \hline \frac{6}{7} \end{array}$$

• Add the numerators and place the sum over the common denominator.

$$\frac{2}{7} + \frac{4}{7} = \frac{2+4}{7} = \frac{6}{7}$$

Example 1   Add: $\frac{5}{12} + \frac{11}{12}$

Solution

$$\begin{array}{r} \frac{5}{12} \\ +\frac{11}{12} \\ \hline \frac{16}{12} = \frac{4}{3} = 1\frac{1}{3} \end{array}$$

• The denominators are the same. Add the numerators. Place the sum over the common denominator.

You Try It 1   Add: $\frac{3}{8} + \frac{7}{8}$

Your solution

Solution on p. S5

Objective B   **To add fractions with different denominators**

Integrating Technology

Some scientific calculators have a fraction key, a^b/c . It is used to perform operations on fractions. To use this key to simplify the expression at the right, enter

$$\underbrace{1 \;\; a^b/c \;\; 2}_{\frac{1}{2}} + \underbrace{1 \;\; a^b/c \;\; 3}_{\frac{1}{3}} =$$

To add fractions with different denominators, first rewrite the fractions as equivalent fractions with a common denominator. The common denominator is the LCM of the denominators of the fractions.

HOW TO   Find the total of $\frac{1}{2}$ and $\frac{1}{3}$.

The common denominator is the LCM of 2 and 3. The LCM = 6. The LCM of denominators is sometimes called the **least common denominator (LCD)**.

Write equivalent fractions using the LCM.

$$\frac{1}{2} = \frac{3}{6}$$
$$+\frac{1}{3} = \frac{2}{6}$$

Add the fractions.

$$\begin{array}{r} \frac{1}{2} = \frac{3}{6} \\ +\frac{1}{3} = \frac{2}{6} \\ \hline \frac{5}{6} \end{array}$$

Example 2 Find $\frac{7}{12}$ more than $\frac{3}{8}$.

Solution

$$\frac{3}{8} = \frac{9}{24}$$

• The LCM of 8 and 12 is 24.

$$+\frac{7}{12} = \frac{14}{24}$$

$$\frac{23}{24}$$

You Try It 2 Find the sum of $\frac{5}{12}$ and $\frac{9}{16}$.

Your solution

Example 3 Add: $\frac{5}{8} + \frac{7}{9}$

Solution

$$\frac{5}{8} = \frac{45}{72}$$

$$+\frac{7}{9} = \frac{56}{72}$$

$$\frac{101}{72} = 1\frac{29}{72}$$

You Try It 3 Add: $\frac{7}{8} + \frac{11}{15}$

Your solution

Example 4 Add: $\frac{2}{3} + \frac{3}{5} + \frac{5}{6}$

Solution

$$\frac{2}{3} = \frac{20}{30}$$

• The LCM of 3, 5, and 6 is 30.

$$\frac{3}{5} = \frac{18}{30}$$

$$+\frac{5}{6} = \frac{25}{30}$$

$$\frac{63}{30} = 2\frac{3}{30} = 2\frac{1}{10}$$

You Try It 4 Add: $\frac{3}{4} + \frac{4}{5} + \frac{5}{8}$

Your solution

Solutions on p. S5

Objective C   **To add whole numbers, mixed numbers, and fractions**

TAKE NOTE

The procedure at the right illustrates why $2 + \frac{2}{3} = 2\frac{2}{3}$. You do not need to show these steps when adding a whole number and a fraction. Here are two more examples:

$$7 + \frac{1}{5} = 7\frac{1}{5}$$

$$6 + \frac{3}{4} = 6\frac{3}{4}$$

The sum of a whole number and a fraction is a mixed number.

HOW TO   Add: $2 + \frac{2}{3}$

$$\boxed{2} + \frac{2}{3} = \boxed{\frac{6}{3}} + \frac{2}{3} = \frac{8}{3} = 2\frac{2}{3}$$

To add a whole number and a mixed number, write the fraction and then add the whole numbers.

HOW TO   Add: $7\frac{2}{5} + 4$

Write the fraction.

$$\begin{array}{r} 7\frac{2}{5} \\ +\,4 \\ \hline \frac{2}{5} \end{array}$$

Add the whole numbers.

$$\begin{array}{r} 7\frac{2}{5} \\ +\,4 \\ \hline 11\frac{2}{5} \end{array}$$

To add two mixed numbers, add the fractional parts and then add the whole numbers. Remember to reduce the sum to simplest form.

Integrating Technology

Use the fraction key on a calculator to enter mixed numbers. For the example at the right, enter

5 a^{b}/c 4 a^{b}/c 9 +

$5\frac{4}{9}$

6 a^{b}/c 14 a^{b}/c 15 =

$6\frac{14}{15}$

HOW TO What is $6\frac{14}{15}$ added to $5\frac{4}{9}$?

The LCM of 9 and 15 is 45.

Add the fractional parts.

$$5\frac{4}{9} = 5\frac{20}{45}$$
$$+ 6\frac{14}{15} = 6\frac{42}{45}$$
$$\frac{62}{45}$$

Add the whole numbers.

$$5\frac{4}{9} = 5\frac{20}{45}$$
$$+ 6\frac{14}{15} = 6\frac{42}{45}$$
$$11\frac{62}{45} = 11 + 1\frac{17}{45} = 12\frac{17}{45}$$

Example 5 Add: $5 + \frac{3}{8}$

Solution $5 + \frac{3}{8} = 5\frac{3}{8}$

You Try It 5 What is 7 added to $\frac{6}{11}$?

Your solution

Example 6 Find 17 increased by $3\frac{3}{8}$.

Solution
$$17$$
$$+ 3\frac{3}{8}$$
$$20\frac{3}{8}$$

You Try It 6 Find the sum of 29 and $17\frac{5}{12}$.

Your solution

Example 7 Add: $5\frac{2}{3} + 11\frac{5}{6} + 12\frac{7}{9}$

Solution
$$5\frac{2}{3} = 5\frac{12}{18} \quad \bullet \text{ LCM} = 18$$
$$11\frac{5}{6} = 11\frac{15}{18}$$
$$+ 12\frac{7}{9} = 12\frac{14}{18}$$
$$28\frac{41}{18} = 30\frac{5}{18}$$

You Try It 7 Add: $7\frac{4}{5} + 6\frac{7}{10} + 13\frac{11}{15}$

Your solution

Example 8 Add: $11\frac{5}{8} + 7\frac{5}{9} + 8\frac{7}{15}$

Solution
$$11\frac{5}{8} = 11\frac{225}{360} \quad \bullet \text{ LCM} = 360$$
$$7\frac{5}{9} = 7\frac{200}{360}$$
$$+ 8\frac{7}{15} = 8\frac{168}{360}$$
$$26\frac{593}{360} = 27\frac{233}{360}$$

You Try It 8 Add: $9\frac{3}{8} + 17\frac{7}{12} + 10\frac{14}{15}$

Your solution

Solutions on p. S5

Objective D   **To solve application problems**

| **Example 9** | **You Try It 9** |

A rain gauge collected $2\frac{1}{3}$ inches of rain in October, $5\frac{1}{2}$ inches in November, and $3\frac{3}{8}$ inches in December. Find the total rainfall for the 3 months.

On Monday, you spent $4\frac{1}{2}$ hours in class, $3\frac{3}{4}$ hours studying, and $1\frac{1}{3}$ hours driving. Find the number of hours spent on these three activities.

Strategy
To find the total rainfall for the 3 months, add the three amounts of rainfall $\left(2\frac{1}{3}, 5\frac{1}{2}, \text{ and } 3\frac{3}{8}\right)$.

Your strategy

Solution

$$2\frac{1}{3} = 2\frac{8}{24}$$

$$5\frac{1}{2} = 5\frac{12}{24}$$

$$+\ 3\frac{3}{8} = 3\frac{9}{24}$$

$$\overline{\qquad\qquad 10\frac{29}{24} = 11\frac{5}{24}}$$

Your solution

The total rainfall for the 3 months was $11\frac{5}{24}$ inches.

| **Example 10** | **You Try It 10** |

Barbara Walsh worked 4 hours, $2\frac{1}{3}$ hours, and $5\frac{2}{3}$ hours this week at a part-time job. Barbara is paid $9 an hour. How much did she earn this week?

Jeff Sapone, a carpenter, worked $1\frac{2}{3}$ hours of overtime on Monday, $3\frac{1}{3}$ hours of overtime on Tuesday, and 2 hours of overtime on Wednesday. At an overtime hourly rate of $36, find Jeff's overtime pay for these 3 days.

Strategy
To find how much Barbara earned:
• Find the total number of hours worked.
• Multiply the total number of hours worked by the hourly wage (9).

Your strategy

Solution

$$
\begin{array}{cc}
4 & 12 \\
2\frac{1}{3} & \times\ 9 \\
+\ 5\frac{2}{3} & \overline{108} \\
\hline
11\frac{3}{3} = 12 \text{ hours worked}
\end{array}
$$

Your solution

Barbara earned $108 this week.

2.4 Exercises

Objective A   **To add fractions with the same denominator**

For Exercises 1 to 20, add.

1. $\dfrac{2}{7} + \dfrac{1}{7}$ **2.** $\dfrac{3}{11} + \dfrac{5}{11}$ **3.** $\dfrac{1}{2} + \dfrac{1}{2}$ **4.** $\dfrac{1}{3} + \dfrac{2}{3}$

5. $\dfrac{8}{11} + \dfrac{7}{11}$ **6.** $\dfrac{9}{13} + \dfrac{7}{13}$ **7.** $\dfrac{8}{5} + \dfrac{9}{5}$ **8.** $\dfrac{5}{3} + \dfrac{7}{3}$

9. $\dfrac{3}{5} + \dfrac{8}{5} + \dfrac{3}{5}$ **10.** $\dfrac{3}{8} + \dfrac{5}{8} + \dfrac{7}{8}$ **11.** $\dfrac{3}{4} + \dfrac{1}{4} + \dfrac{5}{4}$ **12.** $\dfrac{2}{7} + \dfrac{4}{7} + \dfrac{5}{7}$

13. $\dfrac{3}{8} + \dfrac{7}{8} + \dfrac{1}{8}$ **14.** $\dfrac{5}{12} + \dfrac{7}{12} + \dfrac{1}{12}$ **15.** $\dfrac{4}{15} + \dfrac{7}{15} + \dfrac{11}{15}$ **16.** $\dfrac{3}{4} + \dfrac{3}{4} + \dfrac{1}{4}$

17. $\dfrac{3}{16} + \dfrac{5}{16} + \dfrac{7}{16}$ **18.** $\dfrac{5}{18} + \dfrac{11}{18} + \dfrac{17}{18}$ **19.** $\dfrac{3}{11} + \dfrac{5}{11} + \dfrac{7}{11}$ **20.** $\dfrac{5}{7} + \dfrac{4}{7} + \dfrac{5}{7}$

21. Find the sum of $\dfrac{4}{9}$ and $\dfrac{5}{9}$.   **22.** Find the sum of $\dfrac{5}{12}$, $\dfrac{1}{12}$, and $\dfrac{11}{12}$.

23. Find the total of $\dfrac{5}{8}$, $\dfrac{3}{8}$, and $\dfrac{7}{8}$.   **24.** Find the total of $\dfrac{4}{13}$, $\dfrac{7}{13}$, and $\dfrac{11}{13}$.

Objective B   **To add fractions with different denominators**

For Exercises 25 to 48, add.

25. $\dfrac{1}{2} + \dfrac{2}{3}$ **26.** $\dfrac{2}{3} + \dfrac{1}{4}$ **27.** $\dfrac{3}{14} + \dfrac{5}{7}$ **28.** $\dfrac{3}{5} + \dfrac{7}{10}$

29. $\dfrac{8}{15} + \dfrac{7}{20}$ **30.** $\dfrac{1}{6} + \dfrac{7}{9}$ **31.** $\dfrac{3}{8} + \dfrac{9}{14}$ **32.** $\dfrac{5}{12} + \dfrac{5}{16}$

33. $\dfrac{3}{20} + \dfrac{7}{30}$ **34.** $\dfrac{5}{12} + \dfrac{7}{30}$ **35.** $\dfrac{2}{3} + \dfrac{6}{19}$ **36.** $\dfrac{1}{2} + \dfrac{3}{29}$

37. $\dfrac{1}{3} + \dfrac{5}{6} + \dfrac{7}{9}$ **38.** $\dfrac{2}{3} + \dfrac{5}{6} + \dfrac{7}{12}$ **39.** $\dfrac{5}{6} + \dfrac{1}{12} + \dfrac{5}{16}$ **40.** $\dfrac{2}{9} + \dfrac{7}{15} + \dfrac{4}{21}$

41. $\dfrac{2}{3} + \dfrac{1}{5} + \dfrac{7}{12}$ **42.** $\dfrac{3}{4} + \dfrac{4}{5} + \dfrac{7}{12}$ **43.** $\dfrac{1}{4} + \dfrac{4}{5} + \dfrac{5}{9}$ **44.** $\dfrac{2}{3} + \dfrac{3}{5} + \dfrac{7}{8}$

45. $\dfrac{5}{16} + \dfrac{11}{18} + \dfrac{17}{24}$ **46.** $\dfrac{3}{10} + \dfrac{14}{15} + \dfrac{9}{25}$ **47.** $\dfrac{2}{3} + \dfrac{5}{8} + \dfrac{7}{9}$ **48.** $\dfrac{1}{3} + \dfrac{2}{9} + \dfrac{7}{8}$

49. What is $\dfrac{3}{8}$ added to $\dfrac{3}{5}$?   **50.** What is $\dfrac{5}{9}$ added to $\dfrac{7}{12}$?

51. Find the sum of $\dfrac{3}{8}$, $\dfrac{5}{6}$, and $\dfrac{7}{12}$.   **52.** Find the sum of $\dfrac{11}{12}$, $\dfrac{13}{24}$, and $\dfrac{4}{15}$.

53. Find the total of $\dfrac{1}{2}$, $\dfrac{5}{8}$, and $\dfrac{7}{9}$.   **54.** Find the total of $\dfrac{5}{14}$, $\dfrac{3}{7}$, and $\dfrac{5}{21}$.

Objective C   **To add whole numbers, mixed numbers, and fractions**

For Exercises 55 to 82, add.

55. $\begin{array}{r} 1\dfrac{1}{2} \\ + 2\dfrac{1}{6} \\ \hline \end{array}$ **56.** $\begin{array}{r} 2\dfrac{2}{5} \\ + 3\dfrac{3}{10} \\ \hline \end{array}$ **57.** $\begin{array}{r} 4\dfrac{1}{2} \\ + 5\dfrac{7}{12} \\ \hline \end{array}$ **58.** $\begin{array}{r} 3\dfrac{3}{8} \\ + 2\dfrac{5}{16} \\ \hline \end{array}$

59. $\begin{array}{r} 4 \\ + 5\dfrac{2}{7} \\ \hline \end{array}$ **60.** $\begin{array}{r} 6\dfrac{8}{9} \\ + 12 \\ \hline \end{array}$ **61.** $\begin{array}{r} 3\dfrac{5}{8} \\ + 2\dfrac{11}{20} \\ \hline \end{array}$ **62.** $\begin{array}{r} 4\dfrac{5}{12} \\ + 6\dfrac{11}{18} \\ \hline \end{array}$

63. $7\dfrac{5}{12} + 2\dfrac{9}{16}$ **64.** $9\dfrac{1}{2} + 3\dfrac{3}{11}$ **65.** $6 + 2\dfrac{3}{13}$ **66.** $8\dfrac{21}{40} + 6$

67. $8\dfrac{29}{30} + 7\dfrac{11}{40}$ **68.** $17\dfrac{5}{16} + 3\dfrac{11}{24}$ **69.** $17\dfrac{3}{8} + 7\dfrac{7}{20}$ **70.** $14\dfrac{7}{12} + 29\dfrac{13}{21}$

71. $5\dfrac{7}{8} + 27\dfrac{5}{12}$

72. $7\dfrac{5}{6} + 3\dfrac{5}{9}$

73. $7\dfrac{5}{9} + 2\dfrac{7}{12}$

74. $3\dfrac{1}{2} + 2\dfrac{3}{4} + 1\dfrac{5}{6}$

75. $2\dfrac{1}{2} + 3\dfrac{2}{3} + 4\dfrac{1}{4}$

76. $3\dfrac{1}{3} + 7\dfrac{1}{5} + 2\dfrac{1}{7}$

77. $3\dfrac{1}{2} + 3\dfrac{1}{5} + 8\dfrac{1}{9}$

78. $6\dfrac{5}{9} + 6\dfrac{5}{12} + 2\dfrac{5}{18}$

79. $2\dfrac{3}{8} + 4\dfrac{7}{12} + 3\dfrac{5}{16}$

80. $2\dfrac{1}{8} + 4\dfrac{2}{9} + 5\dfrac{17}{18}$

81. $6\dfrac{5}{6} + 17\dfrac{2}{9} + 18\dfrac{5}{27}$

82. $4\dfrac{7}{20} + \dfrac{17}{80} + 25\dfrac{23}{60}$

83. Find the sum of $2\dfrac{4}{9}$ and $5\dfrac{7}{12}$.

84. Find $5\dfrac{5}{6}$ more than $3\dfrac{3}{8}$.

85. What is $4\dfrac{3}{4}$ added to $9\dfrac{1}{3}$?

86. What is $4\dfrac{8}{9}$ added to $9\dfrac{1}{6}$?

87. Find the total of 2, $4\dfrac{5}{8}$, and $2\dfrac{2}{9}$.

88. Find the total of $1\dfrac{5}{8}$, 3, and $7\dfrac{7}{24}$.

Objective D   **To solve application problems**

89. Mechanics   Find the length of the shaft.

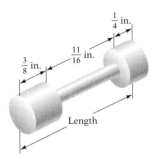

90. Mechanics   Find the length of the shaft.

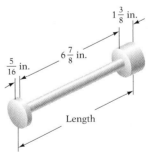

91. Carpentry   A table 30 inches high has a top that is $1\dfrac{1}{8}$ inches thick. Find the total thickness of the table top after a $\dfrac{3}{16}$-inch veneer is applied.

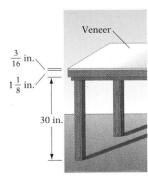

92. Wages   Fred Thomson worked $2\dfrac{2}{3}$ hours of overtime on Monday, $1\dfrac{1}{4}$ hours on Wednesday, $1\dfrac{1}{3}$ hours on Friday, and $6\dfrac{3}{4}$ hours on Saturday.
   a.   Find the total number of overtime hours worked during the week.
   b.   At an overtime hourly wage of $22 per hour, how much overtime pay does Fred receive?

93. **Wages** You are working a part-time job that pays $11 an hour. You worked 5, $3\frac{3}{4}$, $2\frac{1}{3}$, $1\frac{1}{4}$, and $7\frac{2}{3}$ hours during the last five days.

   a. Find the total number of hours you worked during the last five days.
   b. Find your total wages for the five days.

94. **Sports** The course of a yachting race is in the shape of a triangle with sides that measure $4\frac{3}{10}$ miles, $3\frac{7}{10}$ miles, and $2\frac{1}{2}$ miles. Find the total length of the course.

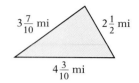

95. **Landscaping** A flower garden in the yard of a colonial home is in the shape of a triangle as shown at the right. The wooden beams lining the edge of the garden need to be replaced. Find the total length of wood beams that must be purchased in order to replace the old beams.

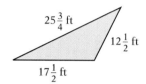

96. 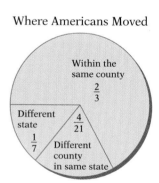 **Food Preferences** When the Heller Research Group conducted a survey to determine favorite doughnut flavors, $\frac{2}{5}$ of the respondents named glazed doughnuts, $\frac{8}{25}$ named filled doughnuts, and $\frac{3}{20}$ named frosted doughnuts. What fraction of the respondents named glazed, filled, *or* frosted as their favorite type of doughnut?

97. **Mobility** During a recent year, over 42 million Americans changed homes. The graph at the right shows what fractions of the people moved within the same county, moved to a different county in the same state, and moved to a different state. (Source: Census Bureau, *Geographical Mobility*) What fractional part of those who changed homes moved outside the county they had been living in?

Where Americans Moved

APPLYING THE CONCEPTS

98. What is a unit fraction? Find the sum of the three largest unit fractions. Is there a smallest unit fraction? If so, write it down. If not, explain why.

99. Use a model to illustrate and explain the addition of fractions with unlike denominators.

100. A survey was conducted to determine people's favorite color from among blue, green, red, purple, and other. The surveyor claims that $\frac{1}{3}$ of the people responded blue, $\frac{1}{6}$ responded green, $\frac{1}{8}$ responded red, $\frac{1}{12}$ responded purple, and $\frac{2}{5}$ responded some other color. Is this possible? Explain your answer.

2.5 Subtraction of Fractions and Mixed Numbers

Objective A   **To subtract fractions with the same denominator**

Fractions with the same denominator are subtracted by subtracting the numerators and placing the difference over the common denominator. After subtracting, write the fraction in simplest form.

HOW TO Subtract: $\dfrac{5}{7} - \dfrac{3}{7}$

$$\begin{array}{r} \dfrac{5}{7} \\[2mm] -\dfrac{3}{7} \\[1mm] \hline \dfrac{2}{7} \end{array}$$

• Subtract the numerators and place the difference over the common denominator.

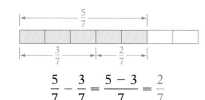

$$\frac{5}{7} - \frac{3}{7} = \frac{5-3}{7} = \frac{2}{7}$$

Example 1 Find $\dfrac{17}{30}$ less $\dfrac{11}{30}$.

Solution

$$\begin{array}{r} \dfrac{17}{30} \\[2mm] -\dfrac{11}{30} \\[1mm] \hline \dfrac{6}{30} = \dfrac{1}{5} \end{array}$$

• The denominators are the same. Subtract the numerators. Place the difference over the common denominator.

You Try It 1 Subtract: $\dfrac{16}{27} - \dfrac{7}{27}$

Your solution

Solution on p. S6

Objective B   **To subtract fractions with different denominators**

To subtract fractions with different denominators, first rewrite the fractions as equivalent fractions with a common denominator. As with adding fractions, the common denominator is the LCM of the denominators of the fractions.

HOW TO Subtract: $\dfrac{5}{6} - \dfrac{1}{4}$

The common denominator is the LCM of 6 and 4. The LCM = 12.

Write equivalent fractions using the LCM.

$$\frac{5}{6} = \frac{10}{12}$$
$$-\frac{1}{4} = \frac{3}{12}$$

Subtract the fractions.

$$\begin{array}{r} \dfrac{5}{6} = \dfrac{10}{12} \\[2mm] -\dfrac{1}{4} = \dfrac{3}{12} \\[1mm] \hline \dfrac{7}{12} \end{array}$$

Example 2 Subtract: $\frac{11}{16} - \frac{5}{12}$

Solution

$$\frac{11}{16} = \frac{33}{48}$$
$$-\frac{5}{12} = \frac{20}{48}$$
$$\frac{13}{48}$$

• LCM = 48

You Try It 2 Subtract: $\frac{13}{18} - \frac{7}{24}$

Your solution

Solution on p. S6

Objective C **To subtract whole numbers, mixed numbers, and fractions**

To subtract mixed numbers without borrowing, subtract the fractional parts and then subtract the whole numbers.

HOW TO Subtract: $5\frac{5}{6} - 2\frac{3}{4}$

Subtract the fractional parts.

$$5\frac{5}{6} = 5\frac{10}{12}$$
$$-2\frac{3}{4} = 2\frac{9}{12}$$
$$\frac{1}{12}$$

• The LCM of 6 and 4 is 12.

Subtract the whole numbers.

$$5\frac{5}{6} = 5\frac{10}{12}$$
$$-2\frac{3}{4} = 2\frac{9}{12}$$
$$3\frac{1}{12}$$

Subtraction of mixed numbers sometimes involves borrowing.

HOW TO Subtract: $5 - 2\frac{5}{8}$

Borrow 1 from 5.

$$5 = \overset{4}{\cancel{5}}\,1$$
$$-2\frac{5}{8} = 2\frac{5}{8}$$

Write 1 as a fraction so that the fractions have the same denominators.

$$5 = 4\frac{8}{8}$$
$$-2\frac{5}{8} = 2\frac{5}{8}$$

Subtract the mixed numbers.

$$5 = 4\frac{8}{8}$$
$$-2\frac{5}{8} = 2\frac{5}{8}$$
$$2\frac{3}{8}$$

HOW TO Subtract: $7\frac{1}{6} - 2\frac{5}{8}$

Write equivalent fractions using the LCM.

$$7\frac{1}{6} = 7\frac{4}{24}$$
$$-2\frac{5}{8} = 2\frac{15}{24}$$

Borrow 1 from 7. Add the 1 to $\frac{4}{24}$. Write $1\frac{4}{24}$ as $\frac{28}{24}$.

$$7\frac{1}{6} = \overset{6}{\cancel{7}}1\frac{4}{24} = 6\frac{28}{24}$$
$$-2\frac{5}{8} = 2\frac{15}{24} = 2\frac{15}{24}$$

Subtract the mixed numbers.

$$7\frac{1}{6} = 6\frac{28}{24}$$
$$-2\frac{5}{8} = 2\frac{15}{24}$$
$$4\frac{13}{24}$$

Example 3 Subtract: $15\frac{7}{8} - 12\frac{2}{3}$

Solution
$$15\frac{7}{8} = 15\frac{21}{24} \quad \bullet \text{ LCM} = 24$$
$$-12\frac{2}{3} = 12\frac{16}{24}$$
$$\rule{4cm}{0.4pt}$$
$$3\frac{5}{24}$$

You Try It 3 Subtract: $17\frac{5}{9} - 11\frac{5}{12}$

Your solution

Example 4 Subtract: $9 - 4\frac{3}{11}$

Solution
$$9 \quad= 8\frac{11}{11} \quad \bullet \text{ LCM} = 11$$
$$-4\frac{3}{11} = 4\frac{3}{11}$$
$$\rule{4cm}{0.4pt}$$
$$4\frac{8}{11}$$

You Try It 4 Subtract: $8 - 2\frac{4}{13}$

Your solution

Example 5 Find $11\frac{5}{12}$ decreased by $2\frac{11}{16}$.

Solution
$$11\frac{5}{12} = 11\frac{20}{48} = 10\frac{68}{48} \quad \bullet \text{ LCM} = 48$$
$$-\ 2\frac{11}{16} = \ 2\frac{33}{48} = \ 2\frac{33}{48}$$
$$\rule{5cm}{0.4pt}$$
$$8\frac{35}{48}$$

You Try It 5 What is $21\frac{7}{9}$ minus $7\frac{11}{12}$?

Your solution

Solutions on p. S6

Objective D   **To solve application problems**

HOW TO The outside diameter of a bushing is $3\frac{3}{8}$ inches and the wall thickness is $\frac{1}{4}$ inch. Find the inside diameter of the bushing.

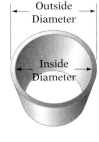

Outside Diameter

Inside Diameter

$$\frac{1}{4} + \frac{1}{4} = \frac{2}{4} = \frac{1}{2}$$

• Add $\frac{1}{4}$ to $\frac{1}{4}$ to find the total thickness of the two walls.

$$3\frac{3}{8} = 3\frac{3}{8} = 2\frac{11}{8}$$
$$-\ \frac{1}{2} = \ \frac{4}{8} = \ \frac{4}{8}$$
$$\rule{4cm}{0.4pt}$$
$$2\frac{7}{8}$$

• Subtract the total thickness of the two walls to find the inside diameter.

The inside diameter of the bushing is $2\frac{7}{8}$ inches.

Example 6

A $2\frac{2}{3}$-inch piece is cut from a $6\frac{5}{8}$-inch board. How much of the board is left?

Strategy

To find the length remaining, subtract the length of the piece cut from the total length of the board.

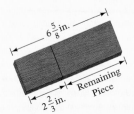

Solution

$$6\frac{5}{8} = 6\frac{15}{24} = 5\frac{39}{24}$$
$$-\,2\frac{2}{3} = 2\frac{16}{24} = 2\frac{16}{24}$$
$$\overline{\phantom{-2\frac{2}{3}} \quad 3\frac{23}{24}}$$

$3\frac{23}{24}$ inches of the board are left.

Example 7

Two painters are staining a house. In 1 day one painter stained $\frac{1}{3}$ of the house, and the other stained $\frac{1}{4}$ of the house. How much of the job remains to be done?

Strategy

To find how much of the job remains:

• Find the total amount of the house already stained $\left(\frac{1}{3} + \frac{1}{4}\right)$.

• Subtract the amount already stained from 1, which represents the complete job.

Solution

$$\frac{1}{3} = \frac{4}{12} \qquad\qquad 1 = \frac{12}{12}$$
$$+\,\frac{1}{4} = \frac{3}{12} \qquad\qquad -\,\frac{7}{12} = \frac{7}{12}$$
$$\overline{\phantom{+\frac{1}{4}}\;\frac{7}{12}} \qquad\qquad \overline{\phantom{-\frac{7}{12}}\;\frac{5}{12}}$$

$\frac{5}{12}$ of the house remains to be stained.

You Try It 6

A flight from New York to Los Angeles takes $5\frac{1}{2}$ hours. After the plane has been in the air for $2\frac{3}{4}$ hours, how much flight time remains?

Your strategy

Your solution

You Try It 7

A patient is put on a diet to lose 24 pounds in 3 months. The patient lost $7\frac{1}{2}$ pounds the first month and $5\frac{3}{4}$ pounds the second month. How much weight must be lost the third month to achieve the goal?

Your strategy

Your solution

Solutions on p. S6

2.5 Exercises

Objective A   **To subtract fractions with the same denominator**

For Exercises 1 to 10, subtract.

1. $\dfrac{9}{17}$
    $-\dfrac{7}{17}$

2. $\dfrac{11}{15}$
    $-\dfrac{3}{15}$

3. $\dfrac{11}{12}$
    $-\dfrac{7}{12}$

4. $\dfrac{13}{15}$
    $-\dfrac{4}{15}$

5. $\dfrac{9}{20}$
    $-\dfrac{7}{20}$

6. $\dfrac{48}{55}$
    $-\dfrac{13}{55}$

7. $\dfrac{42}{65}$
    $-\dfrac{17}{65}$

8. $\dfrac{11}{24}$
    $-\dfrac{5}{24}$

9. $\dfrac{23}{30}$
    $-\dfrac{13}{30}$

10. $\dfrac{17}{42}$
    $-\dfrac{5}{42}$

11. What is $\dfrac{5}{14}$ less than $\dfrac{13}{14}$?

12. What is $\dfrac{7}{19}$ less than $\dfrac{17}{19}$?

13. Find the difference between $\dfrac{7}{8}$ and $\dfrac{5}{8}$.

14. Find the difference between $\dfrac{7}{12}$ and $\dfrac{5}{12}$.

15. What is $\dfrac{18}{23}$ minus $\dfrac{9}{23}$?

16. What is $\dfrac{7}{9}$ minus $\dfrac{3}{9}$?

17. Find $\dfrac{17}{24}$ decreased by $\dfrac{11}{24}$.

18. Find $\dfrac{19}{30}$ decreased by $\dfrac{11}{30}$.

Objective B   **To subtract fractions with different denominators**

For Exercises 19 to 33, subtract.

19. $\dfrac{2}{3}$
    $-\dfrac{1}{6}$

20. $\dfrac{7}{8}$
    $-\dfrac{5}{16}$

21. $\dfrac{5}{8}$
    $-\dfrac{2}{7}$

22. $\dfrac{5}{6}$
    $-\dfrac{3}{7}$

23. $\dfrac{5}{7}$
    $-\dfrac{3}{14}$

24. $\dfrac{5}{9}$
    $-\dfrac{7}{15}$

25. $\dfrac{8}{15}$
    $-\dfrac{7}{20}$

26. $\dfrac{7}{9}$
    $-\dfrac{1}{6}$

27. $\dfrac{9}{14}$
    $-\dfrac{3}{8}$

28. $\dfrac{5}{12}$
    $-\dfrac{5}{16}$

29. $\dfrac{46}{51}$
$-\dfrac{3}{17}$

30. $\dfrac{9}{16}$
$-\dfrac{17}{32}$

31. $\dfrac{21}{35}$
$-\dfrac{5}{14}$

32. $\dfrac{19}{40}$
$-\dfrac{3}{16}$

33. $\dfrac{29}{60}$
$-\dfrac{3}{40}$

34. What is $\dfrac{3}{5}$ less than $\dfrac{11}{12}$?

35. What is $\dfrac{5}{9}$ less than $\dfrac{11}{15}$?

36. Find the difference between $\dfrac{11}{24}$ and $\dfrac{7}{18}$.

37. Find the difference between $\dfrac{9}{14}$ and $\dfrac{5}{42}$.

38. Find $\dfrac{11}{12}$ decreased by $\dfrac{11}{15}$.

39. Find $\dfrac{17}{20}$ decreased by $\dfrac{7}{15}$.

40. What is $\dfrac{13}{20}$ minus $\dfrac{1}{6}$?

41. What is $\dfrac{5}{6}$ minus $\dfrac{7}{9}$?

Objective C **To subtract whole numbers, mixed numbers, and fractions**

For Exercises 42 to 61, subtract.

42. $5\dfrac{7}{12}$
$-2\dfrac{5}{12}$

43. $16\dfrac{11}{15}$
$-11\dfrac{8}{15}$

44. $72\dfrac{21}{23}$
$-16\dfrac{17}{23}$

45. $19\dfrac{16}{17}$
$-9\dfrac{7}{17}$

46. $6\dfrac{1}{3}$
-2

47. $5\dfrac{7}{8}$
-1

48. 10
$-6\dfrac{1}{3}$

49. 3
$-2\dfrac{5}{21}$

50. $6\dfrac{2}{5}$
$-4\dfrac{4}{5}$

51. $16\dfrac{3}{8}$
$-10\dfrac{7}{8}$

52. $25\dfrac{4}{9}$
$-16\dfrac{7}{9}$

53. $8\dfrac{3}{7}$
$-2\dfrac{6}{7}$

54. $16\dfrac{2}{5}$
$-8\dfrac{4}{9}$

55. $23\dfrac{7}{8}$
$-16\dfrac{2}{3}$

56. 6
$-4\dfrac{3}{5}$

57. $65\dfrac{8}{35}$
$-16\dfrac{11}{14}$

58. $82\dfrac{4}{33}$
$-16\dfrac{5}{22}$

59. $101\dfrac{2}{9}$
-16

60. $77\dfrac{5}{18}$
-61

61. 17
$-7\dfrac{8}{13}$

62. What is $5\frac{3}{8}$ less than $8\frac{1}{9}$?

63. What is $7\frac{3}{5}$ less than $23\frac{3}{20}$?

64. Find the difference between $9\frac{2}{7}$ and $3\frac{1}{4}$.

65. Find the difference between $12\frac{3}{8}$ and $7\frac{5}{12}$.

66. What is $10\frac{5}{9}$ minus $5\frac{11}{15}$?

67. Find $6\frac{1}{3}$ decreased by $3\frac{3}{5}$.

Objective D   **To solve application problems**

68. Mechanics   Find the missing dimension.

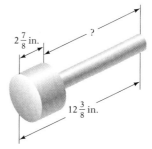

$7\frac{7}{8}$ ft

?

$16\frac{2}{3}$ ft

69. Mechanics   Find the missing dimension.

$2\frac{7}{8}$ in.

?

$12\frac{3}{8}$ in.

70.   **Sports**   In the Kentucky Derby the horses run $1\frac{1}{4}$ miles. In the Belmont Stakes they run $1\frac{1}{2}$ miles, and in the Preakness Stakes they run $1\frac{3}{16}$ miles. How much farther do the horses run in the Kentucky Derby than in the Preakness Stakes? How much farther do they run in the Belmont Stakes than in the Preakness Stakes?

71.   **Sports**   In the running high jump in the 1948 Summer Olympic Games, Alice Coachman's distance was $66\frac{1}{8}$ inches. In the same event in the 1972 Summer Olympics, Urika Meyfarth jumped $75\frac{1}{2}$ inches, and in the 1996 Olympic Games, Stefka Kostadinova jumped $80\frac{3}{4}$ inches. Find the difference between Meyfarth's distance and Coachman's distance. Find the difference between Kostadinova's distance and Meyfarth's distance.

72. Hiking   Two hikers plan a 3-day, $27\frac{1}{2}$-mile backpack trip carrying a total of 80 pounds. The hikers plan to travel $7\frac{3}{8}$ miles the first day and $10\frac{1}{3}$ miles the second day.
a. How many miles do the hikers plan to travel the first two days?
b. How many miles will be left to travel on the third day?

$7\frac{3}{8}$ $10\frac{1}{3}$

Start

73. **Fundraising** A 12-mile walkathon has three checkpoints. The first is $3\frac{3}{8}$ miles from the starting point. The second checkpoint is $4\frac{1}{3}$ miles from the first.

   a. How many miles is it from the starting point to the second checkpoint?

   b. How many miles is it from the second checkpoint to the finish line?

74. **Health** A patient with high blood pressure who weighs 225 pounds is put on a diet to lose 25 pounds in 3 months. The patient loses $8\frac{3}{4}$ pounds the first month and $11\frac{5}{8}$ pounds the second month. How much weight must be lost the third month for the goal to be achieved?

75. **Sports** A wrestler is entered in the 172-pound weight class in the conference finals coming up in 3 weeks. The wrestler needs to lose $12\frac{3}{4}$ pounds. The wrestler loses $5\frac{1}{4}$ pounds the first week and $4\frac{1}{4}$ pounds the second week.

   a. Without doing the calculations, determine whether the wrestler can reach his weight class by losing less in the third week than was lost in the second week.

   b. How many pounds must be lost in the third week for the desired weight to be reached?

76. **Government** The figure at the right shows the sources of federal income. The category "Social Security, Medicare" includes unemployment and other retirement taxes. The category "Miscellaneous Taxes" includes excise, customs, estate, and gift taxes.

   a. What is the difference between the fraction of federal income derived from personal income taxes and the fraction derived from corporate income taxes?

   b. What is the difference between the fraction of federal income derived from the Social Security category and the fraction derived from miscellaneous taxes?

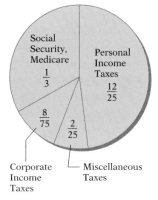

Sources of Federal Income

APPLYING THE CONCEPTS

77. Fill in the square to produce a true statement: $5\frac{1}{3} - \boxed{} = 2\frac{1}{2}$.

78. Fill in the square to produce a true statement: $\boxed{} - 4\frac{1}{2} = 1\frac{5}{8}$.

79. Fill in the blank squares at the right so that the sum of the numbers is the same along any row, column, or diagonal. The resulting square is called a magic square.

80. **Finances** If $\frac{4}{15}$ of an electrician's income is spent for housing, what fraction of the electrician's income is not spent for housing?

2.6 Multiplication of Fractions and Mixed Numbers

Objective A   **To multiply fractions**

The product of two fractions is the product of the numerators over the product of the denominators.

Study Tip

Before the class meeting in which your professor begins a new section, you should read each objective statement for that section. Next, browse through the material in that objective. The purpose of browsing through the material is so that your brain will be prepared to accept and organize the new information when it is presented to you. See *AIM for Success* at the front of the book.

HOW TO   Multiply: $\frac{2}{3} \times \frac{4}{5}$

$$\frac{2}{3} \times \frac{4}{5} = \frac{2 \cdot 4}{3 \cdot 5} = \frac{8}{15}$$

- Multiply the numerators.
- Multiply the denominators.

The product $\frac{2}{3} \times \frac{4}{5}$ can be read "$\frac{2}{3}$ times $\frac{4}{5}$" or "$\frac{2}{3}$ of $\frac{4}{5}$."

Reading the times sign as "of" is useful in application problems.

$\frac{4}{5}$ of the bar is shaded.

Shade $\frac{2}{3}$ of the $\frac{4}{5}$ already shaded.

$\frac{8}{15}$ of the bar is then shaded light yellow.

$$\frac{2}{3} \text{ of } \frac{4}{5} = \frac{2}{3} \times \frac{4}{5} = \frac{8}{15}$$

After multiplying two fractions, write the product in simplest form.

HOW TO   Multiply: $\frac{3}{4} \times \frac{14}{15}$

$$\frac{3}{4} \times \frac{14}{15} = \frac{3 \cdot 14}{4 \cdot 15}$$

- Multiply the numerators.
- Multiply the denominators.

$$= \frac{3 \cdot 2 \cdot 7}{2 \cdot 2 \cdot 3 \cdot 5}$$

- Write the prime factorization of each number.

$$= \frac{\overset{1}{\cancel{3}} \cdot \overset{1}{\cancel{2}} \cdot 7}{2 \cdot 2 \cdot \underset{1}{\cancel{3}} \cdot 5} = \frac{7}{10}$$

- Eliminate the common factors. Then multiply the remaining factors in the numerator and denominator.

This example could also be worked by using the GCF.

$$\frac{3}{4} \times \frac{14}{15} = \frac{42}{60}$$

- Multiply the numerators.
- Multiply the denominators.

$$= \frac{6 \cdot 7}{6 \cdot 10}$$

- The GCF of 42 and 60 is 6. Factor 6 from 42 and 60.

$$= \frac{\overset{1}{\cancel{6}} \cdot 7}{\underset{1}{\cancel{6}} \cdot 10} = \frac{7}{10}$$

- Eliminate the GCF.

Example 1

Multiply $\frac{4}{15}$ and $\frac{5}{28}$.

Solution

$$\frac{4}{15} \times \frac{5}{28} = \frac{4 \cdot 5}{15 \cdot 28} = \frac{\overset{1}{2} \cdot \overset{1}{2} \cdot \overset{1}{5}}{3 \cdot \underset{1}{5} \cdot \underset{1}{2} \cdot \underset{1}{2} \cdot 7} = \frac{1}{21}$$

You Try It 1

Multiply $\frac{4}{21}$ and $\frac{7}{44}$.

Your solution

Example 2

Find the product of $\frac{9}{20}$ and $\frac{33}{35}$.

Solution

$$\frac{9}{20} \times \frac{33}{35} = \frac{9 \cdot 33}{20 \cdot 35} = \frac{3 \cdot 3 \cdot 3 \cdot 11}{2 \cdot 2 \cdot 5 \cdot 5 \cdot 7} = \frac{297}{700}$$

You Try It 2

Find the product of $\frac{2}{21}$ and $\frac{10}{33}$.

Your solution

Example 3

What is $\frac{14}{9}$ times $\frac{12}{7}$?

Solution

$$\frac{14}{9} \times \frac{12}{7} = \frac{14 \cdot 12}{9 \cdot 7} = \frac{2 \cdot \overset{1}{7} \cdot 2 \cdot 2 \cdot \overset{1}{3}}{3 \cdot \underset{1}{3} \cdot \underset{1}{7}} = \frac{8}{3} = 2\frac{2}{3}$$

You Try It 3

What is $\frac{16}{5}$ times $\frac{15}{24}$?

Your solution

Solutions on pp. S6–S7

Objective B   **To multiply whole numbers, mixed numbers, and fractions**

To multiply a whole number by a fraction or mixed number, first write the whole number as a fraction with a denominator of 1.

HOW TO   Multiply: $4 \times \frac{3}{7}$

$$4 \times \frac{3}{7} = \frac{4}{1} \times \frac{3}{7} = \frac{4 \cdot 3}{1 \cdot 7} = \frac{2 \cdot 2 \cdot 3}{7} = \frac{12}{7} = 1\frac{5}{7}$$

• Write 4 with a denominator of 1; then multiply the fractions.

When one or more of the factors in a product is a mixed number, write the mixed number as an improper fraction before multiplying.

HOW TO   Multiply: $2\frac{1}{3} \times \frac{3}{14}$

$$2\frac{1}{3} \times \frac{3}{14} = \frac{7}{3} \times \frac{3}{14} = \frac{7 \cdot 3}{3 \cdot 14} = \frac{\overset{1}{7} \cdot \overset{1}{3}}{\underset{1}{3} \cdot 2 \cdot \underset{1}{7}} = \frac{1}{2}$$

• Write $2\frac{1}{3}$ as an improper fraction; then multiply the fractions.

Example 4

Multiply: $4\frac{5}{6} \times \frac{12}{13}$

Solution

$$4\frac{5}{6} \times \frac{12}{13} = \frac{29}{6} \times \frac{12}{13} = \frac{29 \cdot 12}{6 \cdot 13}$$

$$= \frac{29 \cdot \overset{1}{\cancel{2}} \cdot 2 \cdot \overset{1}{\cancel{3}}}{\underset{1}{\cancel{2}} \cdot \underset{1}{\cancel{3}} \cdot 13} = \frac{58}{13} = 4\frac{6}{13}$$

You Try It 4

Multiply: $5\frac{2}{5} \times \frac{5}{9}$

Your solution

Example 5

Find $5\frac{2}{3}$ times $4\frac{1}{2}$.

Solution

$$5\frac{2}{3} \times 4\frac{1}{2} = \frac{17}{3} \times \frac{9}{2} = \frac{17 \cdot 9}{3 \cdot 2}$$

$$= \frac{17 \cdot \overset{1}{\cancel{3}} \cdot 3}{\underset{1}{\cancel{3}} \cdot 2} = \frac{51}{2} = 25\frac{1}{2}$$

You Try It 5

Multiply: $3\frac{2}{5} \times 6\frac{1}{4}$

Your solution

Example 6

Multiply: $4\frac{2}{5} \times 7$

Solution

$$4\frac{2}{5} \times 7 = \frac{22}{5} \times \frac{7}{1} = \frac{22 \cdot 7}{5 \cdot 1}$$

$$= \frac{2 \cdot 11 \cdot 7}{5} = \frac{154}{5} = 30\frac{4}{5}$$

You Try It 6

Multiply: $3\frac{2}{7} \times 6$

Your solution

Solutions on p. S7

Objective C   **To solve application problems**

Length (ft)	Weight (lb/ft)
$6\frac{1}{2}$	$\frac{3}{8}$
$8\frac{5}{8}$	$1\frac{1}{4}$
$10\frac{3}{4}$	$2\frac{1}{2}$
$12\frac{7}{12}$	$4\frac{1}{3}$

The table at the left lists the length of steel rods and the weight per foot. The weight per foot is measured in pounds for each foot of rod and is abbreviated as lb/ft.

HOW TO   Find the weight of the steel bar that is $10\frac{3}{4}$ feet long.

Strategy
To find the weight of the steel bar, multiply its length by the weight per foot.

Solution $10\frac{3}{4} \times 2\frac{1}{2} = \frac{43}{4} \times \frac{5}{2} = \frac{43 \cdot 5}{4 \cdot 2} = \frac{215}{8} = 26\frac{7}{8}$

The weight of the $10\frac{3}{4}$-foot rod is $26\frac{7}{8}$ pounds.

Example 7

An electrician earns $206 for each day worked. What are the electrician's earnings for working $4\frac{1}{2}$ days?

Strategy

To find the electrician's total earnings, multiply the daily earnings (206) by the number of days worked $\left(4\frac{1}{2}\right)$.

Solution $206 \times 4\frac{1}{2} = \frac{206}{1} \times \frac{9}{2}$

$$= \frac{206 \cdot 9}{1 \cdot 2}$$

$$= 927$$

The electrician's earnings are $927.

You Try It 7

Over the last 10 years, a house increased in value by $2\frac{1}{2}$ times. The price of the house 10 years ago was $170,000. What is the value of the house today?

Your strategy

Your solution

Example 8

The value of a small office building and the land on which it is built is $290,000. The value of the land is $\frac{1}{4}$ the total value. What is the dollar value of the building?

Strategy

To find the value of the building:

• Find the value of the land $\left(\frac{1}{4} \times 290,000\right)$.

• Subtract the value of the land from the total value (290,000).

Solution $\frac{1}{4} \times 290,000 = \frac{290,000}{4}$

$= 72,500$ • Value of the land

$290,000 - 72,500 = 217,500$

The value of the building is $217,500.

You Try It 8

A paint company bought a drying chamber and an air compressor for spray painting. The total cost of the two items was $160,000. The drying chamber's cost was $\frac{4}{5}$ of the total cost. What was the cost of the air compressor?

Your strategy

Your solution

Solutions on p. S7

2.6 Exercises

Objective A   **To multiply fractions**

For Exercises 1 to 36, multiply.

1. $\dfrac{2}{3} \times \dfrac{7}{8}$

2. $\dfrac{1}{2} \times \dfrac{2}{3}$

3. $\dfrac{5}{16} \times \dfrac{7}{15}$

4. $\dfrac{3}{8} \times \dfrac{6}{7}$

5. $\dfrac{1}{6} \times \dfrac{1}{8}$

6. $\dfrac{2}{5} \times \dfrac{5}{6}$

7. $\dfrac{11}{12} \times \dfrac{6}{7}$

8. $\dfrac{11}{12} \times \dfrac{3}{5}$

9. $\dfrac{1}{6} \times \dfrac{6}{7}$

10. $\dfrac{3}{5} \times \dfrac{10}{11}$

11. $\dfrac{1}{5} \times \dfrac{5}{8}$

12. $\dfrac{6}{7} \times \dfrac{14}{15}$

13. $\dfrac{8}{9} \times \dfrac{27}{4}$

14. $\dfrac{3}{5} \times \dfrac{3}{10}$

15. $\dfrac{5}{6} \times \dfrac{1}{2}$

16. $\dfrac{3}{8} \times \dfrac{5}{12}$

17. $\dfrac{16}{9} \times \dfrac{27}{8}$

18. $\dfrac{5}{8} \times \dfrac{16}{15}$

19. $\dfrac{3}{2} \times \dfrac{4}{9}$

20. $\dfrac{5}{3} \times \dfrac{3}{7}$

21. $\dfrac{7}{8} \times \dfrac{3}{14}$

22. $\dfrac{2}{9} \times \dfrac{1}{5}$

23. $\dfrac{1}{10} \times \dfrac{3}{8}$

24. $\dfrac{5}{12} \times \dfrac{6}{7}$

25. $\dfrac{15}{8} \times \dfrac{16}{3}$

26. $\dfrac{5}{6} \times \dfrac{4}{15}$

27. $\dfrac{1}{2} \times \dfrac{2}{15}$

28. $\dfrac{3}{8} \times \dfrac{5}{16}$

29. $\dfrac{5}{7} \times \dfrac{14}{15}$

30. $\dfrac{3}{8} \times \dfrac{15}{41}$

31. $\dfrac{5}{12} \times \dfrac{42}{65}$

32. $\dfrac{16}{33} \times \dfrac{55}{72}$

33. $\dfrac{12}{5} \times \dfrac{5}{3}$

34. $\dfrac{17}{9} \times \dfrac{81}{17}$

35. $\dfrac{16}{85} \times \dfrac{125}{84}$

36. $\dfrac{19}{64} \times \dfrac{48}{95}$

37. Multiply $\frac{7}{12}$ and $\frac{15}{42}$.

38. Multiply $\frac{32}{9}$ and $\frac{3}{8}$.

39. Find the product of $\frac{5}{9}$ and $\frac{3}{20}$.

40. Find the product of $\frac{7}{3}$ and $\frac{15}{14}$.

41. What is $\frac{1}{2}$ times $\frac{8}{15}$?

42. What is $\frac{3}{8}$ times $\frac{12}{17}$?

Objective B   **To multiply whole numbers, mixed numbers, and fractions**

For Exercises 43 to 82, multiply.

43. $4 \times \frac{3}{8}$

44. $14 \times \frac{5}{7}$

45. $\frac{2}{3} \times 6$

46. $\frac{5}{12} \times 40$

47. $\frac{1}{3} \times 1\frac{1}{3}$

48. $\frac{2}{5} \times 2\frac{1}{2}$

49. $1\frac{7}{8} \times \frac{4}{15}$

50. $2\frac{1}{5} \times \frac{5}{22}$

51. $55 \times \frac{3}{10}$

52. $\frac{5}{14} \times 49$

53. $4 \times 2\frac{1}{2}$

54. $9 \times 3\frac{1}{3}$

55. $2\frac{1}{7} \times 3$

56. $5\frac{1}{4} \times 8$

57. $3\frac{2}{3} \times 5$

58. $4\frac{2}{9} \times 3$

59. $\frac{1}{2} \times 3\frac{3}{7}$

60. $\frac{3}{8} \times 4\frac{4}{5}$

61. $6\frac{1}{8} \times \frac{4}{7}$

62. $5\frac{1}{3} \times \frac{5}{16}$

63. $5\frac{1}{8} \times 5$

64. $6\frac{1}{9} \times 2$

65. $\frac{3}{8} \times 4\frac{1}{2}$

66. $\frac{5}{7} \times 2\frac{1}{3}$

67. $6 \times 2\frac{2}{3}$

68. $6\frac{1}{8} \times 0$

69. $1\frac{1}{3} \times 2\frac{1}{4}$

70. $2\frac{5}{8} \times \frac{3}{23}$

71. $2\frac{5}{8} \times 3\frac{2}{5}$

72. $5\frac{3}{16} \times 5\frac{1}{3}$

73. $3\frac{1}{7} \times 2\frac{1}{8}$

74. $16\frac{5}{8} \times 1\frac{1}{16}$

75. $2\frac{2}{5} \times 3\frac{1}{12}$

76. $2\frac{2}{3} \times \frac{3}{20}$

77. $5\frac{1}{5} \times 3\frac{1}{13}$

78. $3\frac{3}{4} \times 2\frac{3}{20}$

79. $10\frac{1}{4} \times 3\frac{1}{5}$

80. $12\frac{3}{5} \times 1\frac{3}{7}$

81. $5\frac{3}{7} \times 5\frac{1}{4}$

82. $6\frac{1}{2} \times 1\frac{3}{13}$

83. Multiply $2\frac{1}{2}$ and $3\frac{3}{5}$.

84. Multiply $4\frac{3}{8}$ and $3\frac{3}{5}$.

85. Find the product of $2\frac{1}{8}$ and $\frac{5}{17}$.

86. Find the product of $12\frac{2}{5}$ and $3\frac{7}{31}$.

87. What is $1\frac{3}{8}$ times $2\frac{1}{5}$?

88. What is $3\frac{1}{8}$ times $2\frac{4}{7}$?

Objective C   **To solve application problems**

89. Consumerism   Salmon costs $4 per pound. Find the cost of $2\frac{3}{4}$ pounds of salmon.

90. Exercise   Maria Rivera can walk $3\frac{1}{2}$ miles in 1 hour. At this rate, how far can Maria walk in $\frac{1}{3}$ hour?

91. Carpentry   A board that costs $6 is $9\frac{1}{4}$ feet long. One-third of the board is cut off.

   a. Without doing the calculation, is the piece being cut off at least 4 feet long?
   b. What is the length of the piece cut off?

92. Geometry   The perimeter of a square is equal to four times the length of a side of the square. Find the perimeter of a square whose side measures $16\frac{3}{4}$ inches.

$16\frac{3}{4}$ in.

93. Geometry   To find the area of a square, multiply the length of one side of the square times itself. What is the area of a square whose side measures $5\frac{1}{4}$ feet? The area of the square will be in square feet.

94. Geometry   The area of a rectangle is equal to the product of the length of the rectangle times its width. Find the area of a rectangle that has a length of $4\frac{2}{5}$ miles and a width of $3\frac{3}{10}$ miles. The area will be in square miles.

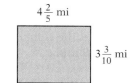

$4\frac{2}{5}$ mi

$3\frac{3}{10}$ mi

95. Finances   A family budgets $\frac{2}{5}$ of its monthly income of $4200 per month for housing and utilities.
   a. What amount is budgeted for housing and utilities?
   b. What amount remains for purposes other than housing and utilities?

96. Education $\frac{5}{6}$ of a chemistry class of 36 students has passing grades. $\frac{1}{5}$ of the students with passing grades received an A.
a. How many students passed the chemistry course?
b. How many students received A grades?

97. Sewing   The Booster Club is making 22 capes for the members of the high school marching band. Each cape is $1\frac{3}{8}$ yards of material at a cost of $12 per yard. Find the total cost of the material.

Measurement   The table at the right shows the length of steel rods and their weight per foot. Use this table for Exercises 98 to 100.

98. Find the weight of the $6\frac{1}{2}$-foot steel rod.

99. Find the weight of the $12\frac{7}{12}$-foot steel rod.

100. Find the total weight of the $8\frac{5}{8}$-foot and the $10\frac{3}{4}$-foot steel rods.

Length (ft)	Weight (lb/ft)
$6\frac{1}{2}$	$\frac{3}{8}$
$8\frac{5}{8}$	$1\frac{1}{4}$
$10\frac{3}{4}$	$2\frac{1}{2}$
$12\frac{7}{12}$	$4\frac{1}{3}$

101. Investments   The manager of a mutual fund has $\frac{1}{2}$ of the portfolio invested in bonds. Of the amount invested in bonds, $\frac{3}{8}$ is invested in corporate bonds. What fraction of the total portfolio is invested in corporate bonds?

APPLYING THE CONCEPTS

102. The product of 1 and a number is $\frac{1}{2}$. Find the number.

103. 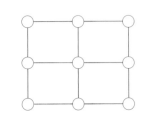   **Time**   Our calendar is based on the solar year, which is $365\frac{1}{4}$ days. Use this fact to explain leap years.

104. Is the product of two positive fractions always greater than either one of the two numbers? If so, explain why. If not, give an example.

105. Which of the labeled points on the number line at the right could be the graph of the product of B and C?

106. Fill in the circles on the square at the right with the fractions $\frac{1}{6}, \frac{5}{18}, \frac{4}{9}, \frac{5}{9}, \frac{2}{3}, \frac{3}{4}, 1\frac{1}{9}, 1\frac{1}{2}$, and $2\frac{1}{4}$ so that the product of any row is equal to $\frac{5}{18}$. (*Note:* There is more than one possible answer.)

2.7 Division of Fractions and Mixed Numbers

Objective A To divide fractions

The **reciprocal of a fraction** is the fraction with the numerator and denominator interchanged.

The reciprocal of $\frac{2}{3}$ is $\frac{3}{2}$.

The process of interchanging the numerator and denominator is called **inverting a fraction.**

To find the reciprocal of a whole number, first write the whole number as a fraction with a denominator of 1; then find the reciprocal of that fraction.

The reciprocal of 5 is $\frac{1}{5}$. $\left(\text{Think } 5 = \frac{5}{1}.\right)$

Reciprocals are used to rewrite division problems as related multiplication problems. Look at the following two problems:

$$8 \div 2 = 4 \qquad\qquad 8 \times \frac{1}{2} = 4$$

8 divided by 2 is 4.   8 times the reciprocal of 2 is 4.

"Divided by" means the same as "times the reciprocal of." Thus "÷ 2" can be replaced with "$\times \frac{1}{2}$," and the answer will be the same. Fractions are divided by making this replacement.

HOW TO   Divide: $\frac{2}{3} \div \frac{3}{4}$

$$\frac{2}{3} \div \frac{3}{4} = \frac{2}{3} \times \frac{4}{3} = \frac{2 \cdot 4}{3 \cdot 3} = \frac{2 \cdot 2 \cdot 2}{3 \cdot 3} = \frac{8}{9}$$ • Multiply the first fraction by the reciprocal of the second fraction.

Example 1 Divide: $\frac{5}{8} \div \frac{4}{9}$

Solution
$$\frac{5}{8} \div \frac{4}{9} = \frac{5}{8} \times \frac{9}{4} = \frac{5 \cdot 9}{8 \cdot 4}$$
$$= \frac{5 \cdot 3 \cdot 3}{2 \cdot 2 \cdot 2 \cdot 2 \cdot 2} = \frac{45}{32} = 1\frac{13}{32}$$

You Try It 1 Divide: $\frac{3}{7} \div \frac{2}{3}$

Your solution

Example 2 Divide: $\frac{3}{5} \div \frac{12}{25}$

Solution
$$\frac{3}{5} \div \frac{12}{25} = \frac{3}{5} \times \frac{25}{12} = \frac{3 \cdot 25}{5 \cdot 12}$$
$$= \frac{\overset{1}{\cancel{3}} \cdot \overset{1}{\cancel{5}} \cdot 5}{\underset{1}{\cancel{5}} \cdot 2 \cdot 2 \cdot \underset{1}{\cancel{3}}} = \frac{5}{4} = 1\frac{1}{4}$$

You Try It 2 Divide: $\frac{3}{4} \div \frac{9}{10}$

Your solution

Solutions on p. S7

Objective B **To divide whole numbers, mixed numbers, and fractions**

To divide a fraction and a whole number, first write the whole number as a fraction with a denominator of 1.

HOW TO Divide: $\frac{3}{7} \div 5$

$$\frac{3}{7} \div \boxed{5} = \frac{3}{7} \div \boxed{\frac{5}{1}} = \frac{3}{7} \times \frac{1}{5} = \frac{3 \cdot 1}{7 \cdot 5} = \frac{3}{35}$$

• Write 5 with a denominator of 1. Then divide the fractions.

When a number in a quotient is a mixed number, write the mixed number as an improper fraction before dividing.

HOW TO Divide: $1\frac{13}{15} \div 4\frac{4}{5}$

Write the mixed numbers as improper fractions. Then divide the fractions.

$$1\frac{13}{15} \div 4\frac{4}{5} = \frac{28}{15} \div \frac{24}{5} = \frac{28}{15} \times \frac{5}{24} = \frac{28 \cdot 5}{15 \cdot 24} = \frac{\overset{1}{\cancel{2}} \cdot \overset{1}{\cancel{2}} \cdot 7 \cdot \overset{1}{\cancel{5}}}{3 \cdot \underset{1}{\cancel{5}} \cdot \underset{1}{\cancel{2}} \cdot \underset{1}{\cancel{2}} \cdot 2 \cdot 3} = \frac{7}{18}$$

Example 3 Divide $\frac{4}{9}$ by 5.

Solution

$$\frac{4}{9} \div 5 = \frac{4}{9} \div \frac{5}{1} = \frac{4}{9} \times \frac{1}{5}$$

• $5 = \frac{5}{1}$. The reciprocal of $\frac{5}{1}$ is $\frac{1}{5}$.

$$= \frac{4 \cdot 1}{9 \cdot 5} = \frac{2 \cdot 2}{3 \cdot 3 \cdot 5} = \frac{4}{45}$$

You Try It 3 Divide $\frac{5}{7}$ by 6.

Your solution

Example 4 Find the quotient of $\frac{3}{8}$ and $2\frac{1}{10}$.

Solution

$$\frac{3}{8} \div 2\frac{1}{10} = \frac{3}{8} \div \frac{21}{10} = \frac{3}{8} \times \frac{10}{21}$$

$$= \frac{3 \cdot 10}{8 \cdot 21} = \frac{\overset{1}{\cancel{3}} \cdot \overset{1}{\cancel{2}} \cdot 5}{2 \cdot 2 \cdot 2 \cdot \underset{1}{\cancel{3}} \cdot 7} = \frac{5}{28}$$

You Try It 4 Find the quotient of $12\frac{3}{5}$ and 7.

Your solution

Example 5 Divide: $2\frac{3}{4} \div 1\frac{5}{7}$

Solution

$$2\frac{3}{4} \div 1\frac{5}{7} = \frac{11}{4} \div \frac{12}{7} = \frac{11}{4} \times \frac{7}{12} = \frac{11 \cdot 7}{4 \cdot 12}$$

$$= \frac{11 \cdot 7}{2 \cdot 2 \cdot 2 \cdot 2 \cdot 3} = \frac{77}{48} = 1\frac{29}{48}$$

You Try It 5 Divide: $3\frac{2}{3} \div 2\frac{2}{5}$

Your solution

Solutions on p. S7

Example 6   Divide: $1\frac{13}{15} \div 4\frac{1}{5}$

Solution

$$1\frac{13}{15} \div 4\frac{1}{5} = \frac{28}{15} \div \frac{21}{5} = \frac{28}{15} \times \frac{5}{21} = \frac{28 \cdot 5}{15 \cdot 21}$$

$$= \frac{2 \cdot 2 \cdot \overset{1}{\cancel{7}} \cdot \overset{1}{\cancel{5}}}{3 \cdot \underset{1}{\cancel{5}} \cdot 3 \cdot \underset{1}{\cancel{7}}} = \frac{4}{9}$$

You Try It 6   Divide: $2\frac{5}{6} \div 8\frac{1}{2}$

Your solution

Example 7   Divide: $4\frac{3}{8} \div 7$

Solution

$$4\frac{3}{8} \div 7 = \frac{35}{8} \div \frac{7}{1} = \frac{35}{8} \times \frac{1}{7}$$

$$= \frac{35 \cdot 1}{8 \cdot 7} = \frac{5 \cdot \overset{1}{\cancel{7}}}{2 \cdot 2 \cdot 2 \cdot \underset{1}{\cancel{7}}} = \frac{5}{8}$$

You Try It 7   Divide: $6\frac{2}{5} \div 4$

Your solution

Solutions on p. S7

Objective C   **To solve application problems**

Example 8

A car used $15\frac{1}{2}$ gallons of gasoline on a 310-mile trip. How many miles can this car travel on 1 gallon of gasoline?

Strategy
To find the number of miles, divide the number of miles traveled by the number of gallons of gasoline used.

Solution

$$310 \div 15\frac{1}{2} = \frac{310}{1} \div \frac{31}{2}$$

$$= \frac{310}{1} \times \frac{2}{31} = \frac{310 \cdot 2}{1 \cdot 31}$$

$$= \frac{2 \cdot 5 \cdot \overset{1}{\cancel{31}} \cdot 2}{1 \cdot \underset{1}{\cancel{31}}} = \frac{20}{1} = 20$$

The car travels 20 miles on 1 gallon of gasoline.

You Try It 8

A factory worker can assemble a product in $7\frac{1}{2}$ minutes. How many products can the worker assemble in 1 hour?

Your strategy

Your solution

Solution on p. S7

Example 9

A 12-foot board is cut into pieces $2\frac{1}{4}$ feet long for use as bookshelves. What is the length of the remaining piece after as many shelves as possible have been cut?

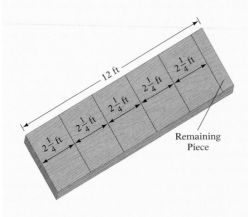

Strategy

To find the length of the remaining piece:

- Divide the total length of the board (12) by the length of each shelf $\left(2\frac{1}{4}\right)$. This will give you the number of shelves cut, with a certain fraction of a shelf left over.
- Multiply the fractional part of the result in step 1 by the length of one shelf to determine the length of the remaining piece.

Solution

$$12 \div 2\frac{1}{4} = \frac{12}{1} \div \frac{9}{4} = \frac{12}{1} \times \frac{4}{9}$$

$$= \frac{12 \cdot 4}{1 \cdot 9} = \frac{16}{3} = 5\frac{1}{3}$$

There are 5 pieces $2\frac{1}{4}$ feet long.

There is 1 piece that is $\frac{1}{3}$ of $2\frac{1}{4}$ feet long.

$$\frac{1}{3} \times 2\frac{1}{4} = \frac{1}{3} \times \frac{9}{4} = \frac{1 \cdot 9}{3 \cdot 4} = \frac{3}{4}$$

The length of the piece remaining is $\frac{3}{4}$ foot.

You Try It 9

A 16-foot board is cut into pieces $3\frac{1}{3}$ feet long for shelves for a bookcase. What is the length of the remaining piece after as many shelves as possible have been cut?

Your strategy

Your solution

Solution on p. S8

2.7 Exercises

For Exercises 1 to 32, divide.

1. $\dfrac{1}{3} \div \dfrac{2}{5}$

2. $\dfrac{3}{7} \div \dfrac{3}{2}$

3. $\dfrac{3}{7} \div \dfrac{3}{7}$

4. $0 \div \dfrac{1}{2}$

5. $0 \div \dfrac{3}{4}$

6. $\dfrac{16}{33} \div \dfrac{4}{11}$

7. $\dfrac{5}{24} \div \dfrac{15}{36}$

8. $\dfrac{11}{15} \div \dfrac{1}{12}$

9. $\dfrac{15}{16} \div \dfrac{16}{39}$

10. $\dfrac{2}{15} \div \dfrac{3}{5}$

11. $\dfrac{8}{9} \div \dfrac{4}{5}$

12. $\dfrac{11}{15} \div \dfrac{5}{22}$

13. $\dfrac{1}{9} \div \dfrac{2}{3}$

14. $\dfrac{10}{21} \div \dfrac{5}{7}$

15. $\dfrac{2}{5} \div \dfrac{4}{7}$

16. $\dfrac{3}{8} \div \dfrac{5}{12}$

17. $\dfrac{1}{2} \div \dfrac{1}{4}$

18. $\dfrac{1}{3} \div \dfrac{1}{9}$

19. $\dfrac{1}{5} \div \dfrac{1}{10}$

20. $\dfrac{4}{15} \div \dfrac{2}{5}$

21. $\dfrac{7}{15} \div \dfrac{14}{5}$

22. $\dfrac{5}{8} \div \dfrac{15}{2}$

23. $\dfrac{14}{3} \div \dfrac{7}{9}$

24. $\dfrac{7}{4} \div \dfrac{9}{2}$

25. $\dfrac{5}{9} \div \dfrac{25}{3}$

26. $\dfrac{5}{16} \div \dfrac{3}{8}$

27. $\dfrac{2}{3} \div \dfrac{1}{3}$

28. $\dfrac{4}{9} \div \dfrac{1}{9}$

29. $\dfrac{5}{7} \div \dfrac{2}{7}$

30. $\dfrac{5}{6} \div \dfrac{1}{9}$

31. $\dfrac{2}{3} \div \dfrac{2}{9}$

32. $\dfrac{5}{12} \div \dfrac{5}{6}$

33. Divide $\dfrac{7}{8}$ by $\dfrac{3}{4}$.

34. Divide $\dfrac{7}{12}$ by $\dfrac{3}{4}$.

35. Find the quotient of $\dfrac{5}{7}$ and $\dfrac{3}{14}$.

36. Find the quotient of $\dfrac{6}{11}$ and $\dfrac{9}{32}$.

Objective B To divide whole numbers, mixed numbers, and fractions

For Exercises 37 to 81, divide.

37. $4 \div \dfrac{2}{3}$

38. $\dfrac{2}{3} \div 4$

39. $\dfrac{3}{2} \div 3$

40. $3 \div \dfrac{3}{2}$

41. $\dfrac{5}{6} \div 25$

42. $22 \div \dfrac{3}{11}$

43. $6 \div 3\dfrac{1}{3}$

44. $5\dfrac{1}{2} \div 11$

45. $6\dfrac{1}{2} \div \dfrac{1}{2}$

46. $\dfrac{3}{8} \div 2\dfrac{1}{4}$

47. $\dfrac{5}{12} \div 4\dfrac{4}{5}$

48. $1\dfrac{1}{2} \div 1\dfrac{3}{8}$

49. $8\dfrac{1}{4} \div 2\dfrac{3}{4}$

50. $3\dfrac{5}{9} \div 32$

51. $4\dfrac{1}{5} \div 21$

52. $6\dfrac{8}{9} \div \dfrac{31}{36}$

53. $\dfrac{11}{12} \div 2\dfrac{1}{3}$

54. $\dfrac{7}{8} \div 3\dfrac{1}{4}$

55. $\dfrac{5}{16} \div 5\dfrac{3}{8}$

56. $\dfrac{9}{14} \div 3\dfrac{1}{7}$

57. $35 \div \dfrac{7}{24}$

58. $\dfrac{3}{8} \div 2\dfrac{3}{4}$

59. $\dfrac{11}{18} \div 2\dfrac{2}{9}$

60. $\dfrac{21}{40} \div 3\dfrac{3}{10}$

61. $2\dfrac{1}{16} \div 2\dfrac{1}{2}$

62. $7\dfrac{3}{5} \div 1\dfrac{7}{12}$

63. $1\dfrac{2}{3} \div \dfrac{3}{8}$

64. $16 \div \dfrac{2}{3}$

65. $1\dfrac{5}{8} \div 4$

66. $13\dfrac{3}{8} \div \dfrac{1}{4}$

67. $16 \div 1\dfrac{1}{2}$

68. $9 \div \dfrac{7}{8}$

69. $16\dfrac{5}{8} \div 1\dfrac{2}{3}$

70. $24\dfrac{4}{5} \div 2\dfrac{3}{5}$

71. $1\dfrac{1}{3} \div 5\dfrac{8}{9}$

72. $13\dfrac{2}{3} \div 0$

73. $82\dfrac{3}{5} \div 19\dfrac{1}{10}$

74. $45\dfrac{3}{5} \div 15$

75. $102 \div 1\dfrac{1}{2}$

76. $0 \div 3\dfrac{1}{2}$

77. $8\dfrac{2}{7} \div 1$

78. $6\dfrac{9}{16} \div 1\dfrac{3}{32}$

79. $8\dfrac{8}{9} \div 2\dfrac{13}{18}$

80. $10\dfrac{1}{5} \div 1\dfrac{7}{10}$

81. $7\dfrac{3}{8} \div 1\dfrac{27}{32}$

82. Divide $7\dfrac{7}{9}$ by $5\dfrac{5}{6}$.

83. Divide $2\dfrac{3}{4}$ by $1\dfrac{23}{32}$.

84. Find the quotient of $8\dfrac{1}{4}$ and $1\dfrac{5}{11}$.

85. Find the quotient of $\dfrac{14}{17}$ and $3\dfrac{1}{9}$.

Objective C   To solve application problems

86. Consumerism   Individual cereal boxes contain $\dfrac{3}{4}$ ounce of cereal. How many boxes can be filled with 600 ounces of cereal?

87. Consumerism   A box of Post's Great Grains cereal costing $4 contains 16 ounces of cereal. How many $1\dfrac{1}{3}$-ounce portions can be served from this box?

88. Gemology   A $\dfrac{5}{8}$-karat diamond was purchased for $1200. What would a similar diamond weighing 1 karat cost?

89. Real Estate   The Inverness Investor Group bought $8\dfrac{1}{3}$ acres of land for $200,000. What was the cost of each acre?

90. Fuel Efficiency   A car used $12\dfrac{1}{2}$ gallons of gasoline on a 275-mile trip. How many miles can their car travel on 1 gallon of gasoline?

91. Mechanics   A nut moves $\dfrac{5}{32}$ inch for each turn. Find the number of turns it will take for the nut to move $1\dfrac{7}{8}$ inches.

92. Real Estate   The Hammond Company purchased $9\dfrac{3}{4}$ acres for a housing project. One and one-half acres were set aside for a park.
a. How many acres are available for housing?
b. How many $\dfrac{1}{4}$-acre parcels of land can be sold after the land for the park is set aside?

93. The Food Industry A chef purchased a roast that weighed $10\frac{3}{4}$ pounds. After the fat was trimmed and the bone removed, the roast weighed $9\frac{1}{3}$ pounds.

a. What was the total weight of the fat and bone?

b. How many $\frac{1}{3}$-pound servings can be cut from the trimmed roast?

94. Carpentry A 15-foot board is cut into pieces $3\frac{1}{2}$ feet long for a bookcase. What is the length of the piece remaining after as many shelves as possible have been cut?

95. Architecture A scale of $\frac{1}{2}$ inch to 1 foot is used to draw the plans for a house. The scale measurements for three walls are given in the table at the right. Complete the table to determine the actual wall lengths for the three walls a, b, and c.

Wall	Scale	Actual Wall Length
a	$6\frac{1}{4}$ in.	?
b	9 in.	?
c	$7\frac{7}{8}$ in.	?

APPLYING THE CONCEPTS

Loans The figure at the right shows how the money borrowed on home equity loans is spent. Use this graph for Exercises 96 and 97.

96. What fractional part of the money borrowed on home equity loans is spent on debt consolidation and home improvement?

97. What fractional part of the money borrowed on home equity loans is spent on home improvement, cars, and tuition?

Real Estate $\frac{1}{25}$ Auto Purchase $\frac{1}{20}$ Tuition $\frac{1}{20}$

Debt Consolidation $\frac{19}{50}$

Home Improvement $\frac{6}{25}$

Other $\frac{6}{25}$

How Money Borrowed on Home Equity Loans Is Spent

Source: Consumer Bankers Association

98. Finances A bank recommends that the maximum monthly payment for a home be $\frac{1}{3}$ of your total monthly income. Your monthly income is $4500. What would the bank recommend as your maximum monthly house payment?

99. Entertainment On Friday evening, 1200 people attended a concert at the music center. The center was $\frac{2}{3}$ full. What is the capacity of the music center?

100. Sports During the second half of the 1900s, greenskeepers mowed the grass on golf putting surfaces progressively lower. The table at the right shows the average grass height by decade. What was the difference between the average height of the grass in the 1980s and its average height in the 1950s?

Average Height of Grass on Golf Putting Surfaces	
Decade	Height (in inches)
1950s	$\frac{1}{4}$
1960s	$\frac{7}{32}$
1970s	$\frac{3}{16}$
1980s	$\frac{5}{32}$
1990s	$\frac{1}{8}$

Source: Golf Course Superintendents Association of America

101. Puzzles You completed $\frac{1}{3}$ of a jigsaw puzzle yesterday and $\frac{1}{2}$ of the puzzle today. What fraction of the puzzle is left to complete?

102. Board Games A wooden travel game board has hinges that allow the board to be folded in half. If the dimensions of the open board are 14 inches by 14 inches by $\frac{7}{8}$ inch, what are the dimensions of the board when it is closed?

103. Wages You have a part-time job that pays $9 an hour. You worked 5 hours, $3\frac{3}{4}$ hours, $1\frac{1}{4}$ hours, and $2\frac{1}{3}$ hours during the four days you worked last week. Find your total earnings for last week's work.

Nutrition According to the Center for Science in the Public Interest, the average teenage boy drinks $3\frac{1}{3}$ cans of soda per day. The average teenage girl drinks $2\frac{1}{3}$ cans of soda per day. Use this information for Exercises 104 to 106.

104. The average teenage boy drinks how many cans of soda per week?

105. If a can of soda contains 150 calories, how many calories does the average teenage boy consume each week in soda?

106. How many more cans of soda per week does the average teenage boy drink than the average teenage girl?

107. Maps On a map, two cites are $4\frac{5}{8}$ inches apart. If $\frac{3}{8}$ inch on the map represents 60 miles, what is the num ber of miles between the two cities?

108. Is the quotient always less than the dividend in a division problem? Explain.

109. Fill in the box to make a true statement.
   a. $\frac{3}{4} \cdot \boxed{} = \frac{1}{2}$ **b.** $\frac{2}{3} \cdot \boxed{} = 1\frac{3}{4}$

110. Publishing A page of type in a certain textbook is $7\frac{1}{2}$ inches wide. If the page is divided into three equal columns, with $\frac{3}{8}$ inch between columns, how wide is each column?

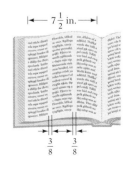

$\longleftarrow 7\frac{1}{2}$ in. $\longrightarrow$

$\frac{3}{8}$ $\frac{3}{8}$

111. A whole number is both multiplied and divided by the same proper fraction. What is greater, the product or the quotient?

2.8 Order, Exponents, and the Order of Operations Agreement

Objective A **To identify the order relation between two fractions**

Point of Interest

Leonardo of Pisa, who was also called Fibonacci (c. 1175–1250), is credited with bringing the Hindu-Arabic number system to the Western world and promoting its use in place of the cumbersome Roman numeral system.

He was also influential in promoting the idea of the fraction bar. His notation, however, was very different from what we have today.

For instance, he wrote $\dfrac{3}{4}\dfrac{5}{7}$

to mean $\dfrac{5}{7} + \dfrac{3}{7 \cdot 4}$, which

equals $\dfrac{23}{28}$.

Recall that whole numbers can be graphed as points on the number line. Fractions can also be graphed as points on the number line.

The graph of $\dfrac{3}{4}$ on the number line

The number line can be used to determine the order relation between two fractions. A fraction that appears to the left of a given fraction is less than the given fraction. A fraction that appears to the right of a given fraction is greater than the given fraction.

$\dfrac{1}{8} < \dfrac{3}{8} \qquad \dfrac{6}{8} > \dfrac{3}{8}$

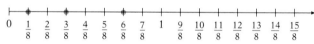

To find the order relation between two fractions with the same denominator, compare the numerators. The fraction that has the smaller numerator is the smaller fraction. When the denominators are different, begin by writing equivalent fractions with a common denominator; then compare numerators.

HOW TO Find the order relation between $\dfrac{11}{18}$ and $\dfrac{5}{8}$.

The LCM of 18 and 8 is 72.

$\dfrac{11}{18} = \dfrac{44}{72} \leftarrow$ Smaller numerator $\qquad \dfrac{11}{18} < \dfrac{5}{8} \quad$ or $\quad \dfrac{5}{8} > \dfrac{11}{18}$

$\dfrac{5}{8} = \dfrac{45}{72} \leftarrow$ Larger numerator

Example 1 Place the correct symbol, $<$ or $>$, between the two numbers.

$\dfrac{5}{12} \qquad \dfrac{7}{18}$

Solution $\dfrac{5}{12} = \dfrac{15}{36} \qquad \dfrac{7}{18} = \dfrac{14}{36}$

$\dfrac{5}{12} > \dfrac{7}{18}$

You Try It 1 Place the correct symbol, $<$ or $>$, between the two numbers.

$\dfrac{9}{14} \qquad \dfrac{13}{21}$

Your solution

Solution on p. S8

Objective B **To simplify expressions containing exponents**

Repeated multiplication of the same fraction can be written in two ways:

$$\dfrac{1}{2} \cdot \dfrac{1}{2} \cdot \dfrac{1}{2} \cdot \dfrac{1}{2} \qquad \text{or} \qquad \left(\dfrac{1}{2}\right)^{4} \leftarrow \text{Exponent}$$

The exponent indicates how many times the fraction occurs as a factor in the multiplication. The expression $\left(\dfrac{1}{2}\right)^{4}$ is in exponential notation.

Example 2 Simplify: $\left(\dfrac{5}{6}\right)^3 \cdot \left(\dfrac{3}{5}\right)^2$

Solution

$$\left(\dfrac{5}{6}\right)^3 \cdot \left(\dfrac{3}{5}\right)^2 = \left(\dfrac{5}{6} \cdot \dfrac{5}{6} \cdot \dfrac{5}{6}\right) \cdot \left(\dfrac{3}{5} \cdot \dfrac{3}{5}\right)$$

$$= \dfrac{\overset{1}{\cancel{5}} \cdot \overset{1}{\cancel{5}} \cdot 5 \cdot \overset{1}{\cancel{3}} \cdot \overset{1}{\cancel{3}}}{2 \cdot \underset{1}{\cancel{3}} \cdot 2 \cdot \underset{1}{\cancel{3}} \cdot 2 \cdot 3 \cdot \underset{1}{\cancel{5}} \cdot \underset{1}{\cancel{5}}} = \dfrac{5}{24}$$

You Try It 2 Simplify: $\left(\dfrac{7}{11}\right)^2 \cdot \left(\dfrac{2}{7}\right)$

Your solution

Solution on p. S8

Objective C   **To use the Order of Operations Agreement to simplify expressions**

The Order of Operations Agreement is used for fractions as well as whole numbers.

> **The Order of Operations Agreement**
>
> **Step 1.** Do all the operations inside parentheses.
> **Step 2.** Simplify any number expressions containing exponents.
> **Step 3.** Do multiplications and divisions as they occur from left to right.
> **Step 4.** Do additions and subtractions as they occur from left to right.

HOW TO Simplify $\dfrac{14}{15} - \left(\dfrac{1}{2}\right)^2 \times \left(\dfrac{2}{3} + \dfrac{4}{5}\right)$.

$$\dfrac{14}{15} - \left(\dfrac{1}{2}\right)^2 \times \left(\underbrace{\dfrac{2}{3} + \dfrac{4}{5}}\right)$$ 1. Perform operations in parentheses.

$$\dfrac{14}{15} - \left(\underbrace{\dfrac{1}{2}}\right)^2 \times \dfrac{22}{15}$$ 2. Simplify expressions with exponents.

$$\dfrac{14}{15} - \underbrace{\dfrac{1}{4} \times \dfrac{22}{15}}$$ 3. Do multiplication and division as they occur from left to right.

$$\underbrace{\dfrac{14}{15} - \dfrac{11}{30}}$$ 4. Do addition and subtraction as they occur from left to right.

$$\dfrac{17}{30}$$

One or more of the above steps may not be needed to simplify an expression. In that case, proceed to the next step in the Order of Operations agreement.

Example 3 Simplify: $\left(\dfrac{3}{4}\right)^2 \div \left(\dfrac{3}{8} - \dfrac{1}{12}\right)$

Solution

$$\left(\dfrac{3}{4}\right)^2 \div \left(\dfrac{3}{8} - \dfrac{1}{12}\right)$$

$$= \left(\dfrac{3}{4}\right)^2 \div \left(\dfrac{7}{24}\right) = \dfrac{9}{16} \div \dfrac{7}{24}$$

$$= \dfrac{9}{16} \cdot \dfrac{24}{7} = \dfrac{27}{14} = 1\dfrac{13}{14}$$

You Try It 3 Simplify: $\left(\dfrac{1}{13}\right)^2 \cdot \left(\dfrac{1}{4} + \dfrac{1}{6}\right) \div \dfrac{5}{13}$

Your solution

Solution on p. S8

2.8 Exercises

To identify the order relation between two fractions

For Exercises 1 to 12, place the correct symbol, $<$ or $>$, between the two numbers.

1. $\dfrac{11}{40}$ $\dfrac{19}{40}$ 2. $\dfrac{92}{103}$ $\dfrac{19}{103}$ 3. $\dfrac{2}{3}$ $\dfrac{5}{7}$ 4. $\dfrac{2}{5}$ $\dfrac{3}{8}$

5. $\dfrac{5}{8}$ $\dfrac{7}{12}$ 6. $\dfrac{11}{16}$ $\dfrac{17}{24}$ 7. $\dfrac{7}{9}$ $\dfrac{11}{12}$ 8. $\dfrac{5}{12}$ $\dfrac{7}{15}$

9. $\dfrac{13}{14}$ $\dfrac{19}{21}$ 10. $\dfrac{13}{18}$ $\dfrac{7}{12}$ 11. $\dfrac{7}{24}$ $\dfrac{11}{30}$ 12. $\dfrac{13}{36}$ $\dfrac{19}{48}$

To simplify expressions containing exponents

For Exercises 13 to 28, simplify.

13. $\left(\dfrac{3}{8}\right)^2$ 14. $\left(\dfrac{5}{12}\right)^2$ 15. $\left(\dfrac{2}{9}\right)^3$ 16. $\left(\dfrac{1}{2}\right)\cdot\left(\dfrac{2}{3}\right)^2$

17. $\left(\dfrac{2}{3}\right)\cdot\left(\dfrac{1}{2}\right)^4$ 18. $\left(\dfrac{1}{3}\right)^2\cdot\left(\dfrac{3}{5}\right)^3$ 19. $\left(\dfrac{2}{5}\right)^3\cdot\left(\dfrac{5}{7}\right)^2$ 20. $\left(\dfrac{5}{9}\right)^3\cdot\left(\dfrac{18}{25}\right)^2$

21. $\left(\dfrac{1}{3}\right)^4\cdot\left(\dfrac{9}{11}\right)^2$ 22. $\left(\dfrac{1}{2}\right)^6\cdot\left(\dfrac{32}{35}\right)^2$ 23. $\left(\dfrac{2}{3}\right)^4\cdot\left(\dfrac{81}{100}\right)^2$ 24. $\left(\dfrac{1}{6}\right)\cdot\left(\dfrac{6}{7}\right)^2\cdot\left(\dfrac{2}{3}\right)$

25. $\left(\dfrac{2}{7}\right)\cdot\left(\dfrac{7}{8}\right)^2\cdot\left(\dfrac{8}{9}\right)$ 26. $3\cdot\left(\dfrac{3}{5}\right)^3\cdot\left(\dfrac{1}{3}\right)^2$ 27. $4\cdot\left(\dfrac{3}{4}\right)^3\cdot\left(\dfrac{4}{7}\right)^2$ 28. $11\cdot\left(\dfrac{3}{8}\right)^3\cdot\left(\dfrac{8}{11}\right)^2$

To use the Order of Operations Agreement to simplify expressions

For Exercises 29 to 47, simplify.

29. $\dfrac{1}{2}-\dfrac{1}{3}+\dfrac{2}{3}$ 30. $\dfrac{2}{5}+\dfrac{3}{10}-\dfrac{2}{3}$ 31. $\dfrac{1}{3}\div\dfrac{1}{2}+\dfrac{3}{4}$ 32. $\dfrac{4}{5}+\dfrac{3}{7}\cdot\dfrac{14}{15}$

33. $\left(\dfrac{3}{4}\right)^2 - \dfrac{5}{12}$

34. $\left(\dfrac{3}{5}\right)^3 - \dfrac{3}{25}$

35. $\dfrac{5}{6} \cdot \left(\dfrac{2}{3} - \dfrac{1}{6}\right) + \dfrac{7}{18}$

36. $\dfrac{3}{4} \cdot \left(\dfrac{11}{12} - \dfrac{7}{8}\right) + \dfrac{5}{16}$

37. $\dfrac{7}{12} - \left(\dfrac{2}{3}\right)^2 + \dfrac{5}{8}$

38. $\dfrac{11}{16} - \left(\dfrac{3}{4}\right)^2 + \dfrac{7}{12}$

39. $\dfrac{3}{4} \cdot \left(\dfrac{4}{9}\right)^2 + \dfrac{1}{2}$

40. $\dfrac{9}{10} \cdot \left(\dfrac{2}{3}\right)^3 + \dfrac{2}{3}$

41. $\left(\dfrac{1}{2} + \dfrac{3}{4}\right) \div \dfrac{5}{8}$

42. $\left(\dfrac{2}{3} + \dfrac{5}{6}\right) \div \dfrac{5}{9}$

43. $\dfrac{3}{8} \div \left(\dfrac{5}{12} + \dfrac{3}{8}\right)$

44. $\dfrac{7}{12} \div \left(\dfrac{2}{3} + \dfrac{5}{9}\right)$

45. $\left(\dfrac{3}{8}\right)^2 \div \left(\dfrac{3}{7} + \dfrac{3}{14}\right)$

46. $\left(\dfrac{5}{6}\right)^2 \div \left(\dfrac{5}{12} + \dfrac{2}{3}\right)$

47. $\dfrac{2}{5} \div \dfrac{3}{8} \cdot \dfrac{4}{5}$

APPLYING THE CONCEPTS

48. **The Food Industry**   The table at the right shows the results of a survey that asked fast-food patrons their criteria for choosing where to go for fast food. For example, 3 out of every 25 people surveyed said that the speed of the service was most important.
   a. According to the survey, do more people choose a fast-food restaurant on the basis of its location or the quality of the food?
   b. Which criterion was cited by the most people?

Fast-Food Patrons' Top Criteria for Fast-Food Restaurants	
Food quality	$\dfrac{1}{4}$
Location	$\dfrac{13}{50}$
Menu	$\dfrac{4}{25}$
Price	$\dfrac{2}{25}$
Speed	$\dfrac{3}{25}$
Other	$\dfrac{3}{100}$

Source: Maritz Marketing Research, Inc.

49.   A farmer died and left 17 horses to be divided among 3 children. The first child was to receive $\dfrac{1}{2}$ of the horses, the second child $\dfrac{1}{3}$ of the horses, and the third child $\dfrac{1}{9}$ of the horses. The executor for the family's estate realized that 17 horses could not be divided by halves, thirds, or ninths and so added a neighbor's horse to the farmer's. With 18 horses, the executor gave 9 horses to the first child, 6 horses to the second child, and 2 horses to the third child. This accounted for the 17 horses, so the executor returned the borrowed horse to the neighbor. Explain why this worked.

50. $\dfrac{2}{3} < \dfrac{3}{4}$. Is $\dfrac{2+3}{3+4}$ less than $\dfrac{2}{3}$, greater than $\dfrac{2}{3}$, or between $\dfrac{2}{3}$ and $\dfrac{3}{4}$?

Focus on Problem Solving

Common Knowledge

An application problem may not provide all the information that is needed to solve the problem. Sometimes, however, the necessary information is common knowledge.

HOW TO You are traveling by bus from Boston to New York. The trip is 4 hours long. If the bus leaves Boston at 10 A.M., what time should you arrive in New York?

What other information do you need to solve this problem?

You need to know that, using a 12-hour clock, the hours run

10 A.M.
11 A.M.
12 P.M.
1 P.M.
2 P.M.

Four hours after 10 A.M. is 2 P.M.

You should arrive in New York at 2 P.M.

HOW TO You purchase a 37¢ stamp at the Post Office and hand the clerk a one-dollar bill. How much change do you receive?

What information do you need to solve this problem?

You need to know that there are 100¢ in one dollar.

Your change is 100¢ − 37¢.

100 − 37 = 63

You receive 63¢ in change.

What information do you need to know to solve each of the following problems?

1. You sell a dozen tickets to a fundraiser. Each ticket costs $10. How much money do you collect?

2. The weekly lab period for your science course is 1 hour and 20 minutes long. Find the length of the science lab period in minutes.

3. An employee's monthly salary is $3750. Find the employee's annual salary.

4. A survey revealed that eighth graders spend an average of 3 hours each day watching television. Find the total time an eighth grader spends watching TV each week.

5. You want to buy a carpet for a room that is 15 feet wide and 18 feet long. Find the amount of carpet that you need.

Projects and Group Activities

Music   In musical notation, notes are printed on a **staff,** which is a set of five horizontal lines and the spaces between them. The notes of a musical composition are grouped into **measures,** or **bars.** Vertical lines separate measures on a staff. The shape of a note indicates how long it should be held. The whole note has the longest time value of any note. Each time value is divided by 2 in order to find the next smallest time value.

The **time signature** is a fraction that appears at the beginning of a piece of music. The numerator of the fraction indicates the number of beats in a measure. The denominator indicates what kind of note receives 1 beat. For example, music written in $\frac{2}{4}$ time has 2 beats to a measure, and a quarter note receives 1 beat. One measure in $\frac{2}{4}$ time may have 1 half note, 2 quarter notes, 4 eighth notes, or any other combination of notes totaling 2 beats. Other common time signatures are $\frac{4}{4}$, $\frac{3}{4}$, and $\frac{6}{8}$.

1. Explain the meaning of the 6 and the 8 in the time signature $\frac{6}{8}$.

2. Give some possible combinations of notes in one measure of a piece written in $\frac{4}{4}$ time.

3. What does a dot at the right of a note indicate? What is the effect of a dot at the right of a half note? At the right of a quarter note? At the right of an eighth note?

4. Symbols called rests are used to indicate periods of silence in a piece of music. What symbols are used to indicate the different time values of rests?

5. Find some examples of musical compositions written in different time signatures. Use a few measures from each to show that the sum of the time values of the notes and rests in each measure equals the numerator of the time signature.

Construction   Suppose you are involved in building your own home. Design a stairway from the first floor of the house to the second floor. Some of the questions you will need to answer follow.

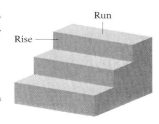

What is the distance from the floor of the first story to the floor of the second story?

Typically, what is the number of steps in a stairway?

What is a reasonable length for the run of each step?

What is the width of the wood being used to build the staircase?

In designing the stairway, remember that each riser should be the same height, that each run should be the same length, and that the width of the wood used for the steps will have to be incorporated into the calculation.

Fractions of Diagrams The diagram that follows has been broken up into nine areas separated by heavy lines. Eight of the areas have been labeled *A* through *H*. The ninth area is shaded. Determine which lettered areas would have to be shaded so that half of the entire diagram is shaded and half is not shaded. Write down the strategy that you or your group use to arrive at the solution. Compare your strategy with that of other individual students or groups.

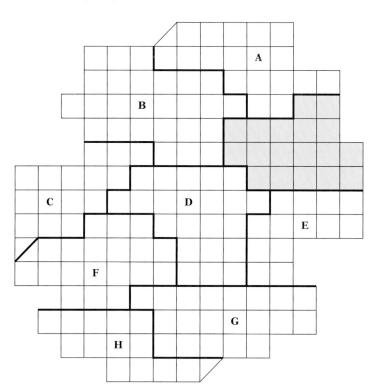

Chapter 2 Summary

Key Words	Examples
A number that is a multiple of two or more numbers is a *common multiple* of those numbers. The *least common multiple (LCM)* is the smallest common multiple of two or more numbers. [2.1A, p. 65]	12, 24, 36, 48, . . . are common multiples of 4 and 6. The LCM of 4 and 6 is 12.
A number that is a factor of two or more numbers is a *common factor* of those numbers. The *greatest common factor (GCF)* is the largest common factor of two or more numbers. [2.1B, p. 66]	The common factors of 12 and 16 are 1, 2, and 4. The GCF of 12 and 16 is 4.
A *fraction* can represent the number of equal parts of a whole. In a fraction, the *fraction bar* separates the *numerator* and the *denominator*. [2.2A, p. 69]	In the fraction $\frac{3}{4}$, the numerator is 3 and the denominator is 4.

In a *proper fraction*, the numerator is smaller than the denominator; a proper fraction is a number less than 1. In an *improper fraction*, the numerator is greater than or equal to the denominator; an improper fraction is a number greater than or equal to 1. A *mixed number* is a number greater than 1 with a whole-number part and a fractional part. [2.2A, p. 69]

$\frac{2}{5}$ is proper fraction.

$\frac{7}{6}$ is an improper fraction.

$4\frac{1}{10}$ is a mixed number; 4 is the whole-number part and $\frac{1}{10}$ is the fractional part.

Equal fractions with different denominators are called *equivalent fractions*. [2.3A, p. 73]

$\frac{3}{4}$ and $\frac{6}{8}$ are equivalent fractions.

A fraction is in *simplest form* when the numerator and denominator have no common factors other than 1. [2.3B, p. 74]

The fraction $\frac{11}{12}$ is in simplest form.

The *reciprocal* of a fraction is the fraction with the numerator and denominator interchanged. [2.7A, p. 101]

The reciprocal of $\frac{3}{8}$ is $\frac{8}{3}$.

The reciprocal of 5 is $\frac{1}{5}$.

Essential Rules and Procedures

Examples

To find the LCM of two or more numbers, find the prime factorization of each number and write the factorization of each number in a table. Circle the greatest product in each column. The LCM is the product of the circled numbers. [2.1A, p. 65]

$$\begin{array}{c|c|c} & 2 & 3 \\ \hline 12 = & \boxed{2 \cdot 2} & 3 \\ \hline 18 = & 2 & \boxed{3 \cdot 3} \end{array}$$

The LCM of 12 and 18 is
$2 \cdot 2 \cdot 3 \cdot 3 = 36$.

To find the GCF of two or more numbers, find the prime factorization of each number and write the factorization of each number in a table. Circle the least product in each column that does not have a blank. The GCF is the product of the circled numbers. [2.1B, p. 66]

$$\begin{array}{c|c|c} & 2 & 3 \\ \hline 12 = & 2 \cdot 2 & ③ \\ \hline 18 = & ② & 3 \cdot 3 \end{array}$$

The GCF of 12 and 18 is $2 \cdot 3 = 6$.

To write an improper fraction as a mixed number or a whole number, divide the numerator by the denominator. [2.2B, p. 70]

$$\frac{29}{6} = 29 \div 6 = 4\frac{5}{6}$$

To write a mixed number as an improper fraction, multiply the denominator of the fractional part of the mixed number by the whole-number part. Add this product and the numerator of the fractional part. The sum is the numerator of the improper fraction. The denominator remains the same. [2.2B, p. 70]

$$3\frac{2}{5} = \frac{5 \times 3 + 2}{5} = \frac{17}{5}$$

To find equivalent fractions by raising to higher terms, multiply the numerator and denominator of the fraction by the same number. [2.3A, p. 73]

$$\frac{3}{4} = \frac{3 \cdot 5}{4 \cdot 5} = \frac{15}{20}$$

$\frac{3}{4}$ and $\frac{15}{20}$ are equivalent fractions.

To write a fraction in simplest form, factor the numerator and denominator of the fraction; then eliminate the common factors. [2.3B, p. 74]

$$\frac{30}{45} = \frac{2 \cdot \overset{1}{\cancel{3}} \cdot \overset{1}{\cancel{5}}}{\underset{1}{\cancel{3}} \cdot 3 \cdot \underset{1}{\cancel{5}}} = \frac{2}{3}$$

To add fractions with the same denominator, add the numerators and place the sum over the common denominator. [2.4A, p. 77]	$\dfrac{5}{12} + \dfrac{11}{12} = \dfrac{16}{12} = 1\dfrac{4}{12} = 1\dfrac{1}{3}$
To add fractions with different denominators, first rewrite the fractions as equivalent fractions with a common denominator. (The common denominator is the LCM of the denominators of the fractions.) Then add the fractions. [2.4B, p. 77]	$\dfrac{1}{4} + \dfrac{2}{5} = \dfrac{5}{20} + \dfrac{8}{20} = \dfrac{13}{20}$
To subtract fractions with the same denominator, subtract the numerators and place the difference over the common denominator. [2.5A, p. 85]	$\dfrac{9}{16} - \dfrac{5}{16} = \dfrac{4}{16} = \dfrac{1}{4}$
To subtract fractions with different denominators, first rewrite the fractions as equivalent fractions with a common denominator. (The common denominator is the LCM of the denominators of the fractions.) Then subtract the fractions. [2.5B, p. 85]	$\dfrac{2}{3} - \dfrac{7}{16} = \dfrac{32}{48} - \dfrac{21}{48} = \dfrac{11}{48}$
To multiply two fractions, multiply the numerators; this is the numerator of the product. Multiply the denominators; this is the denominator of the product. [2.6A, p. 93]	$\dfrac{3}{4} \cdot \dfrac{2}{9} = \dfrac{3 \cdot 2}{4 \cdot 9} = \dfrac{\overset{1}{\cancel{3}} \cdot \overset{1}{\cancel{2}}}{2 \cdot 2 \cdot \underset{1}{\cancel{3}} \cdot 3} = \dfrac{1}{6}$
To divide two fractions, multiply the first fraction by the reciprocal of the second fraction. [2.7A, p. 101]	$\dfrac{8}{15} \div \dfrac{4}{5} = \dfrac{8}{15} \cdot \dfrac{5}{4} = \dfrac{8 \cdot 5}{15 \cdot 4}$ $= \dfrac{\overset{1}{\cancel{2}} \cdot \overset{1}{\cancel{2}} \cdot 2 \cdot \overset{1}{\cancel{5}}}{3 \cdot \underset{1}{\cancel{5}} \cdot \underset{1}{\cancel{2}} \cdot \underset{1}{\cancel{2}}} = \dfrac{2}{3}$
The find the order relation between two fractions with the same denominator, compare the numerators. The fraction that has the smaller numerator is the smaller fraction. [2.8A, p. 110]	$\dfrac{17}{25} \leftarrow$ Smaller numerator $\dfrac{19}{25} \leftarrow$ Larger numerator $\dfrac{17}{25} < \dfrac{19}{25}$
To find the order relation between two fractions with different denominators, first rewrite the fractions with a common denominator. The fraction that has the smaller numerator is the smaller fraction. [2.8A, p. 110]	$\dfrac{3}{5} = \dfrac{24}{40} \qquad \dfrac{5}{8} = \dfrac{25}{40}$ $\dfrac{24}{40} < \dfrac{25}{40}$ $\dfrac{3}{5} < \dfrac{5}{8}$

Order of Operations Agreement [2.8C, p. 111]

Step 1 Do all the operations inside parentheses.	$\left(\dfrac{1}{3}\right)^2 + \left(\dfrac{5}{6} - \dfrac{7}{12}\right) \cdot (4)$
Step 2 Simplify any numerical expressions containing exponents.	$= \left(\dfrac{1}{3}\right)^2 + \left(\dfrac{1}{4}\right) \cdot (4)$
Step 3 Do multiplication and division as they occur from left to right.	$= \dfrac{1}{9} + \left(\dfrac{1}{4}\right) \cdot (4)$
Step 4 Do addition and subtraction as they occur from left to right.	$= \dfrac{1}{9} + 1 = 1\dfrac{1}{9}$

Chapter 2 Review Exercises

1. Write $\frac{30}{45}$ in simplest form.

2. Simplify: $\left(\frac{3}{4}\right)^3 \cdot \frac{20}{27}$

3. Express the shaded portion of the circles as an improper fraction.

4. Find the total of $\frac{2}{3}$, $\frac{5}{6}$, and $\frac{2}{9}$.

5. Place the correct symbol, $<$ or $>$, between the two numbers.

$\frac{11}{18}$ $\frac{17}{24}$

6. Subtract: $18\frac{1}{6}$
$$-\ 3\frac{5}{7}$$

7. Simplify: $\frac{2}{7}\left(\frac{5}{8} - \frac{1}{3}\right) \div \frac{3}{5}$

8. Multiply: $2\frac{1}{3} \times 3\frac{7}{8}$

9. Divide: $1\frac{1}{3} \div \frac{2}{3}$

10. Find $\frac{17}{24}$ decreased by $\frac{3}{16}$.

11. Divide: $8\frac{2}{3} \div 2\frac{3}{5}$

12. Find the GCF of 20 and 48.

13. Write an equivalent fraction with the given denominator.

$\frac{2}{3} = \frac{}{36}$

14. What is $\frac{15}{28}$ divided by $\frac{5}{7}$?

15. Write an equivalent fraction with the given denominator.

$\frac{8}{11} = \frac{}{44}$

16. Multiply: $2\frac{1}{4} \times 7\frac{1}{3}$

17. Find the LCM of 18 and 12.

18. Write $\frac{16}{44}$ in simplest form.

19. Add: $\frac{3}{8} + \frac{5}{8} + \frac{1}{8}$

20. Subtract: $\quad 16$
$$\underline{- \quad 5\frac{7}{8}}$$

21. Add: $4\frac{4}{9} + 2\frac{1}{6} + 11\frac{17}{27}$

22. Find the GCF of 15 and 25.

23. Write $\frac{17}{5}$ as a mixed number.

24. Simplify: $\left(\frac{4}{5} - \frac{2}{3}\right)^2 \div \frac{4}{15}$

25. Add: $\frac{3}{8} + 1\frac{2}{3} + 3\frac{5}{6}$

26. Find the LCM of 18 and 27.

27. Subtract: $\frac{11}{18} - \frac{5}{18}$

28. Write $2\frac{5}{7}$ as an improper fraction.

29. Divide: $\frac{5}{6} \div \frac{5}{12}$

30. Multiply: $\frac{5}{12} \times \frac{4}{25}$

31. What is $\frac{11}{50}$ multiplied by $\frac{25}{44}$?

32. Express the shaded portion of the circles as a mixed number.

33. **Meteorology**   During 3 months of the rainy season, $5\frac{7}{8}$, $6\frac{2}{3}$, and $8\frac{3}{4}$ inches of rain fell. Find the total rainfall for the 3 months.

34. **Real Estate**   A home building contractor bought $4\frac{2}{3}$ acres for \$168,000. What was the cost of each acre?

35. **Sports**   A 15-mile race has three checkpoints. The first checkpoint is $4\frac{1}{2}$ miles from the starting point. The second checkpoint is $5\frac{3}{4}$ miles from the first checkpoint. How many miles is the second checkpoint from the finish line?

36. **Fuel Efficiency**   A compact car gets 36 miles on each gallon of gasoline. How many miles can the car travel on $6\frac{3}{4}$ gallons of gasoline?

Chapter 2 Test

1. Multiply: $\frac{9}{11} \times \frac{44}{81}$

2. Find the GCF of 24 and 80.

3. Divide: $\frac{5}{9} \div \frac{7}{18}$

4. Simplify: $\left(\frac{3}{4}\right)^2 \div \left(\frac{2}{3} + \frac{5}{6}\right) - \frac{1}{12}$

5. Write $9\frac{4}{5}$ as an improper fraction.

6. What is $5\frac{2}{3}$ multiplied by $1\frac{7}{17}$?

7. Write $\frac{40}{64}$ in simplest form.

8. Place the correct symbol, $<$ or $>$, between the two numbers.
   $\frac{3}{8}$ $\frac{5}{12}$

9. Simplify: $\left(\frac{1}{4}\right)^3 \div \left(\frac{1}{8}\right)^2 - \frac{1}{6}$

10. Find the LCM of 24 and 40.

11. Subtract: $\frac{17}{24} - \frac{11}{24}$

12. Write $\frac{18}{5}$ as a mixed number.

13. Find the quotient of $6\frac{2}{3}$ and $3\frac{1}{6}$.

14. Write an equivalent fraction with the given denominator.
    $\frac{5}{8} = \frac{}{72}$

15. Add: $\dfrac{5}{6}$
$\dfrac{7}{9}$
$+\dfrac{1}{15}$

16. Subtract: $23\dfrac{1}{8}$
$-\ 9\dfrac{9}{44}$

17. What is $\dfrac{9}{16}$ minus $\dfrac{5}{12}$?

18. Simplify: $\left(\dfrac{2}{3}\right)^{4} \cdot \dfrac{27}{32}$

19. Add: $\dfrac{7}{12} + \dfrac{11}{12} + \dfrac{5}{12}$

20. What is $12\dfrac{5}{12}$ more than $9\dfrac{17}{20}$?

21. Express the shaded portion of the circles as an improper fraction.

22. **Compensation**   An electrician earns \$240 for each day worked. What is the total of the electrician's earnings for working $3\dfrac{1}{2}$ days?

23. **Real Estate**   Grant Miura bought $7\dfrac{1}{4}$ acres of land for a housing project. One and three-fourths acres were set aside for a park, and the remaining land was developed into $\dfrac{1}{2}$-acre lots. How many lots were available for sale?

24. **Real Estate**   A land developer purchases $25\dfrac{1}{2}$ acres of land and plans to set aside 3 acres for an entranceway to a housing development to be built on the property. Each house will be built on a $\dfrac{3}{4}$-acre plot of land. How many houses does the developer plan to build on the property?

25. **Meterology**   In 3 successive months, the rainfall measured $11\dfrac{1}{2}$ inches, $7\dfrac{5}{8}$ inches, and $2\dfrac{1}{3}$ inches. Find the total rainfall for the 3 months.

Cumulative Review Exercises

1. Round 290,496 to the nearest thousand.

2. Subtract: $\begin{array}{r} 390,047 \\ -\ 98,769 \\ \hline \end{array}$

3. Find the product of 926 and 79.

4. Divide: $57\overline{)30,792}$

5. Simplify: $4 \cdot (6 - 3) \div 6 - 1$

6. Find the prime factorization of 44.

7. Find the LCM of 30 and 42.

8. Find the GCF of 60 and 80.

9. Write $7\frac{2}{3}$ as an improper fraction.

10. Write $\frac{25}{4}$ as a mixed number.

11. Write an equivalent fraction with the given denominator.
$$\frac{5}{16} = \frac{}{48}$$

12. Write $\frac{24}{60}$ in simplest form.

13. What is $\frac{9}{16}$ more than $\frac{7}{12}$?

14. Add: $\begin{array}{r} 3\frac{7}{8} \\ 7\frac{5}{12} \\ +\ 2\frac{15}{16} \\ \hline \end{array}$

15. Find $\frac{3}{8}$ less than $\frac{11}{12}$.

16. Subtract: $\begin{array}{r} 5\frac{1}{6} \\ -\ 3\frac{7}{18} \\ \hline \end{array}$

17. Multiply: $\frac{3}{8} \times \frac{14}{15}$

18. Multiply: $3\frac{1}{8} \times 2\frac{2}{5}$

19. Divide: $\frac{7}{16} \div \frac{5}{12}$

20. Find the quotient of $6\frac{1}{8}$ and $2\frac{1}{3}$.

21. Simplify: $\left(\frac{1}{2}\right)^3 \cdot \frac{8}{9}$

22. Simplify: $\left(\frac{1}{2} + \frac{1}{3}\right) \div \left(\frac{2}{5}\right)^2$

23. **Banking**   Molly O'Brien had $1359 in a checking account. During the week, Molly wrote checks for $128, $54, and $315. Find the amount in the checking account at the end of the week.

24. **Entertainment**   The tickets for a movie were $10 for an adult and $4 for a student. Find the total income from the sale of 87 adult tickets and 135 student tickets.

25. **Measurement**   Find the total weight of three packages that weigh $1\frac{1}{2}$ pounds, $7\frac{7}{8}$ pounds, and $2\frac{2}{3}$ pounds.

26. **Carpentry**   A board $2\frac{5}{8}$ feet long is cut from a board $7\frac{1}{3}$ feet long. What is the length of the remaining piece?

27. **Fuel Efficiency**   A car travels 27 miles on each gallon of gasoline. How many miles can the car travel on $8\frac{1}{3}$ gallons of gasoline?

28. **Real Estate**   Jimmy Santos purchased $10\frac{1}{3}$ acres of land to build a housing development. Jimmy donated 2 acres for a park. How many $\frac{1}{3}$-acre parcels can be sold from the remaining land?

3 Decimals

This woman is the owner and operator of a wholesale groceries store. As such, she is a self-employed person. Anyone who operates a trade, business, or profession is self-employed. There are over 10 million self-employed people in the United States. Among them are authors, musicians, computer technicians, contractors, landscape designers, lawyers, psychologists, sales agents, and dentists. The table associated with **Exercises 28 to 30 on page 136** lists the numbers of self-employed persons in the United States by annual earnings, from less than $5000 per year to $50,000 or more.

OBJECTIVES

Section 3.1

A To write decimals in standard form and in words

B To round a decimal to a given place value

Section 3.2

A To add decimals

B To solve application problems

Section 3.3

A To subtract decimals

B To solve application problems

Section 3.4

A To multiply decimals

B To solve application problems

Section 3.5

A To divide decimals

B To solve application problems

Section 3.6

A To convert fractions to decimals

B To convert decimals to fractions

C To identify the order relation between two decimals or between a decimal and a fraction

Need help? For online student resources, such as section quizzes, visit this textbook's website at **math.college.hmco.com/students.**

Do these exercises to prepare for Chapter 3.

1. Express the shaded portion of the rectangle as a fraction.

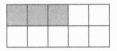

2. Round 36,852 to the nearest hundred.

3. Write 4791 in words.

4. Write six thousand eight hundred forty-two in standard form.

For Exercises 5 to 8, add, subtract, multiply, or divide.

5. 37 + 8892 + 465

6. 2403 − 765

7. 844 × 91

8. 23)6412‾

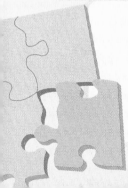

GO FIGURE • • •

Maria and Pedro are siblings. Pedro has as many brothers as sisters. Maria has twice as many brothers as sisters. How many children are in the family?

3.1 Introduction to Decimals

Objective A **To write decimals in standard form and in words**

TAKE NOTE

In decimal notation, that part of the number that appears to the left of the decimal is the **whole-number part.** That part of the number that appears to the right of the decimal point is the **decimal part.** The **decimal point** separates the whole-number part from the decimal part.

The price tag on a sweater reads $61.88. The number 61.88 is in **decimal notation.** A number written in decimal notation is often called simply a **decimal.**

A number written in decimal notation has three parts.

| 61 | . | 88 |
| **Whole-number part** | **Decimal point** | **Decimal part** |

The decimal part of the number represents a number less than 1. For example, $.88 is less than $1. The decimal point (.) separates the whole-number part from the decimal part.

The position of a digit in a decimal determines the digit's place value. The place-value chart is extended to the right to show the place value of digits to the right of a decimal point.

Point of Interest

The idea that all fractions should be represented in tenths, hundredths, and thousandths was presented in 1585 in Simon Stevin's publication *De Thiende* and its French translation, *La Disme*, which was widely read and accepted by the French. This may help to explain why the French accepted the metric system so easily two hundred years later.

In *De Thiende*, Stevin argued in favor of his notation by including examples for astronomers, tapestry makers, surveyors, tailors, and the like. He stated that using decimals would enable calculations to be "performed . . . with as much ease as counterreckoning."

In the decimal 458.302719, the position of the digit 7 determines that its place value is ten-thousandths.

Note the relationship between fractions and numbers written in decimal notation.

Seven tenths	Seven hundredths	Seven thousandths
$\frac{7}{10} = 0.7$	$\frac{7}{100} = 0.07$	$\frac{7}{1000} = 0.007$
1 zero in 10	2 zeros in 100	3 zeros in 1000
1 decimal place in 0.7	2 decimal places in 0.07	3 decimal places in 0.007

To write a decimal in words, write the decimal part of the number as though it were a whole number, and then name the place value of the last digit.

0.9684   Nine thousand six hundred eighty-four ten-thousandths

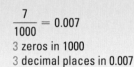

The decimal point in a decimal is read as "and."

372.516   Three hundred seventy-two and five hundred sixteen thousandths

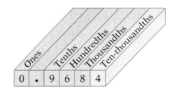

To write a decimal in standard form when it is written in words, write the whole-number part, replace the word *and* with a decimal point, and write the decimal part so that the last digit is in the given place-value position.

Point of Interest

The decimal point did not make its appearance until the early 1600s. Stevin's notation used subscripts with circles around them after each digit: 0 for ones, 1 for tenths (which he called "primes"), 2 for hundredths (called "seconds"), 3 for thousandths ("thirds"), and so on. For example, 1.375 would have been written

1   3   7   5
⓪   ①   ②   ③

Four and twenty-three <u>hundredths</u>

3 is in the hundredths place.   4.2<u>3</u>

When writing a decimal in standard form, you may need to insert zeros after the decimal point so that the last digit is in the given place-value position.

Ninety-one and eight <u>thousandths</u>

8 is in the thousandths place.
Insert two zeros so that the 8 is in the thousandths place.   91.00<u>8</u>

Sixty-five <u>ten-thousandths</u>

5 is in the ten-thousandths place.
Insert two zeros so that the 5 is in the ten-thousandths place.   0.006<u>5</u>

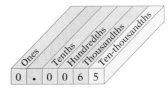

Example 1 Name the place value of the digit 8 in the number 45.687.

Solution The digit 8 is in the hundredths place.

You Try It 1 Name the place value of the digit 4 in the number 907.1342.

Your solution

Example 2 Write $\frac{43}{100}$ as a decimal.

Solution $\frac{43}{100} = 0.43$ • Forty-three hundredths

You Try It 2 Write $\frac{501}{1000}$ as a decimal.

Your solution

Example 3 Write 0.289 as a fraction.

Solution $0.289 = \frac{289}{1000}$ • 289 thousandths

You Try It 3 Write 0.67 as a fraction.

Your solution

Example 4 Write 293.50816 in words.

Solution Two hundred ninety-three and fifty thousand eight hundred sixteen hundred-thousandths

You Try It 4 Write 55.6083 in words.

Your solution

Solutions on p. S8

Example 5 Write twenty-three and two hundred forty-seven millionths in standard form.

Solution   23.000247   • 7 is in the millionths place.

You Try It 5 Write eight hundred six and four hundred ninety-one hundred-thousandths in standard form.

Your solution

Solution on p. S8

Objective B

To round a decimal to a given place value

Study Tip

Have you considered joining a study group? Getting together regularly with other students in the class to go over material and quiz each other can be very beneficial. See *AIM for Success* at the front of the book.

In general, rounding decimals is similar to rounding whole numbers except that the digits to the right of the given place value are dropped instead of being replaced by zeros.

If the digit to the right of the given place value is less than 5, that digit and all digits to the right are dropped.

Round 6.9237 to the nearest hundredth.

┌─── Given place value (hundredths)
6.9237
       └─── 3 < 5   Drop the digits 3 and 7.

6.9237 rounded to the nearest hundredth is 6.92.

If the digit to the right of the given place value is greater or equal to 5, increase the digit in the given place value by 1, and drop all digits to its right.

Round 12.385 to the nearest tenth.

┌─── Given place value (tenths)
12.385
       └─── 8 > 5   Increase 3 by 1 and drop all digits to the right of 3.

12.385 rounded to the nearest tenth is 12.4.

TAKE NOTE

In the example at the right, the zero in the given place value is not dropped. This indicates that the number is rounded to the nearest thousandth. If we dropped the zero and wrote 0.47, it would indicate that the number was rounded to the nearest hundredth.

HOW TO Round 0.46972 to the nearest thousandth.

┌─── Given place value (thousandths)
0.46972
       └─── 7 > 5   Round up by adding 1 to the 9 (9 + 1 = 10). Carry the 1 to the hundredths place (6 + 1 = 7).

0.46972 rounded to the nearest thousandth is 0.470.

Example 6   Round 0.9375 to the nearest thousandth.

Solution

Given place value

0.9375

5 = 5

0.9375 rounded to the nearest thousandth is 0.938.

You Try It 6   Round 3.675849 to the nearest ten-thousandth.

Your solution

Example 7   Round 2.5963 to the nearest hundredth.

Solution

Given place value

2.5963

6 > 5

2.5963 rounded to the nearest hundredth is 2.60.

You Try It 7   Round 48.907 to the nearest tenth.

Your solution

Example 8   Round 72.416 to the nearest whole number.

Solution

Given place value

72.416

4 < 5

72.416 rounded to the nearest whole number is 72.

You Try It 8   Round 31.8652 to the nearest whole number.

Your solution

Example 9

On average, an American goes to the movies 4.56 times per year. To the nearest whole number, how many times per year does an American go to the movies?

Solution
4.56 rounded to the nearest whole number is 5. An American goes to the movies about 5 times per year.

You Try It 9

One of the driest cities in the Southwest is Yuma, Arizona, with an average annual precipitation of 2.65 inch. To the nearest inch, what is the average annual precipitation in Yuma?

Your solution

Solutions on pp. S8–S9

3.1 Exercises

Objective A   **To write decimals in standard form and in words**

For Exercises 1 to 6, name the place value of the digit 5.

1. 76.31587

2. 291.508

3. 432.09157

4. 0.0006512

5. 38.2591

6. 0.0000853

For Exercises 7 to 14, write the fraction as a decimal.

7. $\dfrac{3}{10}$

8. $\dfrac{9}{10}$

9. $\dfrac{21}{100}$

10. $\dfrac{87}{100}$

11. $\dfrac{461}{1000}$

12. $\dfrac{853}{1000}$

13. $\dfrac{93}{1000}$

14. $\dfrac{61}{1000}$

For Exercises 15 to 22, write the decimal as a fraction.

15. 0.1

16. 0.3

17. 0.47

18. 0.59

19. 0.289

20. 0.601

21. 0.09

22. 0.013

For Exercises 23 to 31, write the number in words.

23. 0.37

24. 25.6

25. 9.4

26. 1.004

27. 0.0053

28. 41.108

29. 0.045

30. 3.157

31. 26.04

For Exercises 32 to 39, write the number in standard form.

32. Six hundred seventy-two thousandths

33. Three and eight hundred six ten-thousandths

34. Nine and four hundred seven ten-thousandths

35. Four hundred seven and three hundredths

36. Six hundred twelve and seven hundred four thousandths

37. Two hundred forty-six and twenty-four thousandths

38. Two thousand sixty-seven and nine thousand two ten-thousandths

39. Seventy-three and two thousand six hundred eighty-four hundred-thousandths

To round a decimal to a given place value

For Exercises 40 to 54, round the number to the given place value.

40. 6.249   Tenths

41. 5.398   Tenths

42. 21.007   Tenths

43. 30.0092   Tenths

44. 18.40937   Hundredths

45. 413.5972   Hundredths

46. 72.4983   Hundredths

47. 6.061745   Thousandths

48. 936.2905   Thousandths

49. 96.8027   Whole number

50. 47.3192   Whole number

51. 5439.83   Whole number

52. 7014.96   Whole number

53. 0.023591   Ten-thousandths

54. 2.975268   Hundred-thousandths

55. **Measurement**   A nickel weighs about 0.1763668 ounce. Find the weight of a nickel to the nearest hundredth of an ounce.

56. **Business**   The total cost of a parka, including sales tax, is $124.1093. Round the total cost to the nearest cent to find the amount a customer pays for the parka.

57. **Sports**   Runners in the Boston Marathon run a distance of 26.21875 miles. To the nearest tenth of a mile, find the distance that an entrant who completes the Boston Marathon runs.

APPLYING THE CONCEPTS

58. Indicate which digits of the number, if any, need not be entered on a calculator.

   a. 1.500   **b.** 0.908   **c.** 60.07   **d.** 0.0032

59. **a.** Find a number between 0.1 and 0.2.   **b.** Find a number between 1 and 1.1   **c.** Find a number between 0 and 0.005.

3.2 Addition of Decimals

Objective A **To add decimals**

To add decimals, write the numbers so that the decimal points are on a vertical line. Add as for whole numbers, and write the decimal point in the sum directly below the decimal points in the addends.

HOW TO Add: 0.237 + 4.9 + 27.32

Note that by placing the decimal points on a vertical line, we make sure that digits of the same place value are added.

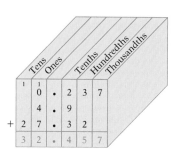

Example 1 Find the sum of 42.3, 162.903, and 65.0729.

Solution
$$
\begin{array}{r}
\overset{1\ 1\ 1}{\ \ 42.3} \\
162.903 \\
+\ \ 65.0729 \\
\hline
270.2759
\end{array}
$$
• Place the decimal points on a vertical line.

You Try It 1 Find the sum of 4.62, 27.9, and 0.62054.

Your solution

Example 2 Add: 0.83 + 7.942 + 15

Solution
$$
\begin{array}{r}
\overset{1\ 1}{\ 0.83} \\
7.942 \\
+\ 15. \\
\hline
23.772
\end{array}
$$

You Try It 2 Add: 6.05 + 12 + 0.374

Your solution

Solutions on p. S9

● E S T I M A T I O N ●

Estimating the Sum of Two or More Decimals

Calculate 23.037 + 16.7892. Then use estimation to determine whether the sum is reasonable.

Add to find the exact sum.

$$23.037 + 16.7892 = 39.8262$$

To estimate the sum, round each number to the same place value. Here we have rounded to the nearest whole number. Then add. The estimated answer is 40, which is very close to the exact sum, 39.8262.

$$
\begin{array}{r}
23.037 \approx 23 \\
+16.7892 \approx +17 \\
\hline
40
\end{array}
$$

Objective B   **To solve application problems**

The graph at the right shows the breakdown by age group of Americans who are hearing-impaired. Use this graph for Example 3 and You Try It 3.

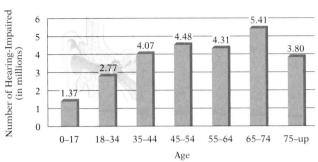

Breakdown by Age Group of Americans Who Are Hearing-Impaired

Source: American Speech-Language-Hearing Association

Example 3

Determine the number of Americans under the age of 45 who are hearing-imparied.

Strategy
To determine the number, add the numbers of hearing impaired ages 0 to 17, 18 to 34, and 35 to 44.

Solution
```
  1.37
  2.77
 +4.07
  8.21
```

8.21 million Americans under the age of 45 are hearing-impaired.

You Try It 3

Determine the number of Americans ages 45 and older who are hearing-impaired.

Your strategy

Your solution

Example 4

Dan Burhoe earned a salary of $138.50 for working 3 days this week as a food server. He also received $42.75, $35.80, and $59.25 in tips during the 3 days. Find his total income for the 3 days of work.

Strategy
To find the total income, add the tips (42.75, 35.80, and 59.25) to the salary (138.50).

Solution
138.50 + 42.75 + 35.80 + 59.25 = 276.30

Dan's total income for the 3 days of work was $276.30.

You Try It 4

Anita Khavari, an insurance executive, earns a salary of $875 every 4 weeks. During the past 4-week period, she received commissions of $985.80, $791.46, $829.75, and $635.42. Find her total income for the past 4-week period.

Your strategy

Your solution

Solutions on p. S9

3.2 Exercises

Objective A   **To add decimals**

For Exercises 1 to 17, add.

1. 16.008 + 2.0385 + 132.06   **2.** 17.32 + 1.0579 + 16.5   **3.** 1.792 + 67 + 27.0526

4. 8.772 + 1.09 + 26.5027   **5.** 3.02 + 62.7 + 3.924   **6.** 9.06 + 4.976 + 59.6

7. 82.006 + 9.95 + 0.927   **8.** 0.826 + 8.76 + 79.005   **9.** 4.307 + 99.82 + 9.078

10. 0.3
   + 0.07

11. 0.29
   + 0.4

12. 1.007
   + 2.1

13. 7.3
   + 9.005

14. 4.9257
   27.05
   + 9.0063

15. 8.72
   99.073
   + 2.9736

16. 62.4
   9.827
   + 692.44

17. 8
   89.43
   + 7.0659

For Exercises 18 to 21, use a calculator to add. Then round the numbers to the nearest whole number and use estimation to determine whether the sum you calculated is reasonable.

18. 342.42
   89.625
   + 176.2

19. 219.9
   0.872
   + 13.42

20. 823.9
   82.65
   + 46.923

21. 678.92
   97.6
   + 5.423

Objective B   **To solve application problems**

22. Finances   A family has a mortgage payment of $814.72, a Visa bill of $216.40, and an electric bill of $87.32.
   a. Calculate the exact amount of the three payments.
   b. Round the numbers to the nearest hundred and use estimation to determine whether the sum you calculated is reasonable.

23. Mechanics   Find the length of the shaft.

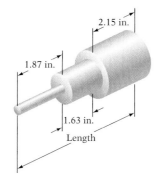

2.15 in.

1.87 in.

1.63 in.

Length

24. Mechanics   Find the length of the shaft.

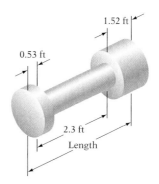

1.52 ft

0.53 ft

2.3 ft

Length

25. Banking You have $2143.57 in your checking account. You make deposits of $210.98, $45.32, $1236.34, and $27.99. Find the amount in your checking account after you have made the deposits if no money has been withdrawn.

26. Geometry The perimeter of a triangle is the sum of the lengths of the three sides of the triangle. Find the perimeter of a triangle that has sides that measure 4.9 meters, 6.1 meters, and 7.5 meters.

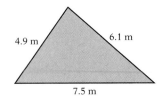

4.9 m   6.1 m

7.5 m

27. 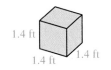 **Demography** The world's population in 2050 is expected to be 8.9 billion people. It is projected that in that year, Asia's population will be 5.3 billion and Africa's population will be 1.8 billion. What are the combined populations of Asia and Africa expected to be in 2050? (*Source: United Nations Population Division, World Population Prospects*)

Employment The table at the right shows the number of self-employed people, in millions, in the United States. They are listed by annual earnings. Use this table for Exercises 28 to 30.

Annual Earnings	Number of Self-Employed (in millions)
Less than $5000	5.1
$5000 – $24,999	3.9
$25,000 – $49,999	1.6
$50,000 or more	1.0

Source: U.S. Small Business Administration

28. How many self-employed people earn less than $50,000?

29. How many self-employed people earn $5000 or more?

30. How many people in the United States are self-employed?

APPLYING THE CONCEPTS

Consumerism The table at the right gives the prices for selected products in a grocery store. Use this table for Exercises 31 and 32.

31. Does a customer with $10 have enough money to purchase raisin bran, bread, milk, and butter?

32. Name three items that would cost more than $7 but less than $8. (There is more than one answer.)

Product	Cost
Raisin bran	$3.29
Butter	$2.79
Bread	$1.49
Popcorn	$1.19
Potatoes	$2.49
Cola (6-pack)	$1.99
Mayonnaise	$2.99
Lunch meat	$3.39
Milk	$2.59
Toothpaste	$2.69

33. Measurement Can a piece of rope 4 feet long be wrapped around the box shown at the right?

1.4 ft

1.4 ft   1.4 ft

3.3 Subtraction of Decimals

Objective A To subtract decimals

To subtract decimals, write the numbers so that the decimal points are on a vertical line. Subtract as for whole numbers, and write the decimal point in the difference directly below the decimal point in the subtrahend.

HOW TO Subtract 21.532 − 9.875 and check.

Placing the decimal points on a vertical line ensures that digits of the same place value are subtracted.

Check:

	Subtrahend	1 1 1 1
		9.875
	+ Difference	+ 11.657
	= Minuend	21.532

HOW TO Subtract 4.3 − 1.7942 and check.

$$
\begin{array}{r}
\overset{3}{\cancel{4}}.\overset{12}{3}\overset{9}{0}\overset{9}{0}\overset{10}{0} \\
- 1.7942 \\
\hline
2.5058
\end{array}
$$

If necessary, insert zeros in the minuend before subtracting.

Check: 1 111
1.7942
+ 2.5058
4.3000

Example 1 Subtract 39.047 − 7.96 and check.

Solution

$$
\begin{array}{r}
\overset{8}{3}\overset{9}{\cancel{9}}.\overset{14}{\cancel{0}}\cancel{4}7 \\
- 7.96 \\
\hline
31.087
\end{array}
$$

Check: 1 1
7.96
+ 31.087
39.047

Example 2 Find 9.23 less than 29 and check.

Solution

$$
\begin{array}{r}
\overset{1}{2}\overset{18}{9}.\overset{9}{0}\overset{10}{0} \\
- 9.23 \\
\hline
19.77
\end{array}
$$

Check: 11 1
9.23
+ 19.77
29.00

Example 3 Subtract 1.2 − 0.8235 and check.

Solution

$$
\begin{array}{r}
\overset{0}{\cancel{1}}.\overset{11}{2}\overset{9}{0}\overset{9}{0}\overset{10}{0} \\
- 0.8235 \\
\hline
0.3765
\end{array}
$$

Check: 1 111
0.8235
+ 0.3765
1.2000

You Try It 1 Subtract 72.039 − 8.47 and check.

Your solution

You Try It 2 Subtract 35 − 9.67 and check.

Your solution

You Try It 3 Subtract 3.7 − 1.9715 and check.

Your solution

Solutions on p. S9

• E S T I M A T I O N •

Estimating the Difference Between Two Decimals

Calculate $820.23 - 475.748$. Then use estimation to determine whether the difference is reasonable.

Subtract to find the exact difference. $820.23 - 475.748 = 344.482$

To estimate the difference, round each number to the same place value. Here we have rounded to the nearest ten. Then subtract. The estimated answer is 340, which is very close to the exact difference, 344.482.

$$\begin{array}{r} 820.23 \approx 820 \\ -475.748 \approx -480 \\ \hline 340 \end{array}$$

Objective B   **To solve application problems**

Example 4

You bought a book for $15.87. How much change did you receive from a $20.00 bill?

Strategy

To find the amount of change, subtract the cost of the book (15.87) from $20.00.

Solution $\begin{array}{r} 20.00 \\ -\ 15.87 \\ \hline 4.13 \end{array}$

You received $4.13 in change.

Example 5

You had a balance of $87.93 on your student debit card. You then used the card, deducting $15.99 for a CD, $6.85 for lunch, and $18.50 for a ticket to the football game. What is your new student debit card balance?

Strategy

To find your new debit card balance:

• Add to find the total of the three deductions (15.99 + 6.85 + 18.50).
• Subtract the total of the three deductions from the old balance (87.93).

Solution

$\begin{array}{r} 15.99 \\ 6.85 \\ +18.50 \\ \hline 41.34 \end{array}$ total of deductions

$\begin{array}{r} 87.93 \\ -\ 41.34 \\ \hline 46.59 \end{array}$

Your new debit card balance is $46.59.

You Try It 4

Your breakfast cost $6.85. How much change did you receive from a $10.00 bill?

Your strategy

Your solution

You Try It 5

You had a balance of $2472.69 in your checking account. You then wrote checks for $1025.60, $79.85, and $162.47. Find the new balance in your checking account.

Your strategy

Your solution

Solutions on p. S9

3.3 Exercises

Objective A **To subtract decimals**

For Exercises 1 to 24, subtract and check.

1. $24.037 - 18.41$ **2.** $26.029 - 19.31$ **3.** $123.07 - 9.4273$ **4.** $214 - 7.143$

5. $16.5 - 9.7902$ **6.** $13.2 - 8.6205$ **7.** $235.79 - 20.093$ **8.** $463.27 - 40.095$

9. $63.005 - 9.1274$ **10.** $23.004 - 7.2175$ **11.** $92 - 19.2909$ **12.** $41.2405 - 25.2709$

13. $\begin{array}{r} 0.32 \\ -\ 0.0058 \end{array}$ **14.** $\begin{array}{r} 0.78 \\ -\ 0.0073 \end{array}$ **15.** $\begin{array}{r} 3.005 \\ -\ 1.982 \end{array}$ **16.** $\begin{array}{r} 6.007 \\ -\ 2.734 \end{array}$

17. $\begin{array}{r} 352.16 \\ -\ 90.994 \end{array}$ **18.** $\begin{array}{r} 872 \\ -\ 80.753 \end{array}$ **19.** $\begin{array}{r} 724.32 \\ -\ 69 \end{array}$ **20.** $\begin{array}{r} 625.46 \\ -\ 77.509 \end{array}$

21. $\begin{array}{r} 362.394 \\ -\ 19.4672 \end{array}$ **22.** $\begin{array}{r} 421.385 \\ -\ 17.5293 \end{array}$ **23.** $\begin{array}{r} 19 \\ -\ 10.372 \end{array}$ **24.** $\begin{array}{r} 23.4 \\ -\ 0.921 \end{array}$

For Exercises 25 to 27, use the relationship between addition and subtraction to complete the statement.

25. _____ $+ 2.325 = 7.01$ **26.** $5.392 +$ _____ $= 8.07$ **27.** _____ $+ 8.967 = 19.35$

For Exercises 28 to 31, use a calculator to subtract. Then round the numbers to the nearest whole number and use estimation to determine whether the difference you calculated is reasonable.

28. $\begin{array}{r} 93.079256 \\ -\ 66.09249 \end{array}$ **29.** $\begin{array}{r} 3.7529 \\ -\ 1.00784 \end{array}$ **30.** $\begin{array}{r} 76.53902 \\ -\ 45.73005 \end{array}$ **31.** $\begin{array}{r} 9.07325 \\ -\ 1.924 \end{array}$

Objective B   **To solve application problems**

32. Business   The manager of the Edgewater Cafe takes a reading of the cash register tape each hour. At 1:00 P.M. the tape read $967.54. At 2:00 P.M. the tape read $1437.15. Find the amount of sales between 1:00 P.M. and 2:00 P.M.

33. Mechanics   Find the missing dimension.

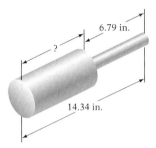

6.79 in.

?

14.34 in.

34. Mechanics   Find the missing dimension.

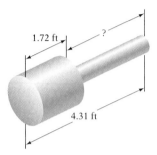

1.72 ft

?

4.31 ft

35. Banking   You had a balance of $1029.74 in your checking account. You then wrote checks for $67.92, $43.10, and $496.34.
a. Find the total amount of the checks written.
b. Find the new balance in your checking account.

36. Consumerism   The price of gasoline is $1.82 per gallon after the price rose $.07 one month and $.12 the next month. Find the price of gasoline before these increases in price.

37. Population Growth   The annual number of births in the United States is projected to rise from 3.98 million in 2003 to 4.37 million in 2012. (*Sources:* U.S. Census Bureau; National Center for Health Statistics) Find the increase in the annual number of births from 2003 to 2012.

38. Investments   Grace Herrera owned 357.448 shares of a mutual fund on January 1. On December 31 of the same year, she had 439.917 shares. What was the increase in the number of shares Grace owned during that year?

E-Commerce   The table at the right shows the actual and projected number of households shopping online, in millions. Use the table for Exercises 39 and 40.

39. Calculate the growth in online shopping from 2000 to 2003.

40. Calculate the growth in online shopping from 1998 to 2003.

Year	Number of Households Shopping Online (in millions)
1998	8.7
1999	13.1
2000	17.7
2001	23.1
2002	30.3
2003	40.3

Source: Forrester Research Inc.

APPLYING THE CONCEPTS

41. Find the largest amount by which the estimate of the sum of two decimals rounded to the given place value could differ from the exact sum.
a. Tenths   **b.** Hundredths   **c.** Thousandths

3.4 Multiplication of Decimals

Objective A   **To multiply decimals**

Point of Interest

Benjamin Banneker (1731–1806) was the first African American to earn distinction as a mathematician and scientist. He was on the survey team that determined the boundaries of Washington, D.C. The mathematics of surveying requires extensive use of decimals.

Decimals are multiplied as though they were whole numbers. Then the decimal point is placed in the product. Writing the decimals as fractions shows where to write the decimal point in the product.

$$0.\underline{3} \times 5 = \frac{3}{10} \times \frac{5}{1} = \frac{15}{10} = 1.\underline{5}$$

1 decimal place   1 decimal place

$$0.\underline{3} \times 0.\underline{5} = \frac{3}{10} \times \frac{5}{10} = \frac{15}{100} = 0.\underline{15}$$

1 decimal place   1 decimal place   2 decimal places

$$0.\underline{3} \times 0.\underline{05} = \frac{3}{10} \times \frac{5}{100} = \frac{15}{1000} = 0.\underline{015}$$

1 decimal place   2 decimal places   3 decimal places

To multiply decimals, multiply the numbers as with whole numbers. Write the decimal point in the product so that the number of decimal places in the product is the sum of the decimal places in the factors.

Integrating Technology

Scientific calculators have a floating decimal point. This means that the decimal point is automatically placed in the answer. For example, for the product at the right, enter

21 · 4 × 0 · 36 =

The display reads 7.704, with the decimal point in the correct position.

HOW TO   Multiply: 21.4×0.36

$$
\begin{array}{r}
21.4 \\
\times\ 0.36 \\
\hline
1284 \\
642\ \ \\
\hline
7.704
\end{array}
$$

1 decimal place
2 decimal places

3 decimal places

HOW TO   Multiply: 0.037×0.08

$$
\begin{array}{r}
0.037 \\
\times\ \ 0.08 \\
\hline
0.00296
\end{array}
$$

3 decimal places
2 decimal places
5 decimal places

• Two zeros must be inserted between the 2 and the decimal point so that there are 5 decimal places in the product.

To multiply a decimal by a power of 10 (10, 100, 1000, . . .), move the decimal point to the right the same number of places as there are zeros in the power of 10.

$3.8925 \times 1\underline{0}$ $= 38.925$

    1 zero   1 decimal place

$3.8925 \times 1\underline{00}$ $= 389.25$

    2 zeros   2 decimal places

$3.8925 \times 1\underline{000}$ $= 3892.5$

    3 zeros   3 decimal places

$3.8925 \times 1\underline{0,000}$ $= 38,925.$

    4 zeros   4 decimal places

$3.8925 \times 1\underline{00,000} = 389,250.$

    5 zeros   5 decimal places

• Note that a zero must be inserted before the decimal point.

Note that if the power of 10 is written in exponential notation, the exponent indicates how many places to move the decimal point.

$$3.8925 \times 10^1 = 38.925$$

1 decimal place

$$3.8925 \times 10^2 = 389.25$$

2 decimal places

$$3.8925 \times 10^3 = 3892.5$$

3 decimal places

$$3.8925 \times 10^4 = 38{,}925.$$

4 decimal places

$$3.8925 \times 10^5 = 389{,}250.$$

5 decimal places

Example 1   Multiply: 920×3.7

Solution

$$\begin{array}{r} 920 \\ \times \quad 3.7 \\ \hline 644\,0 \\ 2760 \\ \hline 3404.0 \end{array}$$

• 1 decimal place

• 1 decimal place

You Try It 1   Multiply: 870×4.6

Your solution

Example 2   Find 0.00079 multiplied by 0.025.

Solution

$$\begin{array}{r} 0.00079 \\ \times \quad 0.025 \\ \hline 395 \\ 158 \\ \hline 0.00001975 \end{array}$$

• 5 decimal places
• 3 decimal places

• 8 decimal places

You Try It 2   Find 0.000086 multiplied by 0.057.

Your solution

Example 3   Find the product of 3.69 and 2.07.

Solution

$$\begin{array}{r} 3.69 \\ \times \, 2.07 \\ \hline 2583 \\ 7380 \\ \hline 7.6383 \end{array}$$

• 2 decimal places
• 2 decimal places

• 4 decimal places

You Try It 3   Find the product of 4.68 and 6.03.

Your solution

Example 4   Multiply: $42.07 \times 10{,}000$

Solution $42.07 \times 10{,}000 = 420{,}700$

You Try It 4   Multiply: 6.9×1000

Your solution

Example 5   Find 3.01 times 10^3.

Solution $3.01 \times 10^3 = 3010$

You Try It 5   Find 4.0273 times 10^2.

Your solution

Solutions on pp. S9–S10

● E S T I M A T I O N ●

Estimating the Product of Two Decimals

Calculate 28.259×0.029. Then use estimation to determine whether the product is reasonable.

Multiply to find the exact product.

$28.259 \times 0.029 = 0.819511$

To estimate the product, round each number so there is one nonzero digit. Then multiply. The estimated answer is 0.90, which is very close to the exact product, 0.819511.

$$
\begin{aligned}
28.259 &\approx 30 \\
\times\ 0.029 &\approx \times 0.03 \\
& \underline{\hphantom{\times}0.90}
\end{aligned}
$$

Objective B   **To solve application problems**

The tables that follow list water rates and meter fees for a city. These tables are used for Example 6 and You Try It 6.

Water Charges	
Commercial	$1.39/1000 gal
Comm Restaurant	$1.39/1000 gal
Industrial	$1.39/1000 gal
Institutional	$1.39/1000 gal
Res—No Sewer	
Residential—SF	
>0 <200 gal per day	$1.15/1000 gal
>200 <1500 gal per day	$1.39/1000 gal
>1500 gal per day	$1.54/1000 gal

Meter Charges	
Meter	Meter Fee
5/8" & 3/4"	$13.50
1"	$21.80
1-1/2"	$42.50
2"	$67.20
3"	$133.70
4"	$208.20
6"	$415.10
8"	$663.70

Example 6

Find the total bill for an industrial water user with a 6-inch meter that used 152,000 gallons of water for July and August.

Strategy

To find the total cost of water:

• Find the cost of water by multiplying the cost per 1000 gallons (1.39) by the number of 1000-gallon units used.
• Add the cost of the water to the meter fee (415.10).

Solution

Cost of water $= \dfrac{152,000}{1000} \cdot 1.39 = 211.28$

Total cost $= 211.28 + 415.10 = 626.38$

The total cost is $626.38.

You Try It 6

Find the total bill for a commercial user that used 5000 gallons of water per day for July and August. The user has a 3-inch meter.

Your strategy

Your solution

Solution on p. S10

Example 7

It costs $.036 an hour to operate an electric motor. How much does it cost to operate the motor for 120 hours?

Strategy

To find the cost of running the motor for 120 hours, multiply the hourly cost (0.036) by the number of hours the motor is run (120).

Solution

```
    0.036
  ×   120
    720
   36
  4.320
```

The cost of running the motor for 120 hours is $4.32.

You Try It 7

The cost of electricity to run a freezer for 1 hour is $.035. This month the freezer has run for 210 hours. Find the total cost of running the freezer this month.

Your strategy

Your solution

Example 8

Jason Ng earns a salary of $440 for a 40-hour workweek. This week he worked 12 hours of overtime at a rate of $16.50 for each hour of overtime worked. Find his total income for the week.

Strategy

To find Jason's total income for the week:

• Find the overtime pay by multiplying the hourly overtime rate (16.50) by the number of hours of overtime worked (12).
• Add the overtime pay to the weekly salary (440).

Solution

```
   16.50              440.00
  ×   12           + 198.00
   33 00              638.00
  165 0
  198.00   Overtime pay
```

Jason's total income for this week is $638.00.

You Try It 8

You make a down payment of $175 on a stereo and agree to make payments of $37.18 a month for the next 18 months to repay the remaining balance. Find the total cost of the stereo.

Your strategy

Your solution

Solutions on p. S10

3.4 Exercises

Objective A   **To multiply decimals**

For Exercises 1 to 94, multiply.

1.   0.9
   $\times$ 0.4

2.   0.7
   $\times$ 0.9

3.   0.5
   $\times$ 0.6

4.   0.3
   $\times$ 0.7

5.   0.5
   $\times$ 0.5

6.   0.7
   $\times$ 0.7

7.   0.9
   $\times$ 0.5

8.   0.2
   $\times$ 0.6

9.   7.7
   $\times$ 0.9

10.   3.4
   $\times$ 0.4

11.   9.2
   $\times$ 0.2

12.   2.6
   $\times$ 0.7

13.   7.2
   $\times$ 0.6

14.   6.8
   $\times$ 0.4

15.   7.4
   $\times$ 0.1

16.   3.8
   $\times$ 0.1

17.   7.9
   $\times$ 5

18.   9.3
   $\times$ 7

19.   0.68
   $\times$ 4

20.   0.83
   $\times$ 9

21.   0.67
   $\times$ 0.9

22.   0.84
   $\times$ 0.3

23.   0.16
   $\times$ 0.6

24.   0.47
   $\times$ 0.8

25.   2.5
   $\times$ 5.4

26.   3.9
   $\times$ 1.9

27.   8.4
   $\times$ 9.5

28.   7.6
   $\times$ 5.8

29.   0.83
   $\times$ 5.2

30.   0.24
   $\times$ 2.7

31.   0.46
   $\times$ 3.9

32.   0.78
   $\times$ 6.8

33.   0.2
   $\times$ 0.3

34.   0.3
   $\times$ 0.3

35.   0.24
   $\times$ 0.3

36.   0.17
   $\times$ 0.5

37.   1.47
   $\times$ 0.09

38.   6.37
   $\times$ 0.05

39.   8.92
   $\times$ 0.004

40.   6.75
   $\times$ 0.007

41.   0.49
     × 0.16

42.   0.38
     × 0.21

43.   7.6
     × 0.01

44.   5.1
     × 0.01

45.   8.62
     ×   4

46.   5.83
     ×   7

47.   64.5
     ×   9

48.   37.8
     ×   8

49.   2.19
     × 9.2

50.   1.25
     × 5.6

51.   1.85
     × 0.023

52.   37.8
     × 0.052

53.   0.478
     × 0.37

54.   0.526
     × 0.22

55.   48.3
     × 0.0041

56.   67.2
     × 0.0086

57.   2.437
     ×   6.1

58.   4.237
     × 0.54

59.   0.413
     × 0.0016

60.   0.517
     × 0.0029

61.   94.73
     × 0.57

62.   89.23
     × 0.62

63.   8.005
     × 0.067

64.   9.032
     × 0.019

65. 4.29×0.1

66. 6.78×0.1

67. 5.29×0.4

68. 6.78×0.5

69. 0.68×0.7

70. 0.56×0.9

71. 1.4×0.73

72. 6.3×0.37

73. 5.2×7.3

74. 7.4×2.9

75. 3.8×0.61

76. 7.2×0.72

77. 0.32×10

78. 6.93×10

79. 0.065×100

80. 0.039×100

81. 6.2856×1000

82. 3.2954×1000

83. 3.2×1000

84. $0.006 \times 10,000$

85. $3.57 \times 10,000$

86. 8.52×10^1

87. 0.63×10^1

88. 82.9×10^2

89. 0.039×10^2

90. 6.8×10^3

91. 4.9×10^4

92. 6.83×10^4

93. 0.067×10^2

94. 0.052×10^2

95. Find the product of 0.0035 and 3.45.

96. Find the product of 237 and 0.34.

97. Multiply 3.005 by 0.00392.

98. Multiply 20.34 by 1.008.

99. Multiply 1.348 by 0.23.

100. Multiply 0.000358 by 3.56.

101. Find the product of 23.67 and 0.0035.

102. Find the product of 0.00346 and 23.1.

103. Find the product of 5, 0.45, and 2.3.

104. Find the product of 0.03, 23, and 9.45.

For Exercises 105 to 120, use a calculator to multiply. Then use estimation to determine whether the product you calculated is reasonable.

105.
$$\begin{array}{r} 28.5 \\ \times\ \ 3.2 \\ \hline \end{array}$$

106.
$$\begin{array}{r} 86.3 \\ \times\ \ 4.4 \\ \hline \end{array}$$

107.
$$\begin{array}{r} 2.38 \\ \times\ 0.44 \\ \hline \end{array}$$

108.
$$\begin{array}{r} 9.82 \\ \times\ 0.77 \\ \hline \end{array}$$

109.
$$\begin{array}{r} 0.866 \\ \times\ \ \ 4.5 \\ \hline \end{array}$$

110.
$$\begin{array}{r} 0.239 \\ \times\ \ \ 8.2 \\ \hline \end{array}$$

111.
$$\begin{array}{r} 4.34 \\ \times\ 2.59 \\ \hline \end{array}$$

112.
$$\begin{array}{r} 6.87 \\ \times\ 9.98 \\ \hline \end{array}$$

113.
$$\begin{array}{r} 8.434 \\ \times\ 0.044 \\ \hline \end{array}$$

114.
$$\begin{array}{r} 7.037 \\ \times\ 0.094 \\ \hline \end{array}$$

115.
$$\begin{array}{r} 28.44 \\ \times\ \ 1.12 \\ \hline \end{array}$$

116.
$$\begin{array}{r} 86.57 \\ \times\ \ 7.33 \\ \hline \end{array}$$

117.
$$\begin{array}{r} 49.6854 \\ \times\ 39.0672 \\ \hline \end{array}$$

118.
$$\begin{array}{r} 2.00547 \\ \times\ \ \ 9.672 \\ \hline \end{array}$$

119.
$$\begin{array}{r} 0.00456 \\ \times\ 0.009542 \\ \hline \end{array}$$

120.
$$\begin{array}{r} 7.00637 \\ \times\ \ 0.0128 \\ \hline \end{array}$$

Objective B **To solve application problems**

121. **Consumerism** An electric motor costing $315.45 has an operating cost of $.027 for 1 hour of operation. Find the cost to run the motor for 56 hours. Round to the nearest cent.

122. **Recycling** Four hundred empty soft drink cans weigh 18.75 pounds. A recycling center pays $.75 per pound for the cans. Find the amount received for the 400 cans. Round to the nearest cent.

123. **Recycling** A recycling center pays $.045 per pound for newspapers.
   a. Estimate the payment for recycling 520 pounds of newspapers.
   b. Find the actual amount received from recycling the newspapers.

124. **Geometry** The perimeter of a square is equal to four times the length of a side of the square. Find the perimeter of a square whose side measures 2.8 meters.

2.8 m

125. **Geometry** The area of a rectangle is equal to the product of the length of the rectangle times its width. Find the area of a rectangle that has a length of 6.75 feet and a width of 3.5 feet. The area will be in square feet.

3.5 ft
6.75 ft

126. **Finance** You bought a car for $5000 down and made payments of $399.50 each month for 36 months.
   a. Find the amount of the payments over the 36 months.
   b. Find the total cost of the car.

127. **Compensation** A nurse earns a salary of $1156 for a 40-hour week. This week the nurse worked 15 hours of overtime at a rate of $43.35 for each hour of overtime worked.
   a. Find the nurse's overtime pay.
   b. Find the nurse's total income for the week.

128. **Consumerism** Bay Area Rental Cars charges $15 a day and $.15 per mile for renting a car. You rented a car for 3 days and drove 235 miles. Find the total cost of renting the car.

129. 🥧 **Shipping** The graph at the right shows United States Postal Service rates for express mail. How much would it cost a company to mail 25 express mail packages, each weighing $\frac{1}{4}$ pound, post office to addressee?

130. **Transportation** A taxi costs $2.50 and $.20 for each $\frac{1}{8}$ mile driven. Find the cost of hiring a taxi to get from the airport to the hotel—a distance of $5\frac{1}{2}$ miles.

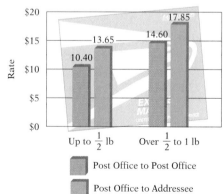
U.S. Postal Service Rates for Express Mail

131. Business   The table at the right lists three pieces of steel required for a repair project.
  a. Find the total cost of grade 1.
  b. Find the total cost of grade 2.
  c. Find the total cost of grade 3.
  d. Find the total cost of the three pieces of steel.

Grade of Steel	Weight (pounds per foot)	Required Number of Feet	Cost per Pound
1	2.2	8	$1.20
2	3.4	6.5	$1.35
3	6.75	15.4	$1.94

132. Business   A confectioner ships holiday packs of candy and nuts anywhere in the United States. At the right is a price list for nuts and candy, and below is a table of shipping charges to zones in the United States. For any fraction of a pound, use the next higher weight. (16 oz = 1 lb)

Code	Description	Price
112	Almonds 16 oz	$4.75
116	Cashews 8 oz	$2.90
117	Cashews 16 oz	$5.50
130	Macadamias 7 oz	$5.25
131	Macadamias 16 oz	$9.95
149	Pecan halves 8 oz	$6.25
155	Mixed nuts 8 oz	$4.80
160	Cashew brittle 8 oz	$1.95
182	Pecan roll 8 oz	$3.70
199	Chocolate peanuts 8 oz	$1.90

Pounds	Zone 1	Zone 2	Zone 3	Zone 4
1–3	$6.55	$6.85	$7.25	$7.75
4–6	$7.10	$7.40	$7.80	$8.30
7–9	$7.50	$7.80	$8.20	$8.70
10–12	$7.90	$8.20	$8.60	$9.10

Find the cost of sending the following orders to the given mail zone.

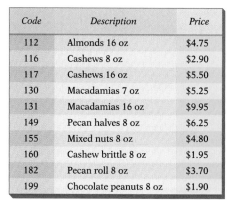

a. Code	Quantity	b. Code	Quantity	c. Code	Quantity
116	2	112	1	117	3
130	1	117	4	131	1
149	3	131	2	155	2
182	4	160	3	160	4
Mail to zone 4.		182	5	182	1
		Mail to zone 3.		199	3
				Mail to zone 2.	

133. Air Pollution   An emissions test for cars requires that of the total engine exhaust, less than 1 part per thousand $\left(\dfrac{1}{1000} = 0.001\right)$ be hydrocarbon emissions. Using this figure, determine which of the cars in the table below would fail the emissions test.

Car	Total Engine Exhaust	Hydrocarbon Emission
1	367,921	360
2	401,346	420
3	298,773	210
4	330,045	320
5	432,989	450

APPLYING THE CONCEPTS

134. Automotive Repair   Chris works at B & W Garage as an auto mechanic and has just completed an engine overhaul for a customer. To determine the cost of the repair job, Chris keeps a list of times worked and parts used. A parts list and a list of the times worked are shown below.

Parts Used		Time Spent	
Item	*Quantity*	*Day*	*Hours*
Gasket set	1	Monday	7.0
Ring set	1	Tuesday	7.5
Valves	8	Wednesday	6.5
Wrist pins	8	Thursday	8.5
Valve springs	16	Friday	9.0
Rod bearings	8		
Main bearings	5		
Valve seals	16		
Timing chain	1		

Price List		
Item Number	*Description*	*Unit Price*
27345	Valve spring	$9.25
41257	Main bearing	$17.49
54678	Valve	$16.99
29753	Ring set	$169.99
45837	Gasket set	$174.90
23751	Timing chain	$50.49
23765	Fuel pump	$429.99
28632	Wrist pin	$13.55
34922	Rod bearing	$4.69
2871	Valve seal	$1.69

a. Organize a table of data showing the parts used, the unit price for each, and the price of the quantity used. *Hint:* Use the following headings for the table.

Quantity   Item Number   Description   Unit Price   Total

b. Add up the numbers in the "Total" column to find the total cost of the parts.

c. If the charge for labor is $46.75 per hour, compute the cost of labor.

d. What is the total cost for parts and labor?

135. Explain how the decimal point is placed when a number is multiplied by 10, 100, 1000, 10,000, etc.

136. Explain how the decimal point is placed in the product of two decimals.

137. Show how the decimal is placed in the product of 1.3×2.31 by first writing each number as a fraction and then multiplying. Then change the product back to decimal notation.

3.5 Division of Decimals

Objective A **To divide decimals**

To divide decimals, move the decimal point in the divisor to the right to make the divisor a whole number. Move the decimal point in the dividend the same number of places to the right. Place the decimal point in the quotient directly over the decimal point in the dividend, and then divide as with whole numbers.

> **HOW TO** Divide: $3.25\overline{)15.275}$
>
> $3.25.\overline{)15.27.5}$ • Move the decimal point 2 places to the right in the divisor and then in the dividend. Place the decimal point in the quotient.
>
> $\begin{array}{r} 4.7 \\ 325.\overline{)\,1527.5} \\ -1300 \\ \hline 227\;5 \\ -227\;5 \\ \hline 0 \end{array}$ • Divide as with whole numbers.

Study Tip

To learn mathematics, you must be an active participant. Listening and watching your professor do mathematics are not enough. Take notes in class, mentally think through every question your instructor asks, and try to answer it even if you are not called on to answer it verbally. Ask questions when you have them. See *AIM for Success* at the front of the book for other ways to be an active learner.

Moving the decimal point the same number of decimal places in the divisor and dividend does not change the value of the quotient, because this process is the same as multiplying the numerator and denominator of a fraction by the same number. In the example above,

$$3.25\overline{)15.275} = \frac{15.275}{3.25} = \frac{15.275 \times 100}{3.25 \times 100} = \frac{1527.5}{325} = 325\overline{)1527.5}$$

When dividing decimals, we usually round the quotient off to a specified place value, rather than writing the quotient with a remainder.

> **HOW TO** Divide: $0.3\overline{)0.56}$
> Round to the nearest hundredth.
>
>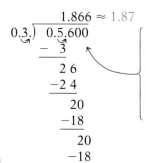
>
> We must carry the division to the thousandths place to round the quotient to the nearest hundredth. Therefore, zeros must be inserted in the dividend so that the quotient has a digit in the thousandths place.

HOW TO Divide 57.93 by 3.24. Round to the nearest thousandth.

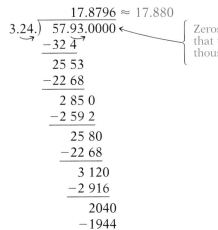

$$17.8796 \approx 17.880$$

$$3.24.\overline{)\;57.93.0000}$$

Zeros must be inserted in the dividend so that the quotient has a digit in the ten-thousandths place.

To divide a decimal by a power of 10 (10, 100, 1000, . . .), move the decimal point to the left the same number of places as there are zeros in the power of 10.

$34.65 \div 1\underline{0} \qquad = 3.465$

1 zero ⁓ 1 decimal place

$34.65 \div 1\underline{00} \qquad = 0.3465$

2 zeros 2 decimal places

$34.65 \div 1\underline{000} \qquad = 0.03465$

3 zeros 3 decimal places

- Note that a zero must be inserted between the 3 and the decimal point.

$34.65 \div 1\underline{0,000} = 0.003465$

4 zeros 4 decimal places

- Note that two zeros must be inserted between the 3 and the decimal point.

If the power of 10 is written in exponential notation, the exponent indicates how many places to move the decimal point.

$34.65 \div 10^1 = 3.465$ \qquad 1 decimal place

$34.65 \div 10^2 = 0.3465$ \qquad 2 decimal places

$34.65 \div 10^3 = 0.03465$ \qquad 3 decimal places

$34.65 \div 10^4 = 0.003465$ \qquad 4 decimal places

Example 1 Divide: $0.1344 \div 0.032$

Solution

$$0.032.\overline{)\;0.134.4}$$
$$\underline{-128}$$
$$6\,4$$
$$\underline{-6\,4}$$
$$0$$

$\quad\quad 4.2$

- Move the decimal point 3 places to the right in the divisor and the dividend.

You Try It 1 Divide: $0.1404 \div 0.052$

Your solution

Solution on p. S10

Example 2   Divide: $58.092 \div 82$
Round to the nearest
thousandth.

Solution

$$
\begin{array}{r}
0.7084 \approx 0.708 \\
82\overline{)\ 58.0920} \\
-57\ 4 \\
\hline
69 \\
-\ \ 0 \\
\hline
692 \\
-656 \\
\hline
360 \\
-328 \\
\end{array}
$$

You Try It 2   Divide: $37.042 \div 76$
Round to the nearest
thousandth.

Your solution

Example 3   Divide: $420.9 \div 7.06$
Round to the nearest tenth.

Solution

$$
\begin{array}{r}
59.61 \approx 59.6 \\
7.06.\overline{)\ 420.90.00} \\
-353\ 0 \\
\hline
67\ 90 \\
-63\ 54 \\
\hline
4\ 36\ 0 \\
-4\ 23\ 6 \\
\hline
12\ 40 \\
-\ 7\ 06 \\
\end{array}
$$

You Try It 3   Divide: $370.2 \div 5.09$
Round to the nearest tenth.

Your solution

Example 4   Divide: $402.75 \div 1000$

Solution $402.75 \div 1000 = 0.40275$

You Try It 4   Divide: $309.21 \div 10,000$

Your solution

Example 5   What is 0.625 divided by 10^2?

Solution $0.625 \div 10^2 = 0.00625$

You Try It 5   What is 42.93 divided by 10^4?

Your solution

Solutions on p. S10

● E S T I M A T I O N ●

Estimating the Quotient of Two Decimals

Calculate $282.18 \div 0.48$. Then use estimation to determine whether the quotient is reasonable.

Divide to find the exact quotient.

$$282.18 \div 0.48 = 587.875$$

To estimate the quotient, round each number so there is one nonzero digit. Then divide. The estimated answer is 600, which is very close to the exact quotient, 587.875.

$$282.18 \div 0.48 \approx 300 \div 0.5$$
$$= 600$$

Objective B **To solve application problems**

The graph at the right shows average hourly earnings in the United States. Use this table for Example 6 and You Try It 6.

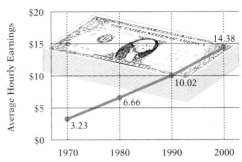

Average Hourly Earnings in the United States

Sources: Statistical Abstract of the United States; Bureau of Labor Statistics

---

Example 6

How many times greater were the average hourly earnings in 2000 than in 1970? Round to the nearest whole number.

Strategy
To find how many times greater the average hourly earnings were, divide the 2000 average hourly earnings (14.38) by the 1970 average hourly earnings (3.23).

Solution
14.38 ÷ 3.23 ≈ 4

The average hourly earnings in 2000 were about 4 times greater than in 1970.

You Try It 6

How many times greater were the average hourly earnings in 1990 than in 1970? Round to the nearest tenth.

Your strategy

Your solution

Example 7

A 1-year subscription to a monthly magazine costs $90. The price of each issue at the newsstand is $9.80. How much would you save per issue by buying a year's subscription rather than buying each issue at the newsstand?

Strategy
To find the amount saved:

• Find the subscription price per issue by dividing the cost of the subscription (90) by the number of issues (12).
• Subtract the subscription price per issue from the newsstand price (9.80).

Solution
90 ÷ 12 = 7.50
9.80 − 7.50 = 2.30

The savings would be $2.30 per issue.

You Try It 7

A Nielsen survey of the number of people (in millions) who watch television each day of the week is given in the table below.

Mon.	*Tues.*	*Wed.*	*Thu.*	*Fri.*	*Sat.*	*Sun.*
91.9	89.8	90.6	93.9	78.0	77.1	87.7

Find the average number of people who watch television per day.

Your strategy

Your solution

Solutions on pp. S10–S11

3.5 Exercises

Objective A   **To divide decimals**

For Exercises 1 to 20, divide.

1. $3\overline{)2.46}$ **2.** $7\overline{)3.71}$ **3.** $0.8\overline{)3.84}$ **4.** $0.9\overline{)6.93}$

5. $0.7\overline{)62.3}$ **6.** $0.4\overline{)52.8}$ **7.** $0.4\overline{)24}$ **8.** $0.5\overline{)65}$

9. $0.7\overline{)59.01}$ **10.** $0.9\overline{)8.721}$ **11.** $0.5\overline{)16.15}$ **12.** $0.8\overline{)77.6}$

13. $0.7\overline{)3.542}$ **14.** $0.6\overline{)2.436}$ **15.** $6.3\overline{)8.19}$ **16.** $3.2\overline{)7.04}$

17. $3.6\overline{)0.396}$ **18.** $2.7\overline{)0.648}$ **19.** $6.9\overline{)26.22}$ **20.** $1.7\overline{)84.66}$

For Exercises 21 to 29, divide. Round to the nearest tenth.

21. $55.62 \div 8.8$ **22.** $25.43 \div 5.4$ **23.** $5.427 \div 9.5$

24. $1.837 \div 1.4$ **25.** $18.4 \div 7.3$ **26.** $52.9 \div 8.1$

27. $0.183 \div 0.17$ **28.** $0.381 \div 0.47$ **29.** $6.924 \div 0.053$

For Exercises 30 to 38, divide. Round to the nearest hundredth.

30. $4.817 \div 16$ **31.** $6.467 \div 8$ **32.** $0.0418 \div 0.53$

33. $0.0647 \div 0.72$ **34.** $7 \div 0.55$ **35.** $38.665 \div 0.95$

36. $13.97 \div 25.4$ **37.** $27.738 \div 60.8$ **38.** $3.171 \div 45.6$

For Exercises 39 to 47, divide. Round to the nearest thousandth.

39. $1.028 \div 54$

40. $6.729 \div 27$

41. $0.0437 \div 0.5$

42. $75.469 \div 77.8$

43. $34.31 \div 95.3$

44. $0.2695 \div 2.67$

45. $0.4871 \div 4.72$

46. $0.1142 \div 17.2$

47. $0.2307 \div 26.7$

For Exercises 48 to 56, divide. Round to the nearest whole number.

48. $16.5 \div 4$

49. $89.76 \div 90$

50. $1.94 \div 0.3$

51. $1.0478 \div 0.413$

52. $2.148 \div 0.519$

53. $0.79 \div 0.778$

54. $3.092 \div 0.075$

55. $392 \div 6.9$

56. $8.729 \div 0.075$

For Exercises 57 to 74, divide.

57. $4.07 \div 10$

58. $0.039 \div 10$

59. $42.67 \div 10$

60. $389.7 \div 100$

61. $1.037 \div 100$

62. $237.835 \div 100$

63. $8.295 \div 1000$

64. $82{,}547 \div 1000$

65. $825.37 \div 1000$

66. $8.35 \div 10^1$

67. $0.32 \div 10^1$

68. $87.65 \div 10^1$

69. $23.627 \div 10^2$

70. $2.954 \div 10^2$

71. $0.0053 \div 10^2$

72. $289.32 \div 10^3$

73. $1.8932 \div 10^3$

74. $0.139 \div 10^3$

75. Divide 44.208 by 2.4.

76. Divide 0.04664 by 0.44.

77. Find the quotient of 723.15 and 45.

78. Find the quotient of 3.3463 and 3.07.

79. Divide 13.5 by 10^3.

80. Divide 0.045 by 10^5.

81. Find the quotient of 23.678 and 1000.

82. Find the quotient of 7.005 and 10,000.

83. What is 0.0056 divided by 0.05?

84. What is 123.8 divided by 0.02?

For Exercises 85 to 96, use a calculator to divide. Round to the nearest ten-thousandth. Then use estimation to determine whether the quotient you calculated is reasonable.

85. $42.42 \div 3.8$

86. $69.8 \div 7.2$

87. $389 \div 0.44$

88. $642 \div 0.83$

89. $6.394 \div 3.5$

90. $8.429 \div 4.2$

91. $1.235 \div 0.021$

92. $7.456 \div 0.072$

93. $95.443 \div 1.32$

94. $423.0925 \div 4.0927$

95. $1.000523 \div 429.07$

96. $0.03629 \div 0.00054$

Objective B   **To solve application problems**

97. **Sports**   Ramon, a high school football player, gained 162 yards on 26 carries in a high school football game. Find the average number of yards gained per carry. Round to the nearest hundredth.

98. **Fuel Efficiency**   A car with an odometer reading of 17,814.2 is filled with 9.4 gallons of gas. At an odometer reading of 18,130.4, the tank is empty and the car is filled with 12.4 gallons of gas. How many miles does the car travel on 1 gallon of gasoline?

99. **Consumerism**   A case of diet cola costs $6.79. If there are 24 cans in a case, find the cost per can. Round to the nearest cent.

100. **Carpentry**   Anne is building bookcases that are 3.4 feet long. How many complete shelves can be cut from a 12-foot board?

101. **Travel**   When the Massachusetts Turnpike opened, the toll for a passenger car that traveled the entire 136 miles of it was $5.60. Calculate the cost per mile. Round to the nearest cent.

102. **Investments** An oil company has issued 3,541,221,500 shares of stock. The company paid $6,090,990,120 in dividends. Find the dividend for each share of stock. Round to the nearest cent.

103. **Insurance** Earl is 52 years old and is buying $70,000 of life insurance for an annual premium of $703.80. If he pays each annual premium in 12 equal installments, how much is each monthly payment?

104. **Email** The graph at the right shows the growth in the number of spam messages sent daily worldwide. Figures given are in billions. How many times greater is the number of spam messages sent daily in 2004 than the number sent in 2000? Round to the nearest tenth.

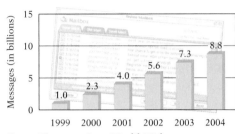

Spam Messages Sent World Wide

Source: IDC

APPLYING THE CONCEPTS

105. **Education** According to the National Center for Education Statistics, 10.2 million women and 7.3 million men will be enrolled at institutions of higher learning in 2010. How many more women than men are expected to be attending institutions of higher learning in 2010?

The Military The table at the right shows the advertising budgets of four branches of the U.S. armed services in a recent year. Use this table for Exercises 106 to 108.

Service	Advertising Budget
Army	$85.3 million
Air Force	$41.1 million
Navy	$20.5 million
Marines	$15.9 million

Source: CMR/TNS Media Intelligence

106. Find the difference between the Army's advertising budget and the Marines' advertising budget.

107. How many times greater was the Army's advertising budget than the Navy's advertising budget? Round to the nearest tenth.

108. What was the total of the advertising budgets for the four branches of the service?

109. **Population Growth** The U.S. population of people ages 85 and over is expected to grow from 4.2 million in 2000 to 8.9 million in 2030. How many times greater is the population of this segment expected to be in 2030 than in 2000? Round to the nearest tenth.

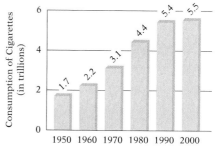

Health   The graph at the right shows that the worldwide consumption of cigarettes has been increasing. Use this table for Exercises 110 to 112.

110. Find the increase in cigarette consumption from 1950 to 1990.

111. How many times greater was the cigarette consumption in 2000 than in 1960?

World Wide Consumption of Cigarettes

Source: The Tobacco Atlas; U.S. Department of Agriculture

112. **a.** During which 10-year period was the increase in cigarette consumption greatest?
    b. During which 10-year period was the increase in cigarette consumption the least?

Forestry   The table at the right shows the number of acres burned in wildfires through July 24 of each year listed. Use this table for Exercises 113 and 114.

113. Find the total number of acres burned in the 4 years listed.

Year	Acres Burned
2000	2.9 million
2001	1.5 million
2002	3.8 million
2003	1.5 million

Source: National Interagency Fire Center

114. How many more acres were burned in 2002 and 2003 than in 2000 and 2001?

115. Explain how the decimal point is moved when a number is divided by 10, 100, 1000, 10,000, etc.

116. **Sports**   Explain how baseball batting averages are determined. Then find Chicago Cubs shortstop Nomar Garciaparra's batting average with 190 hits out of 532 at bats. Round to the nearest thousandth.

117. Explain how the decimal point is placed in the quotient when a number is divided by a decimal.

For Exercises 118 to 123, insert $+$, $-$, $\times$, or $\div$ into the square so that the statement is true.

118. 3.45 ☐ 0.5 = 6.9

119. 3.46 ☐ 0.24 = 0.8304

120. 6.009 ☐ 4.68 = 1.329

121. 0.064 ☐ 1.6 = 0.1024

122. 9.876 ☐ 23.12 = 32.996

123. 3.0381 ☐ 1.23 = 2.47

For Exercises 124 to 126, fill in the square to make a true statement.

124. 6.47 $-$ ☐ = 1.253

125. 6.47 $+$ ☐ = 9

126. 0.009 $\div$ ☐ = 0.36

3.6 Comparing and Converting Fractions and Decimals

Objective A   **To convert fractions to decimals**

Every fraction can be written as a decimal. To write a fraction as a decimal, divide the numerator of the fraction by the denominator. The quotient can be rounded to the desired place value.

> **HOW TO** Convert $\frac{3}{7}$ to a decimal.
>
> $$\frac{0.42857}{7)3.00000}$$
>
> $\frac{3}{7}$ rounded to the nearest hundredth is 0.43.
>
> $\frac{3}{7}$ rounded to the nearest thousandth is 0.429.
>
> $\frac{3}{7}$ rounded to the nearest ten-thousandth is 0.4286.

> **HOW TO** Convert $3\frac{2}{9}$ to a decimal. Round to the nearest thousandth.
>
> $3\frac{2}{9} = \frac{29}{9}$ $\frac{3.2222}{9)29.0000}$ $3\frac{2}{9}$ rounded to the nearest thousandth is 3.222.

Example 1 Convert $\frac{3}{8}$ to a decimal. Round to the nearest hundredth.

Solution $\frac{0.375}{8)3.000} \approx 0.38$

You Try It 1 Convert $\frac{9}{16}$ to a decimal. Round to the nearest tenth.

Your solution

Example 2 Convert $2\frac{3}{4}$ to a decimal. Round to the nearest tenth.

Solution $2\frac{3}{4} = \frac{11}{4}$ $\frac{2.75}{4)11.00} \approx 2.8$

You Try It 2 Convert $4\frac{1}{6}$ to a decimal. Round to the nearest hundredth.

Your solution

Solutions on p. S11

Objective B   **To convert decimals to fractions**

To convert a decimal to a fraction, remove the decimal point and place the decimal part over a denominator equal to the place value of the last digit in the decimal.

$$0.47 \overset{\text{hundredths}}{=} \frac{47}{100}$$

$$7.45 \overset{\text{hundredths}}{=} 7\frac{45}{100} = 7\frac{9}{20}$$

$$0.275 \overset{\text{thousandths}}{=} \frac{275}{1000} = \frac{11}{40}$$

$$0.16\frac{2}{3} \overset{\text{hundredths}}{=} \frac{16\frac{2}{3}}{100} = 16\frac{2}{3} \div 100 = \frac{50}{3} \times \frac{1}{100} = \frac{1}{6}$$

Example 3　Convert 0.82 and 4.75 to fractions.

Solution

$$0.82 = \frac{82}{100} = \frac{41}{50}$$

$$4.75 = 4\frac{75}{100} = 4\frac{3}{4}$$

You Try It 3　Convert 0.56 and 5.35 to fractions.

Your solution

Example 4　Convert $0.15\frac{2}{3}$ to a fraction.

Solution

$$0.15\frac{2}{3} = \frac{15\frac{2}{3}}{100} = 15\frac{2}{3} \div 100$$

$$= \frac{47}{3} \times \frac{1}{100} = \frac{47}{300}$$

You Try It 4　Convert $0.12\frac{7}{8}$ to a fraction.

Your solution

Solutions on p. S11

Objective C　**To identify the order relation between two decimals or between a decimal and a fraction**

Decimals, like whole numbers and fractions, can be graphed as points on the number line. The number line can be used to show the order of decimals. A decimal that appears to the right of a given number is greater than the given number. A decimal that appears to the left of a given number is less than the given number.

3.00　3.05　3.10　3.15　3.20　3.25　3.30　3.35　3.40

Note that 3, 3.0, and 3.00 represent the same number.

HOW TO　Find the order relation between $\frac{3}{8}$ and 0.38.

$$\frac{3}{8} = 0.375 \qquad 0.38 = 0.380$$ • Convert the fraction $\frac{3}{8}$ to a decimal.

$$0.375 < 0.380$$ • Compare the two decimals.

$$\frac{3}{8} < 0.38$$ • Convert 0.375 back to a fraction.

Example 5　Place the correct symbol, < or >, between the numbers.

$$\frac{5}{16} \qquad 0.32$$

Solution

$$\frac{5}{16} \approx 0.313$$ • Convert $\frac{5}{16}$ to a decimal.

$$0.313 < 0.32$$ • Compare the two decimals.

$$\frac{5}{16} < 0.32$$ • Convert 0.313 back to a fraction.

You Try It 5　Place the correct symbol, < or >, between the numbers.

$$0.63 \qquad \frac{5}{8}$$

Your solution

Solution on p. S11

3.6 Exercises

To convert fractions to decimals

For Exercises 1 to 24, convert the fraction to a decimal. Round to the nearest thousandth.

1. $\dfrac{5}{8}$ **2.** $\dfrac{7}{12}$ **3.** $\dfrac{2}{3}$ **4.** $\dfrac{5}{6}$ **5.** $\dfrac{1}{6}$ **6.** $\dfrac{7}{8}$

7. $\dfrac{5}{12}$ **8.** $\dfrac{9}{16}$ **9.** $\dfrac{7}{4}$ **10.** $\dfrac{5}{3}$ **11.** $1\dfrac{1}{2}$ **12.** $2\dfrac{1}{3}$

13. $\dfrac{16}{4}$ **14.** $\dfrac{36}{9}$ **15.** $\dfrac{3}{1000}$ **16.** $\dfrac{5}{10}$ **17.** $7\dfrac{2}{25}$ **18.** $16\dfrac{7}{9}$

19. $37\dfrac{1}{2}$ **20.** $\dfrac{5}{24}$ **21.** $\dfrac{4}{25}$ **22.** $3\dfrac{1}{3}$ **23.** $8\dfrac{2}{5}$ **24.** $5\dfrac{4}{9}$

To convert decimals to fractions

For Exercises 25 to 49, convert the decimal to a fraction.

25. 0.8 **26.** 0.4 **27.** 0.32 **28.** 0.48 **29.** 0.125

30. 0.485 **31.** 1.25 **32.** 3.75 **33.** 16.9 **34.** 17.5

35. 8.4 **36.** 10.7 **37.** 8.437 **38.** 9.279 **39.** 2.25

40. 7.75 **41.** $0.15\dfrac{1}{3}$ **42.** $0.17\dfrac{2}{3}$ **43.** $0.87\dfrac{7}{8}$ **44.** $0.12\dfrac{5}{9}$

45. 7.38 **46.** 0.33 **47.** 0.57 **48.** $0.33\dfrac{1}{3}$ **49.** $0.66\dfrac{2}{3}$

Objective C **To identify the order relation between two decimals or between a decimal and a fraction**

For Exercises 50 to 69, place the correct symbol, < or >, between the numbers.

50. 0.15   0.5

51. 0.6   0.45

52. 6.65   6.56

53. 3.89   3.98

54. 2.504   2.054

55. 0.025   0.105

56. $\frac{3}{8}$ 0.365

57. $\frac{4}{5}$ 0.802

58. $\frac{2}{3}$ 0.65

59. 0.85 $\frac{7}{8}$

60. $\frac{5}{9}$ 0.55

61. $\frac{7}{12}$ 0.58

62. 0.62 $\frac{7}{15}$

63. $\frac{11}{12}$ 0.92

64. 0.161 $\frac{1}{7}$

65. 0.623   0.6023

66. 0.86   0.855

67. 0.87   0.087

68. 1.005   0.5

69. 0.033   0.3

APPLYING THE CONCEPTS

Demography   The graph at the right shows the U.S. population according to the 2000 census. Use this table for Exercises 70 to 72.

70. Are there more individuals ages 0 to 39 or ages 40 and over in the United States?

71. Is the population ages 0 to 19 more than or less than $\frac{1}{4}$ of the total population?

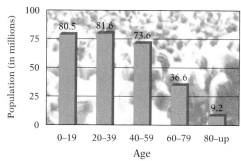

U.S. Population
Source: U.S. Census Bureau

72. Is the population ages 0 to 39 more than or less than $\frac{1}{2}$ of the total population?

73. Is $\frac{7}{13}$ in decimal form a repeating decimal? Why or why not? (*Hint:* See Projects and Group Activities, page 165.)

74. If a number is rounded to the nearest thousandth, is it always greater than if it were rounded to the nearest hundredth? Give examples to support your answer.

75. Explain how terminating, repeating, and nonrepeating decimals differ. Give an example of each kind of decimal.

Focus on Problem Solving

Relevant Information

Problems in mathematics or real life involve a question or a need and information or circumstances related to that question or need. Solving problems in the sciences usually involves a question, an observation, and measurements of some kind.

One of the challenges of problem solving in the sciences is to separate the information that is relevant to the problem from other information. Following is an example from the physical sciences in which some relevant information was omitted.

Hooke's Law states that the distance that a weight will stretch a spring is directly proportional to the weight on the spring. That is, $d = kF$, where d is the distance the spring is stretched and F is the force. In an experiment to verify this law, some physics students were continually getting inconsistent results. Finally, the instructor discovered that the heat produced when the lights were turned on was affecting the experiment. In this case, relevant information was omitted—namely, that the temperature of the spring can affect the distance it will stretch.

A lawyer drove 8 miles to the train station. After a 35-minute ride of 18 miles, the lawyer walked 10 minutes to the office. Find the total time it took the lawyer to get to work.

From this situation, answer the following before reading on.

a. What is asked for?

b. Is there enough information to answer the question?

c. Is information given that is not needed?

Here are the answers.

a. We want the total time for the lawyer to get to work.

b. No. We do not know the time it takes the lawyer to get to the train station.

c. Yes. Neither the distance to the train station nor the distance of the train ride is necessary to answer the question.

For each of the following problems, answer the questions printed in red above.

1. A customer bought 6 boxes of strawberries and paid with a $20 bill. What was the change?

2. A board is cut into two pieces. One piece is 3 feet longer than the other piece. What is the length of the original board?

3. A family rented a car for their vacation and drove 680 miles. The cost of the rental car was $21 per day with 150 free miles per day and $.15 for each mile driven above the number of free miles allowed. How many miles did the family drive per day?

4. An investor bought 8 acres of land for $80,000. One and one-half acres were set aside for a park, and the remainder was developed into one-half-acre lots. How many lots were available for sale?

5. You wrote checks of $43.67, $122.88, and $432.22 after making a deposit of $768.55. How much do you have left in your checking account?

Projects and Group Activities

Fractions as Terminating or Repeating Decimals

The fraction $\frac{3}{4}$ is equivalent to 0.75. The decimal 0.75 is a terminating decimal because there is a remainder of zero when 3 is divided by 4. The fraction $\frac{1}{3}$ is equivalent to 0.333 . . . . The three dots mean the pattern continues on and on. 0.333 . . . is a repeating decimal. To determine whether a fraction can be written as a terminating decimal, first write the fraction in simplest form. Then look at the denominator of the fraction. If it contains prime factors of only 2s and/or 5s, then it can be expressed as a terminating decimal. If it contains prime factors other than 2s or 5s, it represents a repeating decimal.

1. Assume that each of the following numbers is the denominator of a fraction written in simplest form. Does the fraction represent a terminating or repeating decimal?
   a. 4   **b.** 5   **c.** 7   **d.** 9   **e.** 10   **f.** 12   **g.** 15
   h. 16   **i.** 18   **j.** 21   **k.** 24   **l.** 25   **m.** 28   **n.** 40

2. Write two other numbers that, as denominators of fractions in simplest form, represent terminating decimals, and write two other numbers that, as denominators of fractions in simplest form, represent repeating decimals.

Chapter 3 Summary

Key Words	Examples
A number written in *decimal notation* has three parts: a *whole-number part*, a *decimal point*, and a *decimal part*. The decimal part of a number represents a number less than 1. A number written in decimal notation is often simply called a *decimal*. [3.1A, p. 127]	For the decimal 31.25, 31 is the whole-number part and 25 is the decimal part.

Essential Rules and Procedures	Examples
To write a decimal in words, write the decimal part as if it were a whole number. Then name the place value of the last digit. The decimal point is read as "and." [3.1A, p. 127]	The decimal 12.875 is written in words as twelve and eight hundred seventy-five thousandths.
To write a decimal in standard form when it is written in words, write the whole-number part, replace the word *and* with a decimal point, and write the decimal part so that the last digit is in the given place-value position. [3.1A, p. 128]	The decimal forty-nine and sixty-three thousandths is written in standard form as 49.063.
To round a decimal to a given place value, use the same rules used with whole numbers, except drop the digits to the right of the given place value instead of replacing them with zeros. [3.1B, p. 129]	2.7134 rounded to the nearest tenth is 2.7. 0.4687 rounded to the nearest hundredth is 0.47.

To add decimals, write the decimals so that the decimal points are on a vertical line. Add as you would with whole numbers. Then write the decimal point in the sum directly below the decimal points in the addends. [3.2A, p. 133]

$$\begin{array}{r} 1\ 1 \\ 1.35 \\ 20.8 \\ +\ 0.76 \\ \hline 22.91 \end{array}$$

To subtract decimals, write the decimals so that the decimal points are on a vertical line. Subtract as you would with whole numbers. Then write the decimal point in the difference directly below the decimal point in the subtrahend. [3.3A, p. 137]

$$\begin{array}{r} 2\ 15 \quad 6\ 10 \\ 3\,\cancel{5}\,.\,8\,\cancel{7}\,\cancel{0} \\ -\ 9\,.\,6\,4\,1 \\ \hline 2\,6\,.\,2\,2\,9 \end{array}$$

To multiply decimals, multiply the numbers as you would whole numbers. Then write the decimal point in the product so that the number of decimal places in the product is the sum of the decimal places in the factors. [3.4A, p. 141]

$$\begin{array}{r} 26.83 \quad \text{2 decimal places} \\ \times\quad 0.45 \quad \text{2 decimal places} \\ \hline 13415 \\ 10732\quad \\ \hline 12.0735 \quad \text{4 decimal places} \end{array}$$

To multiply a decimal by a power of 10, move the decimal point to the right the same number of places as there are zeros in the power of 10. If the power of 10 is written in exponential notation, the exponent indicates how many places to move the decimal point. [3.4A, pp. 141, 142]

$3.97 \cdot 10{,}000 = 39{,}700$

$0.641 \cdot 10^5 = 64{,}100$

To divide decimals, move the decimal point in the divisor to the right so that it is a whole number. Move the decimal point in the dividend the same number of places to the right. Place the decimal point in the quotient directly above the decimal point in the dividend. Then divide as you would with whole numbers. [3.5A, p. 151]

$$\begin{array}{r} 6.2 \\ 0.39.\overline{)2.41.8} \\ -2\,34 \\ \hline 7\,8 \\ -7\,8 \\ \hline 0 \end{array}$$

To divide a decimal by a power of 10, move the decimal point to the left the same number of places as there are zeros in the power of 10. If the power of 10 is written in exponential notation, the exponent indicates how many places to move the deicmal point. [3.5A, p. 152]

$972.8 \div 1000 = 0.9728$

$61.305 \div 10^4 = 0.0061305$

To convert a fraction to a decimal, divide the numerator of the fraction by the denominator. [3.6A, p. 160]

$\dfrac{7}{8} = 7 \div 8 = 0.875$

To convert a decimal to a fraction, remove the decimal point and place the decimal part over a denominator equal to the place value of the last digit in the decimal. [3.6B, p. 160]

0.85 is eighty-five <u>hundredths</u>.

$0.85 = \dfrac{85}{100} = \dfrac{17}{20}$

To find the order relation between a decimal and a fraction, first rewrite the fraction as a decimal. Then compare the two decimals. [3.6C, p. 161]

Because $\dfrac{3}{11} \approx 0.273$, and

$0.273 > 0.26,\ \dfrac{3}{11} > 0.26.$

Chapter 3 Review Exercises

1. Find the quotient of 3.6515 and 0.067.

2. Find the sum of 369.41, 88.3, 9.774, and 366.474.

3. Place the correct symbol, < or >, between the two numbers.
    0.055   0.1

4. Write 22.0092 in words.

5. Round 0.05678235 to the nearest hundred-thousandth.

6. Convert $2\frac{1}{3}$ to a decimal. Round to the nearest hundredth.

7. Convert 0.375 to a fraction.

8. Add: 3.42 + 0.794 + 32.5

9. Write thirty-four and twenty-five thousandths in standard form.

10. Place the correct symbol, < or >, between the two numbers.
    $\frac{5}{8}$ 0.62

11. Convert $\frac{7}{9}$ to a decimal. Round to the nearest thousandth.

12. Convert 0.66 to a fraction.

13. Subtract: 27.31 − 4.4465

14. Round 7.93704 to the nearest hundredth.

15. Find the product of 3.08 and 2.9.

16. Write 342.37 in words.

17. Write three and six thousand seven hundred fifty-three hundred-thousandths in standard form.

18. Multiply: 34.79
              × 0.74
              ‾‾‾‾‾‾‾

19. Divide: $0.053\overline{)0.349482}$

20. What is 7.796 decreased by 2.9175?

21. **Banking**   You had a balance of $895.68 in your checking account. You then wrote checks of $145.72 and $88.45. Find the new balance in your checking account.

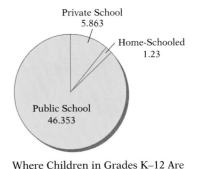

Education   The graph at the right shows where American children in grades K–12 are being educated. Figures are in millions of children. Use this graph for Exercises 22 and 23.

22. Find the total number of American children in grades K–12.

23. How many more children are being educated in public school than in private school?

Private School
5.863

Home-Schooled
1.23

Public School
46.353

Where Children in Grades K–12 Are
Being Educated in America
(in millions)

Sources: U.S. Department of Education;
Home School Legal Defense Association

24.   **Nutrition**   According to the American School Food Service Association, 1.9 million gallons of milk are served in school cafeterias every day. How many gallons of milk are served in school cafeterias during a 5-day school week?

25.   **Travel**   In a recent year, 30.6 million Americans drove to their destinations over Thanksgiving, and 4.8 million Americans traveled by plane. (*Source:* AAA) How many times greater is the number who drove than the number who flew? Round to the nearest tenth.

Chapter 3 Test

1. Place the correct symbol, $<$ or $>$, between the two numbers.

0.66   0.666

2. Subtract: 13.027
    − 8.94

3. Write 45.0302 in words.

4. Convert $\frac{9}{13}$ to a decimal. Round to the nearest thousandth.

5. Convert 0.825 to a fraction.

6. Round 0.07395 to the nearest ten-thousandth.

7. Find 0.0569 divided by 0.037. Round to the nearest thousandth.

8. Find 9.23674 less than 37.003.

9. Round 7.0954625 to the nearest thousandth.

10. Divide: $0.006\overline{)1.392}$

11. Add: 270.93
      97.
      1.976
    + 88.675

12. **Mechanics**   Find the missing dimension.

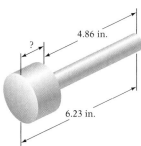

4.86 in.

?

6.23 in.

13. Multiply: 1.37
             $\times\ 0.004$

14. What is the total of 62.3, 4.007, and 189.65?

15. Write two hundred nine and seven thousand eighty-six hundred-thousandths in standard form.

16. Finances   A car was bought for $16,734.40, with a down payment of $2500. The balance was paid in 36 monthly payments. Find the amount of each monthly payment.

17. Compensation   You received a salary of $727.50, a commission of $1909.64, and a bonus of $450. Find your total income.

18. Consumerism   A long-distance telephone call costs $.85 for the first 3 minutes and $.42 for each additional minute. Find the cost of a 12-minute long-distance telephone call.

Computers   The table at the right shows the average number of hours per week that students use a computer. Use this table for Exercises 19 and 20.

19. On average, how many hours per year does a 10th-grade student use a computer? Use a 52-week year.

Grade Level	Average Number of Hours of Computer Use per Week
Prekindergarten – kindergarten	3.9
1st – 3rd	4.9
4th – 6th	4.2
7th – 8th	6.9
9th – 12th	6.7

Source: Find/SVP American Learning Household Survey

20. On average, how many more hours per year does a 2nd-grade student use a computer than a 5th-grade student? Use a 52-week year.

Cumulative Review Exercises

1. Divide: $89\overline{)20,932}$

2. Simplify: $2^3 \cdot 4^2$

3. Simplify: $2^2 - (7 - 3) \div 2 + 1$

4. Find the LCM of 9, 12, and 24.

5. Write $\frac{22}{5}$ as a mixed number.

6. Write $4\frac{5}{8}$ as an improper fraction.

7. Write an equivalent fraction with the given denominator.
$$\frac{5}{12} = \frac{}{60}$$

8. Add: $\frac{3}{8} + \frac{5}{12} + \frac{9}{16}$

9. What is $5\frac{7}{12}$ increased by $3\frac{7}{18}$?

10. Subtract: $9\frac{5}{9} - 3\frac{11}{12}$

11. Multiply: $\frac{9}{16} \times \frac{4}{27}$

12. Find the product of $2\frac{1}{8}$ and $4\frac{5}{17}$.

13. Divide: $\frac{11}{12} \div \frac{3}{4}$

14. What is $2\frac{3}{8}$ divided by $2\frac{1}{2}$?

15. Simplify: $\left(\frac{2}{3}\right)^2 \cdot \left(\frac{3}{4}\right)^3$

16. Simplify: $\left(\frac{2}{3}\right)^2 - \left(\frac{2}{3} - \frac{1}{2}\right) + 2$

17. Write 65.0309 in words.

18. Add:
$$\begin{array}{r} 379.006 \\ 27.523 \\ 9.8707 \\ +\ 88.2994 \\ \hline \end{array}$$

19. What is 29.005 decreased by 7.9286?

20. Multiply: 9.074
   $\times$ 6.09

21. Divide: $8.09\overline{)17.42963}$.
Round to the nearest thousandth.

22. Convert $\frac{11}{15}$ to a decimal. Round to the nearest thousandth.

23. Convert $0.16\frac{2}{3}$ to a fraction.

24. Place the correct symbol, $<$ or $>$, between the two numbers.
$\frac{8}{9}$ 0.98

25. **Vacation**   The graph at the right shows the number of vacation days per year that are legally mandated in several countries. How many more vacation days does Sweden mandate than Germany?

Number of Legally Mandated Vacation Days

Sources: Economic Policy Institute; *World Almanac*

26. **Health**   A patient is put on a diet to lose 24 pounds in 3 months. The patient loses $9\frac{1}{2}$ pounds the first month and $6\frac{3}{4}$ pounds the second month. How much weight must this patient lose the third month to achieve the goal?

27. **Banking**   You have a checking account balance of $814.35. You then write checks for $42.98, $16.43, and $137.56. Find your checking account balance after you write the checks.

28. **Mechanics**   A machine lathe takes 0.017 inch from a brass bushing that is 1.412 inches thick. Find the resulting thickness of the bushing.

29. **Taxes**   The state income tax on your business is $820 plus 0.08 times your profit. You made a profit of $64,860 last year. Find the amount of income tax you paid last year.

30. **Finances**   You bought a camera costing $210.96. The down payment was $20, and the balance is to be paid in 8 equal monthly payments. Find the monthly payment.

4 Ratio and Proportion

Egypt is known around the world for its enormous pyramids, built thousands of years ago by the pharaohs. This photo shows the pyramids at Giza. The largest pyramid at Giza, called the Great Pyramid, dates to approximately 2600 B.C. and is the oldest of the Seven Ancient Wonders of the World. It is also the only ancient wonder that still survives today. Some historians believe that some of the pyramids of Egypt incorporate a special ratio called the golden ratio. This ratio, which is described in the **project on page 192,** has been used extensively in art and architecture for centuries. The ratio of the slant height to a side of the base of the pyramid reflects the golden ratio.

OBJECTIVES

Section 4.1
A To write the ratio of two quantities in simplest form
B To solve application problems

Section 4.2
A To write rates
B To write unit rates
C To solve application problems

Section 4.3
A To determine whether a proportion is true
B To solve proportions
C To solve application problems

Need help? For online student resources, such as section quizzes, visit this textbook's website at **math.college.hmco.com/students.**

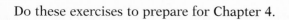
Do these exercises to prepare for Chapter 4.

1. Simplify: $\dfrac{8}{10}$

2. Simplify: $\dfrac{450}{650 + 250}$

3. Write as a decimal: $\dfrac{372}{15}$

4. Which is greater, 4×33 or 62×2?

5. Complete: $? \times 5 = 20$

GO FIGURE • • •

Luis, Kim, Reggie, and Dave are standing in line. Dave is not first. Kim is between Luis and Reggie. Luis is between Dave and Kim. Give the order in which the men are standing.

4.1 Ratio

Objective A — **To write the ratio of two quantities in simplest form**

Point of Interest

In the 1990s, the major-league pitchers with the best strikeout-to-walk ratios (having pitched a minimum of 100 innings) were

Dennis Eckersley	6.46:1
Shane Reynolds	4.13:1
Greg Maddux	4:1
Bret Saberhagen	3.92:1
Rod Beck	3.81:1

The best single-season strikeout-to-walk ratio for starting pitchers in the same period was that of Bret Saberhagen, 11:1.
(*Source:* Elias Sports Bureau)

Quantities such as 3 feet, 12 cents, and 9 cars are number quantities written with units.

3 feet
12 cents
9 cars
   ↑
  units

These are some examples of units. Shirts, dollars, trees, miles, and gallons are further examples.

A **ratio** is a comparison of two quantities that have the *same* units. This comparison can be written three different ways:

1. As a fraction

2. As two numbers separated by a colon (:)

3. As two numbers separated by the word *to*

The ratio of the lengths of two boards, one 8 feet long and the other 10 feet long, can be written as

1. $\dfrac{8 \text{ feet}}{10 \text{ feet}} = \dfrac{8}{10} = \dfrac{4}{5}$

2. 8 feet : 10 feet = 8 : 10 = 4 : 5

3. 8 feet to 10 feet = 8 to 10 = 4 to 5

Writing the **simplest form of a ratio** means writing it so that the two numbers have no common factor other than 1.

This ratio means that the smaller board is $\dfrac{4}{5}$ the length of the longer board.

Example 1

Write the comparison $6 to $8 as a ratio in simplest form using a fraction, a colon, and the word *to*.

Solution

$\dfrac{\$6}{\$8} = \dfrac{6}{8} = \dfrac{3}{4}$

$6 : $8 = 6 : 8 = 3 : 4

$6 to $8 = 6 to 8 = 3 to 4

You Try It 1

Write the comparison 20 pounds to 24 pounds as a ratio in simplest form using a fraction, a colon, and the word *to*.

Your solution

Example 2

Write the comparison 18 quarts to 6 quarts as a ratio in simplest form using a fraction, a colon, and the word *to*.

Solution

$\dfrac{18 \text{ quarts}}{6 \text{ quarts}} = \dfrac{18}{6} = \dfrac{3}{1}$

18 quarts : 6 quarts =
    18 : 6 = 3 : 1

18 quarts to 6 quarts =
    18 to 6 = 3 to 1

You Try It 2

Write the comparison 64 miles to 8 miles as a ratio in simplest form using a fraction, a colon, and the word *to*.

Your solution

Solutions on p. S11

Objective B   **To solve application problems**

Use the table below for Example 3 and You Try It 3.

Board Feet of Wood at a Lumber Store			
Pine	Ash	Oak	Cedar
20,000	18,000	10,000	12,000

Example 3

Find, as a fraction in simplest form, the ratio of the number of board feet of pine to the number of board feet of oak.

Strategy

To find the ratio, write the ratio of board feet of pine (20,000) to board feet of oak (10,000) in simplest form.

Solution

$$\frac{20,000}{10,000} = \frac{2}{1}$$

The ratio is $\frac{2}{1}$.

You Try It 3

Find, as a fraction in simplest form, the ratio of the number of board feet of cedar to the number of board feet of ash.

Your strategy

Your solution

Example 4

The cost of building a patio cover was $500 for labor and $700 for materials. What, as a fraction in simplest form, is the ratio of the cost of materials to the total cost for labor and materials?

Strategy

To find the ratio, write the ratio of the cost of materials ($700) to the total cost ($500 + $700) in simplest form.

Solution

$$\frac{\$700}{\$500 + \$700} = \frac{700}{1200} = \frac{7}{12}$$

The ratio is $\frac{7}{12}$.

You Try It 4

A company spends $60,000 a month for television advertising and $45,000 a month for radio advertising. What, as a fraction in simplest form, is the ratio of the cost of radio advertising to the total cost of radio and television advertising?

Your strategy

Your solution

Solutions on p. S11

4.1 Exercises

Objective A   **To write the ratio of two quantities in simplest form**

For Exercises 1 to 24, write the comparison as a ratio in simplest form using a fraction, a colon (:), and the word *to*.

1. 3 pints to 15 pints

2. 6 pounds to 8 pounds

3. $40 to $20

4. 10 feet to 2 feet

5. 3 miles to 8 miles

6. 2 hours to 3 hours

7. 37 hours to 24 hours

8. 29 inches to 12 inches

9. 6 minutes to 6 minutes

10. 8 days to 12 days

11. 35 cents to 50 cents

12. 28 inches to 36 inches

13. 30 minutes to 60 minutes

14. 25 cents to 100 cents

15. 32 ounces to 16 ounces

16. 12 quarts to 4 quarts

17. 3 cups to 4 cups

18. 6 years to 7 years

19. $5 to $3

20. 30 yards to 12 yards

21. 12 quarts to 18 quarts

22. 20 gallons to 28 gallons

23. 14 days to 7 days

24. 9 feet to 3 feet

Objective B   **To solve application problems**

For Exercises 25 to 28, write ratios in simplest form using a fraction.

Family Budget						
Housing	Food	Transportation	Taxes	Utilities	Miscellaneous	Total
$1600	$800	$600	$700	$300	$800	$4800

25. **Budgets**   Use the table to find the ratio of housing cost to total expenses.

26. **Budgets**   Use the table to find the ratio of food cost to total expenses.

27. **Budgets**   Use the table to find the ratio of utilities cost to food cost.

28. **Budgets**   Use the table to find the ratio of transportation cost to housing cost.

29.  **Sports**   National Collegiate Athletic Association (NCAA) statistics show that for every 154,000 high school seniors playing basketball, only 4000 will play college basketball as first-year students. Write the ratio of the number of first-year students playing college basketball to the number of high school seniors playing basketball.

30. **Sports**   NCAA statistics show that for every 2800 college seniors playing college basketball, only 50 will play as rookies in the National Basketball Association. Write the ratio of the number of National Basketball Association rookies to the number of college seniors playing basketball.

31. **Electricity**   A transformer has 40 turns in the primary coil and 480 turns in the secondary coil. State the ratio of the number of turns in the primary coil to the number of turns in the secondary coil.

Primary coil   Secondary coil

32. **Consumerism**   Rita Sterling bought a computer system for $2400. Five years later she sold the computer for $900. Find the ratio of the amount she received for the computer to the cost of the computer.

33. **Real Estate**   A house with an original value of $90,000 increased in value to $110,000 in 5 years.
    a. Find the increase in the value of the house.
    b. What is the ratio of the increase in value to the original value of the house?

34. **Energy Prices**   The price of gasoline jumped from $1.35 to $1.62 in 1 year.
    a. What was the increase in the price per gallon?
    b. What is the ratio of the increase in price to the original price?

APPLYING THE CONCEPTS

Banking   A bank uses the ratio of a borrower's total monthly debts to the borrower's total monthly income to determine the maximum monthly payment for a potential homeowner. This ratio is called the debt–income ratio. Use the homeowner's debt–income table at the right for Exercises 35 and 36.

Income	Debt
$5500	$1200
$450	$300
$250	$450
	$250

35. Compute the debt–income ratio for the potential homeowner.

36. Central Trust Bank will make a loan to a customer whose debt–income ratio is less than $\frac{1}{3}$. Will the potential homeowner qualify? Explain your answer.

37. **Banking**   To make a home loan, First National Bank requires a debt–income ratio that is less than $\frac{2}{5}$. Would the home-owner whose debt–income table is given at the right qualify for a loan using these standards? Explain.

Income		Debt	
Salary	$3400	Mortgage	$1800
Interest	$83	Property tax	$104
Rent	$650	Insurance	$35
Dividends	$34	Liabilities	$120
		Credit card	$234
		Car loan	$197

38. 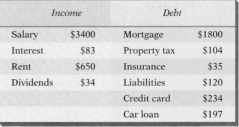 Is the value of a ratio always less than 1? Explain.

4.2 Rates

Objective A To write rates

A **rate** is a comparison of two quantities that have *different* units. A rate is written as a fraction.

A distance runner ran 26 miles in 4 hours. The distance-to-time rate is written

$$\frac{26 \text{ miles}}{4 \text{ hours}} = \frac{13 \text{ miles}}{2 \text{ hours}}$$

Writing the **simplest form of a rate** means writing it so that the two numbers that form the rate have no common factor other than 1.

Example 1 Write "6 roof supports for every 9 feet" as a rate in simplest form.

You Try It 1 Write "15 pounds of fertilizer for 12 trees" as a rate in simplest form.

Solution $\dfrac{6 \text{ supports}}{9 \text{ feet}} = \dfrac{2 \text{ supports}}{3 \text{ feet}}$

Your solution

Solution on p. S11

Objective B To write unit rates

A **unit rate** is a rate in which the number in the denominator is 1.

$$\frac{\$3.25}{1 \text{ pound}}$$ or \$3.25/pound is read "\$3.25 per pound."

To find unit rates, divide the number in the numerator of the rate by the number in the denominator of the rate.

A car traveled 344 miles on 16 gallons of gasoline. To find the miles per gallon (unit rate), divide the numerator of the rate by the denominator of the rate.

$$\frac{344 \text{ miles}}{16 \text{ gallons}}$$ is the rate.

$$16)\overline{344.0} \quad \frac{21.5}{}$$ 21.5 miles/gallon is the unit rate.

Example 2 Write "300 feet in 8 seconds" as a unit rate.

You Try It 2 Write "260 miles in 8 hours" as a unit rate.

Solution $\dfrac{300 \text{ feet}}{8 \text{ seconds}}$ $8)\overline{300.0} \quad \frac{37.5}{}$

37.5 feet/second

Your solution

Solution on p. S11

Objective C   **To solve application problems**

Denver Airport

HOW TO   The table at the right shows air fares for some routes in the continental United States. Find the cost per mile for the four routes in order to determine the most expensive route and the least expensive route on the basis of mileage flown.

Long Routes	Miles	Fare
New York–Los Angeles	2475	$683
San Francisco–Dallas	1464	$536
Denver–Pittsburgh	1302	$525
Minneapolis–Hartford	1050	$483

Strategy
To find the cost per mile, divide the fare by the miles flown for each route. Compare the costs per mile to determine the most expensive and least expensive routes per mile.

Solution

New York–Los Angeles $\dfrac{683}{2475} \approx 0.28$

San Francisco–Dallas $\dfrac{536}{1464} \approx 0.37$

Denver–Pittsburgh $\dfrac{525}{1302} \approx 0.40$

Minneapolis–Hartford $\dfrac{483}{1050} = 0.46$

$0.28 < 0.37 < 0.40 < 0.46$

The Minneapolis–Hartford route is the most expensive per mile, and the New York–Los Angeles route is the least expensive per mile.

Integrating Technology

To calculate the costs per mile using a calculator, perform four divisions:

683 ÷ 2475 =
536 ÷ 1464 =
525 ÷ 1302 =
483 ÷ 1050 =

In each case, round the number in the display to the nearest hundredth.

Example 3

As an investor, Jung Ho purchased 100 shares of stock for $1500. One year later, Jung sold the 100 shares for $1800. What was his profit per share?

Strategy
To find Jung's profit per share:

• Find the total profit by subtracting the original cost ($1500) from the selling price ($1800).
• Find the profit per share (unit rate) by dividing the total profit by the number of shares of stock (100).

Solution
$1800 - 1500 = 300$

$300 \div 100 = 3$

Jung Ho's profit was $3/share.

You Try It 3

Erik Peltier, a jeweler, purchased 5 ounces of gold for $1625. Later, he sold the 5 ounces for $1720. What was Erik's profit per ounce?

Your strategy

Your solution

Solution on p. S11

4.2 Exercises

Objective A   **To write rates**

For Exercises 1 to 10, write each phrase as a rate in simplest form.

1. 3 pounds of meat for 4 people

2. 30 ounces in 24 glasses

3. $80 for 12 boards

4. 84 cents for 3 bars of soap

5. 300 miles on 15 gallons

6. 88 feet in 8 seconds

7. 20 children in 8 families

8. 48 leaves on 9 plants

9. 16 gallons in 2 hours

10. 25 ounces in 5 minutes

Objective B   **To write unit rates**

For Exercises 11 to 24, write each phrase as a unit rate.

11. 10 feet in 4 seconds

12. 816 miles in 6 days

13. $3900 earned in 4 weeks

14. $51,000 earned in 12 months

15. 1100 trees planted on 10 acres

16. 3750 words on 15 pages

17. $131.88 earned in 7 hours

18. $315.70 earned in 22 hours

19. 628.8 miles in 12 hours

20. 388.8 miles in 8 hours

21. 344.4 miles on 12.3 gallons of gasoline

22. 409.4 miles on 11.5 gallons of gasoline

23. $349.80 for 212 pounds

24. $11.05 for 3.4 pounds

Objective C   **To solve application problems**

25. **Fuel Efficiency**   An automobile was driven 326.6 miles on 11.5 gallons of gas. Find the number of miles driven per gallon of gas.

26. **Travel**   You drive 246.6 miles in 4.5 hours. Find the number of miles you drove per hour.

27.   **Fuel Efficiency**   The Saturn-5 rocket uses 534,000 gallons of fuel in 2.5 minutes. How much fuel does the rocket use per minute?

28. Manufacturing   Assume that Regency Computer produced 5000 zip disks for $26,536.32. Of the disks made, 122 did not meet company standards.
   a. How many disks did meet company standards?
   b. What was the cost per disk for those disks that met company standards?

29. Consumerism   The Pierre family purchased a 250-pound side of beef for $365.75 and had it packaged. During the packaging, 75 pounds of beef were discarded as waste.
   a. How many pounds of beef were packaged?
   b. What was the cost per pound for the packaged beef?

30.   Advertising   In 2003, the average price of a 30-second commercial during the sitcom *Friends* was $455,700. (*Source: Time*) Find the price per second.

31.   The Film Industry   During filming, an IMAX camera uses 65-mm film at a rate of 5.6 feet per second.
   a. At what rate per minute does the camera go through film?
   b. At what rate does it use a 500-foot roll of 65-mm film? Round to the nearest second.

32.   Demography   The table at the right shows the population and area of three countries. The population density of a country is the number of people per square mile.
   a. Which country has the least population density?
   b. How many more people per square mile are there in India than in the United States? Round to the nearest whole number.

Country	Population	Area (in square miles)
Australia	19,547,000	2,968,000
India	1,045,845,000	1,269,000
United States	291,929,000	3,619,000

Another application of rates is in the area of international trade. Suppose a company in Canada purchases a shipment of sneakers from an American company. The Canadian company must exchange Canadian dollars for U.S. dollars in order to pay for the order. The number of Canadian dollars that are equivalent to 1 U.S. dollar is called the **exchange rate.**

33.   Exchange Rates   The table at the right shows the exchange rates per U.S. dollar for three foreign countries and for the euro at the time of this writing.
   a. How many euros would be paid for an order of American computer hardware costing $120,000?
   b. Calculate the cost, in Japanese yen, of an American car costing $34,000.

Exchange Rates per U.S. Dollar	
Australian Dollar	1.545
Canadian Dollar	1.386
Japanese Yen	117.000
The Euro	0.9103

APPLYING THE CONCEPTS

34. Compensation   You have a choice of receiving a wage of $34,000 per year, $2840 per month, $650 per week, or $18 per hour. Which pay choice would you take? Assume a 40-hour week with 52 weeks per year.

**35.   The price–earnings ratio of a company's stock is one measure used by stock market analysts to assess the financial well-being of the company. Explain the meaning of the price–earnings ratio.

4.3 Proportions

A **To determine whether a proportion is true**

A **proportion** is an expression of the equality of two ratios or rates.

$$\frac{50 \text{ miles}}{4 \text{ gallons}} = \frac{25 \text{ miles}}{2 \text{ gallons}}$$

Note that the units of the numerators are the same and the units of the denominators are the same.

$$\frac{3}{6} = \frac{1}{2}$$

This is the equality of two ratios.

A proportion is **true** if the fractions are equal when written in lowest terms.

In any true proportion, the **cross products** are equal.

HOW TO Is $\frac{2}{3} = \frac{8}{12}$ a true proportion?

$$\frac{2}{3} \diagdown\!\!\!\diagup \frac{8}{12} \rightarrow \begin{array}{l} 3 \times 8 = 24 \\ 2 \times 12 = 24 \end{array}$$

The cross products *are* equal.

$\frac{2}{3} = \frac{8}{12}$ is a true proportion.

A proportion is **not true** if the fractions are not equal when reduced to lowest terms.

If the cross products are not equal, then the proportion is not true.

HOW TO Is $\frac{4}{5} = \frac{8}{9}$ a true proportion?

$$\frac{4}{5} \diagdown\!\!\!\diagup \frac{8}{9} \rightarrow \begin{array}{l} 5 \times 8 = 40 \\ 4 \times 9 = 36 \end{array}$$

The cross products *are not* equal.

$\frac{4}{5} = \frac{8}{9}$ is not a true proportion.

Example 1 Is $\frac{5}{8} = \frac{10}{16}$ a true proportion?

Solution

$$\frac{5}{8} \diagdown\!\!\!\diagup \frac{10}{16} \rightarrow \begin{array}{l} 8 \times 10 = 80 \\ 5 \times 16 = 80 \end{array}$$

The cross products are equal.
The proportion is true.

You Try It 1 Is $\frac{6}{10} = \frac{9}{15}$ a true proportion?

Your solution

Example 2 Is $\frac{62 \text{ miles}}{4 \text{ gallons}} = \frac{33 \text{ miles}}{2 \text{ gallons}}$ a true proportion?

Solution

$$\frac{62}{4} \diagdown\!\!\!\diagup \frac{33}{2} \rightarrow \begin{array}{l} 4 \times 33 = 132 \\ 62 \times 2 = 124 \end{array}$$

The cross products are not equal.
The proportion is not true.

You Try It 2 Is $\frac{\$32}{6 \text{ hours}} = \frac{\$90}{8 \text{ hours}}$ a true proportion?

Your solution

Solutions on p. S11

Objective B   **To solve proportions**

Sometimes one of the numbers in a proportion is unknown. In this case, it is necessary to *solve* the proportion.

To **solve a proportion**, find a number to replace the unknown so that the proportion is true.

HOW TO   Solve: $\dfrac{9}{6} = \dfrac{3}{n}$

$$\frac{9}{6} = \frac{3}{n}$$

$9 \times n = 6 \times 3$ • Find the cross products.

$9 \times n = 18$

$n = 18 \div 9$ • Think of $9 \times n = 18$ as $9)\overline{18}$.

$n = 2$

Check:

$\dfrac{9}{6} \diagdown\!\!\!\diagup \dfrac{3}{2}$ → $6 \times 3 = 18$
         → $9 \times 2 = 18$

Example 3   Solve $\dfrac{n}{12} = \dfrac{25}{60}$ and check.

Solution $n \times 60 = 12 \times 25$ • Find the cross
$n \times 60 = 300$ products. Then
$n = 300 \div 60$ solve for n.
$n = 5$

Check:

$\dfrac{5}{12} \diagdown\!\!\!\diagup \dfrac{25}{60}$ → $12 \times 25 = 300$
          → $5 \times 60 = 300$

You Try It 3   Solve $\dfrac{n}{14} = \dfrac{3}{7}$ and check.

Your solution

Example 4   Solve $\dfrac{4}{9} = \dfrac{n}{16}$. Round to the nearest tenth.

Solution $4 \times 16 = 9 \times n$ • Find the cross
$64 = 9 \times n$ products. Then
$64 \div 9 = n$ solve for n.
$7.1 \approx n$

Note: A rounded answer is an approximation. Therefore, the answer to a check will not be exact.

You Try It 4   Solve $\dfrac{5}{7} = \dfrac{n}{20}$. Round to the nearest tenth.

Your solution

Solutions on p. S12

Example 5   Solve $\frac{28}{52} = \frac{7}{n}$ and check.

Solution $28 \times n = 52 \times 7$ • Find the cross
$28 \times n = 364$ products. Then
$n = 364 \div 28$ solve for *n*.
$n = 13$

Check:

$\frac{28}{52} \quad \frac{7}{13} \rightarrow \begin{array}{l} 52 \times 7 = 364 \\ 28 \times 13 = 364 \end{array}$

You Try It 5   Solve $\frac{15}{20} = \frac{12}{n}$ and check.

Your solution

Example 6   Solve $\frac{15}{n} = \frac{8}{3}$. Round to the
nearest hundredth.

Solution $15 \times 3 = n \times 8$
$45 = n \times 8$
$45 \div 8 = n$
$5.63 \approx n$

You Try It 6   Solve $\frac{12}{n} = \frac{7}{4}$. Round to the
nearest hundredth.

Your solution

Example 7   Solve $\frac{n}{9} = \frac{3}{1}$ and check.

Solution $n \times 1 = 9 \times 3$
$n \times 1 = 27$
$n = 27 \div 1$
$n = 27$

Check:

$\frac{27}{9} \quad \frac{3}{1} \rightarrow \begin{array}{l} 9 \times 3 = 27 \\ 27 \times 1 = 27 \end{array}$

You Try It 7   Solve $\frac{n}{12} = \frac{4}{1}$ and check.

Your solution

Solutions on p. S12

Objective C   **To solve application problems**

The application problems in this objective require you to write and solve a proportion. When setting up a proportion, remember to keep the same units in the
numerator and the same units in the denominator.

Example 8

The dosage of a certain medication is 2 ounces for every 50 pounds of body weight. How many ounces of this medication are required for a person who weighs 175 pounds?

Strategy

To find the number of ounces of medication for a person weighing 175 pounds, write and solve a proportion using n to represent the number of ounces of medication for a 175-pound person.

Solution

$$\frac{2 \text{ ounces}}{50 \text{ pounds}} = \frac{n \text{ ounces}}{175 \text{ pounds}}$$

• The unit "ounces" is in the numerator. The unit "pounds" is in the denominator.

$$2 \times 175 = 50 \times n$$
$$350 = 50 \times n$$
$$350 \div 50 = n$$
$$7 = n$$

A 175-pound person requires 7 ounces of medication.

You Try It 8

Three tablespoons of a liquid plant fertilizer are to be added to every 4 gallons of water. How many tablespoons of fertilizer are required for 10 gallons of water?

Your strategy

Your solution

Example 9

A mason determines that 9 cement blocks are required for a retaining wall 2 feet long. At this rate, how many cement blocks are required for a retaining wall that is 24 feet long?

Strategy

To find the number of cement blocks for a retaining wall 24 feet long, write and solve a proportion using n to represent the number of blocks required.

Solution

$$\frac{9 \text{ cement blocks}}{2 \text{ feet}} = \frac{n \text{ cement blocks}}{24 \text{ feet}}$$

$$9 \times 24 = 2 \times n$$
$$216 = 2 \times n$$
$$216 \div 2 = n$$
$$108 = n$$

A 24-foot retaining wall requires 108 cement blocks.

You Try It 9

Twenty-four jars can be packed in 6 identical boxes. At this rate, how many jars can be packed in 15 boxes?

Your strategy

Your solution

Solutions on p. S12

4.3 Exercises

Objective A   **To determine whether a proportion is true**

For Exercises 1 to 24, determine whether the proportion is true or not true.

1. $\dfrac{4}{8} = \dfrac{10}{20}$

2. $\dfrac{39}{48} = \dfrac{13}{16}$

3. $\dfrac{7}{8} = \dfrac{11}{12}$

4. $\dfrac{15}{7} = \dfrac{17}{8}$

5. $\dfrac{27}{8} = \dfrac{9}{4}$

6. $\dfrac{3}{18} = \dfrac{4}{19}$

7. $\dfrac{45}{135} = \dfrac{3}{9}$

8. $\dfrac{3}{4} = \dfrac{54}{72}$

9. $\dfrac{16}{3} = \dfrac{48}{9}$

10. $\dfrac{15}{5} = \dfrac{3}{1}$

11. $\dfrac{7}{40} = \dfrac{7}{8}$

12. $\dfrac{9}{7} = \dfrac{6}{5}$

13. $\dfrac{50 \text{ miles}}{2 \text{ gallons}} = \dfrac{25 \text{ miles}}{1 \text{ gallon}}$

14. $\dfrac{16 \text{ feet}}{10 \text{ seconds}} = \dfrac{24 \text{ feet}}{15 \text{ seconds}}$

15. $\dfrac{6 \text{ minutes}}{5 \text{ cents}} = \dfrac{30 \text{ minutes}}{25 \text{ cents}}$

16. $\dfrac{16 \text{ pounds}}{12 \text{ days}} = \dfrac{20 \text{ pounds}}{14 \text{ days}}$

17. $\dfrac{\$15}{4 \text{ pounds}} = \dfrac{\$45}{12 \text{ pounds}}$

18. $\dfrac{270 \text{ trees}}{6 \text{ acres}} = \dfrac{90 \text{ trees}}{2 \text{ acres}}$

19. $\dfrac{300 \text{ feet}}{4 \text{ rolls}} = \dfrac{450 \text{ feet}}{7 \text{ rolls}}$

20. $\dfrac{1 \text{ gallon}}{4 \text{ quarts}} = \dfrac{7 \text{ gallons}}{28 \text{ quarts}}$

21. $\dfrac{\$65}{5 \text{ days}} = \dfrac{\$26}{2 \text{ days}}$

22. $\dfrac{80 \text{ miles}}{2 \text{ hours}} = \dfrac{110 \text{ miles}}{3 \text{ hours}}$

23. $\dfrac{7 \text{ tiles}}{4 \text{ feet}} = \dfrac{42 \text{ tiles}}{20 \text{ feet}}$

24. $\dfrac{15 \text{ feet}}{3 \text{ yards}} = \dfrac{90 \text{ feet}}{18 \text{ yards}}$

To solve proportions

For Exercises 25 to 52, solve. Round to the nearest hundredth, if necessary.

25. $\dfrac{n}{4} = \dfrac{6}{8}$ **26.** $\dfrac{n}{7} = \dfrac{9}{21}$ **27.** $\dfrac{12}{18} = \dfrac{n}{9}$ **28.** $\dfrac{7}{21} = \dfrac{35}{n}$

29. $\dfrac{6}{n} = \dfrac{24}{36}$ **30.** $\dfrac{3}{n} = \dfrac{15}{10}$ **31.** $\dfrac{n}{45} = \dfrac{17}{135}$ **32.** $\dfrac{9}{4} = \dfrac{18}{n}$

33. $\dfrac{n}{6} = \dfrac{2}{3}$ **34.** $\dfrac{5}{12} = \dfrac{n}{144}$ **35.** $\dfrac{n}{5} = \dfrac{7}{8}$ **36.** $\dfrac{4}{n} = \dfrac{9}{5}$

37. $\dfrac{n}{11} = \dfrac{32}{4}$ **38.** $\dfrac{3}{4} = \dfrac{8}{n}$ **39.** $\dfrac{5}{12} = \dfrac{n}{8}$ **40.** $\dfrac{36}{20} = \dfrac{12}{n}$

41. $\dfrac{n}{15} = \dfrac{21}{12}$ **42.** $\dfrac{40}{n} = \dfrac{15}{8}$ **43.** $\dfrac{32}{n} = \dfrac{1}{3}$ **44.** $\dfrac{5}{8} = \dfrac{42}{n}$

45. $\dfrac{18}{11} = \dfrac{16}{n}$ **46.** $\dfrac{25}{4} = \dfrac{n}{12}$ **47.** $\dfrac{28}{8} = \dfrac{12}{n}$ **48.** $\dfrac{n}{30} = \dfrac{65}{120}$

49. $\dfrac{0.3}{5.6} = \dfrac{n}{25}$ **50.** $\dfrac{1.3}{16} = \dfrac{n}{30}$ **51.** $\dfrac{0.7}{9.8} = \dfrac{3.6}{n}$ **52.** $\dfrac{1.9}{7} = \dfrac{13}{n}$

To solve application problems

For Exercises 53 to 71, solve. Round to the nearest hundredth.

53. **Nutrition**   A 6-ounce package of Puffed Wheat contains 600 calories. How many calories are in a 0.5-ounce serving of the cereal?

54. **Fuel Efficiency**   A car travels 70.5 miles on 3 gallons of gas. Find the distance that the car can travel on 14 gallons of gas.

55. Landscaping   Ron Stokes uses 2 pounds of fertilizer for every 100 square feet of lawn for landscape maintenance. At this rate, how many pounds of fertilizer did he use on a lawn that measures 3500 square feet?

56. Gardening   A nursery prepares a liquid plant food by adding 1 gallon of water for each 2 ounces of plant food. At this rate, how many gallons of water are required for 25 ounces of plant food?

57. Manufacturing   A manufacturer of baseball equipment makes 4 aluminum bats for every 15 bats made from wood. On a day when 100 aluminum bats are made, how many wooden bats are produced?

58. Masonry   A brick wall 20 feet in length contains 1040 bricks. At the same rate, how many bricks would it take to build a wall 48 feet in length?

59. Cartography   The scale on the map at the right is "1.25 inches equals 10 miles." Find the distance between Carlsbad and Del Mar, which are 2 inches apart on the map.

60. Architecture   The scale on the plans for a new house is "1 inch equals 3 feet." Find the width and the length of a room that measures 5 inches by 8 inches on the drawing.

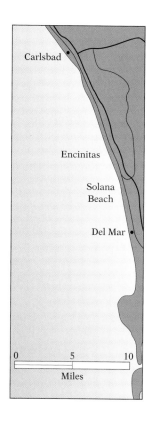

61. Medicine   The dosage for a medication is $\frac{1}{3}$ ounce for every 40 pounds of body weight. At this rate, how many ounces of medication should a physician prescribe for a patient who weighs 150 pounds? Write the answer as a decimal.

62. Banking   A bank requires a monthly payment of $33.45 on a $2500 loan. At the same rate, find the monthly payment on a $10,000 loan.

63. Elections   A pre-election survey showed that 2 out of every 3 eligible voters would cast ballots in the county election. At this rate, how many people in a county of 240,000 eligible voters would vote in the election?

64. Interior Design   A paint manufacturer suggests using 1 gallon of paint for every 400 square feet of a wall. At this rate, how many gallons of paint would be required for a room that has 1400 square feet of wall?

65. Insurance   A 60-year-old male can obtain $10,000 of life insurance for $35.35 per month. At this rate, what is the monthly cost of $50,000 of life insurance?

66. Manufacturing   Suppose a computer chip manufacturer knows from experience that in an average production run of 2000 circuit boards, 60 will be defective. How many defective circuit boards can be expected from a run of 25,000 circuit boards?

67. **Investments** You own 240 shares of stock in a computer company. The company declares a stock split of 5 shares for every 3 owned. How many shares of stock will you own after the stock split?

68. **Computers** The director of data processing at a college estimates that the ratio of student time to administrative time on a certain computer is 3:2. During a month in which the computer was used 200 hours for administration, how many hours was it used by students?

69. **Physics** The ratio of weight on the moon to weight on Earth is 1:6. If a bowling ball weighs 16 pounds on Earth, what would it weigh on the moon?

70. **Automobiles** When engineers designed a new car, they first built a model of the car. The ratio of the size of a part on the model to the actual size of the part is 2:5. If a door is 1.3 feet long on the model, what is the length of the door on the car?

71. **Investments** Carlos Capasso owns 50 shares of Texas Utilities that pay dividends of $153. At this rate, what dividend would Carlos receive after buying 300 additional shares of Texas Utilities?

APPLYING THE CONCEPTS

72. **Publishing** In January 2003, *USA Today* reported that for every 100 copies of *Dr. Atkins' New Diet Revolution* sold, John Grisham's *The Summons* sold 7.3 copies. Explain how a proportion can be used to determine the number of copies of *Dr. Atkins' New Diet Revolution* sold given the number of copies of *The Summons* sold.

73. **Social Security** According to the Social Security Administration, the numbers of workers per retiree in the future are expected to be as given in the table below.

Year	2010	2020	2030	2040
Number of workers per retiree	3.1	2.5	2.1	2.0

Why is the shrinking number of workers per retiree of importance to the Social Security Administration?

74. **Compensation** In June 2002, *Time* magazine reported, "In 1980 the average CEO made 40 times the pay of the average factory worker; by 2000 the ratio had climbed to 531 to 1." What information would you need to know in order to determine the average pay of a CEO in 2000? With that information, how would you calculate the average pay of a CEO in 2000?

75. **Elections** A survey of voters in a city claimed that 2 people of every 5 who voted cast a ballot in favor of city amendment A and that 3 people of every 4 who voted cast a ballot against amendment A. Is this possible? Explain your answer.

76. Write a word problem that requires solving a proportion to find the answer.

Focus on Problem Solving

Looking for a Pattern

A very useful problem-solving strategy is looking for a pattern.

Problem   A legend says that a peasant invented the game of chess and gave it to a very rich king as a present. The king so enjoyed the game that he gave the peasant the choice of anything in the kingdom. The peasant's request was simple: "Place one grain of wheat on the first square, 2 grains on the second square, 4 grains on the third square, 8 on the fourth square, and continue doubling the number of grains until the last square of the chessboard is reached." How many grains of wheat must the king give the peasant?

Solution   A chessboard consists of 64 squares. To find the total number of grains of wheat on the 64 squares, we begin by looking at the amount of wheat on the first few squares.

Square 1	Square 2	Square 3	Square 4	Square 5	Square 6	Square 7	Square 8
1	2	4	8	16	32	64	128
1	3	7	15	31	63	127	255

The bottom row of numbers represents the sum of the number of grains of wheat up to and including that square. For instance, the number of grains of wheat on the first 7 squares is $1 + 2 + 4 + 8 + 16 + 32 + 64 = 127$.

One pattern to observe is that the number of grains of wheat on a square can be expressed as a power of 2.

The number of grains on square $n = 2^{n-1}$.

For example, the number of grains on square $7 = 2^{7-1} = 2^6 = 64$.

A second pattern of interest is that **the number *below* a square** (the total number of grains up to and including that square) **is 1 less than the number of grains of wheat *on the next* square.** For example, the number *below* square 7 is 1 less than the number *on* square 8 ($128 - 1 = 127$). From this observation, the number of grains of wheat on the first 8 squares is the number on square 8 (128) plus 1 less than the number on square 8 (127): The total number of grains of wheat on the first 8 squares is $128 + 127 = 255$.

From this observation,

$$\begin{array}{ll}\text{Number of grains of} \\ \text{wheat on the chessboard}\end{array} = \begin{array}{l}\text{number of grains} \\ \text{on square 64}\end{array} + \begin{array}{l}\text{1 less than the number} \\ \text{of grains on square 64}\end{array}$$

$$= 2^{64-1} + (2^{64-1} - 1)$$

$$= 2^{63} + 2^{63} - 1 \approx 18{,}000{,}000{,}000{,}000{,}000{,}000$$

To give you an idea of the magnitude of this number, this is more wheat than has been produced in the world since chess was invented.

The same king decided to have a banquet in the long banquet room of the palace to celebrate the invention of chess. The king had 50 square tables, and each table could seat only one person on each side. The king pushed the tables together to form one long banquet table. How many people could sit at this table? *Hint:* Try constructing a pattern by using 2 tables, 3 tables, and 4 tables.

Projects and Group Activities

The Golden Ratio

There are certain designs that have been repeated over and over in both art and architecture. One of these involves the **golden rectangle.**

A golden rectangle is drawn at the right. Begin with a square that measures, say, 2 inches on a side. Let *A* be the midpoint of a side (halfway between two corners). Now measure the distance from *A* to *B*. Place this length along the bottom of the square, starting at *A*. The resulting rectangle is a golden rectangle.

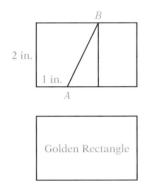

The **golden ratio** is the ratio of the length of the golden rectangle to its width. If you have drawn the rectangle following the procedure above, you will find that the golden ratio is approximately 1.6 to 1.

The golden ratio appears in many different situations. Some historians claim that some of the great pyramids of Egypt are based on the golden ratio. The drawing at the right shows the Pyramid of Giza, which dates from approximately 2600 B.C. The ratio of the height to a side of the base is approximately 1.6 to 1.

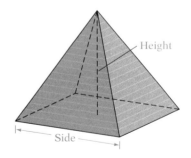

1. There are instances of the golden rectangle in the Mona Lisa painted by Leonardo da Vinci. Do some research on this painting and write a few paragraphs summarizing your findings.
2. What do 3 × 5 and 5 × 8 index cards have to do with the golden rectangle?
3. What does the United Nations Building in New York City have to do with the golden rectangle?
4. When was the Parthenon in Athens, Greece, built? What does the front of that building have to do with the golden rectangle?

Drawing the Floor Plans for a Building

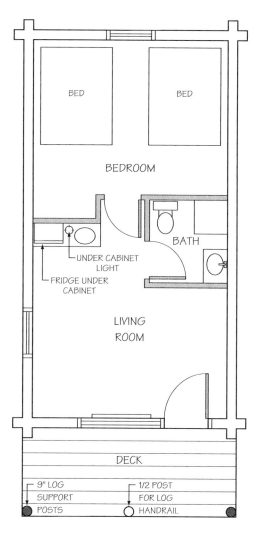

The drawing at the left is a sketch of the floor plan for a cabin at a resort in the mountains of Utah. The measurements are missing. Assume that you are the architect and will finish the drawing. You will have to decide the size of the rooms and put in the measurements to scale.

Design a cabin that you would like to own. Select a scale and draw all the rooms to scale.

If you are interested in architecture, visit an architect who is using CAD (computer-aided design) to create a floor plan. Computer technology has revolutionized the field of architectural design.

The U.S. House of Representatives

The framers of the Constitution decided to use a ratio to determine the number of representatives from each state. It was determined that each state would have one representative for every 30,000 citizens, with a minimum of one representative. Congress has changed this ratio over the years, and we now have 435 representatives.

Find the number of representatives from your state. Determine the ratio of citizens to representatives. Also do this for the most populous state and for the least populous state.

You might consider getting information on the number of representatives for each state and the populations of different states via the Internet.

Chapter 4 Summary

Key Words	**Examples**
A *ratio* is the comparison of two quantities with the same units. A ratio can be written in three ways: as a fraction, as two numbers separated by a colon (:), or as two numbers separated by the word *to*. A ratio is in *simplest form* when the two numbers do not have a common factor. [4.1A, p. 175]	The comparison 16 to 24 ounces can be written as a ratio in simplest form as $\frac{2}{3}$, 2:3, or 2 to 3.
A *rate* is the comparison of two quantities with different units. A rate is written as a fraction. A rate is in *simplest form* when the numbers that form the ratio do not have a common factor. [4.2A, p. 179]	You earned \$63 for working 6 hours. The rate is written in simplest form as $\frac{\$21}{2 \text{ hours}}$.
A *unit rate* is a rate in which the number in the denominator is 1. [4.2B, p. 179]	You traveled 144 miles in 3 hours. The unit rate is 48 miles per hour.
A *proportion* is an expression of the equality of two ratios or rates. A proportion is true if the fractions are equal when written in lowest terms; in any true proportion, the *cross products* are equal. A proportion is not true if the fractions are not equal when written in lowest terms; if the cross products are not equal, the proportion is not true. [4.3A, p. 183]	The proportion $\frac{3}{5} = \frac{12}{20}$ is true because the cross products are equal: $3 \times 20 = 5 \times 12$. The proportion $\frac{3}{4} = \frac{12}{20}$ is not true because the cross products are not equal: $3 \times 20 \neq 4 \times 12$.

Essential Rules and Procedures	**Examples**
To find a unit rate, divide the number in the numerator of the rate by the number in the denominator of the rate. [4.2B, p. 179]	You earned \$41 for working 4 hours. $$41 \div 4 = 10.25$$ The unit rate is \$10.25/hour.
To solve a proportion, find a number to replace the unknown so that the proportion is true. [4.3B, p. 184]	$\frac{6}{24} = \frac{9}{n}$ $6 \times n = 24 \times 9$ • Find the cross products. $6 \times n = 216$ $n = 216 \div 6$ $n = 36$
To set up a proportion, keep the same units in the numerator and the same units in the denominator. [4.3C, p. 185]	Three machines fill 5 cereal boxes per minute. How many boxes can 8 machines fill per minute? $$\frac{3 \text{ machines}}{5 \text{ cereal boxes}} = \frac{8 \text{ machines}}{n \text{ cereal boxes}}$$

Chapter 4 Review Exercises

1. Determine whether the proportion is true or not true.
$$\frac{2}{9} = \frac{10}{45}$$

2. Write the comparison 32 dollars to 80 dollars as a ratio in simplest form using a fraction, a colon (:), and the word *to*.

3. Write "250 miles in 4 hours" as a unit rate.

4. Determine whether the proportion is true or not true.
$$\frac{8}{15} = \frac{32}{60}$$

5. Solve the proportion.
$$\frac{16}{n} = \frac{4}{17}$$

6. Write "$300 earned in 40 hours" as a unit rate.

7. Write "$8.75 for 5 pounds" as a unit rate.

8. Write the comparison 8 feet to 28 feet as a ratio in simplest form using a fraction, a colon (:), and the word *to*.

9. Solve the proportion.
$$\frac{n}{8} = \frac{9}{2}$$

10. Solve the proportion. Round to the nearest hundredth.
$$\frac{18}{35} = \frac{10}{n}$$

11. Write the comparison 6 inches to 15 inches as a ratio in simplest form using a fraction, a colon (:), and the word *to*.

12. Determine whether the proportion is true or not true.
$$\frac{3}{8} = \frac{10}{24}$$

13. Write "$15 in 4 hours" as a rate in simplest form.

14. Write "326.4 miles on 12 gallons" as a unit rate.

15. Write the comparison 12 days to 12 days as a ratio in simplest form using a fraction, a colon (:), and the word *to*.

16. Determine whether the proportion is true or not true.
$$\frac{5}{7} = \frac{25}{35}$$

17. Solve the proportion. Round to the nearest hundredth.

$$\frac{24}{11} = \frac{n}{30}$$

18. Write "100 miles in 3 hours" as a rate in simplest form.

19. **Business** In 5 years, the price of a calculator went from $40 to $24. What is the ratio, as a fraction in simplest form, of the decrease in price to the original price?

20. **Taxes** The property tax on a $245,000 home is $4900. At the same rate, what is the property tax on a home valued at $320,000?

21. **Meteorology** The high temperature during a 24-hour period was 84 degrees, and the low temperature was 42 degrees. Write the ratio, as a fraction in simplest form, of the high temperature to the low temperature for the 24-hour period.

22. **Manufacturing** The total cost of manufacturing 1000 cordless phones was $36,600. Of the phones made, 24 did not pass inspection. What is the cost per phone of the phones that *did* pass inspection?

23. **Masonry** A brick wall 40 feet in length contains 448 concrete blocks. At the same rate, how many blocks would it take to build a wall that is 120 feet in length?

24. **Advertising** A retail computer store spends $30,000 a year on radio advertising and $12,000 on newspaper advertising. Find the ratio, as a fraction in simplest form, of radio advertising to newspaper advertising.

25. **Consumerism** A 15-pound turkey costs $13.95. What is the cost per pound?

26. **Travel** Mahesh drove 198.8 miles in 3.5 hours. Find the average number of miles he drove per hour.

27. **Insurance** An insurance policy costs $9.87 for every $1000 of insurance. At this rate, what is the cost of $50,000 of insurance?

28. **Investments** Pascal Hollis purchased 80 shares of stock for $3580. What was the cost per share?

29. **Landscaping** Monique uses 1.5 pounds of fertilizer for every 200 square feet of lawn. How many pounds of fertilizer will she have to use on a lawn that measures 3000 square feet?

30. **Real Estate** A house had an original value of $80,000, but its value increased to $120,000 in 2 years. Find the ratio, as a fraction in simplest form, of the increase to the original value.

Chapter 4 Test

1. Write "$46,036.80 earned in 12 months" as a unit rate.

2. Write the comparison 40 miles to 240 miles as a ratio in simplest form using a fraction, a colon (:), and the word *to*.

3. Write "18 supports for every 8 feet" as a rate in simplest form.

4. Determine whether the proportion is true or not true.
$$\frac{40}{125} = \frac{5}{25}$$

5. Write the comparison 12 days to 8 days as a ratio in simplest form using a fraction, a colon (:), and the word *to*.

6. Solve the proportion.
$$\frac{5}{12} = \frac{60}{n}$$

7. Write "256.2 miles on 8.4 gallons of gas" as a unit rate.

8. Write the comparison 27 dollars to 81 dollars as a ratio in simplest form using a fraction, a colon (:), and the word *to*.

9. Determine whether the proportion is true or not true.
$$\frac{5}{14} = \frac{25}{70}$$

10. Solve the proportion.
$$\frac{n}{18} = \frac{9}{4}$$

11. Write "$81 for 12 boards" as a rate in simplest form.

12. Write the comparison 18 feet to 30 feet as a ratio in simplest form using a fraction, a colon (:), and the word *to*.

13. **Investments**   Fifty shares of a utility stock pay a dividend of $62.50. At the same rate, what is the dividend paid on 500 shares of the utility stock?

14. **Meteorology**   The average summer temperature in a California desert is 112 degrees. In a city 100 miles away, the average summer temperature is 86 degrees. Write the ratio, as a fraction in simplest form, of the average city temperature to the average desert temperature.

15. **Travel**   A plane travels 2421 miles in 4.5 hours. Find the plane's speed in miles per hour.

16. **Physiology**   A research scientist estimates that the human body contains 88 pounds of water for every 100 pounds of body weight. At this rate, estimate the number of pounds of water in a college student who weighs 150 pounds.

17. **Business**   If 40 feet of lumber costs $69.20, what is the per-foot cost of the lumber?

18. **Medicine**   The dosage of a certain medication is $\frac{1}{4}$ ounce for every 50 pounds of body weight. How many ounces of this medication are required for a person who weighs 175 pounds? Write the answer as a decimal.

19. **Sports**   A basketball team won 20 games and lost 5 games during the season. Write, as a fraction in simplest form, the ratio of the number of games won to the total number of games played.

20. **Manufacturing**   A computer manufacturer discovers through experience that an average of 3 defective hard drives are found in every 100 hard drives manufactured. How many defective hard drives are expected to be found in the production of 1200 hard drives?

Cumulative Review Exercises

1. Subtract: 20,095
                   − 10,937

2. Write $2 \cdot 2 \cdot 2 \cdot 2 \cdot 3 \cdot 3 \cdot 3$ in exponential notation.

3. Simplify: $4 - (5 - 2)^2 \div 3 + 2$

4. Find the prime factorization of 160.

5. Find the LCM of 9, 12, and 18.

6. Find the GCF of 28 and 42.

7. Write $\frac{40}{64}$ in simplest form.

8. Find $4\frac{7}{15}$ more than $3\frac{5}{6}$.

9. What is $4\frac{5}{9}$ less than $10\frac{1}{6}$?

10. Multiply: $\frac{11}{12} \times 3\frac{1}{11}$

11. Find the quotient of $3\frac{1}{3}$ and $\frac{5}{7}$.

12. Simplify: $\left(\frac{2}{5} + \frac{3}{4}\right) \div \frac{3}{2}$

13. Write 4.0709 in words.

14. Round 2.09762 to the nearest hundredth.

15. Divide: $8.09)\overline{16.0976}$
Round to the nearest thousandth.

16. Convert $0.06\frac{2}{3}$ to a fraction.

17. Write the comparison 25 miles to 200 miles as a ratio in simplest form using a fraction.

18. Write "87 cents for 6 pencils" as a rate in simplest form.

19. Write "250.5 miles on 7.5 gallons of gas" as a unit rate.

20. Solve $\dfrac{40}{n} = \dfrac{160}{17}$.

21. Travel   A car traveled 457.6 miles in 8 hours. Find the car's speed in miles per hour.

22. Solve the proportion.
$$\dfrac{12}{5} = \dfrac{n}{15}$$

23. Banking   You had $1024 in your checking account. You then wrote checks for $192 and $88. What is your new checking account balance?

24. Finance   Malek Khatri buys a tractor for $32,360. A down payment of $5000 is required. The balance remaining is paid in 48 equal monthly installments. What is the monthly payment?

25. Homework Assignments   Yuko is assigned to read a book containing 175 pages. She reads $\frac{2}{5}$ of the book during Thanksgiving vacation. How many pages of the assignment remain to be read?

26. Real Estate   A building contractor bought $2\frac{1}{3}$ acres of land for $84,000. What was the cost of each acre?

27. Consumerism   Benjamin Eli bought a shirt for $22.79 and a tie for $9.59. He used a $50 bill to pay for the purchases. Find the amount of change.

28. Compensation   If you earn an annual salary of $41,619, what is your monthly salary?

29. Erosion   A soil conservationist estimates that a river bank is eroding at the rate of 3 inches every 6 months. At this rate, how many inches will be eroded in 50 months?

30. Medicine   The dosage of a certain medication is $\frac{1}{2}$ ounce for every 50 pounds of body weight. How many ounces of this medication are required for a person who weighs 160 pounds? Write the answer as a decimal.

5 Percents

Everyone knows that good health depends on eating right, watching your weight, not smoking, and exercising regularly. In order to get the most out of your workout, the American College of Sports Medicine (ACSM) recommends that you know how to determine your target heart rate. Your target heart rate is the rate at which your heart should beat during any aerobic exercise, such as running, fast walking, or bicycling. Your target heart rate depends on how fit you are, so athletes have higher target heart rates than people who are more sedentary. According to the ACSM, you should reach and then maintain your target heart rate for 20 minutes or more during a workout to achieve cardiovascular fitness. The **Projects and Group Activities on page 224** explain how you can calculate your target heart rate.

OBJECTIVES

Section 5.1
A To write a percent as a fraction or a decimal
B To write a fraction or a decimal as a percent

Section 5.2
A To find the amount when the percent and the base are given
B To solve application problems

Section 5.3
A To find the percent when the base and amount are given
B To solve application problems

Section 5.4
A To find the base when the percent and amount are given
B To solve application problems

Section 5.5
A To solve percent problems using proportions
B To solve application problems

Need help? For online student resources, such as section quizzes, visit this textbook's website at **math.college.hmco.com/students.**

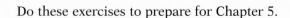

Do these exercises to prepare for Chapter 5.

For Exercises 1 to 6, multiply or divide.

1. $19 \times \dfrac{1}{100}$

2. 23×0.01

3. 0.47×100

4. $0.06 \times 47,500$

5. $60 \div 0.015$

6. $8 \div \dfrac{1}{4}$

7. Multiply $\dfrac{5}{8} \times 100$. Write the answer as a decimal.

8. Write $\dfrac{200}{3}$ as a mixed number.

9. Divide $28 \div 16$. Write the answer as a decimal.

GO FIGURE • • •

A whole number that remains unchanged when its digits are written in reverse order is a palindrome. For example, 818 is a palindrome.

a. Find the smallest three-digit multiple of 6 that is a palindrome.

b. Many nonpalindrome numbers can be converted into palindromes: reverse the digits of the number and add the result to the original; continue until a palindrome is achieved. Using this process, what is the palindrome created from 874?

5.1 Introduction to Percents

Objective A   **To write a percent as a fraction or a decimal**

Percent means "parts of 100." In the figure at the right, there are 100 parts. Because 13 of the 100 parts are shaded, 13% of the figure is shaded. The symbol % is the **percent sign**.

In most applied problems involving percents, it is necessary either to rewrite a percent as a fraction or a decimal or to rewrite a fraction or a decimal as a percent.

To write a percent as a fraction, remove the percent sign and multiply by $\frac{1}{100}$.

$$13\% = 13 \times \frac{1}{100} = \frac{13}{100}$$

TAKE NOTE

Recall that division is defined as multiplication by the reciprocal. Therefore, multiplying by $\frac{1}{100}$ is equivalent to dividing by 100.

To write a percent as a decimal, remove the percent sign and multiply by 0.01.

$$13\% \quad = \quad 13 \times 0.01 \quad = \quad 0.13$$

Move the decimal point two places to the left. Then remove the percent sign.

Example 1   **a.** Write 120% as a fraction.
b. Write 120% as a decimal.

Solution   **a.** $120\% = 120 \times \frac{1}{100} = \frac{120}{100}$

$$= 1\frac{1}{5}$$

b. $120\% = 120 \times 0.01 = 1.2$

Note that percents larger than 100 are greater than 1.

You Try It 1   **a.** Write 125% as a fraction.
b. Write 125% as a decimal.

Your solution

Example 2   Write $16\frac{2}{3}\%$ as a fraction.

Solution $16\frac{2}{3}\% = 16\frac{2}{3} \times \frac{1}{100}$

$$= \frac{50}{3} \times \frac{1}{100} = \frac{50}{300} = \frac{1}{6}$$

You Try It 2   Write $33\frac{1}{3}\%$ as a fraction.

Your solution

Example 3   Write 0.5% as a decimal.

Solution $0.5\% = 0.5 \times 0.01 = 0.005$

You Try It 3   Write 0.25% as a decimal.

Your solution

Solutions on pp. S12–S13

Objective B   **To write a fraction or a decimal as a percent**

A fraction or a decimal can be written as a percent by multiplying by 100%.

> **HOW TO**   Write $\frac{3}{8}$ as a percent.
>
> $$\frac{3}{8} = \frac{3}{8} \times 100\% = \frac{3}{8} \times \frac{100}{1}\% = \frac{300}{8}\% = 37\frac{1}{2}\% \text{ or } 37.5\%$$
>
> **HOW TO**   Write 0.37 as a percent.
>
> $$0.37 \quad = \quad 0.37 \times 100\% \quad = \quad 37\%$$
>
> Move the decimal point two places to the right. Then write the percent sign.

Example 4   Write 0.015 as a percent.

Solution $0.015 = 0.015 \times 100\%$
$\qquad\quad = 1.5\%$

You Try It 4   Write 0.048 as a percent.

Your solution

Example 5   Write 2.15 as a percent.

Solution $2.15 = 2.15 \times 100\% = 215\%$

You Try It 5   Write 3.67 as a percent.

Your solution

Example 6   Write $0.33\frac{1}{3}$ as a percent.

Solution $0.33\frac{1}{3} = 0.33\frac{1}{3} \times 100\%$

$\qquad\quad = 33\frac{1}{3}\%$

You Try It 6   Write $0.62\frac{1}{2}$ as a percent.

Your solution

Example 7   Write $\frac{2}{3}$ as a percent.
Write the remainder in fractional form.

Solution $\frac{2}{3} = \frac{2}{3} \times 100\% = \frac{200}{3}\%$

$\qquad\quad = 66\frac{2}{3}\%$

You Try It 7   Write $\frac{5}{6}$ as a percent.
Write the remainder in fractional form.

Your solution

Example 8   Write $2\frac{2}{7}$ as a percent.
Round to the nearest tenth.

Solution $2\frac{2}{7} = \frac{16}{7} = \frac{16}{7} \times 100\%$

$\qquad\quad = \frac{1600}{7}\% \approx 228.6\%$

You Try It 8   Write $1\frac{4}{9}$ as a percent.
Round to the nearest tenth.

Your solution

Solutions on p. S13

5.1 Exercises

Objective A   **To write a percent as a fraction or a decimal**

For Exercises 1 to 16, write as a fraction and as a decimal.

1. 25%

2. 40%

3. 130%

4. 150%

5. 100%

6. 87%

7. 73%

8. 45%

9. 383%

10. 425%

11. 70%

12. 55%

13. 88%

14. 64%

15. 32%

16. 18%

For Exercises 17 to 28, write as a fraction.

17. $66\frac{2}{3}\%$

18. $12\frac{1}{2}\%$

19. $83\frac{1}{3}\%$

20. $3\frac{1}{8}\%$

21. $11\frac{1}{9}\%$

22. $\frac{3}{8}\%$

23. $45\frac{5}{11}\%$

24. $15\frac{3}{8}\%$

25. $4\frac{2}{7}\%$

26. $5\frac{3}{4}\%$

27. $6\frac{2}{3}\%$

28. $8\frac{2}{3}\%$

For Exercises 29 to 43, write as a decimal.

29. 6.5%

30. 9.4%

31. 12.3%

32. 16.7%

33. 0.55%

34. 0.45%

35. 8.25%

36. 6.75%

37. 5.05%

38. 3.08%

39. 2%

40. 7%

41. 80.4%

42. 36.2%

43. 4.9%

Objective B   **To write a fraction or a decimal as a percent**

For Exercises 44 to 55, write as a percent.

44. 0.16

45. 0.73

46. 0.05

47. 0.01

48. 1.07

49. 2.94

50. 0.004

51. 0.006

52. 1.012

53. 3.106

54. 0.8

55. 0.7

For Exercises 56 to 67, write as a percent. Round to the nearest tenth of a percent.

56. $\dfrac{27}{50}$ **57.** $\dfrac{37}{100}$ **58.** $\dfrac{1}{3}$ **59.** $\dfrac{2}{5}$

60. $\dfrac{5}{8}$ **61.** $\dfrac{1}{8}$ **62.** $\dfrac{1}{6}$ **63.** $1\dfrac{1}{2}$

64. $\dfrac{7}{40}$ **65.** $1\dfrac{2}{3}$ **66.** $1\dfrac{7}{9}$ **67.** $\dfrac{7}{8}$

For Exercises 68 to 75, write as a percent. Write the remainder in fractional form.

68. $\dfrac{15}{50}$ **69.** $\dfrac{12}{25}$ **70.** $\dfrac{7}{30}$ **71.** $\dfrac{1}{3}$

72. $2\dfrac{3}{8}$ **73.** $1\dfrac{2}{3}$ **74.** $2\dfrac{1}{6}$ **75.** $\dfrac{7}{8}$

76. Write the part of the square that is shaded as a fraction, as a decimal, and as a percent. Write the part of the square that is not shaded as a fraction, as a decimal, and as a percent.

APPLYING THE CONCEPTS

77.  **The Food Industry**   In a survey conducted by Opinion Research Corp. for Lloyd's Barbeque Co., people were asked to name their favorite barbeque side dishes. 38% named corn on the cob, 35% named cole slaw, 11% named corn bread, and 10% named fries. What percent of those surveyed named something other than corn on the cob, cole slaw, corn bread, or fries?

78. Consumerism   A sale on computers advertised $\dfrac{1}{3}$ off the regular price. What percent of the regular price does this represent?

79. Consumerism   A suit was priced at 50% off the regular price. What fraction of the regular price does this represent?

80. Elections   If $\dfrac{2}{5}$ of the population voted in an election, what percent of the population did not vote?

81. a. Is the statement "Multiplying a number by a percent always decreases the number" true or false?

b. If it is false, given an example to show that the statement is false.

5.2 Percent Equations: Part I

Objective A ▶ **To find the amount when the percent and the base are given**

A real estate broker receives a payment that is 4% of a $285,000 sale. To find the amount the broker receives requires answering the question "4% of $285,000 is what?"

This sentence can be written using mathematical symbols and then solved for the unknown number.

4%	of	$285,000	is	what?
↓	↓	↓	↓	↓

$$\boxed{\begin{array}{c}\text{Percent}\\4\%\end{array}} \times \boxed{\begin{array}{c}\text{base}\\285{,}000\end{array}} = \boxed{\begin{array}{c}\text{amount}\\n\end{array}}$$

of   is written as × (times)
is   is written as = (equals)
what is written as n (the unknown number)

$$0.04 \times 285{,}000 = n$$
$$11{,}400 = n$$

Note that the percent is written as a decimal.

The broker receives a payment of $11,400.

The solution was found by solving the **basic percent equation** for amount.

> **The Basic Percent Equation**
>
> $$\boxed{\text{Percent}} \times \boxed{\text{base}} = \boxed{\text{amount}}$$

In most cases, the percent is written as a decimal before the basic percent equation is solved. However, some percents are more easily written as a fraction than as a decimal. For example,

$$33\frac{1}{3}\% = \frac{1}{3} \qquad 66\frac{2}{3}\% = \frac{2}{3} \qquad 16\frac{2}{3}\% = \frac{1}{6} \qquad 83\frac{1}{3}\% = \frac{5}{6}$$

Example 1 Find 5.7% of 160.

Solution

Percent × base = amount   • The word *Find* is
$\quad 0.057 \times 160 = n$ used instead of the
$\qquad\qquad 9.12 = n$ words *what is*.

Example 2 What is $33\frac{1}{3}\%$ of 90?

Solution   Percent × base = amount
$$\frac{1}{3} \times 90 = n \qquad \bullet\ 33\frac{1}{3}\% = \frac{1}{3}$$
$$30 = n$$

You Try It 1 Find 6.3% of 150.

Your solution

You Try It 2 What is $16\frac{2}{3}\%$ of 66?

Your solution

Solutions on p. S13

Objective B **To solve application problems**

Solving percent problems requires identifying the three elements of the basic percent equation. Recall that these three parts are the *percent,* the *base,* and the *amount.* Usually the base follows the phrase "percent of."

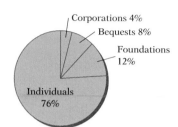

Charitable Giving
Sources: American Association of Fundraising Counsel; AP

 During a recent year, Americans gave $212 billion to charities. The circle graph at the right shows where that money came from. Use these data for Example 3 and You Try It 3.

Example 3

How much of the amount given to charities came from individuals?

Strategy
To determine the amount that came from individuals, write and solve the basic percent equation using n to represent the amount. The percent is 76%. The base is $212 billion.

Solution   Percent × base = amount
$$76\% \times 212 = n$$
$$0.76 \times 212 = n$$
$$161.12 = n$$

Individuals gave $161.12 billion to charities.

You Try It 3

How much of the amount given to charities was given by corporations?

Your strategy

Your solution

Example 4

A quality control inspector found that 1.2% of 2500 telephones inspected were defective. How many telephones inspected were not defective?

Strategy
To find the number of nondefective phones:

• Find the number of defective phones. Write and solve the basic percent equation using n to represent the number of defective phones (amount). The percent is 1.2% and the base is 2500.
• Subtract the number of defective phones from the number of phones inspected (2500).

Solution $1.2\% \times 2500 = n$
$$0.012 \times 2500 = n$$
$$30 = n \text{ defective phones}$$

$$2500 - 30 = 2470$$

2470 telephones were not defective.

You Try It 4

An electrician's hourly wage was $33.50 before an 8% raise. What is the new hourly wage?

Your strategy

Your solution

Solutions on p. S13

5.2 Exercises

Objective A   To find the amount when the percent and the base are given

1. 8% of 100 is what?

2. 16% of 50 is what?

3. 27% of 40 is what?

4. 52% of 95 is what?

5. 0.05% of 150 is what?

6. 0.075% of 625 is what?

7. 125% of 64 is what?

8. 210% of 12 is what?

9. Find 10.7% of 485.

10. Find 12.8% of 625.

11. What is 0.25% of 3000?

12. What is 0.06% of 250?

13. 80% of 16.25 is what?

14. 26% of 19.5 is what?

15. What is $1\frac{1}{2}$% of 250?

16. What is $5\frac{3}{4}$% of 65?

17. $16\frac{2}{3}$% of 120 is what?

18. $83\frac{1}{3}$% of 246 is what?

19. What is $33\frac{1}{3}$% of 630?

20. What is $66\frac{2}{3}$% of 891?

21. Which is larger: 5% of 95, or 75% of 6?

22. Which is larger: 112% of 5, or 0.45% of 800?

23. Which is smaller: 79% of 16, or 20% of 65?

24. Which is smaller: 15% of 80, or 95% of 15?

25. Which is smaller: 2% of 1500, or 72% of 40?

26. Which is larger: 22% of 120, or 84% of 32?

27. ▦ Find 31.294% of 82,460.

28. ▦ Find 123.94% of 275,976.

Objective B   To solve application problems

29. ◕ **Health Insurance**   Approximately 30% of the 44 million people in the United States who do not have health insurance are between the ages of 18 and 24. (*Source:* U.S. Census Bureau) About how many people in the United States aged 18 to 24 do not have health insurance?

30. ◕ **Aviation**   The Federal Aviation Administration reported that 55,422 new student pilots were flying single-engine planes last year. The number of new student pilots flying single-engine planes this year is 106% of the number flying single-engine planes last year. How many new student pilots are flying single-engine planes this year?

Politics The results of a survey in which 32,840 full-time college and university faculty members were asked to describe their political views is shown at the right. Use these data for Exercises 31 and 32.

Political View	Percent of Faculty Members Responding
Far Left	5.3%
Liberal	42.3%
Middle of the road	34.3%
Conservative	17.7%
Far right	0.3%

Source: Higher Education Research Institute, UCLA

31. How many more faculty members described their political views as liberal than described their views as far left?

32. How many fewer faculty members described their political views as conservative than described their views as middle of the road?

33. Taxes A sales tax of 6% of the cost of a car was added to the purchase price of $29,500.
a. How much was the sales tax?
b. What is the total cost of the car, including sales tax?

34. Business During the packaging process for oranges, spoiled oranges are discarded by an inspector. In one day an inspector found that 4.8% of the 20,000 pounds of oranges inspected were spoiled.
a. How many pounds of oranges were spoiled?
b. How many pounds of oranges were not spoiled?

35. Entertainment A USA TODAY.com online poll asked 8878 Internet users, "Would you use software to cut out objectionable parts of movies?" 29.8% of the respondents answered yes. How many respondents did not answer yes to the question? Round to the nearest whole number.

36. Employment Funtimes Amusement Park has 550 employees and must hire an additional 22% for the vacation season. What is the total number of employees needed for the vacation season?

APPLYING THE CONCEPTS

Sociology The two circle graphs at the right show how surveyed employees actually spend their time and the way they would prefer to spend their time. Assuming that employees have 112 hours a week of time that is not spent sleeping, answer Exercises 37 to 39. Round to the nearest tenth of an hour.

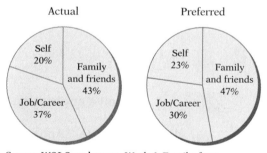

Actual

Self 20%
Family and friends 43%
Job/Career 37%

Preferred

Self 23%
Family and friends 47%
Job/Career 30%

Source: WSJ Supplement, Work & Family, from *Families and Work Institute*

37. What is the actual number of hours per week that employees spend with family and friends?

38. What is the number of hours per week that employees would prefer to spend on job/career?

39. What is the difference between the number of hours an employee preferred to spend on self and the actual amount of time the employee spent on self?

5.3 Percent Equations: Part II

Objective A   **To find the percent when the base and amount are given**

A recent promotional game at a grocery store listed the probability of winning a prize as "1 chance in 2." A percent can be used to describe the chance of winning. This requires answering the question "What percent of 2 is 1?"

The chance of winning can be found by solving the basic percent equation for *percent*.

Integrating Technology

The percent key % on a scientific calculator moves the decimal point to the left two places when pressed after a multiplication or division computation. For the example at the right, enter

1 ÷ 2 % =

The display reads 50.

What percent of   2   is   1?
↓   ↓   ↓   ↓   ↓

$$\boxed{\begin{matrix}\text{Percent}\\n\end{matrix}} \times \boxed{\begin{matrix}\text{base}\\2\end{matrix}} = \boxed{\begin{matrix}\text{amount}\\1\end{matrix}}$$

$$n \times 2 = 1$$
$$n = 1 \div 2$$
$$n = 0.5$$
$$n = 50\%$$

• The solution must be written as a percent to answer the question.

There is a 50% chance of winning a prize.

Example 1   What percent of 40 is 30?

Solution
$$\text{Percent} \times \text{base} = \text{amount}$$
$$n \times 40 = 30$$
$$n = 30 \div 40$$
$$n = 0.75$$
$$n = 75\%$$

You Try It 1   What percent of 32 is 16?

Your solution

Example 2   What percent of 12 is 27?

Solution
$$\text{Percent} \times \text{base} = \text{amount}$$
$$n \times 12 = 27$$
$$n = 27 \div 12$$
$$n = 2.25$$
$$n = 225\%$$

You Try It 2   What percent of 15 is 48?

Your solution

Example 3   25 is what percent of 75?

Solution
$$\text{Percent} \times \text{base} = \text{amount}$$
$$n \times 75 = 25$$
$$n = 25 \div 75$$
$$n = \frac{1}{3} = 33\frac{1}{3}\%$$

You Try It 3   30 is what percent of 45?

Your solution

Solutions on p. S13

Objective B   **To solve application problems**

To solve percent problems, remember that it is necessary to identify the percent, base, and amount. Usually the base follows the phrase "percent of."

Example 4

The monthly house payment for the Kaminski family is $787.50. What percent of the Kaminskis' monthly income of $3750 is the house payment?

Strategy

To find what percent of the income the house payment is, write and solve the basic percent equation using n to represent the percent. The base is $3750 and the amount is $787.50.

Solution

$n \times 3750 = 787.50$

$\qquad n = 787.50 \div 3750$

$\qquad n = 0.21 = 21\%$

The house payment is 21% of the monthly income.

You Try It 4

Tomo Nagata had an income of $33,500 and paid $5025 in income tax. What percent of the income is the income tax?

Your strategy

Your solution

Example 5

On one Monday night, 31.39 million of the approximately 40.76 million households watching television were not watching David Letterman. What percent of these households were watching David Letterman? Round to the nearest percent.

Strategy

To find the percent of households watching David Letterman:

- Subtract to find the number of households that were watching David Letterman (40.76 million − 31.39 million).
- Write and solve the basic percent equation using n to represent the percent. The base is 40.76, and the amount is the number of households watching David Letterman.

Solution

40.76 million − 31.39 million = 9.37 million

9.37 million households were watching David Letterman.

$n \times 40.76 = 9.37$

$\qquad n = 9.37 \div 40.76$

$\qquad n \approx 0.23$

Approximately 23% of the households were watching David Letterman.

You Try It 5

According to the U.S. Department of Defense, of the 518,921 enlisted personnel in the U.S. Army in 1950, 512,370 people were men. What percent of the enlisted personnel in the U.S. Army in 1950 were women? Round to the nearest tenth of a percent.

Your strategy

Your solution

Solutions on p. S13

5.3 Exercises

Objective A   **To find the percent when the base and amount are given**

1. What percent of 75 is 24?

2. What percent of 80 is 20?

3. 15 is what percent of 90?

4. 24 is what percent of 60?

5. What percent of 12 is 24?

6. What percent of 6 is 9?

7. What percent of 16 is 6?

8. What percent of 24 is 18?

9. 18 is what percent of 100?

10. 54 is what percent of 100?

11. 5 is what percent of 2000?

12. 8 is what percent of 2500?

13. What percent of 6 is 1.2?

14. What percent of 2.4 is 0.6?

15. 16.4 is what percent of 4.1?

16. 5.3 is what percent of 50?

17. 1 is what percent of 40?

18. 0.3 is what percent of 20?

19. What percent of 48 is 18?

20. What percent of 11 is 88?

21. What percent of 2800 is 7?

22. What percent of 400 is 12?

23. 4.2 is what percent of 175?

24. 41.79 is what percent of 99.5?

25. What percent of 86.5 is 8.304?

26. What percent of 1282.5 is 2.565?

Objective B   **To solve application problems**

27. **Sociology**   Seven in ten couples disagree about financial issues. (*Source:* Yankelovich Partners for Lutheran Brotherhood) What percent of couples disagree about financial matters?

28. **Sociology**   In a survey, 1236 adults nationwide were asked, "What irks you most about the actions of other motorists?" The response "tailgaters" was given by 293 people. (*Source:* Reuters/Zogby) What percent of those surveyed were most irked by tailgaters? Round to the nearest tenth of a percent.

29. Agriculture   According to the U.S. Department of Agriculture, of the 63 billion pounds of vegetables produced in the United States in 1 year, 16 billion pounds were wasted. What percent of the vegetables produced were wasted? Round to the nearest tenth of a percent.

30. Agriculture   In a recent year, Wisconsin growers produced 281.72 million pounds of the 572 million pounds of cranberries grown in the United States. What percent of the total cranberry crop was produced in Wisconsin? Round to the nearest percent.

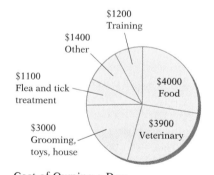

31. Energy   The typical American household spends $1355 a year on energy utilities. Of this amount, approximately $81.30 is spent on lighting. (*Source:* Department of Energy, Owens Corning) What percent of the total amount spent on energy utilities is spent on lighting?

32. Education   To receive a license to sell insurance, an insurance account executive must answer correctly 70% of the 250 questions on a test. Nicholas Mosley answered 177 questions correctly. Did he pass the test?

33. Agriculture   According to the U.S. Department of Agriculture, of the 356 billion pounds of food produced in the United States annually, 260 billion pounds are not wasted. What percent of the food produced in the United States is wasted? Round to the nearest percent.

34. Construction   In a test of the breaking strength of concrete slabs for freeway construction, 3 of the 200 slabs tested did not meet safety requirements. What percent of the slabs did meet safety requirements?

APPLYING THE CONCEPTS

Pets   The graph at the right shows several categories of average lifetime costs of dog ownership. Use this graph for Exercises 35 to 37. Round answers to the nearest tenth of a percent.

35. What percent of the total amount is spent on food?

36. What percent of the total is spent on veterinary care?

37. What percent of the total is spent on all categories except training?

38. Sports   The Fun in the Sun organization claims to have taken a survey of 350 people, asking them to give their favorite outdoor temperature for hiking. The results are given in the table at the right. Explain why these results are not possible.

$1200 Training
$1400 Other
$1100 Flea and tick treatment
$4000 Food
$3000 Grooming, toys, house
$3900 Veterinary

Cost of Owning a Dog

Source: Based on data from the American Kennel Club, *USA Today* research

Favorite Temperature	Percent
Greater than 90	5%
80–89	28%
70–79	35%
60–69	32%
Below 60	13%

5.4 Percent Equations: Part III

Objective A   To find the base when the percent and amount are given

In 1780, the population of Virginia was 538,000. This was 19% of the total population of the United States at that time. To find the total population at that time, you must answer the question "19% of what number is 538,000?"

19%	of	what	is	538,000?
↓		↓		↓
Percent 19%		base *n*		amount 538,000

$$0.19 \times n = 538,000$$
$$n = 538,000 \div 0.19$$
$$n \approx 2,832,000$$

- The population of the United States in 1780 can be found by solving the basic percent equation for the base.

The population of the United States in 1780 was approximately 2,832,000.

Example 1   18% of what is 900?

Solution   Percent × base = amount
$$0.18 \times n = 900$$
$$n = 900 \div 0.18$$
$$n = 5000$$

You Try It 1   86% of what is 215?

Your solution

Example 2   30 is 1.5% of what?

Solution   Percent × base = amount
$$0.015 \times n = 30$$
$$n = 30 \div 0.015$$
$$n = 2000$$

You Try It 2   15 is 2.5% of what?

Your solution

Example 3 $33\frac{1}{3}$% of what is 7?

Solution   Percent × base = amount
$$\frac{1}{3} \times n = 7$$
$$n = 7 \div \frac{1}{3}$$
$$n = 21$$

- Note that the percent is written as a fraction.

You Try It 3 $16\frac{2}{3}$% of what is 5?

Your solution

Solutions on p. S14

Objective B   To solve application problems

To solve percent problems, it is necessary to identify the percent, base, and amount. Usually the base follows the phrase "percent of."

Example 4

A business office bought a used copy machine for $900, which was 75% of the original cost. What was the original cost of the copier?

Strategy

To find the original cost of the copier, write and solve the basic percent equation using n to represent the original cost (base). The percent is 75% and the amount is $900.

Solution

$75\% \times n = 900$
$0.75 \times n = 900$
$n = 900 \div 0.75$
$n = 1200$

The original cost of the copier was $1200.

You Try It 4

A used car has a value of $10,458, which is 42% of the car's original value. What was the car's original value?

Your strategy

Your solution

Example 5

A carpenter's wage this year is $26.40 per hour, which is 110% of last year's wage. What was the increase in the hourly wage over last year?

Strategy

To find the increase in the hourly wage over last year:

• Find last year's wage. Write and solve the basic percent equation using n to represent last year's wage (base). The percent is 110% and the amount is $26.40.
• Subtract last year's wage from this year's wage (26.40).

Solution

$110\% \times n = 26.40$
$1.10 \times n = 26.40$
$n = 26.40 \div 1.10$
$n = 24.00$ • **Last year's wage**

$26.40 - 24.00 = 2.40$

The increase in the hourly wage was $2.40.

You Try It 5

Chang's Sporting Goods has a tennis racket on sale for $89.60, which is 80% of the original price. What is the difference between the original price and the sale price?

Your strategy

Your solution

Solutions on p. S14

5.4 Exercises

Objective A   **To find the base when the percent and amount are given**

For Exercises 1 to 26, solve. Round to the nearest hundredth.

1. 12% of what is 9?

2. 38% of what is 171?

3. 8 is 16% of what?

4. 54 is 90% of what?

5. 10 is 10% of what?

6. 37 is 37% of what?

7. 30% of what is 25.5?

8. 25% of what is 21.5?

9. 2.5% of what is 30?

10. 10.4% of what is 52?

11. 125% of what is 24?

12. 180% of what is 21.6?

13. 18 is 240% of what?

14. 24 is 320% of what?

15. 4.8 is 15% of what?

16. 87.5 is 50% of what?

17. 25.6 is 12.8% of what?

18. 45.014 is 63.4% of what?

19. 0.7% of what is 0.56?

20. 0.25% of what is 1?

21. 30% of what is 2.7?

22. 78% of what is 3.9?

23. 84 is $16\frac{2}{3}$% of what?

24. 120 is $33\frac{1}{3}$% of what?

25. $66\frac{2}{3}$% of what is 72?

26. $83\frac{1}{3}$% of what is 13.5?

Objective B   **To solve application problems**

27. 🔵 **Travel** Of the travelers who, during a recent year, allowed their children to miss school to go along on a trip, approximately 1.738 million allowed their children to miss school for more than a week. This represented 11% of the travelers who allowed their children to miss school. (*Source:* Travel Industry Association) About how many travelers allowed their children to miss school to go along on a trip?

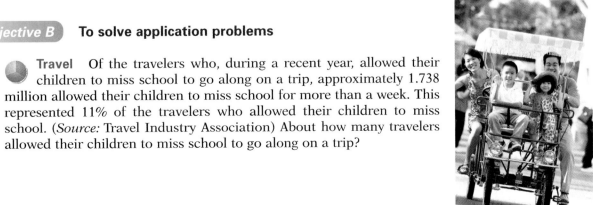

28. Education In the United States today, 23.1% of the women and 27.5% of the men have earned a bachelor's or graduate degree. (*Source:* Census Bureau) How many women in the United States have earned a bachelor's or graduate degree?

29. Taxes A TurboTax online survey asked people how they planned to use their tax refunds. 740 people, or 22% of the respondents, said they would save the money. How many people responded to the survey?

30. Taxes The Internal Revenue Service says that the average deduction for medical expenses for taxpayers in the $40,000–$50,000 bracket is $4500. This is 26% of the medical expenses claimed by taxpayers in the over-$200,000 bracket. How much is the average deduction for medical expenses claimed by taxpayers in the over-$200,000 bracket? Round to the nearest thousand.

31. Manufacturing During a quality control test, Micronics found that 24 computer boards were defective. This amount was 0.8% of the computer boards tested.
a. How many computer boards were tested?
b. How many computer boards tested were not defective?

32. Directory Assistance Of the calls a directory assistance operator received, 441 were requests for telephone numbers listed in the current directory. This accounted for 98% of the calls for assistance that the operator received.
a. How many calls did the operator receive?
b. How many telephone numbers requested were not listed in the current directory?

APPLYING THE CONCEPTS

33. Demography At the last census, of the 281,422,000 people in the United States, 28.6% were under the age of 20. (*Source:* U.S. Census 2000) How many people in the United States were age 20 or older in 2000?

Nutrition The table at the right contains nutrition information about a breakfast cereal. Solve Exercises 34 and 35 using information from this table.

34. The amount of thiamin in one serving of cereal with skim milk is 0.45 milligram. Find the recommended daily allowance of thiamin for an adult.

35. The amount of copper in one serving of cereal with skim milk is 0.08 milligram. Find the recommended daily allowance of copper for an adult.

36. Increase a number by 10%. Now decrease the number by 10%. Is the result the original number? Explain.

NUTRITION INFORMATION

SERVING SIZE: 1.4 OZ WHEAT FLAKES WITH 0.4 OZ. RAISINS: 39.4 g. ABOUT 1/2 CUP
SERVINGS PER PACKAGE: 14

	CEREAL & RAISINS	WITH 1/2 CUP VITAMINS A & D SKIM MILK

PERCENTAGE OF U.S. RECOMMENDED DAILY ALLOWANCES (U.S. RDA)

PROTEIN	4	15
VITAMIN A	15	20
VITAMIN C	**	2
THIAMIN	25	30
RIBOFLAVIN	25	35
NIACIN	25	35
CALCIUM	**	15
IRON	100	100
VITAMIN D	10	25
VITAMIN B₆	25	25
FOLIC ACID..............	25	25
VITAMIN B₁₂	25	30
PHOSPHOROUS.........	10	15
MAGNESIUM	10	20
ZINC	25	30
COPPER.................	2	4

* 2% MILK SUPPLIES AN ADDITIONAL 20 CALORIES.
2 g FAT, AND 10 mg CHOLESTEROL.
** CONTAINS LESS THAN 2% OF THE U.S. RDA OF THIS NUTRIENT

5.5 Percent Problems: Proportion Method

Objective A **To solve percent problems using proportions**

Problems that can be solved using the basic percent equation can also be solved using proportions.

The proportion method is based on writing two ratios. One ratio is the percent ratio, written as $\frac{\text{percent}}{100}$. The second ratio is the amount-to-base ratio, written as $\frac{\text{amount}}{\text{base}}$. These two ratios form the proportion

$$\frac{\text{percent}}{100} = \frac{\text{amount}}{\text{base}}$$

To use the proportion method, first identify the percent, the amount, and the base (the base usually follows the phrase "percent of").

Integrating Technology

To use a calculator to solve the proportions at the right for n, enter

23 × 45 ÷ 100 =

100 × 4 ÷ 25 =

100 × 12 ÷ 60 =

What is 23% of 45?

$$\frac{23}{100} = \frac{n}{45}$$
$$23 \times 45 = 100 \times n$$
$$1035 = 100 \times n$$
$$1035 \div 100 = n$$
$$10.35 = n$$

What percent of 25 is 4?

$$\frac{n}{100} = \frac{4}{25}$$
$$n \times 25 = 100 \times 4$$
$$n \times 25 = 400$$
$$n = 400 \div 25$$
$$n = 16$$

16% of 25 is 4.

12 is 60% of what number?

$$\frac{60}{100} = \frac{12}{n}$$
$$60 \times n = 100 \times 12$$
$$60 \times n = 1200$$
$$n = 1200 \div 60$$
$$n = 20$$

Example 1 15% of what is 7? Round to the nearest hundredth.

Solution
$$\frac{15}{100} = \frac{7}{n}$$
$$15 \times n = 100 \times 7$$
$$15 \times n = 700$$
$$n = 700 \div 15$$
$$n \approx 46.67$$

You Try It 1 26% of what is 22? Round to the nearest hundredth.

Your solution

Example 2 30% of 63 is what?

Solution
$$\frac{30}{100} = \frac{n}{63}$$
$$30 \times 63 = 100 \times n$$
$$1890 = 100 \times n$$
$$1890 \div 100 = n$$
$$18.90 = n$$

You Try It 2 16% of 132 is what?

Your solution

Solutions on p. S14

Objective B To solve application problems

Example 3

An antiques dealer found that 86% of the 250 items that were sold during one month sold for under $1000. How many items sold for under $1000?

Strategy

To find the number of items that sold for under $1000, write and solve a proportion using *n* to represent the number of items sold (amount) for less than $1000. The percent is 86% and the base is 250.

Solution

$$\frac{86}{100} = \frac{n}{250}$$

$$86 \times 250 = 100 \times n$$

$$21{,}500 = 100 \times n$$

$$21{,}500 \div 100 = n$$

$$215 = n$$

215 items sold for under $1000.

You Try It 3

Last year it snowed 64% of the 150 days of the ski season at a resort. How many days did it snow?

Your strategy

Your solution

Example 4

In a test of the strength of nylon rope, 5 pieces of the 25 pieces tested did not meet the test standards. What percent of the nylon ropes tested did meet the standards?

Strategy

To find the percent of ropes tested that met the standards:

• Find the number of ropes that met the test standards (25 − 5).
• Write and solve a proportion using *n* to represent the percent of ropes that met the test standards. The base is 25 and the amount is the number of ropes that met the standards.

Solution

25 − 5 = 20 ropes met test standards

$$\frac{n}{100} = \frac{20}{25}$$

$$n \times 25 = 100 \times 20$$

$$n \times 25 = 2000$$

$$n = 2000 \div 25$$

$$n = 80$$

80% of the ropes tested did meet the test standards.

You Try It 4

Five ballpoint pens in a box of 200 were found to be defective. What percent of the pens were not defective?

Your strategy

Your solution

Solutions on p. S14

5.5 Exercises

Objective A   **To solve percent problems using proportions**

1. 26% of 250 is what?

2. What is 18% of 150?

3. 37 is what percent of 148?

4. What percent of 150 is 33?

5. 68% of what is 51?

6. 126 is 84% of what?

7. What percent of 344 is 43?

8. 750 is what percent of 50?

9. 82 is 20.5% of what?

10. 2.4% of what is 21?

11. What is 6.5% of 300?

12. 96% of 75 is what?

13. 7.4 is what percent of 50?

14. What percent of 1500 is 693?

15. 50.5% of 124 is what?

16. What is 87.4% of 255?

17. 120% of what is 6?

18. 14 is 175% of what?

19. What is 250% of 18?

20. 325% of 4.4 is what?

21. 33 is 220% of what?

22. 160% of what is 40?

Objective B   **To solve application problems**

23. **Charities**   A charitable organization spent $2940 for administrative expenses. This amount is 12% of the money it collected. What is the total amount of money that the organization collected?

24. **Medicine**   A manufacturer of an anti-inflammatory drug claims that the drug will be effective for 6 hours. An independent testing service determined that the drug was effective for only 80% of the length of time claimed by the manufacturer. Find the length of time the drug will be effective as determined by the testing service.

25.   **Geography**   The land area of North America is approximately 9,400,000 square miles. This represents approximately 16% of the total land area of the world. What is the approximate total land area of the world?

26. **Fire Departments**   The Rincon Fire Department received 24 false alarms out of a total of 200 alarms received. What percent of the alarms received were false alarms?

27. ○ **Lodging**   The graph at the right shows the break-
    down of the locations of the 53,500 hotels through-
    out the United States. How many hotels in the United
    States are located along highways?

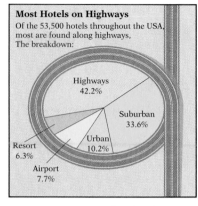

Most Hotels on Highways
Of the 53,500 hotels throughout the USA,
most are found along highways,
The breakdown:

- Highways 42.2%
- Suburban 33.6%
- Urban 10.2%
- Airport 7.7%
- Resort 6.3%

Source: American Hotel and Lodging
Association

28. ○ **Poultry**   In a recent year, North Carolina produced
    1,300,000,000 pounds of turkey. This was 18.6% of
    the U.S. total in that year. Calculate the U.S. total turkey
    production for that year. Round to the nearest billion.

29. ○ **Mining**   During 1 year, approximately 2,240,000
    ounces of gold went into the manufacturing of elec-
    tronic equipment in the United States. This is 16% of all
    the gold mined in the United States that year. How many
    ounces of gold were mined in the United States that year?

30. ○ **Demography**   The table at the right shows the pre-
    dicted increase in population from 2000 to 2040 for
    each of four counties in the Central Valley of California.
    a. What percent of the 2000 population of Sacramento
    County is the increase in population?
    b. What percent of the 2000 population of Kern County is
    the increase in population? Round to the nearest tenth
    of a percent.

County	2000 Population	Projected Increase
Sacramento	1,200,000	900,000
Kern	651,700	948,300
Fresno	794,200	705,800
San Joaquin	562,000	737,400

Source: California Department of Finance

31. ○ **Police Officers**   The graph at the right shows the
    causes of death for all police officers killed in the
    line of duty during a recent year. What percent of the
    deaths were due to traffic accidents? Round to the near-
    est tenth of a percent.

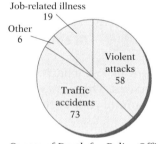

Job-related illness 19
Other 6
Violent attacks 58
Traffic accidents 73

Causes of Death for Police Officers
Killed in the Line of Duty

Source: International Union of Police
Associations

32. ○ **Demography**   According to a 25-city survey of the
    status of hunger and homelessness by the U.S. Con-
    ference of Mayors, 41% of the homeless in the United
    States are single men, 41% are families with children,
    13% are single women, and 5% are unaccompanied
    minors. How many homeless people in the United States
    are single men?

APPLYING THE CONCEPTS

33. ○ **The Federal Government**   In the 108th Senate, there were 51
    Republicans, 48 Democrats, and 1 Independent. In the 108th
    House of Representatives, there were 229 Republicans, 205 Democrats,
    and 1 Independent. Which had the larger percent of Republicans, the
    108th Senate or the 108th House of Representatives?

Focus on Problem Solving

Using a Calculator as a Problem-Solving Tool

A calculator is an important tool for problem solving. Here are a few problems to solve with a calculator. You may need to research some of the questions to find information you do not know.

1. Choose any single-digit positive number. Multiply the number by 1507 and 7373. What is the answer? Choose another positive single-digit number and again multiply by 1507 and 7373. What is the answer? What pattern do you see? Why does this work?

2. The gross domestic product in 2002 was $10,446,200,000. Is this more or less than the amount of money that would be placed on the last square of a standard checkerboard if 1 cent were placed on the first square, 2 cents were placed on the second square, 4 cents were placed on the third square, 8 cents were placed on the fourth square, and so on, until the 64th square was reached?

3. Which of the reciprocals of the first 16 natural numbers have a terminating-decimal representation and which have a repeating-decimal representation?

4. What is the largest natural number n for which $4^n > 1 \cdot 2 \cdot 3 \cdot 4 \cdot 5 \cdots \cdot n$?

5. If $1000 bills are stacked one on top of another, is the height of $1 billion less than or greater than the height of the Washington Monument?

6. What is the value of $1 + \cfrac{1}{1 + \cfrac{1}{1 + \cfrac{1}{1 + \cfrac{1}{1 + 1}}}}$?

7. Calculate 15^2, 35^2, 65^2, and 85^2. Study the results. Make a conjecture about a relationship between a number ending in 5 and its square. Use your conjecture to find 75^2 and 95^2. Does your conjecture work for 125^2?

8. Find the sum of the first 1000 natural numbers. (*Hint:* You could just start adding $1 + 2 + 3 + \cdots$, but even if you performed one operation every 3 seconds, it would take you an hour to find the sum. Instead, try pairing the numbers and then adding the pairs. Pair 1 and 1000, 2 and 999, 3 and 998, and so on. What is the sum of each pair? How many pairs are there? Use this information to answer the original question.)

9. For a borrower to qualify for a home loan, a bank requires that the monthly mortgage payment be less than 25% of a borrower's monthly take-home income. A laboratory technician has deductions for taxes, insurance, and retirement that amount to 25% of the technician's monthly gross income. What minimum monthly income must this technician earn to receive a bank loan that has a mortgage payment of $1200 per month?

Using Estimation as a Problem-Solving Tool

You can use your knowledge of rounding, your understanding of percent, and your experience with the basic percent equation to quickly estimate the answer to a percent problem. Here is an example.

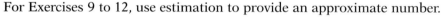

HOW TO What is 11.2% of 978?

Round the given numbers.

$11.2\% \approx 10\%$
$978 \approx 1000$

Mentally calculate with the rounded numbers.

$10\% \text{ of } 1000 = \frac{1}{10} \text{ of } 1000 = 100$

11.2% of 978 is approximately 100.

> **TAKE NOTE**
>
> The exact answer is $0.112 \times 978 = 109.536$. The exact answer 109.536 is close to the approximation of 100.

For Exercises 1 to 8, state which quantity is greater.

1. 49% of 51, or 201% of 15
2. 99% of 19, or 22% of 55
3. 8% of 31, or 78% of 10
4. 24% of 402, or 76% of 205
5. 10.2% of 51, or 20.9% of 41
6. 51.8% of 804, or 25.3% of 1223
7. 26% of 39.217, or 9% of 85.601
8. 66% of 31.807, or 33% of 58.203

For Exercises 9 to 12, use estimation to provide an approximate number.

9. A company survey found that 24% of its 2096 employees favored a new dental plan. How many employees favored the new dental plan?

10. A local newspaper reported that 52.3% of the 29,875 eligible voters in the town voted in the last election. How many people voted in the last election?

11. 19.8% of the 2135 first-year students at a community college have part-time jobs. How many of the first-year students at the college have part-time jobs?

12. A couple made a down payment of 33% of the $310,000 cost of the home. Find the down payment.

Projects and Group Activities

Health The American College of Sports Medicine (ACSM) recommends that you know how to determine your target heart rate in order to get the full benefit of exercise. Your **target heart rate** is the rate at which your heart should beat during any aerobic exercise such as running, cycling, fast walking, or participating in an aerobics class. According to the ACSM, you should reach your target rate and then maintain it for 20 minutes or more to achieve cardiovascular fitness. The intensity level varies for different individuals. A sedentary person might begin at the 60% level and gradually work up to 70%, whereas athletes and very fit individuals might work at the 85% level. The ACSM suggests that you calculate both 50% and 85% of your maximum heart rate. This will give you the low and high ends of the range within which your heart rate should stay.

To calculate your target heart rate:

	Example
Subtract your age from 220. This is your maximum heart rate.	$220 - 20 = 200$
Multiply your maximum heart rate by 50%. This is the low end of your range.	$200(0.50) = 100$
Divide the low end by 6. This is your low 10-second heart rate.	$100 \div 6 \approx 17$
Multiply your maximum heart rate by 85%. This is the high end of your range.	$200(0.85) = 170$
Divide the high end by 6. This is your high 10-second heart rate.	$170 \div 6 \approx 28$

1. Why are the low end and high end divided by 6 in order to determine the low and high 10-second heart rates?

2. Calculate your target heart rate, both the low and high end of your range.

Consumer Price Index

The consumer price index (CPI) is a percent that is written without the percent sign. For instance, a CPI of 160.1 means 160.1%. This number means that an item that cost $100 between 1982 and 1984 (the base years) would cost $160.10 today. Determining the cost is an application of the basic percent equation.

$$\text{Percent} \times \text{base} = \text{amount}$$
$$\text{CPI} \times \text{cost in base year} = \text{cost today}$$
$$1.601 \times 100 = 160.1 \qquad \bullet \ 160.1\% = 1.601$$

The table below gives the CPI for various products in July of 2003. If you have Internet access, you can obtain current data for the items below, as well as other items not on this list, by visiting the website of the Bureau of Labor Statistics.

Product	CPI
All items	183.9
Food and beverages	180.3
Housing	185.9
Clothes	116.2
Transportation	156.8
Medical care	297.6
Entertainment	107.7
Education	108.9

1. Of the items listed, are there any items that in 2003 cost more than twice as much as they cost during the base year? If so, which items?

2. Of the items listed, are there any items that in 2003 cost more than one-and-one-half times as much as they cost during the base years but less than twice as much as they cost during the base years? If so, which items?

3. If the cost for textbooks for one semester was $120 in the base years, how much did similar textbooks cost in 2003? Use the "Education" category.

4. If a new car cost $20,000 in 2003, what would a comparable new car have cost during the base years? Use the "Transportation" category.

5. If a movie ticket cost $8 in 2003, what would a comparable movie ticket have cost during the base years? Use the "Entertainment" category.

6. The base year for the CPI was 1967 before the change to 1982–1984. If 1967 were still used as the base year, the CPI for all items in 2003 (not just those listed above) would be 550.9.
   a. Using the base year of 1967, explain the meaning of a CPI of 550.9.
   b. Using the base year of 1967 and a CPI of 550.9, if textbooks cost $75 for one semester in 1967, how much did similar textbooks cost in 2003?
   c. Using the base year of 1967 and a CPI of 550.9, if a family's food budget in 2003 is $800 per month, what would a comparable family budget have been in 1967?

Chapter 5 Summary

Key Words	**Examples**
Percent means "parts of 100." [5.1A, p. 203]	23% means 23 of 100 equal parts.

Essential Rules and Procedures	**Examples**
To write a percent as a fraction, drop the percent sign and multiply by $\frac{1}{100}$. [5.1A, p. 203]	$56\% = 56\left(\frac{1}{100}\right) = \frac{56}{100} = \frac{14}{25}$
To write a percent as a decimal, drop the percent sign and multiply by 0.01. [5.1A, p. 203]	$87\% = 87(0.01) = 0.87$
To write a fraction as a percent, multiply by 100%. [5.1B, p. 204]	$\frac{7}{20} = \frac{7}{20}(100\%) = \frac{700}{20}\% = 35\%$
To write a decimal as a percent, multiply by 100%. [5.1B, p. 204]	$0.325 = 0.325(100\%) = 32.5\%$
The Basic Percent Equation [5.2A, p. 207] The basic percent equation is $$\text{Percent} \times \text{base} = \text{amount}$$ Solving percent problems requires identifying the three elements of this equation. Usually the base follows the phrase "percent of."	8% of 250 is what number? Percent $\times$ base = amount $0.08 \times 250 = n$ $20 = n$
Proportion Method of Solving a Percent Problem [5.5A, p. 219] The following proportion can be used to solve percent problems. $$\frac{\text{percent}}{100} = \frac{\text{amount}}{\text{base}}$$ To use the proportion method, first identify the percent, the amount, and the base. The base usually follows the phrase "percent of."	8% of 250 is what number? $\frac{\text{percent}}{100} = \frac{\text{amount}}{\text{base}}$ $\frac{8}{100} = \frac{n}{250}$ $8 \times 250 = 100 \times n$ $2000 = 100 \times n$ $2000 \div 100 = n$ $20 = n$

Chapter 5 Review Exercises

1. What is 30% of 200?

2. 16 is what percent of 80?

3. Write $1\frac{3}{4}$ as a percent.

4. 20% of what is 15?

5. Write 12% as a fraction.

6. Find 22% of 88.

7. What percent of 20 is 30?

8. $16\frac{2}{3}\%$ of what is 84?

9. Write 42% as a decimal.

10. What is 7.5% of 72?

11. $66\frac{2}{3}\%$ of what is 105?

12. Write 7.6% as a decimal.

13. Find 125% of 62.

14. Write $16\frac{2}{3}\%$ as a fraction.

15. Use the proportion method to find what percent of 25 is 40.

16. 20% of what number is 15? Use the proportion method.

17. Write 0.38 as a percent.

18. 78% of what is 8.5? Round to the nearest tenth.

19. What percent of 30 is 2.2? Round to the nearest tenth of a percent.

20. What percent of 15 is 92? Round to the nearest tenth of a percent.

21. Education   Trent missed 9 out of 60 questions on a history exam. What percent of the questions did he answer correctly? Use the proportion method.

22. Advertising   A company used 7.5% of its $60,000 advertising budget for newspaper advertising. How much of the advertising budget was spent for newspaper advertising?

23. Energy   The graph at the right shows the amounts that the average U.S. household spends for energy use. What percent of these costs is for electricity? Round to the nearest tenth of a percent.

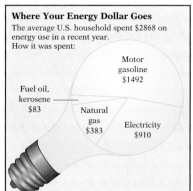

Where Your Energy Dollar Goes
The average U.S. household spent $2868 on energy use in a recent year. How it was spent:

Motor gasoline $1492

Fuel oil, kerosene $83

Natural gas $383

Electricity $910

24. Consumerism   Joshua purchased a video camera for $980 and paid a sales tax of 6.25% of the cost. What was the total cost of the video camera?

Source: Energy Information Administration

25. Health   In a survey of 350 women and 420 men, 275 of the women and 300 of the men reported that they wore sunscreen often. To the nearest tenth of a percent, what percent of the women wore sunscreen often?

26. Demography   It is estimated that the world's population will be 9,100,000,000 by the year 2050. This is 149% of the population in 2000. (*Source:* U.S. Census Bureau). What was the world's population in 2000? Round to the nearest hundred million.

27. Computers   A computer system can be purchased for $1800. This is 60% of what the computer cost 4 years ago. What was the cost of the computer 4 years ago? Use the proportion method.

28. Online Transactions   In a recent year, $25.96 billion worth of online transactions were paid for using a Visa card. This represented 50.4% of the online transactions made during the year. (*Source:* The Nilson Report) Find the dollar value of all the online transactions made that year. Round to the nearest billion.

Chapter 5 Test

1. Write 97.3% as a decimal.

2. Write $83\frac{1}{3}\%$ as a fraction.

3. Write 0.3 as a percent.

4. Write 1.63 as a percent.

5. Write $\frac{3}{2}$ as a percent.

6. Write $\frac{2}{3}$ as a percent.

7. What is 77% of 65?

8. 47.2% of 130 is what?

9. Which is larger:
    7% of 120, or 76% of 13?

10. Which is smaller:
    13% of 200, or 212% of 12?

11. **Advertising** A travel agency uses 6% of its $75,000 budget for advertising. What amount of the budget is spent on advertising?

12. **Agriculture** During the packaging process for vegetables, spoiled vegetables are discarded by an inspector. In one day an inspector found that 6.4% of the 1250 pounds of vegetables were spoiled. How many pounds of vegetables were not spoiled?

Nutrition   The table at the right contains nutrition information about a breakfast cereal. Solve Exercises 13 and 14 with information taken from this table.

13. The recommended amount of potassium per day for an adult is 3000 milligrams (mg). What percent, to the nearest tenth of a percent, of the daily recommended amount of potassium is provided by one serving of this cereal with skim milk?

14. The daily recommended number of calories for a 190-pound man is 2200 calories. What percent, to the nearest tenth of a percent, of the daily recommended number of calories is provided by one serving of this cereal with 2% milk?

NUTRITION INFORMATION

SERVING SIZE: 1.4 OZ WHEAT FLAKES WITH
0.4 OZ. RAISINS: 39.4 g. ABOUT 1/2 CUP
SERVINGS PER PACKAGE: 14

	CEREAL & RAISINS	WITH 1/2 CUP VITAMINS A & D SKIM MILK
CALORIES	120	180
PROTEIN, g	3	7
CARBOHYDRATE, g	28	34
FAT, TOTAL, g	1	1*
UNSATURATED, g 1		
SATURATED, g 0		
CHOLESTEROL, mg	0	0*
SODIUM, mg	125	190
POTASSIUM, mg	240	440

* 2% MILK SUPPLIES AN ADDITIONAL 20 CALORIES.
2 g FAT, AND 10 mg CHOLESTEROL.
** CONTAINS LESS THAN 2% OF THE U.S. RDA OF
THIS NUTRIENT

15. **Employment**   The Urban Center Department Store has 125 permanent employees and must hire an additional 20 temporary employees for the holiday season. What percent of the permanent employees is the number hired as temporary employees for the holiday season?

16. **Education**   Conchita missed 7 out of 80 questions on a math exam. What percent of the questions did she answer correctly? Round to the nearest tenth of a percent.

17. 12 is 15% of what?

18. 42.5 is 150% of what? Round to the nearest tenth.

19. **Manufacturing**   A manufacturer of PDAs found 384 defective PDAs during a quality control study. This amount was 1.2% of the PDAs tested. Find the number of PDAs tested.

20. **Real Estate**   A new house was bought for $95,000. Five years later the house sold for $152,000. The increase was what percent of the original price?

21. 123 is 86% of what number? Use the proportion method. Round to the nearest tenth.

22. What percent of 12 is 120? Use the proportion method.

23. **Wages**   A secretary receives a wage of $16.24 per hour. This amount is 112% of last year's wage. What is the dollar increase in the hourly wage over last year? Use the proportion method.

24. **Demography**   A city has a population of 71,500. Ten years ago the population was 32,500. The population now is what percent of what the population was 10 years ago? Use the proportion method.

25. **Fees**   The annual license fee on a car is 1.4% of the value of the car. If the license fee during a year is $175.00, what is the value of the car? Use the proportion method.

Cumulative Review Exercises

1. Simplify: $18 \div (7 - 4)^2 + 2$.

2. Find the LCM of 16, 24, and 30.

3. Find the sum of $2\frac{1}{3}$, $3\frac{1}{2}$, and $4\frac{5}{8}$.

4. Subtract: $27\frac{5}{12} - 14\frac{9}{16}$

5. Multiply: $7\frac{1}{3} \times 1\frac{5}{7}$

6. What is $\frac{14}{27}$ divided by $1\frac{7}{9}$?

7. Simplify: $\left(\frac{3}{4}\right)^3 \cdot \left(\frac{8}{9}\right)^2$

8. Simplify: $\left(\frac{2}{3}\right)^2 - \left(\frac{3}{8} - \frac{1}{3}\right) \div \frac{1}{2}$

9. Round 3.07973 to the nearest hundredth.

10. Subtract: $\begin{array}{r} 3.0902 \\ -\ 1.9706 \\ \hline \end{array}$

11. Divide: $0.032\overline{)1.097}$
    Round to the nearest ten-thousandth.

12. Convert $3\frac{5}{8}$ to a decimal.

13. Convert 1.75 to a fraction.

14. Place the correct symbol, $<$ or $>$, between the two numbers.
    $\frac{3}{8}$ 0.87

15. Solve the proportion $\frac{3}{8} = \frac{20}{n}$. Round to the nearest tenth.

16. Write "$76.80 earned in 8 hours" as a unit rate.

17. Write $18\frac{1}{3}\%$ as a fraction.

18. Write $\frac{5}{6}$ as a percent.

19. 16.3% of 120 is what? Round to the nearest hundredth.

20. 24 is what percent of 18?

21. 12.4 is 125% of what?

22. What percent of 35 is 120? Round to the nearest tenth.

23. **Taxes**   Sergio has an income of $740 per week. One-fifth of his income is deducted for income tax payments. Find his take-home pay.

24. **Finance**   Eunice bought a used car for $8353, with a down payment of $1000. The balance was paid in 36 equal monthly payments. Find the monthly payment.

25. **Taxes**   The gasoline tax is $.19 a gallon. Find the number of gallons of gasoline used during a month in which $79.80 was paid in gasoline taxes.

26. **Taxes**   The real estate tax on a $172,000 home is $3440. At the same rate, find the real estate tax on a home valued at $250,000.

27. **Consumerism**   Ken purchased a camera for $490 and paid $29.40 in sales tax. What percent of the purchase price was the sales tax?

28. **Elections**   A survey of 300 people showed that 165 people favored a certain candidate for mayor. What percent of the people surveyed did not favor this candidate?

29. **Television**   According to the Cabletelevision Advertising Bureau, cable households watch television 36.5% of the time. On average, how many hours per week do cable households spend watching TV? Round to the nearest tenth.

30. **Health**   The Environmental Protection Agency found that 990 out of 5500 children tested had levels of lead in their blood exceeding federal guidelines. What percent of the children tested had levels of lead in the blood that exceeded federal standards?

chapter

6 Applications for Business and Consumers

When you use a credit card to make a purchase, you are actually receiving a loan. This service allows you to defer payment on your purchase until a predetermined date in the future. In exchange for this convenient service, credit card companies will frequently charge you money for using their credit card. This added cost may be in the form of an annual fee, or it may be in the form of interest charges on balances that are not paid off after a certain deadline. These interest charges on unpaid balances are called finance charges and can be calculated using the simple interest formula. **Exercises 27 to 32 on page 257** ask you to use this formula to calculate the finance charges on unpaid balances.

Need help? For online student resources, such as section quizzes, visit this textbook's website at **math.college.hmco.com/students**.

PREP TEST • • •

Do these exercises to prepare for Chapter 6.

For Exercises 1 to 6, add, subtract, multiply, or divide.

1. Divide: 3.75 ÷ 5

2. Multiply: 3.47 × 15

3. Subtract: 874.50 − 369.99

4. Multiply: 0.065 × 150,000

5. Multiply: 1500 × 0.06 × 0.5

6. Add: 1372.47 + 36.91 + 5.00 + 2.86

7. Divide 10 ÷ 3. Round to the nearest hundredth.

8. Divide 345 ÷ 570. Round to the nearest thousandth.

9. Place the correct symbol, < or >, between the two numbers.
0.379   0.397

GO FIGURE • • •

A store manager priced a pair of earrings in dollars and cents such that when 4% sales tax was added, the result was a whole number of dollars and 0 cents. Find the smallest possible number of dollars the items sold for, including the sales tax.

6.1 Applications to Purchasing

Objective A   **To find unit cost**

Frequently, stores promote items for purchase by advertising, say, 2 Red Baron Bake to Rise Pizzas for $10.50 or 5 cans of StarKist tuna for $4.25.

The **unit cost** is the cost of *one* Red Baron Pizza or of *one* can of StarKist tuna. To find the unit cost, divide the total cost by the number of units.

2 pizzas for $10.50

10.50 ÷ 2 = 5.25

$5.25 is the cost of one pizza.

Unit cost: $5.25 per pizza

5 cans for $4.25

4.25 ÷ 5 = 0.85

$.85 is the cost of one can.

Unit cost: $.85 per can

Example 1

Find the unit cost. Round to the nearest tenth of a cent.
a. 3 gallons of mint chip ice cream for $17
b. 4 ounces of Crest toothpaste for $2.29

Strategy
To find the unit cost, divide the total cost by the number of units.

Solution
a. 17 ÷ 3 ≈ 5.667
$5.667 per gallon
b. 2.29 ÷ 4 = 0.5725
$.573 per ounce

You Try It 1

Find the unit cost. Round to the nearest tenth of a cent.
a. 8 size-AA Energizer batteries for $7.67
b. 15 ounces of Revlon shampoo for $2.29

Your strategy

Your solution

Solution on p. S15

Objective B   **To find the most economical purchase**

Comparison shoppers often find the most economical buy by comparing unit costs.

One store is selling 6 twelve-ounce cans of ginger ale for $2.99, and a second store is selling 24 twelve-ounce cans of ginger ale for $11.79. To find the better buy, compare the unit costs.

2.99 ÷ 6 ≈ 0.498

Unit cost: $.498 per can

11.79 ÷ 24 ≈ 0.491

Unit cost: $.491 per can

Because $.491 < $.498, the better buy is 24 cans for $11.79.

Example 2

Find the more economical purchase:
5 pounds of nails for $4.80, or 4 pounds of nails for $3.78.

Strategy
To find the more economical purchase, compare the unit costs.

Solution
$4.80 \div 5 = 0.96$
$3.78 \div 4 = 0.945$
$\$.945 < \$.96$

The more economical purchase is 4 pounds for $3.78.

You Try It 2

Find the more economical purchase: 6 cans of fruit for $5.70, or 4 cans of fruit for $3.96.

Your strategy

Your solution

Solution on p. S15

Objective C   **To find total cost**

An installer of floor tile found the unit cost of identical floor tiles at three stores.

Store 1	Store 2	Store 3
$1.22 per tile	$1.18 per tile	$1.28 per tile

By comparing the unit costs, the installer determined that store 2 would provide the most economical purchase.

The installer also uses the unit cost to find the total cost of purchasing 300 floor tiles at store 2. The **total cost** is found by multiplying the unit cost by the number of units purchased.

Unit cost	×	number of units	=	total cost
1.18	×	300	=	354

The total cost is $354.

Example 3

Clear redwood lumber costs $5.43 per foot. How much would 25 feet of clear redwood cost?

Strategy
To find the total cost, multiply the unit cost (5.43) by the number of units (25).

Solution

Unit cost	×	number of units	=	total cost
5.43	×	25	=	135.75

The total cost is $135.75.

You Try It 3

Pine saplings cost $9.96 each. How much would 7 pine saplings cost?

Your strategy

Your solution

Solution on p. S15

6.1 Exercises

Objective A   **To find unit cost**

For Exercises 1 to 12, find the unit cost. Round to the nearest tenth of a cent.

1. Heinz B·B·Q sauce, 18 ounces for $.99

2. Birds-eye maple, 6 feet for $18.75

3. Diamond walnuts, $2.99 for 8 ounces

4. A&W root beer, 6 cans for $2.99

5. Ibuprofen, 50 tablets for $3.99

6. Visine eye drops, 0.5 ounce for $3.89

7. Adjustable wood clamps, 2 for $13.95

8. Corn, 6 ears for $1.85

9. Cheerios cereal, 15 ounces for $2.99

10. Doritos Cool Ranch chips, 14.5 ounces for $2.99

11. Sheet metal screws, 8 for $.95

12. Folgers coffee, 11.5 ounces for $4.79

Objective B   **To find the most economical purchase**

For Exercises 13 to 24, suppose your local supermarket offers the following products at the given prices. Find the more economical purchase.

13. Sutter Home pasta sauce, 25.5 ounces for $3.29, or Muir Glen Organic pasta sauce, 26 ounces for $3.79

14. Kraft mayonnaise, 40 ounces for $2.98, or Springfield mayonnaise, 32 ounces for $2.39

15. Ortega salsa, 20 ounces for $3.29 or 12 ounces for $1.99

16. L'Oréal shampoo, 13 ounces for $4.69, or Cortexx shampoo, 12 ounces for $3.99

17. Golden Sun vitamin E, 200 tablets for $7.39 or 400 tablets for $12.99

18. Ultra Mr. Clean, 20 ounces for $2.67, or Ultra Spic and Span, 14 ounces for $2.19

19. 16 ounces of Kraft cheddar cheese, $4.37, or 9 ounces of Land O' Lakes cheddar cheese, $2.29

20. Bertolli olive oil, 34 ounces for $9.49, or Pompeian olive oil, 8 ounces for $2.39

21. Maxwell House coffee, 4 ounces for $3.99, or Sanka coffee, 2 ounces for $2.39

22. Wagner's vanilla extract, $3.29 for 1.5 ounces, or Durkee vanilla extract, 1 ounce for $2.74

23. Purina Cat Chow, $4.19 for 56 ounces, or Friskies Chef's Blend, $3.37 for 50.4 ounces

24. Kleenex tissues, $1.73 for 250 tissues, or Puffs tissues, $1.23 for 175 tissues

Objective C   **To find total cost**

25. If sliced bacon costs $4.59 per pound, find the total cost of 3 pounds.

26. Used red brick costs $.98 per brick. Find the total cost of 75 bricks.

27. Kiwi fruit cost $.23 each. Find the total cost of 8 kiwi.

28. Boneless chicken filets cost $4.69 per pound. Find the cost of 3.6 pounds. Round to the nearest cent.

29. Herbal tea costs $.98 per ounce. Find the total cost of 6.5 ounces.

30. If Stella Swiss Lorraine cheese costs $5.99 per pound, find the total cost of 0.65 pound. Round to the nearest cent.

31. Red Delicious apples cost $1.29 per pound. Find the total cost of 2.1 pounds. Round to the nearest cent.

32. Choice rib eye steak costs $8.49 per pound. Find the total cost of 2.8 pounds. Round to the nearest cent.

33. If Godiva chocolate costs $7.95 per pound, find the total cost of $\frac{3}{4}$ pound. Round to the nearest cent.

34. Color photocopying costs $.89 per page. Find the total cost for photocopying 120 pages.

APPLYING THE CONCEPTS

35. Explain in your own words the meaning of unit pricing.

36. What is the UPC (Universal Product Code) and how is it used?

ISBN 0-395-75524-7

6.2 Percent Increase and Percent Decrease

Objective A   **To find percent increase**

Percent increase is used to show how much a quantity has increased over its original value. The statements "Food prices increased by 2.3% last year" and "City council members received a 4% pay increase" are examples of percent increase.

HOW TO   According to the Energy Information Administration, the number of alternative-fuel vehicles increased from approximately 277,000 to 352,000 in four years. Find the percent increase in alternative-fuel vehicles. Round to the nearest percent.

$$\boxed{\text{New value}} - \boxed{\text{original value}} = \boxed{\text{amount of increase}}$$

$$352{,}000 - 277{,}000 = 75{,}000$$

Now solve the basic percent equation for percent.

$$\text{Percent} \times \text{base} = \text{amount}$$

$$\boxed{\text{Percent increase}} \times \boxed{\text{original value}} = \boxed{\text{amount of increase}}$$

$$n \times 277{,}000 = 75{,}000$$
$$n = 75{,}000 \div 277{,}000$$
$$n \approx 0.27$$

The number of alternative-fuel vehicles increased by approximately 27%.

Amount of increase (75,000)
Original value (277,000)
New value (352,000)

Example 1

The average wholesale price of coffee increased from $2 per pound to $3 per pound in one year. What was the percent increase in the price of 1 pound of coffee?

Strategy

To find the percent increase:

- Find the amount of the increase.
- Solve the basic percent equation for *percent*.

Solution

$$\boxed{\text{New value}} - \boxed{\text{original value}} = \boxed{\text{amount of increase}}$$

$$3 - 2 = 1$$

$$\text{Percent} \times \text{base} = \text{amount}$$
$$n \times 2 = 1$$
$$n = 1 \div 2$$
$$n = 0.5 = 50\%$$

The percent increase was 50%.

You Try It 1

The average price of gasoline rose from $1.46 to $1.83 in 5 months. What was the percent increase in the price of gasoline? Round to the nearest percent.

Your strategy

Your solution

Solution on p. S15

Example 2

Chris Carley was earning $13.50 an hour as a nursing assistant before receiving a 10% increase in pay. What is Chris's new hourly pay?

Strategy

To find the new hourly wage:

- Solve the basic percent equation for *amount*.
- Add the amount of the increase to the original wage.

Solution

Percent × base = amount
0.10 × 13.50 = *n*
1.35 = *n*

The amount of the increase was $1.35.

13.50 + 1.35 = 14.85

The new hourly wage is $14.85.

You Try It 2

Yolanda Liyama was making a wage of $12.50 an hour as a baker before receiving a 14% increase in hourly pay. What is Yolanda's new hourly wage?

Your strategy

Your solution

Solution on p. S15

Objective B — **To apply percent increase to business—markup**

Some of the expenses involved in operating a business are salaries, rent, equipment, and utilities. To pay these expenses and earn a profit, a business must sell a product at a higher price than it paid for the product.

Cost is the price a business pays for a product, and **selling price** is the price at which a business sells a product to a customer. The difference between selling price and cost is called **markup.**

Markup — Cost — Selling price

Point of Interest

According to *Managing a Small Business*, from Liraz Publishing Company, goods in a store are often marked up 50% to 100% of the cost. This allows a business to make a profit of 5% to 10%.

| Selling price | − | cost | = | markup |

or

| Cost | + | markup | = | selling price |

Markup is frequently expressed as a percent of a product's cost. This percent is called the **markup rate.**

| Markup rate | × | cost | = | markup |

HOW TO Suppose Bicycles Galore purchases an AMP Research B-5 bicycle for $2119.20 and sells it for $2649. What markup rate does Bicycles Galore use?

| Selling price | − | cost | = | markup |
| 2649.00 | − 2119.20 = | 529.80 |

- First find the markup.

Percent	×	base	=	amount
Markup rate	×	cost	=	markup
n	× 2119.20 =	529.80

- Then solve the basic percent equation for *percent.*

n = 529.80 ÷ 2119.20 = 0.25

The markup rate is 25%.

Example 3

The manager of a sporting goods store determines that a markup rate of 36% is necessary to make a profit. What is the markup on a pair of skis that costs the store $225?

Strategy

To find the markup, solve the basic percent equation for *amount*.

Solution

Percent $\times$ base $=$ amount

$$\boxed{\begin{array}{c}\text{Markup}\\\text{rate}\end{array}} \times \boxed{\text{cost}} = \boxed{\text{markup}}$$

$$0.36 \quad \times \quad 225 \quad = \quad n$$
$$81 = n$$

The markup is $81.

Example 4

A plant nursery bought a yellow twig dogwood for $4.50 and used a markup rate of 46%. What is the selling price?

Strategy

To find the selling price:
- Find the markup by solving the basic percent equation for *amount*.
- Add the markup to the cost.

Solution

Percent $\times$ base $=$ amount

$$\boxed{\begin{array}{c}\text{Markup}\\\text{rate}\end{array}} \times \boxed{\text{cost}} = \boxed{\text{markup}}$$

$$0.46 \quad \times \quad 4.50 \quad = \quad n$$
$$2.07 = n$$

$$\boxed{\text{Cost}} + \boxed{\text{markup}} = \boxed{\text{selling price}}$$

$$4.50 \quad + \quad 2.07 \quad = \quad 6.57$$

The selling price is $6.57.

You Try It 3

A bookstore manager determines that a markup rate of 20% is necessary to make a profit. What is the markup on a book that costs the bookstore $8?

Your strategy

Your solution

You Try It 4

A clothing store bought a leather suit for $72 and used a markup rate of 55%. What is the selling price?

Your strategy

Your solution

Solutions on p. S15

Objective C   **To find percent decrease**

Percent decrease is used to show how much a quantity has decreased from its original value. The statements "The number of family farms decreased by 2% last year" and "There has been a 50% decrease in the cost of a Pentium chip" are examples of percent decrease.

HOW TO   During a 2-year period, the value of U.S. agricultural products exported decreased from approximately $60.6 billion to $52.0 billion. Find the percent decrease in the value of U.S. agricultural exports. Round to the nearest tenth of a percent.

$$\boxed{\text{Original value}} - \boxed{\text{new value}} = \boxed{\text{amount of decrease}}$$

$$60.6 \quad - \quad 52.0 \quad = \quad 8.6$$

Now solve the basic percent equation for percent.

$$\text{Percent} \quad \times \quad \text{base} \quad = \quad \text{amount}$$

$$\boxed{\text{Percent decrease}} \times \boxed{\text{original value}} = \boxed{\text{amount of decrease}}$$

$$n \quad \times \quad 60.6 \quad = \quad 8.6$$
$$n = 8.6 \div 60.6$$
$$n \approx 0.142$$

The value of agricultural exports decreased approximately 14.2%.

Amount of decrease (8.6)

New value (52.0)

Original value (60.6)

Example 5

During an 8-year period, the population of Baltimore, Maryland, decreased from approximately 736,000 to 646,000. Find the percent decrease in Baltimore's population. Round to the nearest tenth of a percent.

Strategy

To find the percent decrease:
- Find the amount of the decrease.
- Solve the basic percent equation for *percent*.

Solution

$$\boxed{\text{Original value}} - \boxed{\text{new value}} = \boxed{\text{amount of decrease}}$$

$$736{,}000 \quad - \quad 646{,}000 \quad = \quad 90{,}000$$

$$\text{Percent} \times \quad \text{base} \quad = \text{amount}$$
$$n \quad \times 736{,}000 = 90{,}000$$
$$n = 90{,}000 \div 736{,}000$$
$$n \approx 0.122$$

Baltimore's population decreased approximately 12.2%.

You Try It 5

During an 8-year period, the population of Norfolk, Virginia, decreased from approximately 261,000 to 215,000. Find the percent decrease in Norfolk's population. Round to the nearest tenth of a percent.

Your strategy

Your solution

Solution on p. S15

Example 6

The total sales for December for a stationery store were $96,000. For January, total sales showed an 8% decrease from December's sales. What were the total sales for January?

Strategy

To find the total sales for January:

- Find the amount of decrease by solving the basic percent equation for *amount*.
- Subtract the amount of decrease from the December sales.

Solution

Percent $\times$ base = amount
0.08 $\times$ 96,000 = n
              7680 = n

The decrease in sales was $7680.

96,000 − 7680 = 88,320

The total sales for January were $88,320.

You Try It 6

Fog decreased the normal 5-mile visibility at an airport by 40%. What was the visibility in the fog?

Your strategy

Your solution

Solution on p. S16

Objective D   **To apply percent decrease to business—discount**

To promote sales, a store may reduce the regular price of some of its products temporarily. The reduced price is called the **sale price.** The difference between the regular price and the sale price is called the **discount.**

| Regular price | − | sale price | = | discount |

or

| Regular price | − | discount | = | sale price |

Discount is frequently stated as a percent of a product's regular price. This percent is called the **discount rate.**

| Discount rate | × | regular price | = | discount |

Example 7

A GE 25-inch stereo television that regularly sells for $299 is on sale for $250. Find the discount rate. Round to the nearest tenth of a percent.

Strategy

To find the discount rate:

• Find the discount.
• Solve the basic percent equation for *percent*.

Solution

Regular price	−	sale price	=	discount

| 299 | − | 250 | = | 49 |

Percent	×	base	=	amount

Discount rate	×	regular price	=	discount

$$n \times 299 = 49$$
$$n = 49 \div 299$$
$$n \approx 0.164$$

The discount rate is 16.4%.

Example 8

A 20-horsepower lawn mower is on sale for 25% off the regular price of $1125. Find the sale price.

Strategy

To find the sale price:

• Find the discount by solving the basic percent equation for *amount*.
• Subtract to find the sale price.

Solution

Percent	×	base	=	amount

Discount rate	×	regular price	=	discount

$$0.25 \times 1125 = n$$
$$281.25 = n$$

Regular price	−	discount	=	sale price

| 1125 | − | 281.25 | = | 843.75 |

The sale price is $843.75.

You Try It 7

A white azalea that regularly sells for $12.50 is on sale for $10.99. Find the discount rate. Round to the nearest tenth of a percent.

Your strategy

Your solution

You Try It 8

A hardware store is selling a Newport security door for 15% off the regular price of $110. Find the sale price.

Your strategy

Your solution

Solutions on p. S16

6.2 Exercises

Objective A   **To find percent increase**

For Exercises 1 to 5, solve. Round percents to the nearest tenth of a percent.

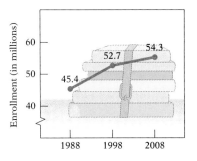

Elementary and Secondary
School Enrollments
Source: National Center for Education

1. **Education**   The figure at the right shows the actual and projected enrollments in grades K–12 in the United States. What percent increase is expected from 1988 to 2008?

2. **Fuel Efficiency**   An automobile manufacturer increased the average mileage on a car from 17.5 miles per gallon to 18.2 miles per gallon. Find the percent increase in mileage.

3. **Business**   In the 1990s, the number of Target stores increased from 420 stores to 914 stores. (*Source:* Target) What was the percent increase in the number of Target stores in the 1990s?

4. **Demography**   The graph at the right shows the number of unmarried American couples living together. (*Source:* U.S. Census Bureau) Find the percent increase in the number of unmarried couples living together from 1980 to 2000. Round to the nearest tenth.

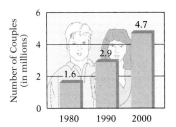

Unmarried U.S. Couples
Living Together

5. **Sports**   In 1924, the number of events in the Winter Olympics was 14. The 2002 Winter Olympics in Salt Lake City included 78 medal events. (*Source:* David Wallenchinsky's *The Complete Book of the Winter Olympics*) Find the percent increase in the number of events in the Winter Olympics from 1924 to 2002.

6. **Wealth**   The table at the right shows the estimated number of millionaire households in the United States. Find the percent increase in the estimated number of households containing millionaires from 1975 to 2005.

Year	Number of Households Containing Millionaires
1975	350,000
1997	3,500,000
2005	5,600,000

Source: Affluent Market Institute

7. **Demography**   The population of Boise City, Idaho, increased 24.3% over an 8-year period. The population initially was approximately 127,000. (*Source:* U.S. Census Bureau) Find the population of Boise City 8 years later.

8. **Television**   During 1 year, the number of people subscribing to direct broadcasting satellite systems increased 87%. If the number of subscribers at the beginning of the year was 2.3 million, how many subscribers were there at the end of the year?

9. **Demography**   From 1970 to 2000, the average age of American mothers giving birth to their first child rose 16.4%. (*Source:* Centers for Disease Control and Prevention) If the average age in 1970 was 21.4 years, what was the average age in 2000? Round to the nearest tenth.

Objective B   **To apply percent increase to business—markup**

10. A window air conditioner cost AirRite Air Conditioning Systems $285. Find the markup on the air conditioner if the markup rate is 25% of the cost.

11. The owner of Kerr Electronics purchased 300 Craig portable CD players at a cost of $85 each. If the owner uses a markup rate of 42%, what is the markup on each of the Craig CD players?

12. The manager of Brass Antiques has determined that a markup rate of 38% is necessary for a profit to be made. What is the markup on a brass doorknob that costs $45?

13. Computer Inc. uses a markup of $975 on a computer system that costs $3250. What is the markup rate on this system?

14. Saizon Pen & Office Supply uses a markup of $12 on a calculator that costs $20. What markup rate does this amount represent?

15. Giant Photo Service uses a markup rate of 48% on its Model ZA cameras, which cost the shop $162.
a. What is the markup?
b. What is the selling price?

16. The Circle R golf pro shop uses a markup rate of 45% on a set of Tour Pro golf clubs that costs the shop $210.
a. What is the markup?
b. What is the selling price?

17. Harvest Time Produce Inc. uses a 55% markup rate and pays $2 for a box of strawberries.
a. What is the markup?
b. What is the selling price of a box of strawberries?

18. Resner Builders' Hardware uses a markup rate of 42% for a table saw that costs $160. What is the selling price of the table saw?

19. Brad Burt's Magic Shop uses a markup rate of 48%. What is the selling price of a telescoping sword that costs $50?

Objective C   **To find percent decrease**

20. **Travel**   A new bridge reduced the normal 45-minute travel time between two cities by 18 minutes. What percent decrease does this represent?

21. **Energy**   By installing energy-saving equipment, the Pala Rey Youth Camp reduced its normal $800-per-month utility bill by $320. What percent decrease does this amount represent?

22. **Depreciation**   It is estimated that the value of a new car is reduced 30% after 1 year of ownership. Using this estimate, find how much value a $18,200 new car loses after 1 year.

23. **Employment**   A department store employs 1200 people during the holiday. At the end of the holiday season, the store reduces the number of employees by 45%. What is the decrease in the number of employees?

24. **Business**   Because of a decrease in demand for super-8 video cameras, Kit's Cameras reduced the orders for these models from 20 per month to 8 per month.
    a. What is the amount of the decrease?
    b. What percent decrease does this amount represent?

25. **Business**   A new computer system reduced the time for printing the payroll from 52 minutes to 39 minutes.
    a. What is the amount of the decrease?
    b. What percent decrease does this amount represent?

26. **Finance**   Juanita's average monthly expense for gasoline was $76. After joining a car pool, she was able to reduce the expense by 20%.
    a. What was the amount of the decrease?
    b. What is the average monthly gasoline bill now?

27. **Investments**   An oil company paid a dividend of $1.60 per share. After a reorganization, the company reduced the dividend by 37.5%.
    a. What was the amount of the decrease?
    b. What is the new dividend?

28. **Traffic Patterns**   Because of an improved traffic pattern at a sports stadium, the average amount of time a fan waits to park decreased from 3.5 minutes to 2.8 minutes. What percent decrease does this amount represent?

29. **Airplanes**   One configuration of the Boeing 777-300 has a seating capacity of 394. This is 26 more than that of the corresponding 777-200 jet. What is the percent decrease in capacity from the 777-300 to the 777-200 model? Round to nearest tenth of a percent.

30. **The Military**   In 2000, the Pentagon revised its account of the number of Americans killed in the Korean War from 54,246 to 36,940. (*Source: Time*, June 12, 2000) What is the percent decrease in the reported number of military personnel killed in the Korean War? Round to nearest tenth of a percent.

Objective D   **To apply percent decrease to business—discount**

31. The Austin College Bookstore is giving a discount of $8 on calculators that normally sell for $24. What is the discount rate?

32. A discount clothing store is selling a $72 sport jacket for $24 off the regular price. What is the discount rate?

33. A disc player that regularly sells for $340 is selling for 20% off the regular price. What is the discount?

34. Dacor Appliances is selling its $450 washing machine for 15% off the regular price. What is the discount?

35. An electric grill that regularly sells for $140 is selling for $42 off the regular price. What is the discount rate?

36. Quick Service Gas Station has its regularly priced $45 tune-up on sale for 16% off the regular price.
   a. What is the discount?
   b. What is the sale price?

37. Tomatoes that regularly sell for $1.25 per pound are on sale for 20% off the regular price.
   a. What is the discount?
   b. What is the sale price?

38. An outdoor supply store has its regularly priced $160 sleeping bags on sale for $120.
   a. What is the discount?
   b. What is the discount rate?

39. Standard Brands paint that regularly sells for $20 per gallon is on sale for $16 per gallon.
   a. What is the discount?
   b. What is the discount rate?

40.   **The Military** The graph at the right shows the number of active-duty U.S. military personnel in 1990 and in 2000.
   a. Which branch of the military had the greatest percent decrease in personnel from 1990 to 2000?
   b. What was the percent decrease for this branch of the service?

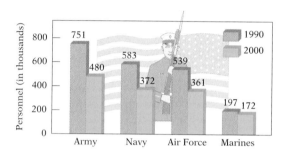

Number of Active-Duty U.S. Military Personnel

Source: Fiscal 2000 Annual Report to the President and Congress by the Secretary of Defense

APPLYING THE CONCEPTS

41. **Compensation** A welder earning $12 per hour is given a 10% raise. To find the new wage, we can multiply $12 by 0.10 and add the product to $12. Can the new wage be found by multiplying $12 by 1.10? Try both methods and compare your answers.

42. **Business** Grocers, florists, bakers, and other businesses must consider spoilage when deciding the markup of a product. For instance, suppose a florist purchased 200 roses at a cost of $.86 per rose. The florist wants a markup rate of 50% of the total cost of all the roses and expects 7% of the roses to wilt and therefore not be salable. Find the selling price per rose by answering each of the following questions.
   a. What is the florist's total cost for the 200 roses?
   b. Find the total selling price without spoilage.
   c. Find the number of roses the florist expects to sell. *Hint:* The number of roses the florist expects to sell is

      % of salable roses × number of roses purchased

   d. To find the selling price per rose, divide the total selling price without spoilage by the number of roses the florist expects to sell. Round to the nearest cent.

43.   **Business** A promotional sale at a department store offers 25% off the sale price. The sale price itself is 25% off the regular price. Is this the same as a sale that offers 50% off the regular price? If not, which sale gives the better price? Explain your answer.

Focus on Problem Solving

Counterexamples

An example that is given to show that a statement is not true is called a **counterexample.** For instance, suppose someone makes the statement "All colors are red." A counterexample to that statement would be to show someone the color blue or some other color.

If a statement is *always* true, there are no counterexamples. The statement "All even numbers are divisible by 2" is always true. It is not possible to give an example of an even number that is not divisible by 2.

In mathematics, statements that are always true are called *theorems,* and mathematicians are always searching for theorems. Sometimes a conjecture by a mathematician appears to be a theorem. That is, the statement appears to be always true, but later on someone finds a counterexample.

One example of this occurred when the French mathematician Pierre de Fermat (1601–1665) conjectured that $2^{(2^n)} + 1$ is always a prime number for any natural number n. For instance, when $n = 3$, we have $2^{(2^3)} + 1 = 2^8 + 1 = 257$, and 257 is a prime number. However, in 1732 Leonhard Euler (1707–1783) showed that when $n = 5$, $2^{(2^5)} + 1 = 4{,}294{,}967{,}297$ and that $4{,}294{,}967{,}297 = 641 \cdot 6{,}700{,}417$—without a calculator! Because $4{,}294{,}967{,}297$ is the product of two numbers (other than itself and 1), it is not a prime number. This counterexample showed that Fermat's conjecture is not a theorem.

For Exercises 1 and 5, find at least one counterexample.

1. All composite numbers are divisible by 2.

2. All prime numbers are odd numbers.

3. The square of any number is always bigger than the number.

4. The reciprocal of a number is always less than 1.

5. A number ending in 9 is always larger than a number ending in 3.

When a problem is posed, it may not be known whether the problem statement is true or false. For instance, Christian Goldbach (1690–1764) stated that every even number greater than 2 can be written as the sum of two prime numbers. For example,

$$12 = 5 + 7 \qquad 32 = 3 + 29$$

Although this problem is approximately 250 years old, mathematicians have not been able to prove it is a theorem, nor have they been able to find a counterexample.

For Exercises 6 to 9, answer true if the statement is always true. If there is an instance in which the statement is false, give a counterexample.

6. The sum of two positive numbers is always larger than either of the two numbers.

7. The product of two positive numbers is always larger than either of the two numbers.

8. Percents always represent a number less than or equal to 1.

9. It is never possible to divide by zero.

Projects and Group Activities

Buying a Car Suppose a student has an after-school job to earn money to buy and maintain a car. We will make assumptions about the monthly costs in several categories in order to determine how many hours per week the student must work to support the car. Assume the student earns $8.50 per hour.

1. Monthly payment

   Assume that the car cost $8500 with a down payment of $1020. The remainder is financed for 3 years at an annual simple interest rate of 9%.

   Monthly payment = _____

2. Insurance

   Assume that insurance costs $1500 per year.

   Monthly insurance payment = _____

3. Gasoline

   Assume that the student travels 750 miles per month, that the car travels 25 miles per gallon of gasoline, and that gasoline costs $1.50 per gallon.

   Number of gallons of gasoline purchased per month = _____

   Monthly cost for gasoline = _____

4. Miscellaneous

   Assume $.33 per mile for upkeep.

   Monthly expense for upkeep = _____

5. Total monthly expenses for the monthly payment, insurance, gasoline, and miscellaneous = _____

6. To find the number of hours per month that the student must work to finance the car, divide the total monthly expenses by the hourly rate.

   Number of hours per month = _____

7. To find the number of hours per week that the student must work, divide the number of hours per month by 4.

   Number of hours per week = _____

   The student has to work _____ hours per week to pay the monthly car expenses.

If you own a car, make out your own expense record. If you do not own a car, make assumptions about the kind of car that you would like to purchase, and calculate the total monthly expenses that you would have. An insurance company will give you rates on different kinds of insurance. An automobile club can give you approximations of miscellaneous expenses.

Chapter 6 Summary

Key Words	Examples
The *unit cost* is the cost of one item. [6.1A, p. 235]	Three paperback books cost $36. The unit cost is the cost of one paperback book, $12.
Percent increase is used to show how much a quantity has increased over its original value. [6.2A, p. 239]	The city's population increased 5%, from 10,000 people to 10,500 people.
Cost is the price a business pays for a product. *Selling price* is the price at which a business sells a product to a customer. *Markup* is the difference between selling price and cost. *Markup rate* is the markup expressed as a percent of a product's cost. [6.2B, p. 240]	A business pays $90 for a pair of cross trainers; the cost is $90. The business sells the cross trainers for $135; the selling price is $135. The markup is $135 − $90 = $45.
Percent decrease is used to show how much a quantity has decreased from its original value. [6.2C, p. 242]	Sales decreased 10%, from 10,000 units in the third quarter to 9000 units in the fourth quarter.
Sale price is the price after a reduction from the regular price. *Discount* is the difference between the regular price and the sale price. *Discount rate* is the discount as a percent of a product's regular price. [6.2D, p. 243]	A movie video that regularly sells for $50 is on sale for $40. The regular price is $50. The sale price is $40. The discount is $50 − $40 = $10.
Interest is the amount paid for the privilege of using someone else's money. *Principal* is the amount of money originally deposited or borrowed. The percent used to determine the amount of interest is the *interest rate*. Interest computed on the original amount is called *simple interest*. The principal plus the interest owed on a loan is called the *maturity value*. [6.3A, p. 249]	Consider a 1-year loan of $5000 at an annual simple interest rate of 8%. The principal is $5000. The interest rate is 8%. The interest paid on the loan is $5000 × 0.08 = $400. The maturity value is $5000 + $400 = $5400.
The interest charged on purchases made with a credit card are called *finance charges*. [6.3B, p. 251]	A credit card company charges 1.5% per month on any unpaid balance. The finance charge on an unpaid balance of $1000 is $1000 × 0.015 × 1 = $15.
Compound interest is computed not only on the original principal but also on the interest already earned. [6.3C, p. 252]	$10,000 is invested at 5% annual interest compounded monthly. The value of the investment after 5 years can be found by multiplying 10,000 by the factor found in the Compound Interest Table in the Appendix. $10,000 × 1.283359 = $12,833.59
A *mortgage* is an amount that is borrowed to buy real estate. The *loan origination fee* is usually a percent of the mortgage and is expressed as *points*. [6.4A, p. 259]	The loan origination fee of 3 points paid on a mortgage of $200,000 is 0.03 × $200,000 = $6000.
A *commission* is usually paid to a salesperson and is calculated as a percent of sales. [6.6A, p. 269]	A commission of 5% on sales of $50,000 is 0.05 × $50,000 = $2500.

An employee who receives an *hourly wage* is paid a certain amount for each hour worked. [6.6A, p. 269]

An employee is paid an hourly wage of $15. The employee's wages for working 10 hours are $15 × 10 = $150.

An employee who is paid a *salary* receives payment based on a weekly, biweekly, monthly, or annual time schedule. [6.6A, p. 269]

An employee paid an annual salary of $60,000 is paid $60,000 ÷ 12 = $5000 per month.

Balancing a checkbook is determining whether the checkbook balance is accurate. [6.7B, pp. 274–275]

To balance a checkbook:
(1) Put a checkmark in the checkbook register by each check paid by the bank and by each deposit recorded by the bank.
(2) Add to the current checkbook balance all checks that have been written but have not yet been paid by the bank and any interest paid on the account.
(3) Subtract any charges and any deposits not yet recorded by the bank. This is the checkbook balance.
(4) Compare the balance with the bank balance listed on the bank statement. If the two numbers are equal, the bank statement and the checkbook "balance."

Essential Rules and Procedures

Examples

To find unit cost, divide the total cost by the number of units. [6.1A, p. 235]

Three paperback books cost $36. The unit cost is $36 ÷ 3 = $12 per book.

To find total cost, multiply the unit cost by the number of units purchased. [6.1C, p. 236]

One melon costs $3. The total cost for 5 melons is $3 × 5 = $15.

Basic Markup Equations [6.2B, p. 240]
Selling price − cost = markup
Cost + markup = selling price
Markup rate × cost = markup

A pair of cross trainers that cost a business $90 has a 50% markup rate. The markup is 0.50 × $90 = $45. The selling price is $90 + $45 = $135.

Basic Discount Equations [6.2D, p. 243]
Regular price − sale price = discount
Regular price − discount = sale price
Discount rate × regular price = discount

A movie video is on sale for 20% off the regular price of $50. The discount is 0.20 × $50 = $10. The sale price is $50 − $10 = $40.

Simple Interest Formula for Annual Interest Rates
[6.3A, p. 249]

Principal × annual interest rate × time (in years) = interest
The simple interest due on a 2-year

Maturity Value Formula for Simple Interest Loan
[6.3A, p. 249]

Principal + interest = maturity value
The interest to be paid on a 2-year loan

Monthly Payment on a Simple Interest Loan [6.3A, p. 250]
Maturity value ÷ length of the loan in months = monthly payment

The maturity value of a simple interest 8-month loan is $8000. The monthly payment is $8000 ÷ 8 = $1000.

Chapter 6 Review Exercises

1. **Consumerism** A 20-ounce box of cereal costs $3.90. Find the unit cost.

2. **Car Expenses** An account executive had car expenses of $1025.58 for insurance, $605.82 for gas, $37.92 for oil, and $188.27 for maintenance during a year in which 11,320 miles were driven. Find the cost per mile for these four items taken as a group. Round to the nearest tenth of a cent.

3. **Investments** An oil stock was bought for $42.375 per share. Six months later, the stock was selling for $55.25 per share. Find the percent increase in the price of the stock for the 6 months. Round to the nearest tenth of a percent.

4. **Markup** A sporting goods store uses a markup rate of 40%. What is the markup on a ski suit that costs the store $180?

5. **Simple Interest** A contractor borrowed $100,000 from a credit union for 9 months at an annual interest rate of 4%. What is the simple interest due on the loan?

6. **Compound Interest** A computer programmer invested $25,000 in a retirement account that pays 6% interest, compounded daily. What is the value of the investment in 10 years? Use the Compound Interest Table in the Appendix. Round to the nearest cent.

7. **Investments** Last year an oil company had earnings of $4.12 per share. This year the earnings are $4.73 per share. What is the percent increase in earnings per share? Round to the nearest percent.

8. **Real Estate** The monthly mortgage payment for a condominium is $523.67. The owner must pay an annual property tax of $658.32. Find the total monthly payment for the mortgage and property tax.

9. **Car Expenses** A used pickup truck is purchased for $24,450. A down payment of 8% is made, and the remaining cost is financed for 4 years at an annual interest rate of 5%. Find the monthly payment. Use the Monthly Payment Table in the Appendix. Round to the nearest cent.

10. **Compound Interest** A fast-food restaurant invested $50,000 in an account that pays 7% annual interest compounded quarterly. What is the value of the investment in 1 year? Use the Compound Interest Table in the Appendix.

11. **Real Estate** Paula Mason purchased a home for $125,000. The lender requires a down payment of 15%. Find the amount of the down payment.

12. **Car Expenses** A plumber bought a truck for $18,500. A state license fee of $315 and a sales tax of 6.25% of the purchase price are required. Find the total cost of the sales tax and the license fee.

13. **Markup** Techno-Center uses a markup rate of 35% on all computer systems. Find the selling price of a computer system that costs the store $1540.

14. **Car Expenses** Mien pays a monthly car payment of $122.78. During a month in which $25.45 is principal, how much of the payment is interest?

15. **Compensation** The manager of the retail store at a ski resort receives a commission of 3% on all sales at the alpine shop. Find the total commission received during a month in which the shop had $108,000 in sales.

16. **Discount** A suit that regularly costs $235 is on sale for 40% off the regular price. Find the sale price.

17. **Banking** Luke had a checking account balance of $1568.45 before writing checks for $123.76, $756.45, and $88.77. He then deposited a check for $344.21. Find Luke's current checkbook balance.

18. **Simple Interest** Pros' Sporting Goods borrowed $30,000 at an annual interest rate of 8% for 6 months. Find the maturity value of the loan.

19. **Real Estate** A credit union requires a borrower to pay $2\frac{1}{2}$ points for a loan. Find the origination fee for a $75,000 loan.

20. **Consumerism** Sixteen ounces of mouthwash cost $3.49. A 33-ounce container of the same brand of mouthwash costs $6.99. Which is the better buy?

21. **Real Estate** The Sweeneys bought a home for $156,000. The family made a 10% down payment and financed the remainder with a 30-year loan at an annual interest rate of 7%. Find the monthly mortgage payment. Use the Monthly Payment Table in the Appendix. Round to the nearest cent.

22. **Compensation** Richard Valdez receives $12.60 per hour for working 40 hours a week and time and a half for working over 40 hours. Find his total income during a week in which he worked 48 hours.

23. **Banking** The business checking account of a donut shop showed a balance of $9567.44 before checks of $1023.55, $345.44, and $23.67 were written and checks of $555.89 and $135.91 were deposited. Find the current checkbook balance.

24. **Simple Interest** The simple interest due on a 4-month loan of $55,000 is $1375. Find the monthly payment on the loan.

25. **Simple Interest** A credit card company charges a customer 1.25% per month on the unpaid balance of charges on the card. What is the finance charge in a month in which the customer has an unpaid balance of $576?

Chapter 6 Test

1. **Consumerism**   Twenty feet of lumber cost $138.40. What is the cost per foot?

2. **Consumerism**   Which is the more economical purchase: 3 pounds of tomatoes for $7.49 or 5 pounds of tomatoes for $12.59?

3. **Consumerism**   Red snapper costs $4.15 per pound. Find the cost of $3\frac{1}{2}$ pounds. Round to the nearest cent.

4. **Business**   An exercise bicycle increased in price from $415 to $498. Find the percent increase in the cost of the exercise bicycle.

5. **Markup**   A department store uses a 40% markup rate. Find the selling price of a compact disc player that the store purchased for $215.

6. **Investments**   The price of gold dropped from $390 per ounce to $360 per ounce. What percent decrease does this amount represent? Round to the nearest tenth of a percent.

7. **Consumerism**   The price of a video camera dropped from $1120 to $896. What percent decrease does this price drop represent?

8. **Discount**   A corner hutch with a regular price of $299 is on sale for 30% off the regular price. Find the sale price.

9. **Discount**   A box of stationery that regularly sells for $9.50 is on sale for $5.70. Find the discount rate.

10. **Simple Interest**   A construction company borrowed $75,000 for 4 months at an annual interest rate of 8%. Find the simple interest due on the loan.

11. **Simple Interest**   Craig Allen borrowed $25,000 at an annual interest rate of 9.2% for 9 months. Find the maturity value of the loan.

12. **Simple Interest**   A credit card company charges a customer 1.2% per month on the unpaid balance of charges on the card. What is the finance charge in a month in which the customer has an unpaid balance of $374.95?

13. **Compound Interest**   Jorge, who is self-employed, placed $30,000 in an account that pays 6% annual interest compounded quarterly. How much interest was earned in 10 years? Use the Compound Interest Table in the Appendix.

14. **Real Estate**   A savings and loan institution is offering mortgage loans that have a loan origination fee of $2\frac{1}{2}$ points. Find the loan origination fee when a home is purchased with a loan of $134,000.

15. **Real Estate** A new housing development offers homes with a mortgage of $222,000 for 25 years at an annual interest rate of 8%. Find the monthly mortgage payment. Use the Monthly Payment Table in the Appendix.

16. **Car Expenses** A Chevrolet was purchased for $23,750, and a 20% down payment was made. Find the amount financed.

17. **Car Expenses** A rancher purchased an SUV for $23,714 and made a down payment of 15% of the cost. The balance was financed for 4 years at an annual interest rate of 7%. Find the monthly truck payment. Use the Monthly Payment Table in the Appendix.

18. **Compensation** Shaney receives an hourly wage of $20.40 an hour as an emergency room nurse. When called in at night, she receives time and a half. How much does Shaney earn in a week when she works 30 hours at normal rates and 15 hours during the night?

19. **Banking** The business checking account for a pottery store had a balance of $7349.44 before checks for $1349.67 and $344.12 were written. The store manager then made a deposit of $956.60. Find the current checkbook balance.

20. **Banking** Balance the checkbook shown.

		RECORD ALL CHARGES OR CREDITS THAT AFFECT YOUR ACCOUNT							BALANCE	
NUMBER	DATE	DESCRIPTION OF TRANSACTION	PAYMENT/DEBIT (−)	√ T	FEE (IF ANY) (−)	DEPOSIT/CREDIT (+)		$ 1422	13
843	8/1	House Payment	$ 713 72		$	$		708	41
	8/4	Deposit				852 60		1561	01
844	8/5	Loan Payment	162 40					1398	61
845	8/6	Groceries	166 44					1232	17
846	8/10	Car Payment	322 37					909	80
	8/15	Deposit				852 60		1762	40
847	8/16	Credit Card	413 45					1348	95
848	8/18	Pharmacy	92 14					1256	81
849	8/22	Utilities	72 30					1184	51
850	8/28	Telephone	78 20					1106	31

CHECKING ACCOUNT Monthly Statement			Account Number: 122-345-1	
Date	Transaction		Amount	Balance
8/1	OPENING BALANCE			1422.13
8/3	CHECK		713.72	708.41
8/4	DEPOSIT		852.60	1561.01
8/8	CHECK		166.44	1394.57
8/8	CHECK		162.40	1232.17
8/15	DEPOSIT		852.60	2084.77
8/23	CHECK		72.30	2012.47
8/24	CHECK		92.14	1920.33
9/1	CLOSING BALANCE			1920.33

Cumulative Review Exercises

1. Simplify: $12 - (10 - 8)^2 \div 2 + 3$

2. Add: $3\frac{1}{3} + 4\frac{1}{8} + 1\frac{1}{12}$

3. Find the difference between $12\frac{3}{16}$ and $9\frac{5}{12}$.

4. Find the product of $5\frac{5}{8}$ and $1\frac{9}{15}$.

5. Divide: $3\frac{1}{2} \div 1\frac{3}{4}$

6. Simplify $\left(\frac{3}{4}\right)^2 \div \left(\frac{3}{8} - \frac{1}{4}\right) + \frac{1}{2}$.

7. Divide: $0.059\overline{)3.0792}$
   Round to the nearest tenth.

8. Convert $\frac{17}{12}$ to a decimal. Round to the nearest thousandth.

9. Write "$410 in 8 hours" as a unit rate.

10. Solve the proportion $\frac{5}{n} = \frac{16}{35}$.
    Round to the nearest hundredth.

11. Write $\frac{5}{8}$ as a percent.

12. Find 6.5% of 420.

13. Write 18.2% as a decimal.

14. What percent of 20 is 8.4?

15. 30 is 12% of what?

16. 65 is 42% of what? Round to the nearest hundredth.

17. **Meteorology**   A series of late-summer storms produced rainfall of $3\frac{3}{4}$, $8\frac{1}{2}$, and $1\frac{2}{3}$ inches during a 3-week period. Find the total rainfall during the 3 weeks.

18. **Taxes**   The Homer family pays $\frac{1}{5}$ of its total monthly income for taxes. The family has a total monthly income of $4850. Find the amount of their monthly income that the Homers pay in taxes.

19. **Consumerism**   In 5 years, the cost of a scientific calculator went from $75 to $30. What is the ratio of the decrease in price to the original price?

20. **Fuel Efficiencies**   A compact car was driven 417.5 miles on 12.5 gallons of gasoline. Find the number of miles driven per gallon of gasoline.

21. **Consumerism**   A 14-pound turkey costs $12.96. Find the unit cost. Round to the nearest cent.

22. **Investments**   Eighty shares of a stock paid a dividend of $112. At the same rate, find the dividend on 200 shares of the stock.

23. **Discount**   A video camera that regularly sells for $900 is on sale for 20% off the regular price. What is the sale price?

24. **Markup**   A department store bought a portable disc player for $85 and used a markup rate of 40%. Find the selling price of the disc player.

25. **Compensation**   Sook Kim, an elementary school teacher, received an increase in salary from $2800 per month to $3024 per month. Find the percent increase in her salary.

26. **Simple Interest**   A contractor borrowed $120,000 for 6 months at an annual interest rate of 4.5%. How much simple interest is due on the loan?

27. **Car Expenses**   A red Ford Mustang was purchased for $26,900, and a down payment of $2000 was made. The balance is financed for 3 years at an annual interest rate of 9%. Find the monthly payment. Use the Monthly Payment Table in the Appendix. Round to the nearest cent.

28. **Banking**   A family had a checking account balance of $1846.78. A check of $568.30 was deposited into the account, and checks of $123.98 and $47.33 were written. Find the new checking account balance.

29. **Car Expenses**   During 1 year, Anna Gonzalez spent $840 on gasoline and oil, $520 on insurance, $185 on tires, and $432 on repairs. Find the cost per mile to drive the car 10,000 miles during the year. Round to the nearest cent.

30. **Real Estate**   A house has a mortgage of $172,000 for 20 years at an annual interest rate of 6%. Find the monthly mortgage payment. Use the Monthly Payment Table in the Appendix. Round to the nearest cent.

8 U.S. Customary Units of Measurement

In this chapter, you will be studying the U.S. Customary Units of length, weight, and capacity. As consumers, we are accustomed to these measurements. We purchase fabric by the yard, lumber by the foot, and tomatoes by the pound. We also buy perfume by the ounce, juice by the fluid ounce, and gasoline by the gallon. It is important to know how to convert between units and to perform operations that include different units. For example, in **Exercise 44 on page 350,** you are asked to determine how many 6-ounce bags of candy a storeowner can package from 12 pounds of candy.

OBJECTIVES

Section 8.1

A To convert measurements of length in the U.S. Customary System
B To perform arithmetic operations with measurements of length
C To solve application problems

Section 8.2

A To convert measurements of weight in the U.S. Customary System
B To perform arithmetic operations with measurements of weight
C To solve application problems

Section 8.3

A To convert measurements of capacity in the U.S. Customary System
B To perform arithmetic operations with measurements of capacity
C To solve application problems

Section 8.4

A To convert units of time

Section 8.5

A To use units of energy in the U.S. Customary System
B To use units of power in the U.S. Customary System

Need help? For online student resources, such as section quizzes, visit this textbook's website at **math.college.hmco.com/students.**

Do these exercises to prepare for Chapter 8.

For Exercises 1 to 8, add, subtract, multiply, or divide.

1.　　485
　　　+ 217

2.　　145
　　　− 87

3.　$36 \times \dfrac{1}{9}$

4.　$\dfrac{5}{3} \times 6$

5.　$400 \times \dfrac{1}{8} \times \dfrac{1}{2}$

6.　$5\dfrac{3}{4} \times 8$

7.　$3\overline{)714}$

8.　$12\overline{)18}$

GO FIGURE • • •

Mandy walks to work at a constant rate. One-third of the way to work, she passes a bank. Three-fourths of the way to work, she passes a book store. At the bank her watch reads 7:52 A.M., and at the book store it reads 8:02 A.M. At what time is Mandy one-half of the way to work?

8.1 Length

Objective A   **To convert measurements of
length in the U.S. Customary System**

A **measurement** includes a number and a unit.

3	feet
7	miles
12	yards

Number   Unit

Standard units of measurement have been established to simplify trade and commerce.

The unit of **length,** or distance, that is called the yard was originally defined as the length of a specified bronze bar located in London.

The standard U.S. Customary System units of length are **inch, foot, yard,** and **mile.**

> **Equivalences Between Units of Length in the U.S. Customary System**
>
> 12 inches (in.) = 1 foot (ft)
> 3 ft = 1 yard (yd)
> 36 in. = 1 yard (yd)
> 5280 ft = 1 mile (mi)

These equivalences can be used to form conversion rates; a **conversion rate** is a relationship used to change one unit of measurement to another. For example, because 3 ft = 1 yd, the conversion rates $\frac{3\text{ ft}}{1\text{ yd}}$ and $\frac{1\text{ yd}}{3\text{ ft}}$ are both equivalent to 1.

HOW TO Convert 27 ft to yards.

$$27\text{ ft} = 27\text{ ft} \times \frac{1\text{ yd}}{3\text{ ft}}$$

$$= 27\ \cancel{\text{ft}} \times \frac{1\text{ yd}}{3\ \cancel{\text{ft}}}$$

$$= \frac{27\text{ yd}}{3}$$

$$= 9\text{ yd}$$

HOW TO Convert 5 yd to feet.

$$5\text{ yd} = 5\text{ yd} \times \frac{3\text{ ft}}{1\text{ yd}}$$

$$= 5\ \cancel{\text{yd}} \times \frac{3\text{ ft}}{1\ \cancel{\text{yd}}}$$

$$= \frac{15\text{ ft}}{1}$$

$$= 15\text{ ft}$$

Note that in the conversion rate chosen, the unit in the numerator is the same as the unit desired in the answer. The unit in the denominator is the same as the unit in the given measurement.

Example 1   Convert 40 in. to feet.

Solution $40 \text{ in.} = 40 \text{ in.} \times \dfrac{1 \text{ ft}}{12 \text{ in.}}$

$= \dfrac{40 \text{ ft}}{12} = 3\dfrac{1}{3} \text{ ft}$

You Try It 1   Convert 14 ft to yards.

Your solution

Example 2   Convert $3\dfrac{1}{4}$ yd to feet.

Solution $3\dfrac{1}{4} \text{ yd} = \dfrac{13}{4} \text{ yd} = \dfrac{13}{4} \text{ yd} \times \dfrac{3 \text{ ft}}{1 \text{ yd}}$

$= \dfrac{39 \text{ ft}}{4} = 9\dfrac{3}{4} \text{ ft}$

You Try It 2   Convert 9240 ft to miles.

Your solution

Solutions on p. S22

Objective B   **To perform arithmetic operations with measurements of length**

When performing arithmetic operations with measurements of length, write the answer in simplest form. For example, 1 ft 14 in. should be written as 2 ft 2 in.

HOW TO   Convert: 50 in. = _____ ft _____ in.

$$
\begin{array}{r}
4 \text{ ft } 2 \text{ in.} \\
12\overline{)\ 50\ } \\
-48 \\
\hline
2
\end{array}
$$

- Because 12 in. = 1 ft, divide 50 in. by 12. The whole-number part of the quotient is the number of feet. The remainder is the number of inches.

50 in. = 4 ft 2 in.

Example 3   Convert: 17 in. = _____ ft _____ in.

Solution

$$
\begin{array}{r}
1 \text{ ft } 5 \text{ in.} \\
12\overline{)\ 17\ } \\
-12 \\
\hline
5
\end{array}
$$

- 12 in. = 1 ft

17 in. = 1 ft 5 in.

You Try It 3   Convert: 42 in. = _____ ft _____ in.

Your solution

Example 4   Convert: 31 ft = _____ yd _____ ft

Solution

$$
\begin{array}{r}
10 \text{ yd } 1 \text{ ft} \\
3\overline{)\ 31\ } \\
-30 \\
\hline
1
\end{array}
$$

- 3 ft = 1 yd

31 ft = 10 yd 1 ft

You Try It 4   Convert: 14 ft = _____ yd _____ ft

Your solution

Solutions on p. S22

Example 5   Find the sum of 4 ft 4 in. and 1 ft 11 in.

Solution

$\begin{array}{r} 4 \text{ ft} \quad 4 \text{ in.} \\ + 1 \text{ ft} \ 11 \text{ in.} \\ \hline 5 \text{ ft} \ 15 \text{ in.} \end{array}$ • **15 in. = 1 ft 3 in.**

5 ft 15 in. = 6 ft 3 in.

You Try It 5   Find the sum of 3 ft 5 in. and 4 ft 9 in.

Your solution

Example 6   Subtract: 9 ft 6 in. − 3 ft 8 in.

Solution

$\begin{array}{r} {}^{8 \text{ ft}} \quad {}^{18 \text{ in.}} \\ \cancel{9 \text{ ft}} \ \cancel{6 \text{ in.}} \\ - \ 3 \text{ ft} \quad 8 \text{ in.} \\ \hline 5 \text{ ft} \ 10 \text{ in.} \end{array}$ • **Borrow 1 ft (12 in.) from 9 ft and add to 6 in.**

You Try It 6   Subtract: 4 ft 2 in. − 1 ft 8 in.

Your solution

Example 7   Multiply: 3 yd 2 ft × 4

Solution

$\begin{array}{r} 3 \text{ yd} \ 2 \text{ ft} \\ \times \quad \ 4 \\ \hline 12 \text{ yd} \ 8 \text{ ft} \end{array}$ • **8 ft = 2 yd 2 ft**

12 yd 8 ft = 14 yd 2 ft

You Try It 7   Multiply: 4 yd 1 ft × 8

Your solution

Example 8   Find the quotient of 4 ft 3 in. and 3.

Solution

$\begin{array}{r} \quad 1 \text{ ft} \qquad 5 \text{ in.} \\ 3 \overline{\smash{)}\ 4 \text{ ft} \qquad 3 \text{ in.}} \\ \underline{- \ 3 \text{ ft}} \qquad \qquad \\ 1 \text{ ft} = \underline{12 \text{ in.}} \\ 15 \text{ in.} \\ \underline{-15 \text{ in.}} \\ 0 \end{array}$

You Try It 8   Find the quotient of 7 yd 1 ft and 2.

Your solution

Example 9   Multiply: $2\frac{3}{4}$ ft × 3

Solution

$2\frac{3}{4} \text{ ft} \times 3 = \frac{11}{4} \text{ ft} \times 3$

$= \frac{33}{4} \text{ ft}$

$= 8\frac{1}{4} \text{ ft}$

You Try It 9   Subtract: $6\frac{1}{4}$ ft − $3\frac{2}{3}$ ft

Your solution

Solutions on p. S22

Objective C To solve application problems

Example 10

A concrete block is 9 in. high. How many rows of blocks are required for a retaining wall that is 6 ft high?

Strategy

To find the number of rows of blocks, convert 9 in. to feet. Then divide the height of the wall (6 ft) by the height of each block.

Solution

$$9 \text{ in.} = \frac{9 \text{ in.}}{1} \cdot \frac{1 \text{ ft}}{12 \text{ in.}} = \frac{9 \text{ ft}}{12} = 0.75 \text{ ft}$$

$$\frac{6 \text{ ft}}{0.75 \text{ ft}} = 8$$

The wall will have 8 rows of blocks.

You Try It 10

The floor of a storage room is being tiled. Eight tiles, each a 9-inch square, fit across the width of the floor. Find the width, in feet, of the storage room.

Your strategy

Your solution

Example 11

A plumber used 3 ft 9 in., 2 ft 6 in., and 11 in. of copper tubing to install a sink. Find the total length of copper tubing used.

Strategy

To find the total length of copper tubing used, add the three lengths of copper tubing (3 ft 9 in., 2 ft 6 in., and 11 in.).

Solution

```
    3 ft   9 in.
    2 ft   6 in.
+         11 in.
    5 ft  26 in.      • 26 in. = 2 ft 2 in.
```

5 ft 26 in. = 7 ft 2 in.

The plumber used 7 ft 2 in. of copper tubing.

You Try It 11

A board 9 ft 8 in. is cut into four pieces of equal length. How long is each piece?

Your strategy

Your solution

Solutions on p. S22

8.1 Exercises

Objective A   To convert measurements of length in the U.S. Customary System

For Exercises 1 to 15, convert.

1. 6 ft = _____ in.

2. 9 ft = _____ in.

3. 30 in. = _____ ft

4. 64 in. = _____ ft

5. 13 yd = _____ ft

6. $4\frac{1}{2}$ yd = _____ ft

7. 16 ft = _____ yd

8. $4\frac{1}{2}$ ft = _____ yd

9. $2\frac{1}{3}$ yd = _____ in.

10. 5 yd = _____ in.

11. 120 in. = _____ yd

12. 66 in. = _____ yd

13. 2 mi = _____ ft

14. $1\frac{1}{2}$ mi = _____ ft

15. $7\frac{1}{2}$ in. = _____ ft

Objective B   To perform arithmetic operations with measurements of length

For Exercises 16 to 30, perform the arithmetic operation.

16. 100 in. = ___ ft ___ in.

17. 6400 ft = ___ mi ___ ft

18. 15 in. = ___ ft ___ in.

19. 6 ft 7 in. + 3 ft 4 in.

20. 9 ft 11 in. + 3 ft 6 in.

21. 5 ft 3 in. − 2 ft 6 in.

22. 9 yd 1 ft − 3 yd 2 ft

23. 2 ft 5 in. × 6

24. $3\frac{2}{3}$ ft × 4

25. 2)5 ft 4 in.

26. $12\frac{1}{2}$ in. ÷ 3

27. $4\frac{2}{3}$ ft + $6\frac{1}{2}$ ft

28. 3 yd 2 ft + 6 yd 2 ft

29. 1 mi 4200 ft + 2 mi 3600 ft

30. 5 yd 1 ft − 2 yd 2 ft

31.   Interior Decorating   A kitchen counter is to be covered with tile that is 4 in. square. How many tiles can be placed along one row of a counter top that is 4 ft 8 in. long?

32.   Interior Decorating   Thirty-two yards of material were used for making pleated draperies. How many feet of material were used?

33.   Measurement   Find the missing dimension.

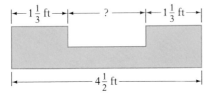

34.   Measurement   Find the total length of the shaft.

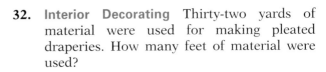

35.   Measurement   What length of material is needed to drill two holes 3 in. in diameter and leave $\frac{1}{2}$ in. between the holes and on either side as shown in the diagram?

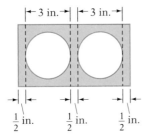

36.   Measurement   Find the missing dimension in the figure.

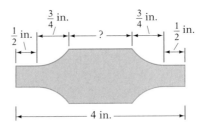

37.   Carpentry   A board $6\frac{2}{3}$ ft long is cut into four equal pieces. How long is each piece?

38.   Carpentry   How long must a board be if four pieces, each 3 ft 4 in. long, are to be cut from it?

39.   Interior Decorating   A picture is 1 ft 9 in. high and 1 ft 6 in. wide. Find the length of framing needed to frame the picture.

40.   Interior Decorating   You bought 32 ft of baseboard to install in the kitchen of your house. How many inches of baseboard did you purchase?

41.   Masonry   Forty-five bricks, each 9 in. long, are laid end to end to make the base for a wall. Find the length of the wall in feet.

42.   Construction   A roof is constructed with nine rafters, each 8 ft 4 in. long. Find the total number of feet of material needed to build the rafters.

APPLYING THE CONCEPTS

43.   Measurement   There are approximately 200,000,000 adults living in the United States. Assume that the average adult is 19 in. wide from shoulder to shoulder. If all the adults in the United States are standing shoulder to shoulder, could they reach around Earth at the equator, a distance of approximately 25,000 mi?

**44.   How good are you at estimating lengths or distances? Estimate the length of a pencil, the width of your room, the length of a block, and the distance to the grocery store. Then measure these lengths and compare the results with your estimates.

8.2 Weight

Objective A **To convert measurements of weight in the U.S. Customary System**

Point of Interest

The Romans used two different systems of weights. In both systems, the smallest unit was the *uncia,* abbreviated to "oz," from which the term *ounce* is derived. In one system, there were 16 ounces to 1 pound. In the second system, a pound, which was called the libra, equaled 12 unciae. The abbreviation "lb" for pound comes from the word *libra.*

The avoirdupois system of measurement and the troy system of measurement have their heritage in the two Roman systems.

Weight is a measure of how strongly Earth is pulling on an object. The unit of weight called the pound is defined as the weight of a standard solid kept at the Bureau of Standards in Washington, D.C. The U.S. Customary System units of weight are **ounce, pound,** and **ton.**

> **Equivalences Between Units of Weight in the U.S. Customary System**
> 16 ounces (oz) = 1 pound (lb)
> 2000 lb = 1 ton

These equivalences can be used to form conversion rates to change one unit of measurement to another. For example, because 16 oz = 1 lb, the conversion rates $\frac{16\ oz}{1\ lb}$ and $\frac{1\ lb}{16\ oz}$ are both equivalent to 1.

HOW TO Convert 62 oz to pounds.

$$62\ oz = 62\ oz \times \boxed{\frac{1\ lb}{16\ oz}}$$

$$= \frac{62\ \cancel{oz}}{1} \times \frac{1\ lb}{16\ \cancel{oz}}$$

$$= \frac{62\ lb}{16}$$

$$= 3\frac{7}{8}\ lb$$

- The conversion rate must contain lb (the unit desired in the answer) in the numerator and must contain oz (the original unit) in the denominator.

Example 1 Convert $3\frac{1}{2}$ tons to pounds.

Solution
$$3\frac{1}{2}\ tons = \frac{7}{2}\ \cancel{tons} \times \frac{2000\ lb}{1\ \cancel{ton}}$$
$$= \frac{14{,}000\ lb}{2} = 7000\ lb$$

You Try It 1 Convert 3 lb to ounces.

Your solution

Example 2 Convert 42 oz to pounds.

Solution
$$42\ oz = 42\ \cancel{oz} \times \frac{1\ lb}{16\ \cancel{oz}}$$
$$= \frac{42\ lb}{16} = 2\frac{5}{8}\ lb$$

You Try It 2 Convert 4200 lb to tons.

Your solution

Solutions on p. S22

Objective B **To perform arithmetic operations with measurements of weight**

When performing arithmetic operations with measurements of weight, write the answer in simplest form. For example, 1 lb 22 oz should be written 2 lb 6 oz.

Example 3 Find the difference between 14 lb 5 oz and 8 lb 14 oz.

Solution

$$
\begin{array}{r}
\overset{13\ lb}{\cancel{14\ lb}} \quad \overset{21\ oz}{\cancel{5\ oz}} \\
-\quad 8\ lb\ 14\ oz \\
\hline
5\ lb\ \ 7\ oz
\end{array}
$$

• Borrow 1 lb (16 oz) from 14 lb and add it to 5 oz.

You Try It 3 Find the difference between 7 lb 1 oz and 3 lb 4 oz.

Your solution

Example 4 Divide: 7 lb 14 oz ÷ 3

Solution

$$
\begin{array}{r}
2\ lb \quad\ 10\ oz \\
3\overline{)\ 7\ lb \quad\ 14\ oz} \\
-6\ lb \\
\hline
1\ lb = 16\ oz \\
\quad\quad 30\ oz \\
\quad -30\ oz \\
\hline
\quad\quad\quad 0
\end{array}
$$

You Try It 4 Multiply: 3 lb 6 oz × 4

Your solution

Solutions on pp. S22–S23

Objective C **To solve application problems**

Example 5

Sirina Jasper purchased 4 lb 8 oz of oat bran and 2 lb 11 oz of wheat bran. She plans to blend the two brans and then repackage the mixture in 3-ounce packages for a diet supplement. How many 3-ounce packages can she make?

Strategy

To find the number of 3-ounce packages:

• Add the amount of oat bran (4 lb 8 oz) to the amount of wheat bran (2 lb 11 oz).
• Convert the sum to ounces.
• Divide the total ounces by the weight of each package (3 oz).

Solution

$$
\begin{array}{r}
4\ lb\ \ 8\ oz \\
+\ 2\ lb\ 11\ oz \\
\hline
6\ lb\ 19\ oz = 7\ lb\ 3\ oz = 115\ oz
\end{array}
$$

$$\frac{115\ oz}{3\ oz} \approx 38.3$$

She can make 38 packages.

You Try It 5

Find the weight in pounds of 12 bars of soap. Each bar weighs 7 oz.

Your strategy

Your solution

Solution on p. S23

8.2 Exercises

Objective A   **To convert measurements of weight in the U.S. Customary System**

For Exercises 1 to 18, convert.

1. 64 oz = _____ lb

2. 36 oz = _____ lb

3. 8 lb = _____ oz

4. 7 lb = _____ oz

5. 3200 lb = _____ tons

6. 9000 lb = _____ tons

7. 6 tons = _____ lb

8. $1\frac{1}{4}$ tons = _____ lb

9. 66 oz = _____ lb

10. 90 oz = _____ lb

11. $1\frac{1}{2}$ lb = _____ oz

12. $2\frac{5}{8}$ lb = _____ oz

13. $1\frac{3}{10}$ tons = _____ lb

14. $\frac{4}{5}$ ton = _____ lb

15. 500 lb = _____ ton

16. 5000 lb = _____ tons

17. 180 oz = _____ lb

18. 12 oz = _____ lb

Objective B   **To perform arithmetic operations with measurements of weight**

For Exercises 19 to 33, perform the arithmetic operation.

19. 9000 lb =
     _____ tons _____ lb

20. 85 oz =
     _____ lb _____ oz

21. 40 oz =
     _____ lb _____ oz

22. $\begin{array}{r} 4\text{ lb }\ 7\text{ oz} \\ +\ 3\text{ lb }12\text{ oz} \\ \hline \end{array}$

23. $\begin{array}{r} 1\text{ ton }\ \ 800\text{ lb} \\ +\ 3\text{ tons }1600\text{ lb} \\ \hline \end{array}$

24. $\begin{array}{r} 7\text{ lb }5\text{ oz} \\ -\ 3\text{ lb }8\text{ oz} \\ \hline \end{array}$

25. $\begin{array}{r} 3\text{ tons }500\text{ lb} \\ -\ 1\text{ ton }\ \ 800\text{ lb} \\ \hline \end{array}$

26. $\begin{array}{r} 3\text{ lb }6\text{ oz} \\ \times\ \ \ \ \ \ \ 4 \\ \hline \end{array}$

27. $5\frac{1}{2}$ lb × 6

28. $2\overline{)3\text{ lb }8\text{ oz}}$

29. $4\frac{2}{3}$ lb × 3

30. $\begin{array}{r} 7\text{ lb }7\text{ oz} \\ +\ 6\text{ lb }9\text{ oz} \\ \hline \end{array}$

31. $\begin{array}{r} 6\frac{1}{2}\text{ oz} \\ +\ 2\frac{1}{2}\text{ oz} \\ \hline \end{array}$

32. $\begin{array}{r} 6\frac{3}{8}\text{ lb} \\ -\ 2\frac{5}{6}\text{ lb} \\ \hline \end{array}$

33. 5 lb 12 oz ÷ 4

Objective C   **To solve application problems**

34. **Iron Works**   A machinist has 25 iron rods to mill. Each rod weighs 20 oz. Find the total weight of the rods in pounds.

35. **Masonry**   A fireplace brick weighs $2\frac{1}{2}$ lb. What is the weight of a load of 800 bricks?

36. **Weights**   A college bookstore received 1200 textbooks, each weighing 9 oz. Find the total weight of the 1200 textbooks in pounds.

37. **Weights**   A 4- × 4-inch tile weighs 7 oz. Find the weight, in pounds, of a package of 144 tiles.

38. **Ranching**   A farmer ordered 20 tons of feed for 100 cattle. After 15 days, the farmer has 5 tons of feed left. On average, how many pounds of food has each cow eaten per day?

39. **Weights**   A case of soft drinks contains 24 cans, each weighing 6 oz. Find the weight, in pounds, of the case of soft drinks.

40. **Child Development**   A baby weighed 7 lb 8 oz at birth. At 6 months of age, the baby weighed 15 lb 13 oz. Find the baby's increase in weight during the 6 months.

41. **Packaging**   Shampoo weighing 5 lb 4 oz is divided equally and poured into four containers. How much shampoo is in each container?

42. **Weights**   A steel rod weighing 16 lb 11 oz is cut into three pieces. Find the weight of each piece of steel rod.

43. **Consumerism**   Find the cost of a ham roast that weighs 5 lb 10 oz if the price per pound is $4.80.

44. **Markup**   A candy store buys candy weighing 12 lb for $14.40. The candy is repackaged and sold in 6-ounce packages for $1.15 each. Find the markup on the 12 lb of candy.

45. **Shipping**   A manuscript weighing 2 lb 3 oz is mailed at the parcel post rate of $.25 per ounce. Find the cost of mailing the manuscript.

APPLYING THE CONCEPTS

46. Write a paragraph describing the growing need for precision in our measurements as civilization progressed. Include a discussion of the need for precision in the space industry.

47. Estimate the weight of a nickel, a textbook, a friend, and a car. Then find the actual weights and compare them with your estimates.

8.3 Capacity

Objective A

To convert measurements of capacity in the U.S. Customary System

Point of Interest

The word *quart* has its root in the Medieval Latin word *quartus*, which means "fourth." Thus a quart is $\frac{1}{4}$ of a gallon. The same Latin word is the source of such other English words as *quarter*, *quartile*, *quadrilateral*, and *quartet*.

Liquid substances are measured in units of **capacity.** The standard U.S. Customary units of capacity are the **fluid ounce, cup, pint, quart,** and **gallon.**

> **Equivalences Between Units of Capacity in the U.S. Customary System**
>
> 8 fluid ounces (fl oz) = 1 cup (c)
> 2 c = 1 pint (pt)
> 2 pt = 1 quart (qt)
> 4 qt = 1 gallon (gal)

These equivalences can be used to form conversion rates to change one unit of measurement to another. For example, because 8 fl oz = 1 c, the conversion rates $\frac{8 \text{ fl oz}}{1 \text{ c}}$ and $\frac{1 \text{ c}}{8 \text{ fl oz}}$ are both equivalent to 1.

HOW TO Convert 36 fl oz to cups.

$$36 \text{ fl oz} = 36 \text{ fl oz} \times \frac{1 \text{ c}}{8 \text{ fl oz}}$$

$$= \frac{36 \text{ fl oz}}{1} \times \frac{1 \text{ c}}{8 \text{ fl oz}}$$

$$= \frac{36 \text{ c}}{8}$$

$$= 4\frac{1}{2} \text{ c}$$

- The conversion rate must contain c in the numerator and fl oz in the denominator.

HOW TO Convert 3 qt to cups.

$$3 \text{ qt} = 3 \text{ qt} \times \frac{2 \text{ pt}}{1 \text{ qt}} \times \frac{2 \text{ c}}{1 \text{ pt}}$$

$$= \frac{3 \text{ qt}}{1} \times \frac{2 \text{ pt}}{1 \text{ qt}} \times \frac{2 \text{ c}}{1 \text{ pt}}$$

$$= \frac{12 \text{ c}}{1}$$

$$= 12 \text{ c}$$

- The direct equivalence is not given above. Use two conversion rates. First convert quarts to pints, and then convert pints to cups. The unit in the denominator of the second conversion rate and the unit in the numerator of the first conversion rate must be the same in order to cancel.

Example 1 Convert 42 c to quarts.

Solution

$$42 \text{ c} = 42 \text{ c} \times \frac{1 \text{ pt}}{2 \text{ c}} \times \frac{1 \text{ qt}}{2 \text{ pt}}$$

$$= \frac{42 \text{ qt}}{4} = 10\frac{1}{2} \text{ qt}$$

You Try It 1 Convert 18 pt to gallons.

Your solution

Solution on p. S23

Objective B   **To perform arithmetic operations with measurements of capacity**

When performing arithmetic operations with measurements of capacity, write the answer in simplest form. For example, 1 c 12 fl oz should be written as 2 c 4 fl oz.

Example 2   What is 4 gal 1 qt decreased by 2 gal 3 qt?

You Try It 2   Find the quotient of 4 gal 2 qt and 3.

Solution

$$\begin{array}{r} \overset{\text{3 gal}}{\cancel{4\ \text{gal}}}\ \overset{\text{5 qt}}{\cancel{1\ \text{qt}}} \\ -\ 2\ \text{gal}\ 3\ \text{qt} \\ \hline 1\ \text{gal}\ 2\ \text{qt} \end{array}$$

• **Borrow 1 gal (4 qt) from 4 gal and add to 1 qt.**

Your solution

Solution on p. S23

Objective C   **To solve application problems**

Example 3

A can of apple juice contains 25 fl oz. Find the number of quarts of apple juice in a case of 24 cans.

You Try It 3

Five students are going backpacking in the desert. Each student requires 5 qt of water per day. How many gallons of water should they take for a 3-day trip?

Strategy
To find the number of quarts of apple juice in one case:

• Multiply the number of cans (24) by the number of fluid ounces per can (25) to find the total number of fluid ounces in the case.
• Convert the number of fluid ounces in the case to quarts.

Your strategy

Solution
24 × 25 fl oz = 600 fl oz

$$600\ \text{fl oz} = \frac{600\ \cancel{\text{fl oz}}}{1} \cdot \frac{1\ \cancel{c}}{8\ \cancel{\text{fl oz}}} \cdot \frac{1\ \cancel{\text{pt}}}{2\ \cancel{c}} \cdot \frac{1\ \text{qt}}{2\ \cancel{\text{pt}}}$$

$$= \frac{600\ \text{qt}}{32} = 18\frac{3}{4}\ \text{qt}$$

One case of apple juice contains $18\frac{3}{4}$ qt.

Your solution

Solution on p. S23

8.3 Exercises

Objective A To convert measurements of capacity in the U.S. Customary System

For Exercises 1 to 18, convert.

1. 60 fl oz = _____ c

2. 48 fl oz = _____ c

3. 3 c = _____ fl oz

4. $2\frac{1}{2}$ c = _____ fl oz

5. 8 c = _____ pt

6. 5 c = _____ pt

7. $3\frac{1}{2}$ pt = _____ c

8. 12 pt = _____ qt

9. 22 qt = _____ gal

10. 10 qt = _____ gal

11. $2\frac{1}{4}$ gal = _____ qt

12. 7 gal = _____ qt

13. $7\frac{1}{2}$ pt = _____ qt

14. $3\frac{1}{2}$ qt = _____ pt

15. 20 fl oz = _____ pt

16. $1\frac{1}{2}$ pt = _____ fl oz

17. 17 c = _____ qt

18. $1\frac{1}{2}$ qt = _____ c

Objective B To perform arithmetic operations with measurements of capacity

For Exercises 19 to 36, perform the arithmetic operation.

19. 14 qt = _____ gal _____ qt

20. 9 pt = _____ qt _____ pt

21. 5 pt = _____ qt _____ pt

22. 3 gal 2 qt
     + 4 gal 3 qt

23. 4 qt 1 pt
     + 2 qt 1 pt

24. 3 gal 1 qt
     − 1 gal 2 qt

25. 3 c 3 fl oz
     − 2 c 5 fl oz

26. 2 qt 1 pt
     ×   5

27. $3\frac{1}{2}$ pt × 5

28. 5)6 gal 1 qt

29. $3\frac{1}{2}$ gal ÷ 4

30. 5 c 3 fl oz
     + 3 c 6 fl oz

31. 3 gal 3 qt
     + 1 gal 2 qt

32. 4 c 6 fl oz
     − 2 c 7 fl oz

33. 3 gal
     − 1 gal 2 qt

34. $1\dfrac{1}{2}$ pt $+ 2\dfrac{2}{3}$ pt

35. $4\dfrac{1}{2}$ gal $- 1\dfrac{3}{4}$ gal

36. $2\overline{)3 \text{ gal } 2 \text{ qt}}$

Objective C   **To solve application problems**

37. Catering   Sixty adults are expected to attend a book signing. Each adult will drink 2 c of coffee. How many gallons of coffee should be prepared?

38. Catering   The Bayside Playhouse serves punch during intermission. Assume that 200 people will each drink 1 c of punch. How many gallons of punch should be ordered?

39. Chemistry   A solution needed for a chemistry class required 72 fl oz of water, 16 fl oz of one solution, and 48 fl oz of another solution. Find the number of quarts of the final solution.

40. Food Service   A cafeteria sold 124 cartons of milk in 1 day. Each carton contained 1 c of milk. How many quarts of milk were sold that day?

41. Vehicle Maintenance   A farmer changed the oil in a tractor seven times during the year. Each oil change required 5 qt of oil. How many gallons of oil did the farmer use in the seven oil changes?

42. Capacity   There are 24 cans in a case of tomato juice. Each can contains 10 fl oz of tomato juice. Find the number of 1-cup servings in the case of tomato juice.

43. Consumerism   One brand of tomato juice costs $1.59 for 1 qt. Another brand costs $1.25 for 24 fl oz. Which is the more economical purchase?

44. Camping   Mandy carried 12 qt of water for 3 days of desert camping. Water weighs $8\dfrac{1}{3}$ lb per gallon. Find the weight of water that she carried.

45. Business   A department store bought hand lotion in 5-quart containers and then repackaged the lotion in 8-fluid-ounce bottles. The lotion and bottles cost $81.50, and each 8-fluid-ounce bottle was sold for $8.25. How much profit was made on each 5-quart package of lotion?

46. Business   Orlando bought oil in 50-gallon containers for changing the oil in his customers' cars. He paid $240 for the 50 gal of oil and charged customers $2.10 per quart. Find the profit Orlando made on one 50-gallon container of oil.

APPLYING THE CONCEPTS

47. Define the following units: grain, dram, furlong, and rod. Give an example where each would be used.

48. ✎ Assume that you wanted to invent a new measuring system. Discuss some of the features that would have to be incorporated into the system.

8.4 Time

Objective A   **To convert units of time**

The units in which time is generally measured are the **second, minute, hour, day,** and **week**.

> ### Equivalences Between Units of Time
> 60 seconds (s) = 1 minute (min)
> 60 min = 1 hour (h)
> 24 h = 1 day
> 7 days = 1 week

These equivalences can be used to form conversion rates to change one unit of time to another. For example, because 24 h = 1 day, the conversion rates $\frac{24\ h}{1\ day}$ and $\frac{1\ day}{24\ h}$ are both equivalent to 1. An example using each of these two rates is shown below.

HOW TO   Convert $5\frac{1}{2}$ days to hours.

$$5\frac{1}{2}\ \text{days} = 5\frac{1}{2}\ \text{days} \times \boxed{\frac{24\ h}{1\ day}}$$

$$= \frac{11\ \cancel{days}}{2} \times \frac{24\ h}{1\ \cancel{day}}$$

$$= \frac{264\ h}{2}$$

$$= 132\ h$$

• The conversion rate must contain h (the unit desired in the answer) in the numerator and must contain day (the original unit) in the denominator.

HOW TO   Convert 156 h to days.

$$156\ h = 156\ h \times \boxed{\frac{1\ day}{24\ h}}$$

$$= \frac{156\ \cancel{h}}{1} \times \frac{1\ day}{24\ \cancel{h}}$$

$$= \frac{156\ \text{days}}{24}$$

$$= 6\frac{1}{2}\ \text{days}$$

• The conversion rate must contain day (the unit desired in the answer) in the numerator and must contain h (the original unit) in the denominator.

Example 1   Convert 2880 min to days.

Solution

$$2880\ \text{min} = 2880\ \cancel{\text{min}} \times \frac{1\ \cancel{h}}{60\ \cancel{\text{min}}} \times \frac{1\ day}{24\ \cancel{h}}$$

$$= \frac{2880\ \text{days}}{1440} = 2\ \text{days}$$

You Try It 1   Convert 18,000 s to hours.

Your solution

Solution on p. S23

8.4 Exercises

Objective A   **To convert units of time**

For Exercises 1 to 24, convert.

1. 98 days = _____ weeks

2. 12 weeks = _____ days

3. $6\frac{1}{4}$ days = _____ h

4. 114 h = _____ days

5. 555 min = _____ h

6. $7\frac{3}{4}$ h = _____ min

7. $18\frac{1}{2}$ min = _____ s

8. 750 s = _____ min

9. 12,600 s = _____ h

10. 15,300 s = _____ h

11. $6\frac{1}{2}$ h = _____ s

12. $5\frac{3}{4}$ h = _____ s

13. 5040 min = _____ days

14. 6840 min = _____ days

15. $2\frac{1}{2}$ days = _____ min

16. $6\frac{1}{4}$ days = _____ min

17. 672 h = _____ weeks

18. 588 h = _____ weeks

19. 3 weeks = _____ h

20. $5\frac{1}{2}$ weeks = _____ h

21. 172,800 s = _____ days

22. 20,160 min = _____ weeks

23. 3 days = _____ s

24. 3 weeks = _____ min

APPLYING THE CONCEPTS

Another unit of time is the year. One year is equivalent to $365\frac{1}{4}$ days. However, our calendar does not include quarter days. Instead, we say that a year is 365 days, and every fourth year is a leap year of 366 days. If a year is divisible by 4, it is a leap year, unless it is a year at the beginning of a century not divisible by 400. 1600, 2000, 2004, 2008, and 2012 are leap years. 1700, 1800, and 1900 are not leap years. For Exercises 25 to 27, state whether the given year is a leap year.

25. 1984

26. 1994

27. 2144

For Exercises 28 to 33, convert. Use a 365-day year.

28. 1825 days = _____ years

29. 2555 days = _____ years

30. 4 years = _____ days

31. 6 years = _____ days

32. 2 years = _____ h

33. $3\frac{1}{2}$ years = _____ h

8.5 Energy and Power

Objective A **To use units of energy in the U.S. Customary System**

Energy can be defined as the ability to do work. Energy is stored in coal, in gasoline, in water behind a dam, and in one's own body.

One **foot-pound** (ft · lb) of energy is the amount of energy necessary to lift 1 pound a distance of 1 foot.

To lift 50 lb a distance of 5 ft requires
50 × 5 = 250 ft · lb of energy.

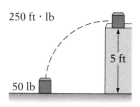

Consumer items that use energy, such as furnaces, stoves, and air conditioners, are rated in terms of the **British thermal unit** (Btu). For example, a furnace might have a rating of 35,000 Btu per hour, which means that it releases 35,000 Btu of energy in one hour (1 h).

Because 1 Btu = 778 ft · lb, the following conversion rate, equivalent to 1, can be written:

$$\frac{778 \text{ ft} \cdot \text{lb}}{1 \text{ Btu}} = 1$$

Example 1

Convert 250 Btu to foot-pounds.

Solution

$$250 \text{ Btu} = 250 \text{ Btu} \times \frac{778 \text{ ft} \cdot \text{lb}}{1 \text{ Btu}}$$
$$= 194,500 \text{ ft} \cdot \text{lb}$$

You Try It 1

Convert 4.5 Btu to foot-pounds.

Your solution

Example 2

Find the energy required for a 125-pound person to climb a mile-high mountain.

Solution

In climbing the mountain, the person is lifting 125 lb a distance of 5280 ft.

Energy = 125 lb × 5280 ft
     = 660,000 ft · lb

You Try It 2

Find the energy required for a motor to lift 800 lb a distance of 16 ft.

Your solution

Solutions on p. S23

Example 3

A furnace is rated at 80,000 Btu per hour. How many foot-pounds of energy are released in 1 h?

Solution

$$80{,}000 \text{ Btu} = 80{,}000 \text{ Btu} \times \frac{778 \text{ ft} \cdot \text{lb}}{1 \text{ Btu}}$$

$$= 62{,}240{,}000 \text{ ft} \cdot \text{lb}$$

You Try It 3

A furnace is rated at 56,000 Btu per hour. How many foot-pounds of energy are released in 1 h?

Your solution

Solution on p. S23

Objective B   **To use units of power in the U.S. Customary System**

Power is the rate at which work is done or the rate at which energy is released. Power is measured in **foot-pounds per second** $\left(\frac{\text{ft} \cdot \text{lb}}{\text{s}} \right)$. In each of the following examples, the amount of energy released is the same, but the time taken to release the energy is different; thus the power is different.

100 lb is lifted 10 ft in 10 s.

$$\text{Power} = \frac{10 \text{ ft} \times 100 \text{ lb}}{10 \text{ s}} = 100 \frac{\text{ft} \cdot \text{lb}}{\text{s}}$$

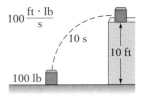

100 lb is lifted 10 ft in 5 s.

$$\text{Power} = \frac{10 \text{ ft} \times 100 \text{ lb}}{5 \text{ s}} = 200 \frac{\text{ft} \cdot \text{lb}}{\text{s}}$$

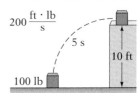

The U.S. Customary unit of power is the **horsepower.** A horse doing average work can pull 550 lb a distance of 1 ft in 1 s and can continue this work all day.

$$\textbf{1 horsepower (hp)} = \textbf{550} \frac{\textbf{ft} \cdot \textbf{lb}}{\textbf{s}}$$

Example 4

Find the power needed to raise 300 lb a distance of 30 ft in 15 s.

Solution $\text{Power} = \dfrac{30 \text{ ft} \times 300 \text{ lb}}{15 \text{ s}}$

$$= 600 \frac{\text{ft} \cdot \text{lb}}{\text{s}}$$

You Try It 4

Find the power needed to raise 1200 lb a distance of 90 ft in 24 s.

Your solution

Example 5

A motor has a power of 2750 $\frac{\text{ft} \cdot \text{lb}}{\text{s}}$. Find the horsepower of the motor.

Solution $\dfrac{2750}{550} = 5 \text{ hp}$

You Try It 5

A motor has a power of 3300 $\frac{\text{ft} \cdot \text{lb}}{\text{s}}$. Find the horsepower of the motor.

Your solution

Solutions on p. S23

8.5 Exercises

Objective A   To use units of energy in the U.S. Customary System

1. Convert 25 Btu to foot-pounds.

2. Convert 6000 Btu to foot-pounds.

3. Convert 25,000 Btu to foot-pounds.

4. Convert 40,000 Btu to foot-pounds.

5. Find the energy required to lift 150 lb a distance of 10 ft.

6. Find the energy required to lift 300 lb a distance of 16 ft.

7. Find the energy required to lift a 3300-pound car a distance of 9 ft.

8. Find the energy required to lift a 3680-pound elevator a distance of 325 ft.

9. Three tons are lifted 5 ft. Find the energy required in foot-pounds.

10. Seven tons are lifted 12 ft. Find the energy required in foot-pounds.

11. A construction worker carries 3-pound blocks up a 10-foot flight of stairs. How many foot-pounds of energy are required to carry 850 blocks up the stairs?

12. A crane lifts an 1800-pound steel beam to the roof of a building 36 ft high. Find the amount of energy the crane requires in lifting the beam.

13. A furnace is rated at 45,000 Btu per hour. How many foot-pounds of energy are released by the furnace in 1 h?

14. A furnace is rated at 22,500 Btu per hour. How many foot-pounds of energy does the furnace release in 1 h?

15. Find the amount of energy in foot-pounds given off when 1 lb of coal is burned. One pound of coal gives off 12,000 Btu of energy when burned.

16. Find the amount of energy in foot-pounds given off when 1 lb of gasoline is burned. One pound of gasoline gives off 21,000 Btu of energy when burned.

Objective B   **To use units of power in the U.S. Customary System**

17. Convert $1100 \frac{ft \cdot lb}{s}$ to horsepower.

18. Convert $6050 \frac{ft \cdot lb}{s}$ to horsepower.

19. Convert $4400 \frac{ft \cdot lb}{s}$ to horsepower.

20. Convert $1650 \frac{ft \cdot lb}{s}$ to horsepower.

21. Convert 9 hp to foot-pounds per second.

22. Convert 4 hp to foot-pounds per second.

23. Convert 7 hp to foot-pounds per second.

24. Convert 8 hp to foot-pounds per second.

25. Find the power in foot-pounds per second needed to raise 125 lb a distance of 12 ft in 3 s.

26. Find the power in foot-pounds per second needed to raise 500 lb a distance of 60 ft in 8 s.

27. Find the power in foot-pounds per second needed to raise 3000 lb a distance of 40 ft in 25 s.

28. Find the power in foot-pounds per second of an engine that can raise 12,000 lb to a height of 40 ft in 60 s.

29. Find the power in foot-pounds per second of an engine that can raise 180 lb to a height of 40 ft in 5 s.

30. Find the power in foot-pounds per second of an engine that can raise 1200 lb to a height of 18 ft in 30 s.

31. A motor has a power of $4950 \frac{ft \cdot lb}{s}$. Find the horsepower of the motor.

32. A motor has a power of $16,500 \frac{ft \cdot lb}{s}$. Find the horsepower of the motor.

33. A motor has a power of $6600 \frac{ft \cdot lb}{s}$. Find the horsepower of the motor.

APPLYING THE CONCEPTS

34. Pick a source of energy and write an article about it. Include the source, possible pollution problems, and future prospects associated with this form of energy.

Focus on Problem Solving

Applying Solutions to Other Problems

Problem solving in the previous chapters concentrated on solving specific problems. After a problem is solved, however, there is an important question to be asked: "Does the solution to this problem apply to other types of problems?"

To illustrate this extension of problem solving, we will consider *triangular numbers*, which were studied by ancient Greek mathematicians. The numbers 1, 3, 6, 10, 15, and 21 are the first six triangular numbers. What is the next triangular number?

To answer this question, note in the diagram below that a triangle can be formed using the number of dots that correspond to a triangular number.

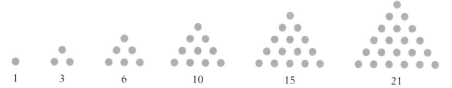

Observe that the number of dots in each row is one more than the number of dots in the row above. The total number of dots can be found by addition.

The pattern suggests that the next triangular number (the seventh one) is the sum of the first 7 natural numbers. The seventh triangular number is 28. The diagram at the right shows the seventh triangular number.

Using the pattern for triangular numbers, it is easy to determine that the tenth triangular number is

$$1 + 2 + 3 + 4 + 5 + 6 + 7 + 8 + 9 + 10 = 55$$

Now consider a situation that may seem to be totally unrelated to triangular numbers. Suppose you are in charge of scheduling softball games for a league. There are seven teams in the league, and each team must play every other team once. How many games must be scheduled?

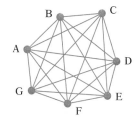

We label the teams A, B, C, D, E, F, and G. (See the figure at the left.) A line between two teams indicates that the two teams play each other. Beginning with A, there are 6 lines for the 6 teams that A must play. There are 6 teams that B must play, but the line between A and B has already been drawn, so there are only 5 remaining games to schedule for B. Now move on to C. The lines between C and A and between C and B have already been drawn, so there are only 4 additional lines to be drawn to represent the teams C will play. Moving on to D, we see that the lines between D and A, D and B, and D and C have already been drawn, so there are 3 more lines to be drawn to represent the teams D will play.

Note that each time we move from team to team, one fewer line needs to be drawn. When we reach F, there is only one line to be drawn, the one between F and G. The total number of lines drawn is 6 + 5 + 4 + 3 + 2 + 1 = 21, the sixth triangular number. For a league with 7 teams, the number of games that must be scheduled so that each team plays every other team once is the sixth triangular number. If there were ten teams in the league, the number of games that must be scheduled would be the ninth triangular number, which is 45.

A college chess team wants to schedule a match so that each of its 15 members plays each other member of the team once. How many matches must be scheduled?

Projects and Group Activities

Nomographs

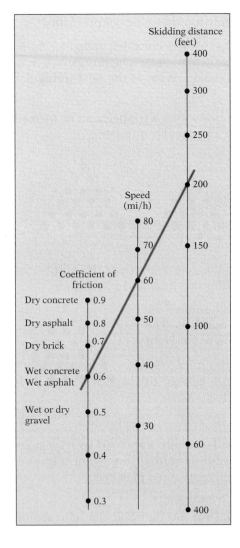

A chart is another tool that is used in problem solving. The chart at the left is a nomograph. A **nomograph** is a chart that represents numerical relationships among variables.

One of the details a traffic accident investigator checks when looking into a car accident is the length of the skid marks of the car. This length can help the investigator determine the speed of the car when the brakes were applied.

The nomograph at the left can be used to determine the speed of a car under given conditions. It shows the relationship among the speed of the car, the skidding distance, and the *coefficient of friction*.

The coefficient of friction is an experimentally obtained value that reflects how easy or hard it is to drag one object over another. For instance, it is easier to drag a box across ice than to drag it across a carpet. The coefficient of friction is smaller for the box and ice than it is for the box and carpet.

To use the nomograph at the left, an investigator would draw a line from the coefficient of friction to the skidding distance. The point at which the line crosses the speed line shows how fast the car was going when the brakes were applied. The line from 0.6 to 200 intersects the speed line at 60. This indicates that a car that skidded 200 ft on wet asphalt or wet concrete was traveling at 60 mi/h.

1. Use the nomograph to determine the speed of a car when the brakes were applied for a car traveling on gravel and for skid marks of 100 ft.

2. Use the nomograph to determine the speed of a car when the brakes were applied for a car traveling on dry concrete and for skid marks of 150 ft.

3. Suppose a car is traveling 80 mi/h when the brakes are applied. Find the difference in skidding distance if the car is traveling on wet concrete rather than dry concrete.

Averages

If two towns are 150 mi apart and you drive between the two towns in 3 h, then your

$$\text{Average speed} = \frac{\text{total distance}}{\text{total time}} = \frac{150 \text{ mi}}{3 \text{ h}} = 50 \text{ mi/h}$$

It is highly unlikely that your speed was *exactly* 50 mi/h the entire time of the trip. Sometimes you will have traveled faster than 50 mi/h, and other times you will have traveled slower than 50 mi/h. Dividing the total distance you traveled by the total time it took to go that distance is an example of calculating an average.

There are many other averages that may be calculated. For instance, the Environmental Protection Agency calculates an estimated miles per gallon (mpg) for new cars. Miles per gallon is an average calculated from the formula

$$\frac{\text{Miles traveled}}{\text{Gallons of gasoline consumed}}$$

For instance, the miles per gallon for a car that travels 308 mi on 11 gal of gas is $\frac{308 \text{ mi}}{11 \text{ gal}} = 28 \text{ mpg}$.

A pilot would not use miles per gallon as a measure of fuel efficiency. Rather, pilots use gallons per hour. A plane that travels 5 h and uses 400 gal of fuel has an average that is calculated as

$$\frac{\text{Gallons of fuel}}{\text{Hours flown}} = \frac{400 \text{ gal}}{5 \text{ h}} = 80 \text{ gal/h}$$

Using the examples above, calculate the following averages.

1. Determine the average speed of a car that travels 355 mi in 6 h. Round to the nearest tenth.

2. Determine the miles per gallon of a car that can travel 405 mi on 12 gal of gasoline. Round to the nearest tenth.

3. If a plane flew 2000 mi in 5 h and used 1000 gal of fuel, determine the average number of gallons per hour that the plane used.

Another type of average is grade-point average (GPA). It is calculated by multiplying the units for each class by the grade point for that class, adding the results, and dividing by the total number of units taken. Here is an example using the grading scale $A = 4$, $B = 3$, $C = 2$, $D = 1$, and $F = 0$.

Class	Units	Grade
Math	4	B (= 3)
English	3	A (= 4)
French	5	C (= 2)
Biology	3	B (= 3)

$$\text{GPA} = \frac{4 \cdot 3 + 3 \cdot 4 + 5 \cdot 2 + 3 \cdot 3}{4 + 3 + 5 + 3} = \frac{43}{15} \approx 2.87$$

4. A grading scale that provides for plus or minus grades uses $A = 4$, $A- = 3.7$, $B+ = 3.3$, $B = 3$, $B- = 2.7$, $C+ = 2.3$, $C = 2$, $C- = 1.7$, $D+ = 1.3$, $D = 1$, $D- = 0.7$, and $F = 0$. Calculate the GPA of the student whose grades are given below.

Class	Units	Grade
Math	5	B +
English	3	C +
Spanish	5	A –
Physical science	3	B –

Chapter 8 Summary

Key Words	Examples
A *measurement* includes a number and a unit. [8.1A, p. 341]	9 inches, 6 feet, 3 yards, and 50 miles are measurements.
Equivalent measures are used to form *conversion rates* to change one unit in the U.S. Customary System of measurement to another. In the conversion rate chosen, the unit in the numerator is the same as the unit desired in the answer. The unit in the denominator is the same as the unit in the given measurement. [8.1A, p. 341]	Because 12 in. = 1 ft, the conversion rate $\frac{12 \text{ in.}}{1 \text{ ft}}$ is used to convert feet to inches. The conversion rate $\frac{1 \text{ ft}}{12 \text{ in.}}$ is used to convert inches to feet.

Energy is the ability to do work. One *foot-pound* (ft · lb) of energy is the amount of energy necessary to lift 1 pound a distance of 1 foot. Consumer items that use energy are rated in *British thermal units* (Btu). [8.5A, p. 357]

Find the energy required for a 110-pound person to climb a set of stairs 12 ft high.

Energy = 110 lb × 12 ft = 1320 ft · lb

Power is the rate at which work is done or energy is released. Power is measured in *foot-pounds per second* $\left(\frac{ft \cdot lb}{s}\right)$ and *horsepower* (hp). [8.5B, p. 358]

Find the power needed to raise 250 lb a distance of 20 ft in 10 s.

$$\text{Power} = \frac{20 \text{ ft} \times 250 \text{ lb}}{10 \text{ s}} = 500\frac{ft \cdot lb}{s}$$

Essential Rules and Procedures

Examples

Equivalences Between Units of Length [8.1A, p. 341]
The U.S. Customary units of length are inch (in.), foot (ft), yard (yd), and mile (mi).
12 in. = 1 ft
3 ft = 1 yd
36 in. = 1 yd
5280 ft = 1 mi

Convert 52 in. to ft.

$$52 \text{ in.} = 52 \text{ in.} \times \frac{1 \text{ ft}}{12 \text{ in.}}$$
$$= \frac{52 \text{ ft}}{12} = 4\frac{1}{3} \text{ ft}$$

Equivalences Between Units of Weight [8.2A, p. 347]
Weight is a measure of how strongly Earth is pulling on an object. The U.S. Customary units of weight are ounce (oz), pound (lb), and ton.
16 oz = 1 lb
2000 lb = 1 ton

Convert 9 lb to ounces.

$$9 \text{ lb} = 9 \text{ lb} \times \frac{16 \text{ oz}}{1 \text{ lb}} = 144 \text{ oz}$$

Equivalences Between Units of Capacity [8.3A, p. 351]
Liquid substances are measured in units of *capacity*. The U.S. Customary units of capacity are fluid ounce (fl oz), cup (c), pint (pt), quart (qt), and gallon (gal).
8 fl oz = 1 c
2 c = 1 pt
2 pt = 1 qt
4 qt = 1 gal

Convert 14 qt to gallons.

$$14 \text{ qt} = 14 \text{ qt} \times \frac{1 \text{ gal}}{4 \text{ qt}}$$
$$= \frac{14 \text{ gal}}{4} = 3\frac{1}{2} \text{ gal}$$

Equivalences Between Units of Time [8.4A, p. 355]
Units of time are seconds (s), minutes (min), hours (h), days, and weeks.
60 s = 1 min
60 min = 1 h
24 h = 1 day
7 days = 1 week

Convert 8 days to hours.

$$8 \text{ days} = 8 \text{ days} \times \frac{24 \text{ h}}{1 \text{ day}} = 192 \text{ h}$$

Equivalences Between Units of Energy [8.5A, p. 357]
1 Btu = 778 ft · lb

Convert 70 Btu to foot-pounds.

$$70 \text{ Btu} = 70 \text{ Btu} \times \frac{778 \text{ ft} \cdot \text{lb}}{1 \text{ Btu}}$$
$$= 54,460 \text{ ft} \cdot \text{lb}$$

Equivalences Between Units of Power [8.5B, p. 358]
The U.S. Customary unit of power is the horsepower (hp).

$$1 \text{ hp} = 550 \frac{ft \cdot lb}{s}$$

Convert 5 hp to foot-pounds per second.

$$5 \times 550 = 2750 \frac{ft \cdot lb}{s}$$

Chapter 8 Review Exercises

1. Convert 4 ft to inches.

2. What is 7 ft 6 in. divided by 3?

3. Find the energy needed to lift 200 lb a distance of 8 ft.

4. Convert $2\frac{1}{2}$ pt to fluid ounces.

5. Convert 14 ft to yards.

6. Convert 2400 lb to tons.

7. Find the quotient of 7 lb 5 oz and 3.

8. Convert $3\frac{3}{8}$ lb to ounces.

9. Add: 3 ft 9 in.
         + 5 ft 6 in.

10. Subtract: 3 tons   500 lb
           − 1 ton   1500 lb

11. Add: 4 c 7 fl oz
         + 2 c 3 fl oz

12. Subtract: 5 yd 1 ft
           − 3 yd 2 ft

13. Convert 12 c to quarts.

14. Convert 375 min to hours.

15. Convert 2.5 hp to foot-pounds per second. $\left(1 \text{ hp} = 550 \, \frac{\text{ft} \cdot \text{lb}}{\text{s}}.\right)$

16. Multiply: 5 lb 8 oz
            $\times$ 8
            _____

17. Convert 50 Btu to foot-pounds. (1 Btu = 778 ft · lb.)

18. Convert 3850 $\frac{\text{ft} \cdot \text{lb}}{\text{s}}$ to horsepower. $\left(1 \text{ hp} = 550 \, \frac{\text{ft} \cdot \text{lb}}{\text{s}}.\right)$

19. **Carpentry**   A board 6 ft 11 in. long is cut from a board 10 ft 5 in. long. Find the length of the remaining piece of board.

20. **Shipping**   A book weighing 2 lb 3 oz is mailed at the parcel post rate of $.24 per ounce. Find the cost of mailing the book.

21. **Capacity**   A can of pineapple juice contains 18 fl oz. Find the number of quarts in a case of 24 cans.

22. **Food Service**   A cafeteria sold 256 cartons of milk in one school day. Each carton contains 1 c of milk. How many gallons of milk were sold that day?

23. **Energy**   A furnace is rated at 35,000 Btu per hour. How many foot-pounds of energy does the furnace release in 1 h? (1 Btu = 778 ft · lb)

24. **Power**   Find the power in foot-pounds per second of an engine that can raise 800 lb to a height of 15 ft in 25 s.

Chapter 8 Test

1. Convert $2\frac{1}{2}$ ft to inches.

2. Subtract: 4 ft 2 in. − 1 ft 9 in.

3. **Carpentry** A board $6\frac{2}{3}$ ft long is cut into five equal pieces. How long is each piece?

4. **Masonry** Seventy-two bricks, each 8 in. long, are laid end to end to make the base for a wall. Find the length of the wall in feet.

5. Convert $2\frac{7}{8}$ lb to ounces.

6. Convert: 40 oz = ___ lb ___ oz

7. Find the sum of 9 lb 6 oz and 7 lb 11 oz.

8. Divide: 6 lb 12 oz ÷ 4

9. **Weights** A college bookstore received 1000 workbooks, each weighing 12 oz. Find the total weight of the 1000 workbooks in pounds.

10. **Recycling** An elementary school class gathered 800 aluminum cans for recycling. Four aluminum cans weigh 3 oz. Find the amount the class received if the rate of pay was $.75 per pound for the aluminum cans. Round to the nearest cent.

11. Convert 13 qt to gallons.

12. Convert $3\frac{1}{2}$ gal to pints.

13. What is $1\frac{3}{4}$ gal times 7?

14. Add: 5 gal 2 qt + 2 gal 3 qt

15. Convert 756 h to weeks.

16. Convert $3\frac{1}{4}$ days to minutes.

17. **Capacity** A can of grapefruit juice contains 20 fl oz. Find the number of cups of grapefruit juice in a case of 24 cans.

18. **Business** Nick, a mechanic, bought oil in 40-gallon containers for changing the oil in customers' cars. He paid $200 for the 40 gal of oil and charged customers $2.15 per quart. Find the profit Nick made on one 40-gallon container of oil.

19. **Energy** Find the energy required to lift 250 lb a distance of 15 ft.

20. **Energy** A furnace is rated at 40,000 Btu per hour. How many foot-pounds of energy are released by the furnace in 1 h? (1 Btu = 778 ft · lb)

21. **Power** Find the power needed to lift 200 lb a distance of 20 ft in 25 s.

22. **Power** A motor has a power of 2200 $\frac{\text{ft} \cdot \text{lb}}{\text{s}}$. Find the motor's horsepower. $\left(1 \text{ hp} = 550 \frac{\text{ft} \cdot \text{lb}}{\text{s}}\right)$

Cumulative Review Exercises

1. Find the LCM of 9, 12, and 15.

2. Write $\frac{43}{8}$ as a mixed number.

3. Subtract: $5\frac{7}{8} - 2\frac{7}{12}$

4. What is $5\frac{1}{3}$ divided by $2\frac{2}{3}$?

5. Simplify: $\frac{5}{8} \div \left(\frac{3}{8} - \frac{1}{4}\right) - \frac{5}{8}$

6. Round 2.0972 to the nearest hundredth.

7. Multiply: $\begin{array}{r} 0.0792 \\ \times \quad 0.49 \\ \hline \end{array}$

8. Solve the proportion: $\frac{n}{12} = \frac{44}{60}$

9. Find $2\frac{1}{2}\%$ of 50.

10. 18 is 42% of what? Round to the nearest hundredth.

11. **Consumerism** A 7.2-pound roast costs $37.08. Find the unit cost.

12. Add: $3\frac{2}{5}$ in. $+ 5\frac{1}{3}$ in.

13. Convert: 24 oz = ___ lb ___ oz

14. Multiply: 3 lb 8 oz $\times$ 9

15. Subtract: $4\frac{1}{3}$ qt $- 1\frac{5}{6}$ qt

16. Find 2 lb 10 oz less than 4 lb 6 oz.

17. Investments   An investor receives a dividend of $56 from 40 shares of stock. At the same rate, find the dividend that 200 shares of stock would yield.

18. Banking   Anna had a balance of $578.56 in her checkbook. She wrote checks for $216.98 and $34.12 and made a deposit of $315.33. What is her new checking account balance?

19. Compensation   An account executive receives a salary of $1800 per month plus a commission of 2% on all sales over $25,000. Find the total monthly income of an account executive who has monthly sales of $140,000.

20. Produce   A health inspector found that 3% of a 2500-pound shipment of carrots were spoiled and could not be sold. Find the amount of carrots that could be sold.

21. Education   The scores on the final exam of a trigonometry class are recorded in the histogram in the figure to the right. What percent of the class received a score between 80% and 90%? Round to the nearest percent.

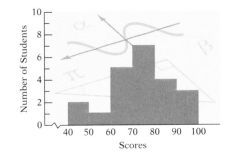

22. Markup   Hayes Department Store uses a markup rate of 40% on all merchandise. What is the selling price of a compact disc player that cost the store $220?

23. Simple Interest   A construction firm received a loan of $200,000 for 8 months at a simple interest rate of 6%. Find the interest paid on the loan.

24. Income   Six college students spent several weeks panning for gold during their summer vacation. The students obtained 1 lb 3 oz of gold, which they sold for $200 per ounce. How much money did each student receive if they shared the money equally? Round to the nearest dollar.

25. Shipping   Four books were mailed at the postal rate of $.28 per ounce. The books weighed 1 lb 3 oz, 13 oz, 1 lb 8 oz, and 1 lb. Find the cost of mailing the books.

26. Consumerism   One brand of yogurt costs $.79 for 8 oz, and 36 oz of another brand can be bought for $2.98. Which purchase is the better buy?

27. Probability   Two dice are rolled. What is the probability that the sum of the dots on the upward faces is 9?

28. Energy   Find the energy required to lift 400 lb a distance of 8 ft.

29. Power   Find the power, in foot-pounds per second, needed to raise 600 lb a distance of 8 ft in 12 s.

These tourists took an excursion boat in order to get a closer look at the icebergs at the end of the glaciers in Antarctica's Paradise Bay. Temperatures in places such as this fall below zero. When this happens, the temperatures are described in negative numbers. Negative numbers are used to express any value below zero, such as debt, altitude below sea level, decreases in stock prices, and golf scores under par. In **Exercises 86 to 89 on page 436,** you will be solving problems involving extreme temperature changes in parts of the United States, as well as the boiling points of certain chemical elements.

OBJECTIVES

Section 10.1

A To identify the order relation between two integers
B To evaluate expressions that contain the absolute value symbol

Section 10.2

A To add integers
B To subtract integers
C To solve application problems

Section 10.3

A To multiply integers
B To divide integers
C To solve application problems

Section 10.4

A To add or subtract rational numbers
B To multiply or divide rational numbers
C To solve application problems

Section 10.5

A To write a number in scientific notation
B To use the Order of Operations Agreement to simplify expressions

Need help? For online student resources, such as section quizzes, visit this textbook's website at **math.college.hmco.com/students.**

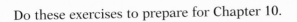

PREP TEST ● ● ●

Do these exercises to prepare for Chapter 10.

1. Place the correct symbol, < or >, between the two numbers.

54   45

2. What is the distance from 4 to 8 on the number line?

For Exercises 3 to 14, add, subtract, multiply, or divide.

3. $7654 + 8193$

4. $6097 - 2318$

5. 472×56

6. $\dfrac{144}{24}$

7. $\dfrac{2}{3} + \dfrac{3}{5}$

8. $\dfrac{3}{4} - \dfrac{5}{16}$

9. $0.75 + 3.9 + 6.408$

10. $5.4 - 1.619$

11. $\dfrac{3}{4} \times \dfrac{8}{15}$

12. $\dfrac{5}{12} \div \dfrac{3}{4}$

13. 23.5×0.4

14. $0.96 \div 2.4$

15. Simplify: $(8 - 6)^2 + 12 \div 4 \cdot 3^2$

GO FIGURE ● ● ●

Super Yeast causes bread to double in volume each minute. If it takes one loaf of bread made with Super Yeast 30 minutes to fill the oven, how long does it take two loaves of bread made with Super Yeast to fill one-half the oven?

10.1 Introduction to Integers

Objective A To identify the order relation between two integers

Thus far in the text, we have encountered only zero and the numbers greater than zero. The numbers greater than zero are called **positive numbers.** However, the phrases "12 degrees below zero," "$25 in debt," and "15 feet below sea level" refer to numbers less than zero. These numbers are called **negative numbers.**

The **integers** are . . . , −4, −3, −2, −1, 0, 1, 2, 3, 4, ...

Point of Interest

Among the slang words for zero are *zilch*, *zip*, and *goose egg.* The word *love* for zero in scoring a tennis game comes from the French word *l'oeuf*, which means "the egg."

Each integer can be shown on a number line. The integers to the left of zero on the number line are called **negative integers** and are represented by a negative sign (−) placed in front of the number. The integers to the right of zero are called **positive integers.** The positive integers are also called **natural numbers.** Zero is neither a positive nor a negative integer.

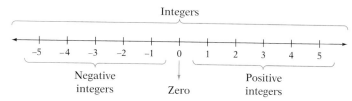

A number line can be used to visualize the order relation between two integers. A number that appears to the left of a given number is less than (<) the given number. A number that appears to the right of a given number is greater than (>) the given number.

2 is greater than negative 4.

2 > −4

Negative 5 is less than negative 3.

−5 < −3

Example 1

The temperature at the North Pole was recorded as 87° below zero. Represent this temperature as an integer.

Solution −87°

Example 2

Graph −2 on the number line.

Solution

Example 3

Place the correct symbol, < or >, between the numbers −5 and −7.

Solution −5 > −7   • −5 is to the right of −7 on the number line.

You Try It 1

The surface of the Salton Sea is 232 ft below sea level. Represent this depth as an integer.

Your solution

You Try It 2

Graph −4 on the number line.

Your solution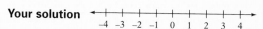

You Try It 3

Place the correct symbol, < or >, between the numbers −12 and −8.

Your solution

Solutions on p. S25

Objective B   **To evaluate expressions that contain the absolute value symbol**

Two numbers that are the same distance from zero on the number line but on opposite sides of zero are called **opposites.**

−4 is the opposite of 4

            and

4 is the opposite of −4.

Note that a negative sign can be read as "the opposite of."

−(4) = −4   The opposite of positive 4 is negative 4.

−(−4) = 4   The opposite of negative 4 is positive 4.

The **absolute value of a number** is the distance between zero and the number on the number line. Therefore, the absolute value of a number is a positive number or zero. The symbol for absolute value is | |.

The distance from 0 to 4 is 4. Thus |4| = 4 (the absolute value of 4 is 4).

The distance from 0 to −4 is 4. Thus |−4| = 4 (the absolute value of −4 is 4).

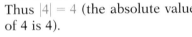

The absolute value of a positive number is the number itself. The absolute value of a negative number is the opposite of the negative number. The absolute value of zero is zero.

Example 4   Find the absolute value of 2 and −3.

Solution |2| = 2

            |−3| = 3

You Try It 4   Find the absolute value of −7 and 21.

Your solution

Example 5   Evaluate |−34| and |0|.

Solution |−34| = 34

            |0| = 0

You Try It 5   Evaluate |2| and |−9|.

Your solution

Example 6   Evaluate −|−4|.

Solution   −|−4| = −4
The minus sign *in front of* the absolute value sign is not affected by the absolute value sign.

You Try It 6   Evaluate −|−12|.

Your solution

Solutions on p. S25

10.1 Exercises

Objective A **To identify the order relation between two integers**

For Exercises 1 to 4, represent the quantity as an integer.

1. A lake 120 ft below sea level

2. A temperature that is 15° below zero

3. A share of stock up 2 dollars

4. A loss of 324 dollars

For Exercises 5 to 8, graph the numbers on the number line.

5. 3 and −3

6. −2 and 0

7. −4 and 1

8. 4 and −1

For Exercises 9 to 14, state which number on the number line is in the location given.

9. 3 units to the right of −2

10. 5 units to the right of −3

11. 4 units to the left of 3

12. 2 units to the left of −1

13. 6 units to the right of −3

14. 4 units to the right of −4

For Exercises 15 to 18, use the following number line.

A   B   C   D   E   F   G   H   I

15. **a.** If *F* is 1 and *G* is 2, what number is *A*?

16. **a.** If *G* is 1 and *H* is 2, what number is *B*?

b. If *F* is 1 and *G* is 2, what number is *C*?

b. If *G* is 1 and *H* is 2, what number is *D*?

17. **a.** If *H* is 0 and *I* is 1, what number is *A*?

18. **a.** If *G* is 2 and *I* is 4, what number is *B*?

b. If *H* is 0 and *I* is 1, what number is *D*?

b. If *G* is 2 and *I* is 4, what number is *E*?

For Exercises 19 to 42, place the correct symbol, < or >, between the two numbers.

19. −2   −5

20. −6   −1

21. −16   1

22. −2   13

23. 3   −7

24. 5   −6

25. −11   −8

26. −4   −10

27. 35   28

28. 42   19

29. −42   27

30. −36   49

31. 21   −34

32. 53   −46

33. −27   −39

34. −51   −20

35. −87   63

36. −75   92

37. 86   −79

38. 95   −71

39. −62   −84

40. −91   −70

41. −131   101

42. 127   −150

For Exercises 43 to 51, write the given numbers in order from smallest to largest.

43. 3, −7, 0, −2

44. −4, 8, 6, −1

45. −3, 1, −5, 4

46. −6, 2, −8, 7

47. 9, −4, 5, 0

48. 6, −9, −12, 8

49. −10, 4, 12, −5, −7

50. 11, −8, −1, 7, −6

51. 10, −11, −2, 5, −7

Objective B   **To evaluate expressions that contain the absolute value symbol**

For Exercises 52 to 61, find the opposite number.

52. 4

53. 16

54. −2

55. −3

56. 22

57. 45

58. −31

59. −59

60. 70

61. −88

For Exercises 62 to 69, find the absolute value of the number.

62. 4   **63.** -4 **64.** -7 **65.** 9

66. -1 **67.** -11 **68.** 10   **69.** -12

For Exercises 70 to 99, evaluate.

70. $|2|$ **71.** $|-2|$ **72.** $|-6|$ **73.** $|6|$ **74.** $|8|$

75. $|5|$ **76.** $|-9|$ **77.** $|-1|$ **78.** $-|-1|$ **79.** $-|-5|$

80. $-|0|$ **81.** $|16|$ **82.** $|19|$ **83.** $|-12|$ **84.** $|-22|$

85. $-|29|$ **86.** $-|20|$ **87.** $-|-14|$ **88.** $-|-18|$ **89.** $|-15|$

90. $|-23|$ **91.** $-|33|$ **92.** $-|27|$ **93.** $|32|$ **94.** $|25|$

95. $-|-42|$ **96.** $|-74|$ **97.** $|-61|$ **98.** $-|88|$ **99.** $-|52|$

For Exercises 100 to 107, place the correct symbol, $<$, $=$, or $>$, between the two numbers.

100. $|7|$ $|-9|$ **101.** $|-12|$ $|8|$ **102.** $|-5|$ $|-2|$ **103.** $|6|$ $|13|$

104. $|-8|$ $|3|$ **105.** $|-1|$ $|-17|$ **106.** $|-14|$ $|14|$ **107.** $|17|$ $|-17|$

For Exercises 108 to 113, write the given numbers in order from smallest to largest.

108. $|-8|, -3, |2|, -|-5|$ **109.** $-|6|, -4, |-7|, -9$ **110.** $-1, |-6|, |0|, -|3|$

111. $-|-7|, -9, 5, |4|$ **112.** $-|2|, -8, 6, |1|$ **113.** $-3, -|-8|, |5|, -|10|$

APPLYING THE CONCEPTS

114. 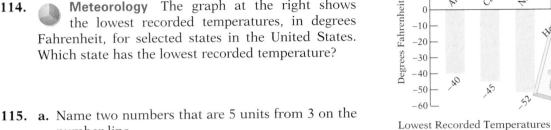 **Meteorology** The graph at the right shows the lowest recorded temperatures, in degrees Fahrenheit, for selected states in the United States. Which state has the lowest recorded temperature?

Lowest Recorded Temperatures

Sources: National Climatic Data Center; NESDIS; NOAA; U.S. Dept. of Commerce

115. a. Name two numbers that are 5 units from 3 on the number line.
   b. Name two numbers that are 3 units from −1 on the number line.

116. a. Find a number that is halfway between −7 and −5.
   b. Find a number that is halfway between −10 and −6.
   c. Find a number that is one-third of the way between −12 and −3.

117. Rocketry Which is closer to blastoff, −12 min and counting or −17 min and counting?

118. Investments In the stock market, the net change in the price of a share of stock is recorded as a positive or a negative number. If the price rises, the net change is positive. If the price falls, the net change is negative. If the net change for a share of Stock A is −2 and the net change for a share of Stock B is −1, which stock showed the least net change?

119. Business Some businesses show a profit as a positive number and a loss as a negative number. During the first quarter of this year, the loss experienced by a company was recorded as −12,575. During the second quarter of this year, the loss experienced by the company was −11,350. During which quarter was the loss greater?

120. Find the values of a for which $|a| = 7$.

121. Find the values of y for which $|y| = 11$.

122. 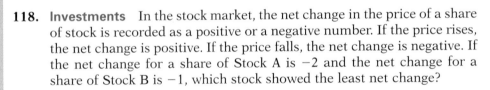 **a.** Describe the *opposite of a number* in your own words.
   b. Describe the *absolute value of a number* in your own words.

10.2   Addition and Subtraction of Integers

Objective A   **To add integers**

An integer can be graphed as a dot on a number line, as shown in the last section. An integer also can be represented anywhere along a number line by an arrow. A positive number is represented by an arrow pointing to the right. A negative number is represented by an arrow pointing to the left. The absolute value of the number is represented by the length of the arrow. The integers 5 and −4 are shown on the number lines below.

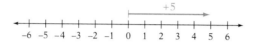

The sum of two integers can be shown on a number line. To add two integers, use arrows to represent the addends, with the first arrow starting at zero. The sum is the number directly below the tip of the arrow that represents the second addend.

$4 + 2 = 6$

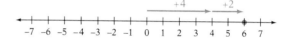

$-4 + (-2) = -6$

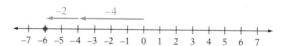

$-4 + 2 = -2$

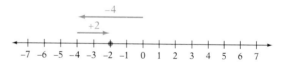

$4 + (-2) = 2$

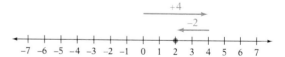

The sums of the integers shown above can be categorized by the signs of the addends.

Here the addends have the same sign:

$4 + 2$ *positive* 4 plus *positive* 2
$-4 + (-2)$ *negative* 4 plus *negative* 2

Here the addends have different signs:

$-4 + 2$ *negative* 4 plus *positive* 2
$4 + (-2)$ *positive* 4 plus *negative* 2

The rule for adding two integers depends on whether the signs of the addends are the same or different.

Rule for Adding Two Numbers

To add numbers with the same sign, add the absolute values of the numbers. Then attach the sign of the addends.

To add numbers with different signs, find the difference between the absolute values of the numbers. Then attach the sign of the addend with the greater absolute value.

Point of Interest

Although mathematical symbols are fairly standard in every country, that has not always been true. Italian mathematicians in the 15th century used a "p" to indicate plus. The "p" was from the Italian word *piu*.

HOW TO Add: $(-4) + (-9)$

$|-4| = 4, |-9| = 9$
$4 + 9 = 13$

$(-4) + (-9) = -13$

- Because the signs of the addends are the same, add the absolute values of the numbers.
- Then attach the sign of the addends.

HOW TO Add: $6 + (-13)$

$|6| = 6, |-13| = 13$
$13 - 6 = 7$

$6 + (-13) = -7$

- Because the signs of the addends are different, subtract the smaller absolute value from the larger absolute value.
- Then attach the sign of the number with the larger absolute value. Because $|-13| > |6|$, attach the negative sign.

HOW TO Add: $162 + (-247)$

$162 + (-247) = -85$

- Because the signs are different, find the difference between the absolute values of the numbers and attach the sign of the number with the greater absolute value.

Integrating Technology

To add $-14 + (-47)$ on your calculator, enter the following:

14 $+/-$ $+$ 47 $+/-$ $=$

HOW TO Find the sum of -14 and -47.

$-14 + (-47) = -61$

- Because the signs are the same, add the absolute values of the numbers and attach the sign of the addends.

When adding more than two integers, start from the left and add the first two numbers. Then add the sum to the third number. Continue this process until all the numbers have been added.

HOW TO Add: $(-4) + (-6) + (-8) + 9$

$(-4) + (-6) + (-8) + 9 = (-10) + (-8) + 9$
$= (-18) + 9$

$= -9$

- Add the first two numbers.
- Add the sum to the next number.
- Continue adding until all numbers have been added.

Example 1 What is -162 added to 98?

Solution $98 + (-162) = -64$
- The signs of the addends are different.

You Try It 1 Add: $-154 + (-37)$

Your solution

Solution on p. S25

Example 2

Add: $-2 + (-7) + 4 + (-6)$

Solution

$$-2 + (-7) + 4 + (-6) = -9 + 4 + (-6)$$
$$= -5 + (-6)$$
$$= -11$$

You Try It 2

Add: $-5 + (-2) + 9 + (-3)$

Your solution

Solution on p. S25

Objective B   **To subtract integers**

Study Tip

Be sure to do all you need to do in order to be successful at adding and subtracting integers: Read through the introductory material, work through the examples indicated by the HOW TO feature, study the paired Examples, do the You Try Its and check your solutions against those in the back of the book, and do the exercises on pages 415 to 418. See *AIM for Success* at the front of the book.

Before the rules for subtracting two integers are explained, look at the translation into words of an expression that is the difference of two integers:

$9 - 3$	positive 9 minus positive 3
$(-9) - 3$	negative 9 minus positive 3
$9 - (-3)$	positive 9 minus negative 3
$(-9) - (-3)$	negative 9 minus negative 3

Note that the sign $-$ is used in two different ways. One way is as a negative sign, as in (-9), *negative* 9. The second way is to indicate the operation of subtraction, as in $9 - 3$, 9 *minus* 3.

Look at the next four subtraction expressions and decide whether the second number in each expression is a positive number or a negative number.

1. $(-10) - 8$ **2.** $(-10) - (-8)$ **3.** $10 - (-8)$ **4.** $10 - 8$

In expressions 1 and 4, the second number is a positive 8. In expressions 2 and 3, the second number is a negative 8.

Rule for Subtracting Two Numbers

To subtract two numbers, add the opposite of the second number to the first number.

This rule states that to subtract two integers, we rewrite the subtraction expression as the sum of the first number and the opposite of the second number.

Here are some examples:

First number	−	second number	=	first number	+	the opposite of the second number	
8	−	15	=	8	+	(-15)	$= -7$
8	−	(-15)	=	8	+	15	$= 23$
(-8)	−	15	=	(-8)	+	(-15)	$= -23$
(-8)	−	(-15)	=	(-8)	+	15	$= 7$

Integrating Technology

The $+/-$ key on your calculator is used to find the opposite of a number. The $-$ is used to perform the operation of subtraction.

HOW TO   Subtract: $(-15) - 75$

$$(-15) - 75 = (-15) + (-75)$$
$$= -90$$

• To subtract, add the opposite of the second number to the first number.

HOW TO   Subtract: $27 - (-32)$

$$27 - (-32) = 27 + 32$$
$$= 59$$

• To subtract, add the opposite of the second number to the first number.

When subtraction occurs several times in an expression, rewrite each subtraction as addition of the opposite and then add.

HOW TO   Subtract: $-13 - 5 - (-8)$

$$-13 - 5 - (-8) = -13 + (-5) + 8$$
$$= -18 + 8$$
$$= -10$$

• Rewrite each subtraction as the addition of the opposite and then add.

Example 3

Find 8 less than -12.

Solution
$$-12 - 8 = -12 + (-8)$$
$$= -20$$

• Rewrite "$-$" as "$+$"; the opposite of 8 is -8.

You Try It 3

Find -8 less 14.

Your solution

Example 4

Subtract: $6 - (-20)$

Solution
$$6 - (-20) = 6 + 20$$
$$= 26$$

• Rewrite "$-$" as "$+$"; the opposite of -20 is 20.

You Try It 4

Subtract: $3 - (-15)$

Your solution

Example 5

Subtract: $-8 - 30 - (-12) - 7$

Solution
$$-8 - 30 - (-12) - 7$$
$$= -8 + (-30) + 12 + (-7)$$
$$= -38 + 12 + (-7)$$
$$= -26 + (-7)$$
$$= -33$$

You Try It 5

Subtract: $4 - (-3) - 12 - (-7) - 20$

Your solution

Solutions on pp. S25–S26

Objective C   **To solve application problems**

Example 6

Find the temperature after an increase of 9°C from -6°C.

Strategy
To find the temperature, add the increase (9°C) to the previous temperature (-6°C).

Solution
$$-6 + 9 = 3$$

The temperature is 3°C.

You Try It 6

Find the temperature after an increase of 12°C from -10°C.

Your strategy

Your solution

Solution on p. S26

10.2 Exercises

Objective A **To add integers**

For Exercises 1 and 2, name the negative integers in the list of numbers.

1. $-14, 28, 0, -\dfrac{5}{7}, -364, -9.5$

2. $-37, 90, -\dfrac{7}{10}, -88.8, 42, -561$

For Exercises 3 to 30, add.

3. $3 + (-5)$

4. $-4 + 2$

5. $8 + 12$

6. $16 + 23$

7. $-3 + (-8)$

8. $-12 + (-1)$

9. $-4 + (-5)$

10. $-12 + (-12)$

11. $6 + (-9)$

12. $4 + (-9)$

13. $-6 + 7$

14. $-12 + 6$

15. $2 + (-3) + (-4)$

16. $7 + (-2) + (-8)$

17. $-3 + (-12) + (-15)$

18. $9 + (-6) + (-16)$

19. $-17 + (-3) + 29$

20. $13 + 62 + (-38)$

21. $-3 + (-8) + 12$

22. $-27 + (-42) + (-18)$

23. $13 + (-22) + 4 + (-5)$

24. $-14 + (-3) + 7 + (-6)$

25. $-22 + 10 + 2 + (-18)$

26. $-6 + (-8) + 13 + (-4)$

27. $-16 + (-17) + (-18) + 10$

28. $-25 + (-31) + 24 + 19$

29. $-126 + (-247) + (-358) + 339$

30. $-651 + (-239) + 524 + 487$

31. What is -8 more than -12?

32. What is -5 more than 3?

33. What is -7 added to -16?

34. What is 7 added to -25?

35. What is -4 plus 2?

36. What is -22 plus -17?

37. Find the sum of -2, 8, and -12.

38. Find the sum of 4, -4, and -6.

39. What is the total of 2, -3, 8, and -13?

40. What is the total of -6, -8, 13, and -2?

Objective B   **To subtract integers**

For Exercises 41 to 44, translate the expression into words. Represent each number as positive or negative.

41. $-6 - 4$ **42.** $-6 - (-4)$ **43.** $6 - (-4)$ **44.** $6 - 4$

For Exercises 45 to 48, rewrite the subtraction as the sum of the first number and the opposite of the second number.

45. $9 - (-5)$ **46.** $-3 - 7$ **47.** $1 - 8$ **48.** $-2 - (-10)$

For Exercises 49 to 76, subtract.

49. $16 - 8$ **50.** $12 - 3$ **51.** $7 - 14$ **52.** $6 - 9$

53. $-7 - 2$ **54.** $-9 - 4$ **55.** $7 - (-29)$ **56.** $3 - (-4)$

57. $-6 - (-3)$ **58.** $-4 - (-2)$ **59.** $6 - (-12)$ **60.** $-12 - 16$

61. $-4 - 3 - 2$ **62.** $4 - 5 - 12$ **63.** $12 - (-7) - 8$

64. $-12 - (-3) - (-15)$ **65.** $4 - 12 - (-8)$ **66.** $13 - 7 - 15$

67. $-6 - (-8) - (-9)$ **68.** $7 - 8 - (-1)$

69. $-30 - (-65) - 29 - 4$ **70.** $42 - (-82) - 65 - 7$

71. $-16 - 47 - 63 - 12$ **72.** $42 - (-30) - 65 - (-11)$

73. $47 - (-67) - 13 - 15$ **74.** $-18 - 49 - (-84) - 27$

75. $167 - 432 - (-287) - 359$

76. $-521 - (-350) - 164 - (-299)$

77. Subtract -8 from -4.

78. Subtract -12 from 3.

79. What is the difference between -8 and 4?

80. What is the difference between 8 and -3?

81. What is -4 decreased by 8?

82. What is -13 decreased by 9?

83. Find -2 less than 1.

84. Find -3 less than -5.

Objective C   **To solve application problems**

85. Temperature   Find the temperature after a rise of 7°C from -8°C.

86. Temperature   Find the temperature after a rise of 5°C from -19°C.

87. Games   During a card game of Hearts, Nick had a score of 11 points before his opponent "shot the moon," subtracting a score of 26 from Nick's total. What was Nick's score after his opponent shot the moon?

88. Games   In a card game of Hearts, Monique had a score of -19 before she "shot the moon," entitling her to add 26 points to her score. What was Monique's score after she shot the moon?

89. Investments   The price of Byplex Corporation's stock fell each trading day of the first week of June. Use the figure at the right to find the change in the price of Byplex stock over the week's time.

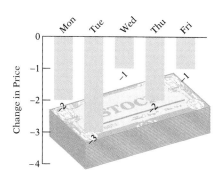

Change in Price of Byplex
Corporation Stock (in dollars)

90.   **Astronomy**   The daytime temperature on the moon can reach 266°F, and the nighttime temperature can go as low as -292°F. Find the difference between these extremes.

91.   **Earth Science**   The average temperature throughout Earth's stratosphere is -70°F. The average temperature on Earth's surface is 45°F. Find the difference between these average temperatures.

Geography The elevation, or height, of places on Earth is measured in relation to sea level, or the average level of the ocean's surface. The table below shows height above sea level as a positive number and depth below sea level as a negative number. Use the table for Exercises 92 to 94.

Continent	Highest Elevation (in meters)		Lowest Elevation (in meters)	
Africa	Mt. Kilimanjaro	5895	Lake Assal	−156
Asia	Mt. Everest	8850	Dead Sea	−411
North America	Mt. McKinley	5642	Death Valley	−28
South America	Mt. Aconcagua	6960	Valdes Peninsula	−86

Mt. Everest

92. What is the difference in elevation between Mt. Kilimanjaro and Lake Assal?

93. What is the difference in elevation between Mt. Aconcagua and the Valdes Peninsula?

94. For which continent shown is the difference between the highest and lowest elevations greatest?

Meteorology The figure at the right shows the highest and lowest temperatures ever recorded for selected regions of the world. Use this graph for Exercises 95 to 97.

95. What is the difference between the highest and lowest temperatures recorded in Africa?

96. What is the difference between the highest and lowest temperatures recorded in South America?

97. What is the difference between the lowest temperature recorded in Europe and the lowest temperature recorded in Asia?

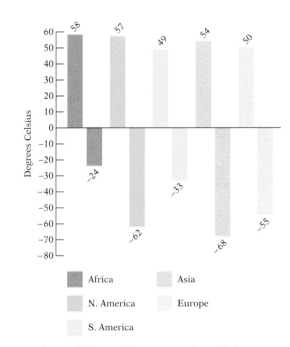

Highest and Lowest Temperatures Recorded (in degrees Celsius)

Source: National Climatic Data Center

APPLYING THE CONCEPTS

98. **Number Problems** Consider the numbers 4, −7, −5, 13, and −9. What is the largest difference that can be obtained by subtracting one number in the list from another number in the list? Find the smallest positive difference.

99. **Number Problems** Fill in the blank squares at the right with integers so that the sum of the integers along any row, column, or diagonal is zero.

−3		1
		3

100. **Number Problems** The sum of two negative integers is −8. Find the integers.

101. ✎ Explain the difference between the words *negative* and *minus*.

 Multiplication and Division of Integers

Objective A   **To multiply integers**

Multiplication is the repeated addition of the same number.

Several different symbols are used to indicate multiplication:

$$3 \times 2 = 6 \qquad\qquad 3 \cdot 2 = 6 \qquad\qquad (3)(2) = 6$$

When 5 is multiplied by a sequence of decreasing integers, the products decrease by 5.

$$5 \times 3 = 15$$
$$5 \times 2 = 10$$
$$5 \times 1 = 5$$
$$5 \times 0 = 0$$

The pattern developed can be continued so that 5 is multiplied by a sequence of negative numbers. The resulting products must be negative in order to maintain the pattern of decreasing by 5.

$$5 \times (-1) = -5$$
$$5 \times (-2) = -10$$
$$5 \times (-3) = -15$$
$$5 \times (-4) = -20$$

This example illustrates that the product of a positive number and a negative number is negative.

When -5 is multiplied by a sequence of decreasing integers, the products increase by 5.

$$-5 \times 3 = -15$$
$$-5 \times 2 = -10$$
$$-5 \times 1 = -5$$
$$-5 \times 0 = 0$$

The pattern developed can be continued so that -5 is multiplied by a sequence of negative numbers. The resulting products must be positive in order to maintain the pattern of increasing by 5.

$$-5 \times (-1) = 5$$
$$-5 \times (-2) = 10$$
$$-5 \times (-3) = 15$$
$$-5 \times (-4) = 20$$

This example illustrates that the product of two negative numbers is positive.

The pattern for multiplication shown above is summarized in the following rules for multiplying integers.

Integrating Technology

To multiply $(-4)(-8)$ on your calculator, enter the following:

4 +/−   × 8 +/−   =

Rule for Multiplying Two Numbers

To multiply numbers with the same sign, multiply the absolute values of the factors. The product is positive.

To multiply numbers with different signs, multiply the absolute values of the factors. The product is negative.

$$4 \cdot 8 = 32$$

$$(-4)(-8) = 32$$

$$-4 \cdot 8 = -32$$

$$(4)(-8) = -32$$

HOW TO   Multiply: $2(-3)(-5)(-7)$

$$2(-3)(-5)(-7) = -6(-5)(-7)$$

- To multiply more than two numbers, multiply the first two numbers.

$$= 30(-7)$$

- Then multiply the product by the third number.

$$= -210$$

- Continue until all the numbers have been multiplied.

Example 1

Multiply: $(-2)(6)$

Solution

$(-2)(6) = -12$ • The signs are different. The product is negative.

You Try It 1

Multiply: $(-3)(-5)$

Your solution

Example 2

Find the product of -42 and 62.

Solution

$-42 \cdot 62 = -2604$ • The signs are different. The product is negative.

You Try It 2

Find -38 multiplied by 51.

Your solution

Example 3

Multiply: $-5(-4)(6)(-3)$

Solution

$$-5(-4)(6)(-3) = 20(6)(-3)$$
$$= 120(-3)$$
$$= -360$$

You Try It 3

Multiply: $-7(-8)(9)(-2)$

Your solution

Solutions on p. S26

Objective B   **To divide integers**

For every division problem, there is a related multiplication problem.

Division: $\dfrac{8}{2} = 4$ Related multiplication: $4 \cdot 2 = 8$

This fact can be used to illustrate the rules for dividing signed numbers.

Rule for Dividing Two Numbers

To divide numbers with the same sign, divide the absolute values of the numbers. The quotient is positive.

To divide numbers with different signs, divide the absolute values of the numbers. The quotient is negative.

$\dfrac{8}{2} = 4$ because $4 \cdot 2 = 8$.

$\dfrac{-8}{-2} = 4$ because $4(-2) = -8$.

$\dfrac{8}{-2} = -4$ because $-4(-2) = 8$.

$\dfrac{-8}{2} = -4$ because $-4(2) = -8$.

Note that $\frac{8}{-2}$, $\frac{-8}{2}$, and $-\frac{8}{2}$ are all equal to -4.

If a and b are two integers, then $\frac{a}{-b} = \frac{-a}{b} = -\frac{a}{b}$.

<table>
<tr><td rowspan="4">

Properties of Zero and One in Division

Zero divided by any number other than zero is zero.

Any number other than zero divided by itself is 1.

Any number divided by 1 is the number.

Division by zero is not defined.

</td><td>

$\frac{0}{a} = 0$ because $0 \cdot a = 0$

</td></tr>
<tr><td>

$\frac{a}{a} = 1$ because $1 \cdot a = a$

</td></tr>
<tr><td>

$\frac{a}{1} = a$ because $a \cdot 1 = a$

</td></tr>
<tr><td>

$\frac{4}{0} = ?$ $? \cdot 0 = 4$

There is no number whose product with zero is 4.

</td></tr>
</table>

The examples below illustrate these properties of division.

$$\frac{0}{-8} = 0 \qquad \frac{-7}{-7} = 1 \qquad \frac{-9}{1} = -9 \qquad \frac{-3}{0} \text{ is undefined.}$$

Example 4

Divide: $(-120) \div (-8)$

Solution

$(-120) \div (-8) = 15$ • The signs are the same. The quotient is positive.

You Try It 4

Divide: $(-135) \div (-9)$

Your solution

Example 5

Divide: $95 \div (-5)$

Solution

$95 \div (-5) = -19$ • The signs are different. The quotient is negative.

You Try It 5

Divide: $84 \div (-6)$

Your solution

Example 6

Find the quotient of -81 and 3.

Solution

$-81 \div 3 = -27$

You Try It 6

What is -72 divided by 4?

Your solution

Example 7

Divide: $0 \div (-24)$

Solution

$0 \div (-24) = 0$ • Zero divided by a nonzero number is zero.

You Try It 7

Divide: $-39 \div 0$

Your solution

Solutions on p. S26

Objective C   **To solve application problems**

Example 8

The combined scores of the top five golfers in a tournament equaled −10 (10 under par). What was the average score of the five golfers?

Strategy
To find the average score, divide the combined scores (−10) by the number of golfers (5).

Solution
−10 ÷ 5 = −2

The average score was −2.

You Try It 8

The melting point of mercury is −38°C. The melting point of argon is five times the melting point of mercury. Find the melting point of argon.

Your strategy

Your solution

Example 9

The daily high temperatures during one week were recorded as follows: −9°F, 3°F, 0°F, −8°F, 2°F, 1°F, 4°F. Find the average daily high temperature for the week.

Strategy
To find the average daily high temperature:
• Add the seven temperature readings.
• Divide by 7.

Solution
−9 + 3 + 0 + (−8) + 2 + 1 + 4 = −7

−7 ÷ 7 = −1

The average daily high temperature was −1°F.

You Try It 9

The daily low temperatures during one week were recorded as follows: −6°F, −7°F, 1°F, 0°F, −5°F, −10°F, −1°F. Find the average daily low temperature for the week.

Your strategy

Your solution

Solutions on p. S26

10.3 Exercises

Objective A   **To multiply integers**

For Exercises 1 to 4, state whether the operation in the expression is addition, subtraction, or multiplication.

1. $5 - (-6)$ 　　　　**2.** $4(-9)$ 　　　　**3.** $-8(-5)$ 　　　　**4.** $-3 + (-7)$

For Exercises 5 to 46, multiply.

5. 14×3 　　　　**6.** 62×9 　　　　**7.** $-4 \cdot 6$

8. $-7 \cdot 3$ 　　　　**9.** $-2 \cdot (-3)$ 　　　　**10.** $-5 \cdot (-1)$

11. $(9)(2)$ 　　　　**12.** $(3)(8)$ 　　　　**13.** $5(-4)$

14. $4(-7)$ 　　　　**15.** $-8(2)$ 　　　　**16.** $-9(3)$

17. $(-5)(-5)$ 　　　　**18.** $(-3)(-6)$ 　　　　**19.** $(-7)(0)$

20. -32×4 　　　　**21.** -24×3 　　　　**22.** $19 \cdot (-7)$

23. $6(-17)$ 　　　　**24.** $-8(-26)$ 　　　　**25.** $-4(-35)$

26. $-5 \cdot (23)$ 　　　　**27.** $-6 \cdot (38)$ 　　　　**28.** $9(-27)$

29. $8(-40)$ 　　　　**30.** $-7(-34)$ 　　　　**31.** $-4(39)$

32. $4 \cdot (-8) \cdot 3$ 　　　　**33.** $5 \times 7 \times (-2)$ 　　　　**34.** $8 \cdot (-6) \cdot (-1)$

35. $(-9)(-9)(2)$ 　　　　**36.** $-8(-7)(-4)$ 　　　　**37.** $-5(8)(-3)$

38. $(-6)(5)(7)$ 　　　　**39.** $-1(4)(-9)$ 　　　　**40.** $6(-3)(-2)$

41. $4(-4) \cdot 6(-2)$

42. $-5 \cdot 9(-7) \cdot 3$

43. $-9(4) \cdot 3(1)$

44. $8(8)(-5)(-4)$

45. $(-6) \cdot 7 \cdot (-10)(-5)$

46. $-9(-6)(11)(-2)$

47. What is -5 multiplied by -4?

48. What is 6 multiplied by -5?

49. What is -8 times 6?

50. What is -8 times -7?

51. Find the product of -4, 7, and -5.

52. Find the product of -2, -4, and -7.

Objective B   **To divide integers**

For Exercises 53 to 56, write the related multiplication problem.

53. $\dfrac{-36}{-12} = 3$

54. $\dfrac{28}{-7} = -4$

55. $\dfrac{-55}{11} = -5$

56. $\dfrac{-20}{-10} = 2$

For Exercises 57 to 107, divide.

57. $12 \div (-6)$

58. $18 \div (-3)$

59. $(-72) \div (-9)$

60. $(-64) \div (-8)$

61. $0 \div (-6)$

62. $-49 \div 7$

63. $45 \div (-5)$

64. $-24 \div 4$

65. $-36 \div 4$

66. $-56 \div 7$

67. $-81 \div (-9)$

68. $-40 \div (-5)$

69. $72 \div (-3)$

70. $44 \div (-4)$

71. $-60 \div 5$

72. $-66 \div 6$

73. $-93 \div (-3)$

74. $-98 \div (-7)$

75. $(-85) \div (-5)$

76. $(-60) \div (-4)$

77. $120 \div 8$

78. $144 \div 9$

79. $78 \div (-6)$

80. $84 \div (-7)$

81. $-72 \div 4$

82. $-80 \div 5$

83. $-114 \div (-6)$

84. $-91 \div (-7)$

85. $-104 \div (-8)$

86. $-126 \div (-9)$

87. $57 \div (-3)$

88. $162 \div (-9)$

89. $-136 \div (-8)$

90. $-128 \div 4$

91. $-130 \div (-5)$

92. $(-280) \div 8$

93. $(-92) \div (-4)$

94. $-196 \div (-7)$

95. $-150 \div (-6)$

96. $(-261) \div 9$

97. $204 \div (-6)$

98. $165 \div (-5)$

99. $-132 \div (-12)$

100. $-156 \div (-13)$

101. $-182 \div 14$

102. $-144 \div 12$

103. $143 \div 11$

104. $168 \div 14$

105. $-180 \div (-15)$

106. $-169 \div (-13)$

107. $154 \div (-11)$

108. Find the quotient of -132 and -11.

109. Find the quotient of 182 and -13.

110. What is -60 divided by -15?

111. What is 144 divided by -24?

112. Find the quotient of -135 and 15.

113. Find the quotient of -88 and 22.

Objective C   **To solve application problems**

114. **Meteorology** The daily low temperatures during one week were recorded as follows: 4°F, −5°F, 8°F, −1°F, −12°F, −14°F, −8°F. Find the average daily low temperature for the week.

115. **Meteorology** The daily high temperatures during one week were recorded as follows: −6°F, −11°F, 1°F, 5°F, −3°F, −9°F, −5°F. Find the average daily high temperature for the week.

116. 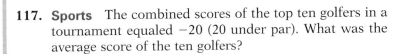 **Chemistry** The graph at the right shows the boiling points of three chemical elements. The boiling point of neon is seven times the highest boiling point shown in the table.
   a. Without actually calculating the boiling point, determine whether the boiling point of neon is above 0°C or below 0°C.
   b. What is the boiling point of neon?

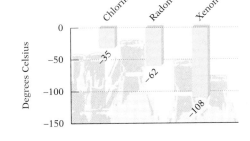

117. **Sports** The combined scores of the top ten golfers in a tournament equaled −20 (20 under par). What was the average score of the ten golfers?

118. **Sports** The combined scores of the top four golfers in a tournament equaled −12 (12 under par). What was the average score of the four golfers?

119.  **Meteorology** The wind chill factor when the temperature is −20°F and the wind is blowing at 15 mph is five times the wind chill factor when the temperature is 10°F and the wind is blowing at 20 mph. If the wind chill factor at 10°F with a 20-mph wind is −9°F, what is the wind chill factor at −20°F with a 15-mph wind?

120. **Education** To discourage guessing on a multiple-choice exam, an instructor graded the test by giving 5 points for a correct answer, −2 points for an answer left blank, and −5 points for an incorrect answer. How many points did a student score who answered 20 questions correctly, answered 5 questions incorrectly, and left 2 questions blank?

APPLYING THE CONCEPTS

121. **a. Number Problems** Find the greatest possible product of two negative integers whose sum is −10.
   b. Number Problems Find the least possible sum of two negative integers whose product is 16.

122. Use repeated addition to show that the product of two integers with different signs is a negative number.

123. Determine whether the statement is true or false.
   a. The product of a nonzero number and its opposite is negative.
   b. The square of a negative number is a positive number.

124. In your own words, describe the rules for multiplying and dividing integers.

10.4 Operations with Rational Numbers

Objective A   **To add or subtract rational numbers**

In this section, operations with rational numbers are discussed. A **rational number** is the quotient of two integers.

> **Rational Numbers**
>
> A rational number is a number that can be written in the form $\frac{a}{b}$, where a and b are integers and $b \neq 0$.

Each of the three numbers shown at the right is a rational number.

$$\frac{3}{4} \qquad \frac{-2}{9} \qquad \frac{13}{-5}$$

An integer can be written as the quotient of the integer and 1. Therefore, **every integer is a rational number.**

$$6 = \frac{6}{1} \qquad -8 = \frac{-8}{1}$$

A mixed number can be written as the quotient of two integers. Therefore, **every mixed number is a rational number.**

$$1\frac{4}{7} = \frac{11}{7} \qquad 3\frac{2}{5} = \frac{17}{5}$$

Recall that every fraction can be written as a decimal by dividing the numerator of the fraction by the denominator. The result is either a terminating decimal or a repeating decimal.

We can write the fraction $\frac{3}{4}$ as the terminating decimal 0.75.

TAKE NOTE

The fraction bar can be read "divided by."
$$\frac{3}{4} = 3 \div 4$$

$$\begin{array}{r} 0.75 \\ 4)\overline{3.00} \\ -2\,8 \\ \hline 20 \\ -20 \\ \hline 0 \end{array}$$

0.75 ⟵ This is a **terminating decimal.**

0 ⟵ The remainder is zero.

We can write the fraction $\frac{2}{3}$ as the repeating decimal $0.\overline{6}$.

TAKE NOTE

A **terminating decimal** is a decimal that has a finite number of digits after the decimal point, which means that it comes to an end and does not go on forever. A **repeating decimal** is a decimal that does not end; it has a repeating pattern of digits after the decimal point.

$$\begin{array}{r} 0.666 \\ 3)\overline{2.000} \\ -1\,8 \\ \hline 20 \\ -18 \\ \hline 20 \\ -18 \\ \hline 2 \end{array}$$

$0.666 = 0.\overline{6}$ ⟵ This is a **repeating decimal.**
The bar over the digit 6 in $0.\overline{6}$ is used to show that this digit repeats.

2 ⟵ The remainder is never zero.

All terminating and repeating decimals are rational numbers.

To add or subtract rational numbers in fractional form, first find the least common multiple (LCM) of the denominators.

HOW TO   Add: $-\dfrac{7}{8} + \dfrac{5}{6}$

$8 = 2 \cdot 2 \cdot 2$
$6 = 2 \cdot 3$
$\text{LCM} = 2 \cdot 2 \cdot 2 \cdot 3 = 24$

- Find the LCM of the denominators.

$-\dfrac{7}{8} + \dfrac{5}{6} = -\dfrac{21}{24} + \dfrac{20}{24}$

- Rewrite each fraction using the LCM of the denominators as the common denominator.

$= \dfrac{-21 + 20}{24}$

- Add the numerators.

$= \dfrac{-1}{24} = -\dfrac{1}{24}$

TAKE NOTE

In this text, answers that are negative fractions are written with the negative sign in front of the fraction.

HOW TO   Subtract: $-\dfrac{7}{9} - \dfrac{5}{12}$

$9 = 3 \cdot 3$
$12 = 2 \cdot 2 \cdot 3$
$\text{LCM} = 2 \cdot 2 \cdot 3 \cdot 3 = 36$

- Find the LCM of the denominators.

$-\dfrac{7}{9} - \dfrac{5}{12} = -\dfrac{28}{36} - \dfrac{15}{36}$

- Rewrite each fraction using the LCM of the denominators as the common denominator.

$= \dfrac{-28}{36} + \dfrac{-15}{36}$

- Rewrite subtraction as addition of the opposite. Rewrite negative fractions with the negative sign in the numerator.

$= \dfrac{-28 + (-15)}{36}$

- Add the numerators.

$= \dfrac{-43}{36} = -\dfrac{43}{36} = -1\dfrac{7}{36}$

To add or subtract rational numbers in decimal form, use the sign rules for adding integers.

HOW TO   Add: $47.034 + (-56.91)$

$\begin{array}{r} 56.910 \\ -\,47.034 \\ \hline 9.876 \end{array}$

- The signs are different. Find the difference between the absolute values of the numbers.

$47.034 + (-56.91)$
$= -9.876$

- Attach the sign of the number with the greater absolute value.

HOW TO   Subtract: $-39.09 - 102.98$

$-39.09 - 102.98$
$= -39.09 + (-102.98)$

* Rewrite subtraction as addition of the opposite number.

$$\begin{array}{r} 39.09 \\ + 102.98 \\ \hline 142.07 \end{array}$$

* The signs of the addends are the same. Find the sum of the absolute values of the numbers.

$-39.09 - 102.98 = -142.07$

* Attach the sign of the addends.

Example 1

Subtract: $\dfrac{5}{16} - \dfrac{7}{40}$

Solution

$$\dfrac{5}{16} - \dfrac{7}{40} = \dfrac{25}{80} - \dfrac{14}{80}$$

* The LCM of 16 and 40 is 80.

$$= \dfrac{25}{80} + \dfrac{-14}{80}$$

* Rewrite as addition of the opposite.

$$= \dfrac{25 + (-14)}{80} = \dfrac{11}{80}$$

You Try It 1

Subtract: $\dfrac{5}{9} - \dfrac{11}{12}$

Your solution

Example 2

Simplify: $-\dfrac{3}{4} + \dfrac{1}{6} - \dfrac{5}{8}$

Solution

$$-\dfrac{3}{4} + \dfrac{1}{6} - \dfrac{5}{8} = -\dfrac{18}{24} + \dfrac{4}{24} - \dfrac{15}{24}$$

* The LCM of 4, 6, and 8 is 24.

$$= \dfrac{-18}{24} + \dfrac{4}{24} + \dfrac{-15}{24}$$

$$= \dfrac{-18 + 4 + (-15)}{24}$$

$$= \dfrac{-29}{24} = -\dfrac{29}{24} = -1\dfrac{5}{24}$$

You Try It 2

Simplify: $-\dfrac{7}{8} - \dfrac{5}{6} + \dfrac{2}{3}$

Your solution

Example 3

Subtract: $42.987 - 98.61$

Solution

$42.987 - 98.61 = 42.987 + (-98.61)$

$$\begin{array}{r} 98.610 \\ - 42.987 \\ \hline 55.623 \end{array}$$

$42.987 - 98.61 = -55.623$

You Try It 3

Subtract: $16.127 - 67.91$

Your solution

Example 4

Simplify: $1.02 + (-3.6) + 9.24$

Solution

$$1.02 + (-3.6) + 9.24 = -2.58 + 9.24$$
$$= 6.66$$

You Try It 4

Simplify: $2.7 + (-9.44) + 6.2$

Your solution

Solution on p. S26

Objective B   **To multiply or divide rational numbers**

The product of two rational numbers written as fractions is the product of the numerators over the product of the denominators. Use the sign rules for multiplying integers.

HOW TO   Simplify: $-\frac{3}{8} \times \frac{12}{17}$

$$-\frac{3}{8} \times \frac{12}{17} = -\left(\frac{3 \cdot 12}{8 \cdot 17}\right) = -\frac{9}{34}$$

• The signs are different.
  The product is negative.

To divide rational numbers written as fractions, invert the divisor and then multiply. Use the sign rules for dividing integers.

HOW TO   Simplify: $-\frac{3}{10} \div \left(-\frac{18}{25}\right)$

$$-\frac{3}{10} \div \left(-\frac{18}{25}\right) = \frac{3}{10} \times \frac{25}{18} = \frac{3 \cdot 25}{10 \cdot 18} = \frac{5}{12}$$

• The signs are the same.
  The quotient is positive.

To multiply or divide rational numbers written in decimal form, use the sign rules for integers.

HOW TO   Simplify: $(-6.89) \times (-0.00035)$

$$
\begin{array}{r}
6.89 \\
\times \quad 0.00035 \\
\hline
3445 \\
2067 \quad\;\; \\
\hline
0.0024115
\end{array}
$$

2 decimal places
5 decimal places

7 decimal places

• The signs are the same. Multiply the absolute values.

$(-6.89) \times (-0.00035) = 0.0024115$

• The product is positive.

HOW TO   Divide $1.32 \div (-0.27)$. Round to the nearest tenth.

$$
\begin{array}{r}
4.88 \approx 4.9 \\
0.27\overline{)1.32.00} \\
-1\ 08 \\
\hline
24\ 0 \\
-21\ 6 \\
\hline
2\ 40 \\
-2\ 16 \\
\hline
24
\end{array}
$$

• Divide the absolute values. Move the decimal point two places in the divisor and then in the dividend. Place the decimal point in the quotient.

$1.32 \div (-0.27) \approx -4.9$

• The signs are different. The quotient is negative.

Example 5

Multiply: $-\dfrac{7}{12} \times \dfrac{9}{14}$

Solution   The product is negative.

$$-\frac{7}{12} \times \frac{9}{14} = -\left(\frac{7 \cdot 9}{12 \cdot 14}\right)$$

$$= -\frac{3}{8}$$

You Try It 5

Multiply: $\left(-\dfrac{2}{3}\right)\left(-\dfrac{9}{10}\right)$

Your solution

Example 6

Divide: $-\dfrac{3}{8} \div \left(-\dfrac{5}{12}\right)$

Solution   The quotient is positive.

$$-\frac{3}{8} \div \left(-\frac{5}{12}\right) = \frac{3}{8} \times \frac{12}{5}$$

$$= \frac{3 \cdot 12}{8 \cdot 5}$$

$$= \frac{9}{10}$$

You Try It 6

Divide: $-\dfrac{5}{8} \div \dfrac{5}{40}$

Your solution

Example 7   Multiply: -4.29×8.2

Solution   The product is negative.

$$
\begin{array}{r}
4.29 \\
\times\ \ 8.2 \\
\hline
858 \\
3432 \\
\hline
35.178
\end{array}
$$

$-4.29 \times 8.2 = -35.178$

You Try It 7   Multiply: -5.44×3.8

Your solution

Solutions on pp. S26–S27

Example 8   Multiply: $-3.2 \times (-0.4) \times 6.9$

Solution
$-3.2 \times (-0.4) \times 6.9$
$= 1.28 \times 6.9$
$= 8.832$

You Try It 8   Multiply: $3.44 \times (-1.7) \times 0.6$

Your solution

Example 9   Divide: $-0.0792 \div (-0.42)$
Round to the nearest hundredth.

Solution

$$
\begin{array}{r}
0.188 \approx 0.19 \\
0.42.\overline{)0.07.920} \\
-4\ 2 \\
\hline
3\ 72 \\
-3\ 36 \\
\hline
360 \\
-336 \\
\hline
24
\end{array}
$$

$-0.0792 \div (-0.42) \approx 0.19$

You Try It 9   Divide: $-0.394 \div 1.7$
Round to the nearest
hundredth.

Your solution

Solutions on p. S27

Objective C   **To solve application problems**

Example 10

In Fairbanks, Alaska, the average temperature during the month of July is 61.5°F. During the month of January, the average temperature in Fairbanks is −12.7°F. What is the difference between the average temperature in Fairbanks during July and the average temperature during January?

Strategy
To find the difference, subtract the average temperature in January (−12.7°F) from the average temperature in July (61.5°F).

Solution
$61.5 - (-12.7) = 61.5 + 12.7 = 74.2$

The difference between the average temperature during July and the average temperature during January in Fairbanks is 74.2°F.

You Try It 10

On January 10, 1911, in Rapid City, South Dakota, the temperature fell from 12.78°C at 7:00 A.M. to −13.33°C at 7:15 A.M. How many degrees did the temperature fall during the 15-min period?

Your strategy

Your solution

Solution on p. S27

10.4 Exercises

Objective A   To add or subtract rational numbers

For Exercises 1 to 43, simplify.

1. $\dfrac{5}{8} - \dfrac{5}{6}$

2. $\dfrac{1}{9} - \dfrac{5}{27}$

3. $-\dfrac{5}{12} - \dfrac{3}{8}$

4. $-\dfrac{5}{6} - \dfrac{5}{9}$

5. $-\dfrac{6}{13} + \dfrac{17}{26}$

6. $-\dfrac{7}{12} + \dfrac{5}{8}$

7. $-\dfrac{5}{8} - \left(-\dfrac{11}{12}\right)$

8. $-\dfrac{7}{12} - \left(-\dfrac{7}{8}\right)$

9. $\dfrac{5}{12} - \dfrac{11}{15}$

10. $\dfrac{2}{5} - \dfrac{14}{15}$

11. $-\dfrac{3}{4} - \dfrac{5}{8}$

12. $-\dfrac{2}{3} - \dfrac{5}{8}$

13. $-\dfrac{5}{2} - \left(-\dfrac{13}{4}\right)$

14. $-\dfrac{7}{3} - \left(-\dfrac{3}{2}\right)$

15. $-\dfrac{3}{8} - \dfrac{5}{12} - \dfrac{3}{16}$

16. $-\dfrac{5}{16} + \dfrac{3}{4} - \dfrac{7}{8}$

17. $\dfrac{1}{2} - \dfrac{3}{8} - \left(-\dfrac{1}{4}\right)$

18. $\dfrac{3}{4} - \left(-\dfrac{7}{12}\right) - \dfrac{7}{8}$

19. $\dfrac{1}{3} - \dfrac{1}{4} - \dfrac{1}{5}$

20. $\dfrac{5}{16} + \dfrac{1}{8} - \dfrac{1}{2}$

21. $\dfrac{1}{2} + \left(-\dfrac{3}{8}\right) + \dfrac{5}{12}$

22. $-\dfrac{3}{8} + \dfrac{3}{4} - \left(-\dfrac{3}{16}\right)$

23. $3.4 + (-6.8)$

24. $-4.9 + 3.27$

25. $-8.32 + (-0.57)$

26. $-3.5 + 7$

27. $-4.8 + (-3.2)$

28. $6.2 + (-4.29)$

29. $-4.6 + 3.92$

30. $7.2 + (-8.42)$

31. $-45.71 + (-135.8)$

32. $-35.274 + 12.47$

33. $4.2 + (-6.8) + 5.3$

34. $6.7 + 3.2 + (-10.5)$

35. $-4.5 + 3.2 + (-19.4)$

36. $2.09 - 6.72 - 5.4$

37. $-18.39 + 4.9 - 23.7$

38. $19 - (-3.72) - 82.75$

39. $-3.09 - 4.6 - 27.3$

40. $-3.89 + (-2.9) + 4.723 + 0.2$

41. $-4.02 + 6.809 - (-3.57) - (-0.419)$

42. $0.0153 + (-1.0294) + (-1.0726)$

43. $0.27 + (-3.5) - (-0.27) + (-5.44)$

Objective B   **To multiply or divide rational numbers**

For Exercises 44 to 79, simplify.

44. $\dfrac{1}{2} \times \left(-\dfrac{3}{4}\right)$

45. $-\dfrac{2}{9} \times \left(-\dfrac{3}{14}\right)$

46. $\left(-\dfrac{3}{8}\right)\left(-\dfrac{4}{15}\right)$

47. $\left(-\dfrac{3}{4}\right)\left(-\dfrac{8}{27}\right)$

48. $-\dfrac{1}{2} \times \dfrac{8}{9}$

49. $\dfrac{5}{12} \times \left(-\dfrac{8}{15}\right)$

50. $\left(-\dfrac{5}{12}\right)\left(\dfrac{42}{65}\right)$

51. $\left(\dfrac{3}{8}\right)\left(-\dfrac{15}{41}\right)$

52. $\left(-\dfrac{15}{8}\right)\left(-\dfrac{16}{3}\right)$

53. $\left(-\dfrac{5}{7}\right)\left(-\dfrac{14}{15}\right)$

54. $\dfrac{5}{8} \times \left(-\dfrac{7}{12}\right) \times \dfrac{16}{25}$

55. $\left(\dfrac{1}{2}\right)\left(-\dfrac{3}{4}\right)\left(-\dfrac{5}{8}\right)$

56. $\dfrac{1}{3} \div \left(-\dfrac{1}{2}\right)$

57. $-\dfrac{3}{8} \div \dfrac{7}{8}$

58. $\left(-\dfrac{3}{4}\right) \div \left(-\dfrac{7}{40}\right)$

59. $\dfrac{5}{6} \div \left(-\dfrac{3}{4}\right)$

60. $-\dfrac{5}{12} \div \dfrac{15}{32}$

61. $-\dfrac{5}{16} \div \left(-\dfrac{3}{8}\right)$

62. $\left(-\dfrac{3}{8}\right) \div \left(-\dfrac{5}{12}\right)$

63. $\left(-\dfrac{8}{19}\right) \div \dfrac{7}{38}$

64. $\left(-\dfrac{2}{3}\right) \div 4$

65. $-6 \div \dfrac{4}{9}$

66. $-6.7 \times (-4.2)$

67. $-8.9 \times (-3.5)$

68. -1.6×4.9

69. -14.3×7.9

70. $(-0.78)(-0.15)$

71. $(-1.21)(-0.03)$

72. $(-8.919) \div (-0.9)$

73. $-77.6 \div (-0.8)$

74. $59.01 \div (-0.7)$

75. $(-7.04) \div (-3.2)$

76. $(-84.66) \div 1.7$

77. $-3.312 \div (0.8)$

78. $1.003 \div (-0.59)$

79. $26.22 \div (-6.9)$

 For Exercises 80 to 85, divide.

80. $(-19.08) \div 0.45$

81. $21.792 \div (-0.96)$

82. $(-38.665) \div (-9.5)$

83. $(-3.171) \div (-45.3)$

84. $27.738 \div (-60.3)$

85. $(-13.97) \div (-25.4)$

Objective C **To solve application problems**

86. **Meteorology** On January 23, 1916, the temperature in Browing, Montana, was 6.67°C. On January 24, 1916, the temperature in Browing was −48.9°C. Find the difference between the temperatures in Browing on these two days.

87. **Meteorology** On January 22, 1943, in Spearfish, South Dakota, the temperature fell from 12.22°C at 9 A.M. to −20°C at 9:27 A.M. How many degrees did the temperature fall during the 27-min period?

88. **Chemistry** The boiling point of nitrogen is −195.8°C and the melting point is −209.86°C. Find the difference between the boiling point and the melting point of nitrogen.

89. **Chemistry** The boiling point of oxygen is −182.962°C. Oxygen's melting point is −218.4°C. What is the difference between the boiling point and the melting point of oxygen?

Investments The chart at the right shows the closing price of a share of stock on September 15, 2003, for each of five companies. Also shown is the change in the price from the previous day. To find the closing price on the previous day, subtract the change in price from the closing price on September 15. Use this chart for Exercises 90 and 91.

Company	Closing Price	Change in Price
Del Monte Foods Co.	8.77	−0.06
General Mills, Inc.	47.10	−0.11
Hershey Foods, Inc.	72.57	+0.11
Hormel Food Corp.	22.42	−0.08
Sara Lee Corp.	19.18	−0.21

90. **a.** Find the closing price on the previous day for General Mills.
    b. Find the closing price on the previous day for Hormel Foods.

91. **a.** Find the closing price on the previous day for Sara Lee.
    b. Find the closing price on the previous day for Hershey Foods.

APPLYING THE CONCEPTS

92. Determine whether the statement is true or false.
    a. Every integer is a rational number.
    b. Every whole number is an integer.
    c. Every integer is a positive number.
    d. Every rational number is an integer.

93. **Number Problems** Find a rational number between $-\frac{3}{4}$ and $-\frac{2}{3}$.

94. **Number Problems**
    a. Find a rational number between 0.1 and 0.2.
    b. Find a rational number between 1 and 1.1.
    c. Find a rational number between 0 and 0.005.

95. Given any two different rational numbers, is it always possible to find a rational number between them? If so, explain how. If not, give an example of two different rational numbers for which there is no rational number between them.

10.5 Scientific Notation and the Order of Operations Agreement

Objective A To write a number in scientific notation

Point of Interest

The first woman mathematician for whom documented evidence exists is Hypatia (370–415). She lived in Alexandria, Egypt, and lectured at the Museum, the forerunner of our modern university. She made important contributions in mathematics, astronomy, and philosophy.

Scientific notation uses negative exponents. Therefore, we will discuss that topic before presenting scientific notation.

Look at the powers of 10 shown at the right. Note the pattern: The exponents are decreasing by 1, and each successive number on the right is one-tenth of the number above it. ($100,000 \div 10 = 10,000$; $10,000 \div 10 = 1000$; etc.)

$$10^5 = 100,000$$
$$10^4 = 10,000$$
$$10^3 = 1000$$
$$10^2 = 100$$
$$10^1 = 10$$

If we continue this pattern, the next exponent on 10 is $1 - 1 = 0$, and the number on the right side is $10 \div 10 = 1$.

$$10^0 = 1$$

The next exponent on 10 is $0 - 1 = -1$, and 10^{-1} is equal to $1 \div 10 = 0.1$.

$$10^{-1} = 0.1$$

The pattern is continued on the right. Note that a negative exponent does not indicate a negative number. Rather, each power of 10 with a negative exponent is equal to a number between 0 and 1. Also note that as the exponent on 10 decreases, so does the number it is equal to.

$$10^{-2} = 0.01$$
$$10^{-3} = 0.001$$
$$10^{-4} = 0.0001$$
$$10^{-5} = 0.00001$$
$$10^{-6} = 0.000001$$

Very large and very small numbers are encountered in the natural sciences. For example, the mass of an electron is 0.0000000000000000000000000000911 kg. Numbers such as this are difficult to read, so a more convenient system called **scientific notation** is used. In scientific notation, a number is expressed as the product of two factors, one a number between 1 and 10, and the other a power of 10.

To express a number in scientific notation, write it in the form $a \times 10^n$, where a is a number between 1 and 10 and n is an integer.

For numbers greater than 10, move the decimal point to the right of the first digit. The exponent n is positive and equal to the number of places the decimal point has been moved.

$$240,000 = 2.4 \times 10^5$$

$$93,000,000 = 9.3 \times 10^7$$

For numbers less than 1, move the decimal point to the right of the first nonzero digit. The exponent n is negative. The absolute value of the exponent is equal to the number of places the decimal point has been moved.

$$0.0003 = 3 \times 10^{-4}$$

$$0.0000832 = 8.32 \times 10^{-5}$$

Changing a number written in scientific notation to decimal notation also requires moving the decimal point.

When the exponent on 10 is positive, move the decimal point to the right the same number of places as the exponent.

$$3.45 \times 10^{9} = 3,450,000,000$$

$$2.3 \times 10^{8} = 230,000,000$$

When the exponent on 10 is negative, move the decimal point to the left the same number of places as the absolute value of the exponent.

$$8.1 \times 10^{-3} = 0.0081$$

$$6.34 \times 10^{-6} = 0.00000634$$

Example 1   Write 824,300,000,000 in scientific notation.

Solution   The number is greater than 10. Move the decimal point 11 places to the left. The exponent on 10 is 11.

$$824,300,000,000 = 8.243 \times 10^{11}$$

You Try It 1   Write 0.000000961 in scientific notation.

Your solution

Example 2   Write 6.8×10^{-10} in decimal notation.

Solution   The exponent on 10 is negative. Move the decimal point 10 places to the left.

$$6.8 \times 10^{-10} = 0.00000000068$$

You Try It 2   Write 7.329×10^{6} in decimal notation.

Your solution

Solutions on p. S27

Objective B   **To use the Order of Operations Agreement to simplify expressions**

The Order of Operations Agreement has been used throughout this book. In simplifying expressions with rational numbers, the same Order of Operations Agreement is used. This agreement is restated here.

> **The Order of Operations Agreement**
>
> **Step 1** Do all operations inside parentheses.
> **Step 2** Simplify any number expressions containing exponents.
> **Step 3** Do multiplication and division as they occur from left to right.
> **Step 4** Rewrite subtraction as addition of the opposite. Then do additions as they occur from left to right.

Exponents may be confusing in expressions with signed numbers.

$$(-3)^2 = (-3) \times (-3) = 9$$
$$-3^2 = -(3)^2 = -(3 \times 3) = -9$$

Note that -3 is squared only when the negative sign is *inside* the parentheses.

HOW TO   Simplify: $(-3)^2 - 2 \times (8 - 3) + (-5)$

$(-3)^2 - 2 \times \underbrace{(8 - 3)} + (-5)$

$\quad (-3)^2 - \underbrace{2 \times 5} + (-5)$

$\quad\quad \underbrace{9} - 2 \times 5 + (-5)$

$\quad\quad 9 - 10 + (-5)$

$\quad\quad \underbrace{9 + (-10)} + (-5)$

$\quad\quad\quad \underbrace{(-1) + (-5)}$

$\quad\quad\quad\quad -6$

1. Perform operations inside parentheses.

2. Simplify expressions with exponents.

3. Do multiplications and divisions as they occur from left to right.

4. Rewrite subtraction as the addition of the opposite. Then add from left to right.

HOW TO   Simplify: $\left(\dfrac{1}{4} - \dfrac{1}{2}\right)^2 \div \dfrac{3}{8}$

$\underbrace{\left(\dfrac{1}{4} - \dfrac{1}{2}\right)^2} \div \dfrac{3}{8}$

$\underbrace{\left(-\dfrac{1}{4}\right)^2} \div \dfrac{3}{8}$

$\underbrace{\dfrac{1}{16} \div \dfrac{3}{8}}$

$\underbrace{\dfrac{1}{16} \times \dfrac{8}{3}}$

$\quad \dfrac{1}{6}$

1. Perform operations inside parentheses.

2. Simplify expressions with exponents.

3. Do multiplication and division as they occur from left to right.

Example 3   Simplify: $8 - 4 \div (-2)$

Solution
$8 - 4 \div (-2)$
$= 8 - (-2)$ • Do the division.
$= 8 + 2$ • Rewrite as addition. Add.
$= 10$

You Try It 3   Simplify: $9 - 9 \div (-3)$

Your solution

Solution on p. S27

Example 4 Simplify: $12 \div (-2)^2 + 5$

Solution
$$12 \div (-2)^2 + 5$$
$$= 12 \div 4 + 5 \qquad \bullet \ \text{Exponents}$$
$$= 3 + 5 \qquad\qquad \bullet \ \text{Division}$$
$$= 8 \qquad\qquad\quad\ \bullet \ \text{Addition}$$

You Try It 4 Simplify: $8 \div 4 \cdot 4 - (-2)^2$

Your solution

Example 5 Simplify: $12 - (-10) \div (8 - 3)$

Solution
$$12 - (-10) \div (8 - 3)$$
$$= 12 - (-10) \div 5$$
$$= 12 - (-2)$$
$$= 12 + 2$$
$$= 14$$

You Try It 5 Simplify: $8 - (-15) \div (2 - 7)$

Your solution

Example 6 Simplify:
$(-3)^2 \times (5 - 7)^2 - (-9) \div 3$

Solution
$$(-3)^2 \times (5 - 7)^2 - (-9) \div 3$$
$$= (-3)^2 \times (-2)^2 - (-9) \div 3$$
$$= 9 \times 4 - (-9) \div 3$$
$$= 36 - (-9) \div 3$$
$$= 36 - (-3)$$
$$= 36 + 3$$
$$= 39$$

You Try It 6 Simplify:
$(-2)^2 \times (3 - 7)^2 - (-16) \div (-4)$

Your solution

Example 7 Simplify: $3 \div \left(\dfrac{1}{2} - \dfrac{1}{4} \right) - 3$

Solution
$$3 \div \left(\dfrac{1}{2} - \dfrac{1}{4} \right) - 3$$
$$= 3 \div \dfrac{1}{4} - 3$$
$$= 3 \times \dfrac{4}{1} - 3$$
$$= 12 - 3$$
$$= 12 + (-3)$$
$$= 9$$

You Try It 7 Simplify: $7 \div \left(\dfrac{1}{7} - \dfrac{3}{14} \right) - 9$

Your solution

Solutions on p. S27

10.5 Exercises

To write a number in scientific notation

For Exercises 1 to 12, write the number in scientific notation.

1. 2,370,000

2. 75,000

3. 0.00045

4. 0.000076

5. 309,000

6. 819,000,000

7. 0.000000601

8. 0.00000000096

9. 57,000,000,000

10. 934,800,000,000

11. 0.000000017

12. 0.0000009217

For Exercises 13 to 24, write the number in decimal notation.

13. 7.1×10^5

14. 2.3×10^7

15. 4.3×10^{-5}

16. 9.21×10^{-7}

17. 6.71×10^8

18. 5.75×10^9

19. 7.13×10^{-6}

20. 3.54×10^{-8}

21. 5×10^{12}

22. 1.0987×10^{11}

23. 8.01×10^{-3}

24. 4.0162×10^{-9}

25. **Physics** Light travels 16,000,000,000 mi in 1 day. Write this number in scientific notation.

26. **Earth Science** Write the mass of Earth, which is approximately 5,980,000,000,000,000,000,000,000 kg, in scientific notation.

27. **Wars** The graph at the right shows the monetary cost of four wars. Write the monetary cost of World War II in scientific notation.

28. **Chemistry** The electric charge on an electron is 0.00000000000000000016 coulomb. Write this number in scientific notation.

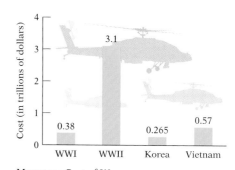

Monetary Cost of Wars

Source: Congressional Research Service, using numbers from the *Statistical Abstract of the United States*

29. **Physics** The length of an infrared light wave is approximately 0.0000037 m. Write this number in scientific notation.

30. **Computers** One unit used to measure the speed of a computer is the picosecond. One picosecond is 0.000000000001 of a second. Write this number in scientific notation.

Objective B **To use the Order of Operations Agreement to simplify expressions**

For Exercises 31 to 92, simplify.

31. $8 \div 4 + 2$

32. $3 - 12 \div 2$

33. $4 + (-7) + 3$

34. $-16 \div 2 + 8$

35. $4^2 - 4$

36. $6 - 2^2$

37. $2 \times (3 - 5) - 2$

38. $2 - (8 - 10) \div 2$

39. $4 - (-3)^2$

40. $(-2)^2 - 6$

41. $4 - (-3) - 5$

42. $6 + (-8) - (-3)$

43. $4 - (-2)^2 + (-3)$

44. $-3 + (-6)^2 - 1$

45. $3^2 - 4 \times 2$

46. $9 \div 3 - (-3)^2$

47. $3 \times (6 - 2) \div 6$

48. $4 \times (2 - 7) \div 5$

49. $2^2 - (-3)^2 + 2$

50. $3 \times (8 - 5) + 4$

51. $6 - 2 \times (1 - 5)$

52. $4 \times 2 \times (3 - 6)$

53. $(-2)^2 - (-3)^2 + 1$

54. $4^2 - 3^2 - 4$

55. $6 - (-3) \times (-3)^2$

56. $4 - (-5) \times (-2)^2$

57. $4 \times 2 - 3 \times 7$

58. $16 \div 2 - 9 \div 3$

59. $(-2)^2 - 5 \times 3 - 1$

60. $4 - 2 \times 7 - 3^2$

61. $7 \times 6 - 5 \times 6 + 3 \times 2 - 2 + 1$

62. $3 \times 2^2 + 5 \times (3 + 2) - 17$

63. $-4 \times 3 \times (-2) + 12 \times (3 - 4) + (-12)$

64. $3 \times 4^2 - 16 - 4 + 3 - (1 - 2)^2$

65. $-12 \times (6 - 8) + 1^2 \times 3^2 \times 2 - 6 \times 2$

66. $-3 \times (-2)^2 \times 4 \div 8 - (-12)$

67. $10 \times 9 - (8 + 7) \div 5 + 6 - 7 + 8$

68. $-27 - (-3)^2 - 2 - 7 + 6 \times 3$

69. $3^2 \times (4 - 7) \div 9 + 6 - 3 - 4 \times 2$

70. $16 - 4 \times 8 + 4^2 - (-18) \div (-9)$

71. $(-3)^2 \times (5 - 7)^2 - (-9) \div 3$

72. $-2 \times 4^2 - 3 \times (2 - 8) - 3$

73. $4 - 6(2 - 5)^3 \div (17 - 8)$

74. $5 + 7(3 - 8)^2 \div (-14 + 9)$

75. $(1.2)^2 - 4.1 \times 0.3$

76. $2.4 \times (-3) - 2.5$

77. $1.6 - (-1.6)^2$

78. $4.1 \times 8 \div (-4.1)$

79. $(4.1 - 3.9) - 0.7^2$

80. $1.8 \times (-2.3) - 2$

81. $(-0.4)^2 \times 1.5 - 2$

82. $(6.2 - 1.3) \times (-3)$

83. $4.2 - (-3.9) - 6$

84. $-\dfrac{1}{2} + \dfrac{3}{8} \div \left(-\dfrac{3}{4}\right)$

85. $\left(\dfrac{3}{4}\right)^{2} - \dfrac{3}{8}$

86. $\left(\dfrac{1}{2}\right)^{2} - \left(-\dfrac{1}{2}\right)^{2}$

87. $\dfrac{5}{16} - \dfrac{3}{8} + \dfrac{1}{2}$

88. $\dfrac{2}{7} \div \dfrac{5}{7} - \dfrac{3}{14}$

89. $\dfrac{1}{2} \times \dfrac{1}{4} \times \dfrac{1}{2} - \dfrac{3}{8}$

90. $\dfrac{2}{3} \times \dfrac{5}{8} \div \dfrac{2}{7}$

91. $\dfrac{1}{2} - \left(\dfrac{3}{4} - \dfrac{3}{8}\right) \div \dfrac{1}{3}$

92. $\dfrac{3}{8} \div \left(-\dfrac{1}{2}\right)^{2} + 2$

APPLYING THE CONCEPTS

93. Place the correct symbol, $<$ or $>$, between the two numbers.
    a. 3.45×10^{-14} 3.45×10^{-15}
    b. 5.23×10^{18} 5.23×10^{17}
    c. 3.12×10^{12} 3.12×10^{11}

94. **Astronomy**   Light travels 3×10^{8} m in 1 s. How far does light travel in 1 year? (Astronomers refer to this distance as 1 light year.)

95. a. Evaluate $1^{3} + 2^{3} + 3^{3} + 4^{3}$.
    b. Evaluate $(-1)^{3} + (-2)^{3} + (-3)^{3} + (-4)^{3}$.
    c. Evaluate $1^{3} + 2^{3} + 3^{3} + 4^{3} + 5^{3}$.
    d. On the basis of your answers to parts a, b, and c, evaluate $(-1)^{3} + (-2)^{3} + (-3)^{3} + (-4)^{3} + (-5)^{3}$.

96. Evaluate $2^{(3^{2})}$ and $(2^{3})^{2}$. Are the answers the same? If not, which is larger?

97. Abdul, Becky, Carl, and Diana were being questioned by their teacher. One of the students had left an apple on the teacher's desk, but the teacher did not know which one. Abdul said it was either Becky or Diana. Diana said it was neither Becky nor Carl. If both those statements are false, who left the apple on the teacher's desk? Explain how you arrived at your solution.

98. In your own words, explain how you know that a number is written in scientific notation.

99. a. Express the mass of the sun in kilograms using scientific notation.
    b. Express the mass of a neutron in kilograms using scientific notation.

Focus on Problem Solving

Drawing Diagrams How do you best remember something? Do you remember best what you hear? The word *aural* means "pertaining to the ear"; people with a strong aural memory remember best those things that they hear. The word *visual* means "pertaining to the sense of sight"; people with a strong visual memory remember best that which they see written down. Some people claim that their memory is in their writing hand—they remember something only if they write it down! The method by which you best remember something is probably also the method by which you can best learn something new.

In problem-solving situations, try to capitalize on your strengths. If you tend to understand the material better when you hear it spoken, read application problems aloud or have someone else read them to you. If writing helps you to organize ideas, rewrite application problems in your own words.

No matter what your main strength, visualizing a problem can be a valuable aid in problem solving. A drawing, sketch, diagram, or chart can be a useful tool in problem solving, just as calculators and computers are tools. A diagram can be helpful in gaining an understanding of the relationships inherent in a problem-solving situation. A sketch will help you to organize the given information and can lead to your being able to focus on the method by which the solution can be determined.

> **HOW TO** A tour bus drives 5 mi south, then 4 mi west, then 3 mi north, then 4 mi east. How far is the tour bus from the starting point?
>
> Draw a diagram of the given information.
>
> From the diagram, we can see that the solution can be determined by subtracting 3 from 5: $5 - 3 = 2$.
>
> The bus is 2 mi from the starting point.

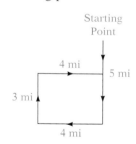

> **HOW TO** If you roll two ordinary six-sided dice and multiply the two numbers that appear on top, how many different possible products are there?
>
> Make a chart of the possible products. In the chart below, repeated products are marked with an asterisk.

$1 \cdot 1 = 1$	$2 \cdot 1 = 2$ (*)	$3 \cdot 1 = 3$ (*)	$4 \cdot 1 = 4$ (*)	$5 \cdot 1 = 5$ (*)	$6 \cdot 1 = 6$ (*)
$1 \cdot 2 = 2$	$2 \cdot 2 = 4$ (*)	$3 \cdot 2 = 6$ (*)	$4 \cdot 2 = 8$ (*)	$5 \cdot 2 = 10$ (*)	$6 \cdot 2 = 12$ (*)
$1 \cdot 3 = 3$	$2 \cdot 3 = 6$ (*)	$3 \cdot 3 = 9$	$4 \cdot 3 = 12$ (*)	$5 \cdot 3 = 15$ (*)	$6 \cdot 3 = 18$ (*)
$1 \cdot 4 = 4$	$2 \cdot 4 = 8$	$3 \cdot 4 = 12$ (*)	$4 \cdot 4 = 16$	$5 \cdot 4 = 20$ (*)	$6 \cdot 4 = 24$ (*)
$1 \cdot 5 = 5$	$2 \cdot 5 = 10$	$3 \cdot 5 = 15$	$4 \cdot 5 = 20$	$5 \cdot 5 = 25$	$6 \cdot 5 = 30$ (*)
$1 \cdot 6 = 6$	$2 \cdot 6 = 12$	$3 \cdot 6 = 18$	$4 \cdot 6 = 24$	$5 \cdot 6 = 30$	$6 \cdot 6 = 36$

By counting the products that are not repeats, we can see that there are 18 different possible products.

Look at Sections 10.1 and 10.2. You will notice that number lines are used to help you visualize the integers, as an aid in ordering integers, to help you understand the concepts of opposite and absolute value, and to illustrate addition of integers. As you begin your work with integers, you may find that sketching a number line proves helpful in coming to understand a problem or in working through a calculation that involves integers.

Projects and Group Activities

Deductive Reasoning

Suppose that during the last week of your math class, your instructor tells you that if you receive an A on the final exam, you will earn an A in the course. When the final exam grades are posted, you learn that you received an A on the final exam. You can then assume that you will earn an A in the course.

The process used to determine your grade in the math course is deductive reasoning. **Deductive reasoning** involves drawing a conclusion that is based on given facts. The problems below require deductive reasoning.

1. Given that $\Delta\Delta\Delta = \Diamond\Diamond\Diamond\Diamond$ and $\Diamond\Diamond\Diamond\Diamond = \acute{O}\acute{O}$, then $\Delta\Delta\Delta\Delta\Delta\Delta =$ how many $\acute{O}$s?

2. Given that $\ddagger\ddagger = \bullet\bullet\bullet$ and $\bullet\bullet\bullet = \Lambda$, then $\ddagger\ddagger\ddagger\ddagger =$ how many Λs?

3. Given that $\acute{O}\acute{O}\acute{O} = \Omega\Omega$ and $\square = \Omega\Omega$, then $\square\square =$ how many $\acute{O}$s?

4. Given that $\int\int\int\int\int = \partial\partial$ and $\partial\partial\partial\partial = ¥¥¥$, then $¥¥¥¥¥¥ =$ how many $\int$s?

5. Given that $\hat{O}\hat{O}\hat{O}\hat{O}\hat{O} = \square\square\square$ and $\square\square\square\square\square\square = §§§§$, then $§§§§§§ =$ how many $\hat{O}$s?

6. Chris, Dana, Leslie, and Pat are neighbors. Each drives a different type of vehicle: a compact car, a sedan, a sports car, or a station wagon. From the following statements, determine which type of vehicle each of the neighbors drives. It may be helpful to use the chart provided below.
   a. Although the vehicle owned by Chris has more mileage on it than does either the sedan or the sports car, it does not have the highest mileage of all four cars.
   b. Pat and the owner of the sports car live on one side of the street, and Leslie and the owner of the compact car live on the other side of the street.
   c. Leslie owns the vehicle with the most mileage on it.

TAKE NOTE

To use the chart to solve this problem, write an X in a box to indicate that a possibility has been eliminated. Write a $\surd$ to show that a match has been found. When a row or column has 3 X's, a $\surd$ is written in the remaining open box in that row or column of the chart.

	Compact	*Sedan*	*Sports Car*	*Wagon*
Chris				
Dana				
Leslie				
Pat				

7. Four neighbors, Anna, Kay, Michelle, and Nicole, each plant a different vegetable (beans, cucumbers, squash, or tomatoes) in their garden. From the following statements, determine which vegetable each neighbor plants.
   a. Nicole's garden is bigger than the one that has tomatoes but smaller than the one that has cucumbers.
   b. Anna, who planted the largest garden, didn't plant the beans.
   c. The person who planted the beans has a garden the same size as Nicole's.
   d. Kay and the person who planted the tomatoes also have flower gardens.

8. The Ontkeans, Kedrovas, McIvers, and Levinsons are neighbors. Each of the four families specializes in a different national cuisine (Chinese, French, Italian, or Mexican). From the following statements, determine which cuisine each family specializes in.
   a. The Ontkeans invited the family that specializes in Chinese cuisine and the family that specializes in Mexican cuisine for dinner last night.
   b. The McIvers live between the family that specializes in Italian cuisine and the Ontkeans. The Levinsons live between the Kedrovas and the family that specializes in Chinese cuisine.
   c. The Kedrovas and the family that specializes in Italian cuisine both subscribe to the same culinary magazine.

Chapter 10 Summary

Key Words

	Examples
Positive numbers are numbers greater than zero. *Negative numbers* are numbers less than zero. The *integers* are . . . −4, −3, −2, −1, 0, 1, 2, 3, 4, ... *Positive integers* are to the right of zero on the number line. *Negative integers* are to the left of zero on the number line. [10.1A, p. 405]	9, 87, and 603 are positive numbers. They are also positive integers. −5, −41, and −729 are negative numbers. They are also negative integers.
Opposite numbers are two numbers that are the same distance from zero on the number line but on opposite sides of zero. [10.1B, p. 406]	8 is the opposite of −8. −2 is the opposite of 2.
The *absolute value of a number* is its distance from zero on a number line. The absolute value of a number is a positive number or zero. The symbol for absolute value is | |. [10.1B, p. 406]	$\|9\| = 9$ $\|-9\| = 9$ $-\|9\| = -9$
A *rational number* is a number that can be written in the form $\frac{a}{b}$, where a and b are integers and $b \neq 0$. [10.4A, p. 427]	$\frac{3}{7}$, $-\frac{5}{8}$, 9, −2, $4\frac{1}{2}$, 0.6, and $0.\overline{3}$ are rational numbers.

Essential Rules and Procedures

	Examples
Order Relations [10.1A, p. 405] A number that appears to the left of a given number on the number line is less than (<) the given number. A number that appears to the right of a given number on the number line is greater than (>) the given number.	$-6 > -12$ $-8 < 4$

To add numbers with the same sign, add the absolute values of the numbers. Then attach the sign of the addends. [10.2A, p. 412]

$$6 + 4 = 10$$
$$-6 + (-4) = -10$$

To add numbers with different signs, find the difference between the absolute values of the numbers. Then attach the sign of the addend with the greater absolute value. [10.2A, p. 412]

$$-6 + 4 = -2$$
$$6 + (-4) = 2$$

To subtract two numbers, add the opposite of the second number to the first number. [10.2B, p. 413]

$$6 - 4 = 6 + (-4) = 2$$
$$6 - (-4) = 6 + 4 = 10$$
$$-6 - 4 = -6 + (-4) = -10$$
$$-6 - (-4) = -6 + 4 = -2$$

To multiply numbers with the same sign, multiply the absolute values of the factors. The product is positive. [10.3A, p. 419]

$$3 \cdot 5 = 15$$
$$-3(-5) = 15$$

To multiply numbers with different signs, multiply the absolute values of the factors. The product is negative. [10.3A, p. 419]

$$-3(5) = -15$$
$$3(-5) = -15$$

To divide two numbers with the same sign, divide the absolute values of the numbers. The quotient is positive. [10.3B, p. 420]

$$15 \div 3 = 5$$
$$(-15) \div (-3) = 5$$

To divide two numbers with different signs, divide the absolute values of the numbers. The quotient is negative. [10.3B, p. 420]

$$-15 \div 3 = -5$$
$$15 \div (-3) = -5$$

Properties of Zero and One in Division [10.3B, p. 421]
Zero divided by any number other than zero is zero.
Any number other than zero divided by itself is 1.
Any number divided by 1 is the number.
Division by zero is not defined.

$$0 \div (-5) = 0$$
$$-5 \div (-5) = 1$$
$$-5 \div 1 = -5$$
$$-5 \div 0 \text{ is undefined.}$$

Scientific Notation [10.5A, pp. 437–438]
To express a number in scientific notation, write it in the form $a \times 10^n$, where a is a number between 1 and 10 and n is an integer.
If the number is greater than 10, the exponent on 10 will be positive.
If the number is less than 1, the exponent on 10 will be negative.

$$367,000,000 = 3.67 \times 10^8$$
$$0.0000059 = 5.9 \times 10^{-6}$$

To change a number written in scientific notation to decimal notation, move the decimal point to the right if the exponent on 10 is positive and to the left if the exponent is negative. Move the decimal point the same number of places as the absolute value of the exponent on 10.

$$2.418 \times 10^7 = 24,180,000$$
$$9.06 \times 10^{-5} = 0.0000906$$

The Order of Operations Agreement [10.5B, p. 439]

Step 1 Do all operations inside parentheses.

Step 2 Simplify any numerical expressions containing exponents.

Step 3 Do multiplication and division as they occur from left to right.

Step 4 Rewrite subtraction as addition of the opposite. Then do additions as they occur from left to right.

$$(-4)^2 - 3(1 - 5) = (-4)^2 - 3(-4)$$
$$= 16 - 3(-4)$$
$$= 16 - (-12)$$
$$= 16 + 12$$
$$= 28$$

Chapter 10 Review Exercises

1. Find the opposite of 22.

2. Subtract: $-8 - (-2) - (-10) - 3$

3. Subtract: $\dfrac{5}{8} - \dfrac{5}{6}$

4. Simplify: $-0.33 + 1.98 - 1.44$

5. Multiply: $\left(-\dfrac{2}{3}\right)\left(\dfrac{6}{11}\right)\left(-\dfrac{22}{25}\right)$

6. Multiply: -0.08×16

7. Simplify: $12 - 6 \div 3$

8. Simplify: $\left(\dfrac{2}{3}\right)^2 - \dfrac{5}{6}$

9. Find the opposite of -4.

10. Place the correct symbol, $<$ or $>$, between the two numbers.
$0 \quad -3$

11. Evaluate $-|-6|$.

12. Divide: $-18 \div (-3)$

13. Add: $-\dfrac{3}{8} + \dfrac{5}{12} + \dfrac{2}{3}$

14. Multiply: $\dfrac{1}{3} \times \left(-\dfrac{3}{4}\right)$

15. Divide: $-\dfrac{7}{12} \div \left(-\dfrac{14}{39}\right)$

16. Simplify: $16 \div 4(8 - 2)$

17. Add: $-22 + 14 + (-18)$

18. Simplify: $3^2 - 9 + 2$

19. Write 0.0000397 in scientific notation.

20. Divide: $-1.464 \div 18.3$

21. Simplify: $-\dfrac{5}{12} + \dfrac{7}{9} - \dfrac{1}{3}$

22. Multiply: $\dfrac{6}{34} \times \dfrac{17}{40}$

23. Multiply: $1.2 \times (-0.035)$

24. Simplify: $-\dfrac{1}{2} + \dfrac{3}{8} \div \dfrac{9}{20}$

25. Evaluate $|-5|$.

26. Place the correct symbol, $<$ or $>$, between the two numbers.
$-2 \quad -40$

27. Find 2 times -13.

28. Simplify: $-0.4 \times 5 - (-3.33)$

29. Add: $\dfrac{5}{12} + \left(-\dfrac{2}{3}\right)$

30. Simplify: $-33.4 + 9.8 - (-16.2)$

31. Divide: $\left(-\dfrac{3}{8}\right) \div \left(-\dfrac{4}{5}\right)$

32. Write 2.4×10^5 in decimal notation.

33. **Temperatures**   Find the temperature after a rise of $18°$ from $-22°$.

34. **Education**   To discourage guessing on a multiple-choice exam, an instructor graded the test by giving 3 points for a correct answer, -1 point for an answer left blank, and -2 points for an incorrect answer. How many points did a student score who answered 38 questions correctly, answered 4 questions incorrectly, and left 8 questions blank?

35.   **Chemistry**   The boiling point of mercury is $356.58°$C. The melting point of mercury is $-38.87°$C. Find the difference between the boiling point and the melting point of mercury.

Chapter 10 Test

1. Subtract: $-5 - (-8)$

2. Evaluate $-|-2|$.

3. Add: $-\frac{2}{5} + \frac{7}{15}$

4. Find the product of 0.032 and -1.9.

5. Place the correct symbol, $<$ or $>$, between the two numbers.
$-8 \quad -10$

6. Add: $1.22 + (-3.1)$

7. Simplify: $4 \times (4 - 7) \div (-2) - 4 \times 8$

8. Multiply: $-5 \times (-6) \times 3$

9. What is -1.004 decreased by 3.01?

10. Divide: $-72 \div 8$

11. Find the sum of -2, 3, and -8.

12. Add: $-\frac{3}{8} + \frac{2}{3}$

13. Write 87,600,000,000 in scientific notation.

14. Find the product of -4 and 12.

15. Divide: $\frac{0}{-17}$

16. Subtract: $16 - 4 - (-5) - 7$

17. Find the quotient of $-\frac{2}{3}$ and $\frac{5}{6}$.

18. Place the correct symbol, $<$ or $>$, between the two numbers.

   0   -4

19. Add: $16 + (-10) + (-20)$

20. Simplify: $(-2)^2 - (-3)^2 \div (1 - 4)^2 \times 2 - 6$

21. Subtract: $-\frac{2}{5} - \left(-\frac{7}{10}\right)$

22. Write 9.601×10^{-8} in decimal notation.

23. Divide: $-15.64 \div (-4.6)$

24. Find the sum of $-\frac{1}{2}, \frac{1}{3}$, and $\frac{1}{4}$.

25. Multiply: $\frac{3}{8} \times \left(-\frac{5}{6}\right) \times \left(-\frac{4}{15}\right)$

26. Subtract: $2.113 - (-1.1)$

27. Temperatures   Find the temperature after a rise of 11°C from −4°C.

28.   **Chemistry**   The melting point of radon is −71°C. The melting point of oxygen is three times the melting point of radon. Find the melting point of oxygen.

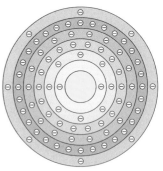

Radon

29.   **Meteorology**   On December 24, 1924, in Fairfield, Montana, the temperature fell from 17.22°C at noon to −29.4°C at midnight. How many degrees did the temperature fall in the 12-h period?

30. Meteorology   The daily low temperature readings for a 3-day period were as follows: −7°F, 9°F, −8°F. Find the average low temperature for the 3-day period.

Cumulative Review Exercises

1. Simplify: $16 - 4 \cdot (3 - 2)^2 \cdot 4$

2. Find the difference between $8\frac{1}{2}$ and $3\frac{4}{7}$.

3. Divide: $3\frac{7}{8} \div 1\frac{1}{2}$

4. Simplify: $\frac{3}{8} \div \left(\frac{3}{8} - \frac{1}{4}\right) \div \frac{7}{3}$

5. Subtract: $2.907 - 1.09761$

6. Solve the proportion $\frac{7}{12} = \frac{n}{32}$. Round to the nearest hundredth.

7. 22 is 160% of what number?

8. Convert: 7 qt = _____ gal _____ qt

9. Convert: 6692 ml = _____ L

10. Convert 4.2 ft to meters. Round to the nearest hundredth. (1 m = 3.28 ft.)

11. Find 32% of 180.

12. Convert $3\frac{2}{5}$ to a percent.

13. Add: $-8 + 5$

14. Add: $3\frac{1}{4} + \left(-6\frac{5}{8}\right)$

15. Subtract: $-6\frac{1}{8} - 4\frac{5}{12}$

16. Simplify: $-12 - (-7) - 3(-8)$

17. What is -3.2 times -1.09?

18. Multiply: $-6 \times 7 \times \left(-\frac{3}{4}\right)$

19. Find the quotient of 42 and −6.

20. Divide: $-2\frac{1}{7} \div \left(-3\frac{3}{5}\right)$

21. Simplify: $3 \times (3 - 7) \div 6 - 2$

22. Simplify: $4 - (-2)^2 \div (1 - 2)^2 \times 3 + 4$

23. Carpentry A board $5\frac{2}{3}$ ft long is cut from a board 8 ft long. What is the length of the board remaining?

24. Banking Nimisha had a balance of $763.56 in her checkbook before writing checks for $135.88 and $47.81 and making a deposit of $223.44. Find her new checkbook balance.

25. Consumerism A suit that regularly sells for $165 is on sale for $120. Find the percent decrease in price. Round to the nearest tenth of a percent.

26. Measurement A reception is planned for 80 guests. How many gallons of coffee should be prepared to provide 2 c of coffee for each guest?

27. Investments A stock selling for $82.625 per share paid a dividend of $1.50 per share before the dividend was increased by 12%. Find the dividend per share after the increase.

28. Compensation The hourly wages for five job classifications at a company are $11.40, $9.32, $15.25, $10.73, and $13.10. Find the median hourly pay.

29. Elections A pre-election survey showed that 5 out of every 8 registered voters would cast ballots in a city election. At this rate, how many people would vote in a city of 960,000 registered voters?

30. Meteorology The daily high temperature readings for a 4-day period were recorded as follows: −19°F, −7°F, 1°F, and 9°F. Find the average high temperature for the 4-day period.

11 Introduction to Algebra

This family is getting ready to head off on their vacation. They plan to drive 500 miles to their destination, and their car averages 25 miles per gallon of gasoline on the highway. How many gallons of gasoline will the car consume in driving the family there and back? We can use the formula $D = M \cdot G$, where D is the distance traveled, M is the miles per gallon, and G is the number of gallons consumed. Using this formula, we find that the car will need 40 gallons to make the trip. **Exercises 98 to 101 on pages 475 and 476** use this formula to answer other questions about gasoline consumption.

Need help? For online student resources, such as section quizzes, visit this textbook's website at **math.college.hmco.com/students.**

OBJECTIVES

Section 11.1

A To evaluate variable expressions
B To simplify variable expressions containing no parentheses
C To simplify variable expressions containing parentheses

Section 11.2

A To determine whether a given number is a solution of an equation
B To solve an equation of the form $x + a = b$
C To solve an equation of the form $ax = b$
D To solve application problems using formulas

Section 11.3

A To solve an equation of the form $ax + b = c$
B To solve application problems using formulas

Section 11.4

A To solve an equation of the form $ax + b = cx + d$
B To solve an equation containing parentheses

Section 11.5

A To translate a verbal expression into a mathematical expression given the variable
B To translate a verbal expression into a mathematical expression by assigning the variable

Section 11.6

A To translate a sentence into an equation and solve
B To solve application problems

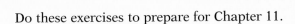
Do these exercises to prepare for Chapter 11.

For Exercises 1 to 9, simplify.

1. $2 - 9$

2. $-5(4)$

3. $-16 + 16$

4. $\dfrac{-7}{-7}$

5. $-\dfrac{3}{8}\left(-\dfrac{8}{3}\right)$

6. $\left(\dfrac{3}{5}\right)^3 \cdot \left(\dfrac{5}{9}\right)^2$

7. $\dfrac{2}{3} + \left(\dfrac{3}{4}\right)^2 \cdot \dfrac{2}{9}$

8. $-8 \div (-2)^2 + 6$

9. $4 + 5(2 - 7)^2 \div (-8 + 3)$

GO FIGURE • • •

In the addition at the right, each letter stands for a different digit. If N = 1, I = 5, U = 7, F = 2, and T = 3, what is the value of S?

$$
\begin{array}{r}
\text{FUN} \\
\text{IN} \\
+\,\text{THE} \\
\hline
\text{SUN}
\end{array}
$$

11.1 Variable Expressions

Objective A   **To evaluate variable expressions**

Point of Interest

There are historical records indicating that mathematics has been studied for at least 4000 years. However, only in the last 400 years have variables been used. Prior to that, mathematics was written in words.

Often we discuss a quantity without knowing its exact value—for example, next year's inflation rate, the price of gasoline next summer, or the interest rate on a new-car loan next fall. In mathematics, a letter of the alphabet is used to stand for a quantity that is unknown or that can change, or *vary*. The letter is called a **variable.** An expression that contains one or more variables is called a **variable expression.**

A company's business manager has determined that the company will make a $10 profit on each radio it sells. The manager wants to describe the company's total profit from the sale of radios. Because the number of radios that the company will sell is unknown, the manager lets the variable n stand for that number. Then the variable expression $10 \cdot n$, or simply $10n$, describes the company's profit from selling n radios.

The company's profit from selling n radios is $\$10 \cdot n = \$10n$.

If the company sells 12 radios, its profit is $\$10 \cdot 12 = \$120$.

If the company sells 75 radios, its profit is $\$10 \cdot 75 = \$750$.

Replacing the variable or variables in a variable expression and then simplifying the resulting numerical expression is called **evaluating a variable expression.**

HOW TO   Evaluate $3x^2 + xy - z$ when $x = -2$, $y = 3$, and $z = -4$.

$3x^2 + xy - z$

$3(-2)^2 + (-2)(3) - (-4)$ • Replace each variable in the expression with the number it stands for.

$= 3 \cdot 4 + (-2)(3) - (-4)$ • Use the Order of Operations Agreement to simplify the resulting numerical expression.

$= 12 + (-6) - (-4)$

$= 12 + (-6) + 4$

$= 6 + 4$

$= 10$

The value of the variable expression $3x^2 + xy - z$ when $x = -2$, $y = 3$, and $z = -4$ is 10.

Example 1

Evaluate $3x - 4y$ when $x = -2$ and $y = 3$.

Solution

$3x - 4y$

$3(-2) - 4(3) = -6 - 12$
$= -6 + (-12) = -18$

You Try It 1

Evaluate $6a - 5b$ when $a = -3$ and $b = 4$.

Your solution

Example 2

Evaluate $-x^2 - 6 \div y$ when $x = -3$ and $y = 2$.

Solution

$-x^2 - 6 \div y$

$-(-3)^2 - 6 \div 2 = -9 - 6 \div 2$
$= -9 - 3$
$= -9 + (-3) = -12$

You Try It 2

Evaluate $-3s^2 - 12 \div t$ when $s = -2$ and $t = 4$.

Your solution

Example 3

Evaluate $-\dfrac{1}{2}y^2 - \dfrac{3}{4}z$ when $y = 2$ and $z = -4$.

Solution

$-\dfrac{1}{2}y^2 - \dfrac{3}{4}z$

$-\dfrac{1}{2}(2)^2 - \dfrac{3}{4}(-4) = -\dfrac{1}{2} \cdot 4 - \dfrac{3}{4}(-4)$
$= -2 - (-3)$
$= -2 + (3) = 1$

You Try It 3

Evaluate $-\dfrac{2}{3}m + \dfrac{3}{4}n^3$ when $m = 6$ and $n = 2$.

Your solution

Example 4

Evaluate $-2ab + b^2 + a^2$ when $a = -\dfrac{3}{5}$ and $b = \dfrac{2}{5}$.

Solution

$-2ab + b^2 + a^2$

$-2\left(-\dfrac{3}{5}\right)\left(\dfrac{2}{5}\right) + \left(\dfrac{2}{5}\right)^2 + \left(-\dfrac{3}{5}\right)^2$

$= -2\left(-\dfrac{3}{5}\right)\left(\dfrac{2}{5}\right) + \left(\dfrac{4}{25}\right) + \left(\dfrac{9}{25}\right)$

$= \dfrac{12}{25} + \dfrac{4}{25} + \dfrac{9}{25} = \dfrac{25}{25} = 1$

You Try It 4

Evaluate $-3yz - z^2 + y^2$ when $y = -\dfrac{2}{3}$ and $z = \dfrac{1}{3}$.

Your solution

Solutions on p. S28

Objective B   **To simplify variable expressions containing no parentheses**

The **terms of a variable expression** are the addends of the expression. The variable expression at the right has four terms.

$$\underbrace{7x^2 \;+\; \overbrace{(-6xy) \;+\; x}^{\text{4 terms}} \;+\; (-8)}$$

$$\underbrace{7x^2 \;+\; (-6xy) \;+\; x}_{\text{Variable terms}} \quad \underbrace{(-8)}_{\substack{\text{Constant} \\ \text{term}}}$$

TAKE NOTE

A variable term is a term composed of a numerical coefficient and a variable part. The numerical coefficient is the number part of the term.

Three of the terms are **variable terms:** $7x^2$, $-6xy$, and x.

One of the terms is a **constant term:** -8. A constant term has no variables.

Each variable term is composed of a **numerical coefficient** (the number part of a variable term) and a **variable part** (the variable or variables and their exponents). When the numerical coefficient is 1, the 1 is usually not written. ($1x = x$)

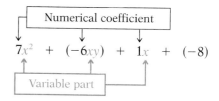

Like terms of a variable expression are the terms with the same variable part. (Because $y^2 = y \cdot y$, y^2 and y are not like terms.)

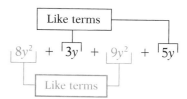

In variable expressions that contain constant terms, the constant terms are like terms.

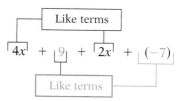

The Commutative and Associative Properties of Addition are used to simplify variable expressions. These properties can be stated in general form using variables.

Commutative Property of Addition

If a and b are two numbers, then $a + b = b + a$.

TAKE NOTE

With the Commutative Property, the order in which the numbers appear changes. With the Associative Property, the order in which the numbers appear remains the same.

Associative Property of Addition

If a, b, and c are three numbers, then $a + (b + c) = (a + b) + c$.

The phrase **simplifying a variable expression** means *combining* like terms by adding their numerical coefficients. For example, to simplify $2y + 3y$, think

$$2y + 3y = (y + y) + (y + y + y) = 5y$$

HOW TO   Simplify: $8z - 5 + 2z$

$8z - 5 + 2z = 8z + 2z - 5$ • Use the **Commutative and Associative**
$\quad\quad\quad\quad = 10z - 5$ **Properties of Addition** to group like terms.
         Combine the like terms $8z + 2z$.

HOW TO Simplify: $12a - 4b - 8a + 2b$

$$12a - 4b - 8a + 2b = 12a + (-4)b + (-8)a + 2b$$

- Change subtraction to addition of the opposite.

$$= 12a + (-8)a + (-4)b + 2b$$
$$= 4a + (-2)b$$

- Use the Commutative and Associative Properties of Addition to group like terms. Combine like terms.

$$= 4a - 2b$$

- Recall that $a + (-b) = a - b$.

HOW TO Simplify: $6z^2 + 3 - z^2 - 7$

$$6z^2 + 3 - z^2 - 7 = 6z^2 + 3 + (-1)z^2 + (-7)$$

- Change subtraction to addition of the opposite.

$$= 6z^2 + (-1)z^2 + 3 + (-7)$$
$$= 5z^2 + (-4)$$
$$= 5z^2 - 4$$

- Use the Commutative and Associative Properties of Addition to group like terms. Combine like terms.

Example 5

Simplify: $6xy - 8x + 5x - 9xy$

Solution
$6xy - 8x + 5x - 9xy$
$\quad = 6xy + (-8)x + 5x + (-9)xy$
$\quad = 6xy + (-9)xy + (-8)x + 5x$
$\quad = (-3)xy + (-3)x$
$\quad = -3xy - 3x$

You Try It 5

Simplify: $5a^2 - 6b^2 + 7a^2 - 9b^2$

Your solution

Example 6

Simplify: $-4z^2 + 8 + 5z^2 - 3$

Solution
$-4z^2 + 8 + 5z^2 - 3$
$\quad = -4z^2 + 8 + 5z^2 + (-3)$
$\quad = -4z^2 + 5z^2 + 8 + (-3)$
$\quad = z^2 + 5$

You Try It 6

Simplify: $-6x + 7 + 9x - 10$

Your solution

Example 7

Simplify: $\frac{1}{4}m^2 - \frac{1}{2}n^2 + \frac{1}{2}m^2$

Solution
$$\frac{1}{4}m^2 - \frac{1}{2}n^2 + \frac{1}{2}m^2 = \frac{1}{4}m^2 + \left(-\frac{1}{2}\right)n^2 + \frac{1}{2}m^2$$
$$= \frac{1}{4}m^2 + \frac{1}{2}m^2 + \left(-\frac{1}{2}\right)n^2$$
$$= \frac{1}{4}m^2 + \frac{2}{4}m^2 + \left(-\frac{1}{2}\right)n^2$$
$$= \frac{3}{4}m^2 + \left(-\frac{1}{2}\right)n^2$$
$$= \frac{3}{4}m^2 - \frac{1}{2}n^2$$

You Try It 7

Simplify: $\frac{3}{8}w + \frac{1}{2} - \frac{1}{4}w - \frac{2}{3}$

Your solution

Solutions on p. S28

Objective C **To simplify variable expressions containing parentheses**

The Commutative and Associative Properties of Multiplication and the Distributive Property are used to simplify variable expressions that contain parentheses. These properties can be stated in general form using variables.

> **Commutative Property of Multiplication**
>
> If a and b are two numbers, then $a \cdot b = b \cdot a$.

> **Associative Property of Multiplication**
>
> If a, b, and c are three numbers, then $a \cdot (b \cdot c) = (a \cdot b) \cdot c$.

The Associative and Commutative Properties of Multiplication are used to simplify variable expressions such as the following.

HOW TO Simplify: $-5(4x)$

$$-5(4x) = (-5 \cdot 4)x$$ • Use the Associative Property of Multiplication.
$$= -20x$$

HOW TO Simplify: $(6y) \cdot 5$

$$(6y) \cdot 5 = 5 \cdot (6y)$$ • Use the Commutative Property of Multiplication.
$$= (5 \cdot 6)y = 30y$$ • Use the Associative Property of Multiplication.

The **Distributive Property** is used to remove parentheses from variable expressions that contain both multiplication and addition.

> **Distributive Property**
>
> If a, b, and c are three numbers, then $a(b + c) = ab + ac$.

HOW TO Simplify: $4(z + 5)$

$$4(z + 5) = 4z + 4(5)$$ • The Distributive Property is used to rewrite the
$$= 4z + 20$$ variable expression without parentheses.

HOW TO Simplify: $-3(2x + 7)$

$$-3(2x + 7) = -3(2x) + (-3)(7)$$ • Use the Distributive Property.
$$= -6x + (-21)$$
$$= -6x - 21$$ • Recall that $a + (-b) = a - b$.

The Distributive Property can also be stated in terms of subtraction.

$$a(b - c) = ab - ac$$

HOW TO Simplify: $8(2r - 3s)$

$$8(2r - 3s) = 8(2r) - 8(3s)$$
• Use the Distributive Property.
$$= 16r - 24s$$

HOW TO Simplify: $-5(2x - 4y)$

$$-5(2x - 4y) = (-5)(2x) - (-5)(4y)$$
• Use the Distributive Property.
$$= -10x - (-20y)$$
$$= -10x + 20y$$
• Recall that $a - (-b) = a + b$.

HOW TO Simplify: $12 - 5(m + 2) + 2m$

$$12 - 5(m + 2) + 2m = 12 - 5m + (-5)(2) + 2m$$
• Use the Distributive Property to simplify the expression $-5(m + 2)$.
$$= 12 - 5m + (-10) + 2m$$

$$= -5m + 2m + 12 + (-10)$$
• Use the Commutative and Associative Properties to group like terms.

$$= -3m + 2$$
• Combine like terms by adding their numerical coefficients. Add constant terms.

The answer $-3m + 2$ can also be written as $2 - 3m$. In this text, we will write answers with variable terms first, followed by the constant term.

Example 8

Simplify: $4(x - 3)$

Solution
$$4(x - 3) = 4x - 4(3)$$
$$= 4x - 12$$

You Try It 8

Simplify: $5(a - 2)$

Your solution

Example 9

Simplify: $5n - 3(2n - 4)$

Solution
$$5n - 3(2n - 4) = 5n - 3(2n) - (-3)(4)$$
$$= 5n - 6n - (-12)$$
$$= 5n - 6n + 12$$
$$= -n + 12$$

You Try It 9

Simplify: $8s - 2(3s - 5)$

Your solution

Example 10

Simplify: $3(c - 2) + 2(c + 6)$

Solution
$$3(c - 2) + 2(c + 6) = 3c - 3(2) + 2c + 2(6)$$
$$= 3c - 6 + 2c + 12$$
$$= 3c + 2c - 6 + 12$$
$$= 5c + 6$$

You Try It 10

Simplify: $4(x - 3) - 2(x + 1)$

Your solution

Solutions on p. S28

11.1 Exercises

To evaluate variable expressions

For Exercises 1 to 34, evaluate the variable expression when $a = -3$, $b = 6$, and $c = -2$.

1. $5a - 3b$

2. $4c - 2b$

3. $2a + 3c$

4. $2c + 4a$

5. $-c^2$

6. $-a^2$

7. $b - a^2$

8. $b - c^2$

9. $ab - c^2$

10. $bc - a^2$

11. $2ab - c^2$

12. $3bc - a^2$

13. $a - (b \div a)$

14. $c - (b \div c)$

15. $2ac - (b \div a)$

16. $4ac \div (b \div a)$

17. $b^2 - c^2$

18. $b^2 - a^2$

19. $b^2 \div (ac)$

20. $3c^2 \div (ab)$

21. $c^2 - (b \div c)$

22. $a^2 - (b \div a)$

23. $a^2 + b^2 + c^2$

24. $a^2 - b^2 - c^2$

25. $ac + bc + ab$

26. $ac - bc - ab$

27. $a^2 + b^2 - ab$

28. $b^2 + c^2 - bc$

29. $2b - (3c + a^2)$

30. $\frac{2}{3}b + \left(\frac{1}{2}c - a\right)$

31. $\frac{1}{3}a + \left(\frac{1}{2}b - \frac{2}{3}a\right)$

32. $-\frac{2}{3}b - \left(\frac{1}{2}c + a\right)$

33. $\frac{1}{6}b + \frac{1}{3}(c + a)$

34. $\frac{1}{2}c + \left(\frac{1}{3}b - a\right)$

For Exercises 35 to 38, evaluate the variable expression when $a = -\frac{1}{2}$, $b = \frac{3}{4}$, and $c = \frac{1}{4}$.

35. $4a + (3b - c)$

36. $2b + (c - 3a)$

37. $2a - b^2 \div c$

38. $b \div (-c) + 2a$

For Exercises 39 to 42, evaluate the variable expression when $a = 3.72$, $b = -2.31$, and $c = -1.74$.

39. $a^2 - b^2$

40. $a^2 - b \cdot c$

41. $3ac - (c \div a)$

42. $2c + (b^2 - c)$

Objective B **To simplify variable expressions containing no parentheses**

For Exercises 43 to 46, name the terms of the variable expression. Then underline the constant term.

43. $2x^2 + 3x - 4$

44. $-4y^2 + 5$

45. $3a^2 - 4a + 8$

46. $7 - b$

For Exercises 47 to 50, name the variable terms of the expression. Then underline the coefficients of the variable terms.

47. $3x^2 - 4x + 9$

48. $-5a^2 + a - 4$

49. $y^2 + 6a - 1$

50. $8 - c$

For Exercises 51 to 94, simplify.

51. $7z + 9z$

52. $6x + 5x$

53. $12m - 3m$

54. $5y - 12y$

55. $5at + 7at$

56. $12mn + 11mn$

57. $-4yt + 7yt$

58. $-12yt + 5yt$

59. $-3x - 12y$

60. $-12y - 7y$

61. $3t^2 - 5t^2$

62. $7t^2 + 8t^2$

63. $6c - 5 + 7c$

64. $7x - 5 + 3x$

65. $2t + 3t - 7t$

66. $9x^2 - 5 - 3x^2$

67. $7y^2 - 2 - 4y^2$

68. $3w - 7u + 4w$

69. $6w - 8u + 8w$

70. $4 - 6xy - 7xy$

71. $10 - 11xy - 12xy$

72. $7t^2 - 5t^2 - 4t^2$

73. $3v^2 - 6v^2 - 8v^2$

74. $5ab - 7a - 10ab$

75. $-10ab - 3a + 2ab$

76. $-4x^2 - x + 2x^2$

77. $-3y^2 - y + 7y^2$

78. $4x^2 - 8y - x^2 + y$

79. $2a - 3b^2 - 5a + b^2$

80. $8y - 4z - y + 2z$

81. $3x^2 - 7x + 4x^2 - x$

82. $5y^2 - y + 6y^2 - 5y$

83. $6s - t - 9s + 7t$

84. $5w - 2v - 9w + 5v$

85. $4m + 8n - 7m + 2n$

86. $z + 9y - 4z + 3y$

87. $-5ab + 7ac + 10ab - 3ac$

88. $-2x^2 - 3x - 11x^2 + 14x$

89. $\frac{4}{9}a^2 - \frac{1}{5}b^2 + \frac{2}{9}a^2 + \frac{4}{5}b^2$

90. $\frac{6}{7}x^2 + \frac{2}{5}x - \frac{3}{7}x^2 - \frac{4}{5}x$

91. $4.235x - 0.297x + 3.056x$

92. $8.092y - 3.0793y + 0.063y$

93. $7.81m + 3.42n - 6.25m - 7.19n$

94. $8.34y^2 - 4.21y - 6.07y^2 - 5.39y$

Objective C   **To simplify variable expressions containing parentheses**

For Exercises 95 to 130, simplify.

95. $5(x + 4)$

96. $3(m + 6)$

97. $(y - 3)4$

98. $(z - 3)7$

99. $-2(a + 4)$

100. $-5(b + 3)$

101. $3(5x + 10)$

102. $2(4m - 7)$

103. $5(3c - 5)$

104. $-4(w - 3)$

105. $-3(y - 6)$

106. $3m + 4(m + z)$

107. $5x + 2(x + 7)$

108. $6z - 3(z + 4)$

109. $8y - 4(y + 2)$

110. $7w - 2(w - 3)$

111. $9x - 4(x - 6)$

112. $-5m + 3(m + 4)$

113. $-2y + 3(y - 2)$

114. $5m + 3(m + 4) - 6$

115. $4n + 2(n + 1) - 5$

116. $8z - 2(z - 3) + 8$

117. $9y - 3(y - 4) + 8$

118. $6 - 4(a + 4) + 6a$

119. $3x + 2(x + 2) + 5x$

120. $7x + 4(x + 1) + 3x$

121. $-7t + 2(t - 3) - t$

122. $-3y + 2(y - 4) - y$

123. $z - 2(1 - z) - 2z$

124. $2y - 3(2 - y) + 4y$

125. $3(y - 2) - 2(y - 6)$

126. $7(x + 2) + 3(x - 4)$

127. $2(t - 3) + 7(t + 3)$

128. $3(y - 4) - 2(y - 3)$

129. $3t - 6(t - 4) + 8t$

130. $5x + 3(x - 7) - 9x$

APPLYING THE CONCEPTS

131. The square and the rectangle at the right can be used to illustrate algebraic expressions. The illustration below represents the expression $2x + 1$.

a. Using similar squares and rectangles, draw a figure that represents the expression $3 + 2x$.

b. Draw a figure that represents the expression $4x + 6$.

c. Draw a figure that represents the expression $3x + 2$.

d. Draw a figure that represents the expression $2x + 4$.

e. The illustration below represents the expression $3(x + 1)$. Rearrange these rectangles so that the x's are together and the 1's are together.

f. Write a mathematical expression for the rearranged figure.

132. a. Using squares and rectangles similar to those in Exercise 131, draw a figure that represents the expression $2 + 3x$.

b. Draw a figure that represents the expression $2(2x + 3)$.

c. Draw a figure that represents the expression $4x + 3$.

d. Draw a figure that represents the expression $4x + 6$.

e. Does the figure $2(2x + 3)$ equal the figure $4x + 6$? Explain how this equivalence is related to the Distributive Property.

f. Does the figure $2 + 3x$ equal the figure $5x$? Explain how this equivalence is related to combining like terms.

133. a. Simplifying variable expressions requires combining like terms. Give some examples of how this applies to everyday experience.

b. It was stated in this section that the variable terms y^2 and y are not like terms. Use measurements of area and distance to show that these terms would not be combined as measurements.

134. Explain why the simplification of the expression $2 + 3(2x + 4)$ shown at the right is incorrect. What is the correct simplification?

Why is this incorrect?
$$2 + 3(2x + 4) = 5(2x + 4)$$
$$= 10x + 20$$

11.2 Introduction to Equations

Objective A **To determine whether a given number is a solution of an equation**

Point of Interest

Finding solutions of equations has been a principal aim of mathematics for thousands of years. However, the equals sign did not appear in any text until 1557.

An **equation** expresses the equality of two mathematical expressions. These expressions can be either numerical or variable expressions.

$$\left. \begin{array}{l} 5 + 4 = 9 \\ 3x + 13 = x - 8 \\ y^2 + 4 = 6y + 1 \\ x = -3 \end{array} \right\} \text{Equations}$$

In the equation at the right, if the variable is replaced by 4, the equation is true.

$x + 3 = 7$
$4 + 3 = 7$ A true equation

If the variable is replaced by 6, the equation is false.

$6 + 3 = 7$ A false equation

A **solution of an equation** is a number that, when substituted for the variable, results in a true equation. 4 is a solution of the equation $x + 3 = 7$. 6 is not a solution of the equation $x + 3 = 7$.

HOW TO Is -2 a solution of the equation $-2x + 1 = 2x + 9$?

$$-2x + 1 = 2x + 9$$

$-2(-2) + 1$	$2(-2) + 9$
$4 + 1$	$-4 + 9$

$$5 = 5$$

• Replace the variable by the given number.

• Evaluate the numerical expressions.

• Compare the results. If the results are equal, the given number is a solution. If the results are not equal, the given number is not a solution.

Yes, -2 is a solution of the equation $-2x + 1 = 2x + 9$.

Example 1 Is $\frac{1}{2}$ a solution of $2x(x + 2) = 3x + 1$?

Solution

$$2x(x + 2) = 3x + 1$$

$2\left(\dfrac{1}{2}\right)\left(\dfrac{1}{2} + 2\right)$	$3\left(\dfrac{1}{2}\right) + 1$
$2\left(\dfrac{1}{2}\right)\left(\dfrac{5}{2}\right)$	$\dfrac{3}{2} + 1$
$\dfrac{5}{2}$	$= \dfrac{5}{2}$

Yes, $\frac{1}{2}$ is a solution.

You Try It 1 Is -2 a solution of $x(x + 3) = 4x + 6$?

Your solution

Solution on p. S28

Example 2   Is 5 a solution of
$(x - 2)^2 = x^2 - 4x + 2$?

You Try It 2   Is -3 a solution of
$x^2 - x = 3x + 7$?

Solution

$$(x - 2)^2 = x^2 - 4x + 2$$

$(5 - 2)^2$	$5^2 - 4(5) + 2$
3^2	$25 - 4(5) + 2$
9	$25 - 20 + 2$
	$25 + (-20) + 2$
$9 \neq 7$	($\neq$ means "is not equal to")

No, 5 is not a solution.

Your solution

Solution on p. S28

Objective B   **To solve an equation of the form $x + a = b$**

A solution of an equation is a number that, when substituted for the variable, results in a true equation. The phrase **solving an equation** means finding a solution of the equation.

The simplest equation to solve is an equation of the form *variable = constant*. The constant is the solution of the equation.

If $x = 7$, then 7 is the solution of the equation because $7 = 7$ is a true equation.

In solving an equation of the form $x + a = b$, the goal is to simplify the given equation to one of the form *variable = constant*. The Addition Properties that follow are used to simplify equations to this form.

> **Addition Property of Zero**
>
> The sum of a term and zero is the term.
> $$a + 0 = a \qquad 0 + a = a$$

> **Addition Property of Equations**
>
> If a, b, and c are algebraic expressions, then the equations $a = b$ and $a + c = b + c$ have the same solutions.

The Addition Property of Equations states that the same quantity can be added to each side of an equation without changing the solution of the equation.

The Addition Property of Equations is used to rewrite an equation in the form *variable = constant*. Remove a term from one side of the equation by adding the opposite of that term to each side of the equation.

TAKE NOTE

TAKE NOTE

Always check the solution to an equation.

Check: $x - 7 = -2$
$$\frac{5 - 7 \mid -2}{-2 = -2 \text{ True}}$$

HOW TO Solve: $x - 7 = -2$

$$x - 7 = -2$$
$$x - 7 + 7 = -2 + 7$$
$$x + 0 = 5$$
$$x = 5$$

• The goal is to simplify the equation to one of the form *variable = constant*.

• Add the opposite of the constant term -7 to each side of the equation. After we simplify and use the Addition Property of Zero, the equation will be in the form *variable = constant*.

The solution is 5.

Because subtraction is defined in terms of addition, the Addition Property of Equations allows the same number to be subtracted from each side of an equation.

Study Tip

When we suggest that you check a solution, substitute the solution into the original equation. For instance,

$$x + 8 = 5$$
$$\frac{-3 + 8 \mid 5}{5 = 5}$$

The solution checks.

HOW TO Solve: $x + 8 = 5$

$$x + 8 = 5$$
$$x + 8 - 8 = 5 - 8$$
$$x + 0 = -3$$
$$x = -3$$

• The goal is to simplify the equation to one of the form *variable = constant*.

• Add the opposite of the constant term 8 to each side of the equation. This procedure is equivalent to subtracting 8 from each side of the equation.

The solution is -3. You should check this solution.

Example 3 Solve: $4 + m = -2$

Solution
$$4 + m = -2$$
$$4 - 4 + m = -2 - 4 \quad \bullet \text{ Subtract 4 from}$$
$$0 + m = -6 \qquad \text{each side.}$$
$$m = -6$$

The solution is -6.

You Try It 3 Solve: $-2 + y = -5$

Your solution

Example 4 Solve: $3 = y - 2$

Solution
$$3 = y - 2$$
$$3 + 2 = y - 2 + 2 \quad \bullet \text{ Add 2 to each}$$
$$5 = y + 0 \qquad \text{side.}$$
$$5 = y$$

The solution is 5.

You Try It 4 Solve: $7 = y + 8$

Your solution

Example 5 Solve: $\frac{2}{7} = \frac{5}{7} + t$

Solution
$$\frac{2}{7} = \frac{5}{7} + t$$
$$\frac{2}{7} - \frac{5}{7} = \frac{5}{7} - \frac{5}{7} + t \quad \bullet \text{ Subtract } \frac{5}{7} \text{ from}$$
$$-\frac{3}{7} = 0 + t \qquad \text{each side.}$$
$$-\frac{3}{7} = t$$

The solution is $-\frac{3}{7}$.

You Try It 5 Solve: $\frac{1}{5} = z + \frac{4}{5}$

Your solution

Solutions on p. S28

Objective C   **To solve an equation of the form *ax* = *b***

In solving an equation of the form $ax = b$, the goal is to simplify the given equation to one of the form *variable = constant*. The Multiplication Properties that follow are used to simplify equations to this form.

Multiplication Property of Reciprocals

The product of a nonzero term and its reciprocal equals 1.

Because $a = \dfrac{a}{1}$, the reciprocal of a is $\dfrac{1}{a}$.

$$a\left(\dfrac{1}{a}\right) = 1 \qquad \dfrac{1}{a}(a) = 1$$

The reciprocal of $\dfrac{a}{b}$ is $\dfrac{b}{a}$.

$$\left(\dfrac{a}{b}\right)\left(\dfrac{b}{a}\right) = 1 \qquad \left(\dfrac{b}{a}\right)\left(\dfrac{a}{b}\right) = 1$$

Multiplication Property of One

The product of a term and 1 is the term.
$$a \cdot 1 = a \qquad 1 \cdot a = a$$

Multiplication Property of Equations

If *a*, *b*, and *c* are algebraic expressions and $c \neq 0$, then the equation $a = b$ has the same solutions as the equation $ac = bc$.

The Multiplication Property of Equations states that each side of an equation can be multiplied by the same nonzero number without changing the solutions of the equation.

Recall that the goal of solving an equation is to rewrite the equation in the form *variable = constant*. The Multiplication Property of Equations is used to rewrite an equation in this form by multiplying each side of the equation by the reciprocal of the coefficient.

HOW TO   Solve: $\dfrac{2}{3}x = 8$

$$\dfrac{2}{3}x = 8$$

$$\left(\dfrac{3}{2}\right)\left(\dfrac{2}{3}\right)x = \left(\dfrac{3}{2}\right)8$$

$$1 \cdot x = 12$$

$$x = 12$$

• Multiply each side of the equation by $\dfrac{3}{2}$, the reciprocal of $\dfrac{2}{3}$. After simplifying, the equation will be in the form *variable = constant*.

Check: $\dfrac{2}{3}x = 8$

$$\dfrac{2}{3}(12) \;\Big|\; 8$$

$$8 = 8$$

The solution is 12.

Because division is defined in terms of multiplication, the Multiplication Property of Equations allows each side of an equation to be divided by the same nonzero quantity.

Study Tip

When we suggest that you check a solution, substitute the solution into the original equation. For instance,

$$\frac{-4x = 24}{-4(-6) \mid 24}$$
$$24 = 24$$

The solution checks.

HOW TO Solve: $-4x = 24$

$$-4x = 24$$

$$\frac{-4x}{-4} = \frac{24}{-4}$$
$$1x = -6$$
$$x = -6$$

• The goal is to rewrite the equation in the form *variable = constant*.

• Multiply each side of the equation by the reciprocal of -4. This is equivalent to dividing each side of the equation by -4. Then simplify.

The solution is -6. You should check this solution.

In using the Multiplication Property of Equations, it is usually easier to multiply each side of the equation by the reciprocal of the coefficient when the coefficient is a fraction. Divide each side of the equation by the coefficient when the coefficient is an integer or a decimal.

Example 6 Solve: $-2x = 6$

Solution

$$-2x = 6$$
$$\frac{-2x}{-2} = \frac{6}{-2}$$ • Divide each side by -2.
$$1x = -3$$
$$x = -3$$

The solution is -3.

You Try It 6 Solve: $4z = -20$

Your solution

Example 7 Solve: $-9 = \frac{3}{4}y$

Solution

$$-9 = \frac{3}{4}y$$
$$\left(\frac{4}{3}\right)(-9) = \left(\frac{4}{3}\right)\left(\frac{3}{4}y\right)$$ • Multiply each side by $\frac{4}{3}$.
$$-12 = 1y$$
$$-12 = y$$

The solution is -12.

You Try It 7 Solve: $8 = \frac{2}{5}n$

Your solution

Example 8 Solve: $6z - 8z = -5$

Solution

$$6z - 8z = -5$$
$$-2z = -5$$ • Combine like terms.
$$\frac{-2z}{-2} = \frac{-5}{-2}$$ • Divide each side by -2.
$$1z = \frac{5}{2}$$
$$z = \frac{5}{2} = 2\frac{1}{2}$$

The solution is $2\frac{1}{2}$.

You Try It 8 Solve: $\frac{2}{3}t - \frac{1}{3}t = -2$

Your solution

Solutions on p. S29

> **Objective D** **To solve application problems using formulas**

A **formula** is an equation that expresses a relationship among variables. Formulas are used in the examples below.

Example 9

An accountant for a greeting card store found that the weekly profit for the store was $1700 and that the total amount spent during the week was $2400. Use the formula $P = R - C$, where P is the profit, R is the revenue, and C is the amount spent, to find the revenue for the week.

Strategy

To find the revenue for the week, replace the variables P and C in the formula by the given values, and solve for R.

Solution

$$P = R - C$$
$$1700 = R - 2400$$
$$1700 + 2400 = R - 2400 + 2400$$
$$4100 = R + 0$$
$$4100 = R$$

The revenue for the week was $4100.

You Try It 9

A clothing store's sale price for a pair of slacks is $44. This is a discount of $16 off the regular price. Use the formula $S = R - D$, where S is the sale price, R is the regular price, and D is the discount, to find the regular price.

Your strategy

Your solution

Example 10

A store manager uses the formula $S = R - d \cdot R$, where S is the sale price, R is the regular price, and d is the discount rate. During a clearance sale, all items are discounted 20%. Find the regular price of a jacket that is on sale for $120.

Strategy

To find the regular price of the jacket, replace the variables S and d in the formula by the given values, and solve for R.

Solution

$$S = R - d \cdot R$$
$$120 = R - 0.20R$$
$$120 = 0.80R \qquad \bullet \; R - 0.20R = 1R - 0.20R$$
$$\frac{120}{0.80} = \frac{0.80R}{0.80}$$
$$150 = R$$

The regular price of the jacket is $150.

You Try It 10

Find the monthly payment when the total amount paid on a loan is $6840 and the loan is paid off in 24 months. Use the formula $A = MN$, where A is the total amount paid on a loan, M is the monthly payment, and N is the number of monthly payments.

Your strategy

Your solution

Solutions on p. S29

11.2 Exercises

Objective A To determine whether a given number is a solution of an equation

1. Is -3 a solution of $2x + 9 = 3$?

2. Is -2 a solution of $5x + 7 = 12$?

3. Is 2 a solution of $4 - 2x = 8$?

4. Is 4 a solution of $5 - 2x = 4x$?

5. Is 3 a solution of $3x - 2 = x + 4$?

6. Is 2 a solution of $4x + 8 = 4 - 2x$?

7. Is 3 a solution of $x^2 - 5x + 1 = 10 - 5x$?

8. Is -5 a solution of $x^2 - 3x - 1 = 9 - 6x$?

9. Is -1 a solution of $2x(x - 1) = 3 - x$?

10. Is 2 a solution of $3x(x - 3) = x - 8$?

11. Is 2 a solution of $x(x - 2) = x^2 - 4$?

12. Is -4 a solution of $x(x + 4) = x^2 + 16$?

13. Is $-\frac{2}{3}$ a solution of $3x + 6 = 4$?

14. Is $\frac{1}{2}$ a solution of $2x - 7 = -3$?

15. Is $\frac{1}{4}$ a solution of $2x - 3 = 1 - 14x$?

16. Is $-\frac{1}{3}$ a solution of $5x - 2 = 1 - 2x$?

17. Is $\frac{3}{4}$ a solution of $3x(x - 2) = x - 4$?

18. Is $\frac{2}{5}$ a solution of $5x(x + 1) = x + 3$?

19. Is 1.32 a solution of $x^2 - 3x = -0.8776 - x$?

20. Is -1.9 a solution of $x^2 - 3x = x + 3.8$?

21. Is 1.05 a solution of $x^2 + 3x = x(x + 3)$?

Objective B To solve an equation of the form $x + a = b$

For Exercises 22 to 57, solve.

22. $x + 3 = 9$

23. $x + 7 = 5$

24. $y - 6 = 16$

25. $z - 4 = 10$

26. $3 + n = 4$

27. $6 + x = 8$

28. $z + 7 = 2$

29. $w + 9 = 5$

30. $x - 3 = -7$ **31.** $m - 4 = -9$ **32.** $y + 6 = 6$ **33.** $t - 3 = -3$

34. $v - 7 = -4$ **35.** $x - 3 = -1$ **36.** $1 + x = 0$ **37.** $3 + y = 0$

38. $x - 10 = 5$ **39.** $y - 7 = 3$ **40.** $x + 4 = -7$ **41.** $t - 3 = -8$

42. $w + 5 = -5$ **43.** $z + 6 = -6$ **44.** $x + 7 = -8$ **45.** $x + 2 = -5$

46. $x + \dfrac{1}{2} = -\dfrac{1}{2}$ **47.** $x - \dfrac{5}{6} = -\dfrac{1}{6}$ **48.** $y + \dfrac{7}{11} = -\dfrac{3}{11}$ **49.** $\dfrac{2}{5} + x = -\dfrac{3}{5}$

50. $\dfrac{7}{8} + y = -\dfrac{1}{8}$ **51.** $\dfrac{1}{3} + x = \dfrac{2}{3}$ **52.** $x + \dfrac{1}{2} = -\dfrac{1}{3}$ **53.** $y + \dfrac{3}{8} = \dfrac{1}{4}$

54. $y + \dfrac{2}{3} = -\dfrac{3}{8}$ **55.** $t + \dfrac{1}{4} = -\dfrac{1}{2}$ **56.** $x + \dfrac{1}{3} = \dfrac{5}{12}$ **57.** $y + \dfrac{2}{3} = -\dfrac{5}{12}$

Objective C   **To solve an equation of the form $ax = b$**

For Exercises 58 to 93, solve.

58. $3y = 12$ **59.** $5x = 30$ **60.** $5z = -20$ **61.** $3z = -27$

62. $-2x = 6$ **63.** $-4t = 20$ **64.** $-5x = -40$ **65.** $-2y = -28$

66. $40 = 8x$ **67.** $24 = 3y$ **68.** $-24 = 4x$ **69.** $-21 = 7y$

70. $\dfrac{x}{3} = 5$ **71.** $\dfrac{y}{2} = 10$ **72.** $\dfrac{n}{4} = -2$ **73.** $\dfrac{y}{7} = -3$

74. $-\dfrac{x}{4} = 1$ **75.** $-\dfrac{y}{3} = 5$ **76.** $\dfrac{2}{3}w = 4$ **77.** $\dfrac{5}{8}x = 10$

78. $\dfrac{3}{4}v = -3$ **79.** $\dfrac{2}{7}x = -12$ **80.** $-\dfrac{1}{3}x = -2$ **81.** $-\dfrac{1}{5}y = -3$

82. $\dfrac{3}{8}x = -24$ **83.** $\dfrac{5}{12}y = -16$ **84.** $-4 = -\dfrac{2}{3}z$ **85.** $-8 = -\dfrac{5}{6}x$

86. $-12 = -\dfrac{3}{8}y$ **87.** $-9 = \dfrac{5}{6}t$ **88.** $\dfrac{2}{3}x = -\dfrac{2}{7}$ **89.** $\dfrac{3}{7}y = \dfrac{5}{6}$

90. $4x - 2x = 7$ **91.** $3a - 6a = 8$ **92.** $\dfrac{4}{5}m - \dfrac{1}{5}m = 9$ **93.** $\dfrac{1}{3}b - \dfrac{2}{3}b = -1$

Objective D   **To solve application problems using formulas**

Investments   In Exercises 94 to 97, use the formula $A = P + I$, where A is the value of the investment after 1 year, P is the original investment, and I is the increase in value of the investment.

94. The value of an investment in a high-tech company after 1 year was $17,700. The increase in value during the year was $2700. Find the amount of the original investment.

95. The value of an investment in a software company after 1 year was $26,440. The increase in value during the year was $2830. Find the amount of the original investment.

96. The original investment in a mutual fund was $8000. The value of the mutual fund after 1 year was $11,420. Find the increase in value of the investment.

97. The original investment in a money market fund was $7500. The value of the mutual fund after 1 year was $8690. Find the increase in value of the investment.

Fuel Efficiency   In Exercises 98 to 101, use the formula $D = M \cdot G$, where D is the distance, M is the miles per gallon, and G is the number of gallons. Round to the nearest tenth.

98. Julio, a sales executive, averages 28 mi/gal on a 621-mile trip. Find the number of gallons of gasoline used on the trip.

99. Over a 3-day weekend, you take a 592-mile trip. If you average 32 mi/gal on the trip, how many gallons of gasoline did you use?

100. The manufacturer of a subcompact car estimates that the car can travel 560 mi on a 15-gallon tank of gas. Find the miles per gallon.

101. You estimate that your car can travel 410 mi on 12 gal of gasoline. Find the miles per gallon.

Markup In Exercises 102 and 103, use the formula $S = C + M$, where S is the selling price, C is the cost, and M is the markup.

102. A computer store sells a computer for $2240. The computer has a markup of $420. Find the cost of the computer.

103. A toy store buys stuffed animals for $23.50 and sells them for $39.80. Find the markup on each stuffed animal.

Markup In Exercises 104 and 105, use the formula $S = C + R \cdot C$, where S is the selling price, C is cost, and R is the markup rate.

104. A store manager uses a markup rate of 24% on all appliances. Find the cost of a blender that sells for $77.50.

105. A music store uses a markup rate of 30%. Find the cost of a compact disc that sells for $18.85.

APPLYING THE CONCEPTS

106. Write out the steps for solving the equation $x - 3 = -5$. Identify each property of real numbers and each property of equations as you use it.

107. Write out the steps for solving the equation $\frac{3}{4}x = 6$. Identify each property of real numbers and each property of equations as you use it.

108. Is 2 a solution of $x = x + 4$? Try -2, 0, 3, 6, and 10. Do you think there is a solution of this equation? Why or why not?

109. Write an equation of the form $x + a = b$ that has -4 as its solution.

110. Write an equation of the form $a - x = b$ that has -2 as its solution.

111. **a.** In your own words, state the Addition Property of Equations.
      b. In your own words, state the Multiplication Property of Equations.

11.3 General Equations: Part I

Objective A   To solve an equation of the form $ax + b = c$

To solve an equation of the form $ax + b = c$, it is necessary to use both the Addition and the Multiplication Properties to simplify the equation to one of the form *variable = constant*.

HOW TO   Solve: $\frac{x}{4} - 1 = 3$

$\frac{x}{4} - 1 = 3$ • The goal is to simplify the equation to one of the form *variable = constant*.

$\frac{x}{4} - 1 + 1 = 3 + 1$ • Add the opposite of the constant term −1 to each side of the equation. Then simplify (Addition Properties).

$\frac{x}{4} + 0 = 4$

$\frac{x}{4} = 4$

$4 \cdot \frac{x}{4} = 4 \cdot 4$ • Multiply each side of the equation by the reciprocal of the numerical coefficient of the variable term. Then simplify (Multiplication Properties).

$1x = 16$

$x = 16$

The solution is 16.   • Write the solution.

TAKE NOTE

$\frac{x}{4} = \frac{1}{4}x$

The reciprocal of $\frac{1}{4}$ is 4.

Example 1   Solve: $3x + 7 = 2$

Solution

$3x + 7 = 2$
$3x + 7 - 7 = 2 - 7$ • Subtract 7 from each side.
$3x = -5$
$\frac{3x}{3} = \frac{-5}{3}$ • Divide each side by 3.

$x = -\frac{5}{3} = -1\frac{2}{3}$

The solution is $-1\frac{2}{3}$.

You Try It 1   Solve: $5x + 8 = 6$

Your solution

Example 2   Solve: $5 - x = 6$

Solution

$5 - x = 6$
$5 - 5 - x = 6 - 5$ • Subtract 5 from each side.
$-x = 1$
$(-1)(-x) = (-1) \cdot 1$ • Multiply each side by −1.
$x = -1$

The solution is −1.

You Try It 2   Solve: $7 - x = 3$

Your solution

Solutions on p. S29

Objective B   **To solve application problems using formulas**

Anders Celsius

The Fahrenheit temperature scale was devised by Daniel Gabriel Fahrenheit (1686–1736), a German physicist and maker of scientific instruments. He invented the mercury thermometer in 1714. On the Fahrenheit scale, the temperature at which water freezes is 32°F, and the temperature at which water boils is 212°F. *Note:* The small raised circle is the symbol for degrees, and the capital F is for Fahrenheit. The Fahrenheit scale is used only in the United States.

In the metric system, temperature is measured on the Celsius scale. The Celsius temperature scale was devised by Anders Celsius (1701–1744), a Swedish astronomer. On the Celsius scale, the temperature at which water freezes is 0°C, and the temperature at which water boils is 100°C. *Note:* The small raised circle is the symbol for degrees, and the capital C is for Celsius.

On both the Celsius scale and the Fahrenheit scale, temperatures below 0° are negative numbers.

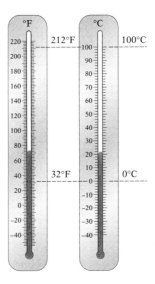

The relationship between Celsius temperatures and Fahrenheit temperatures is given by the formula

$$F = 1.8C + 32$$

where F represents degrees Fahrenheit and C represents degrees Celsius.

Integrating Technology

You can check the solution to this equation using a calculator. Evaluate the right side of the equation after substituting 37 for C. Enter

1.8 × 37 + 32 =

The display reads 98.6, the given Fahrenheit temperature. The solution checks.

HOW TO   Normal body temperature is 98.6°F. Convert this temperature to degrees Celsius.

$$F = 1.8C + 32$$
$$98.6 = 1.8C + 32$$ • Substitute 98.6 for F.
$$98.6 - 32 = 1.8C + 32 - 32$$ • Subtract 32 from each side.
$$66.6 = 1.8C$$ • Combine like terms on each side.
$$\frac{66.6}{1.8} = \frac{1.8C}{1.8}$$ • Divide each side by 1.8.
$$37 = C$$

Normal body temperature is 37°C.

Example 3

Find the Celsius temperature when the Fahrenheit temperature is 212°. Use the formula $F = 1.8C + 32$, where F is the Fahrenheit temperature and C is the Celsius temperature.

Strategy

To find the Celsius temperature, replace the variable F in the formula by the given value and solve for C.

Solution

$$F = 1.8C + 32$$
$$212 = 1.8C + 32$$
$$212 - 32 = 1.8C + 32 - 32$$
$$180 = 1.8C$$
$$\frac{180}{1.8C} = \frac{1.8C}{1.8}$$
$$100 = C$$

• Substitute 212 for F.
• Subtract 32 from each side.
• Combine like terms.
• Divide each side by 1.8.

The Celsius temperature is 100°.

You Try It 3

Find the Celsius temperature when the Fahrenheit temperature is $-22°$. Use the formula $F = 1.8C + 32$, where F is the Fahrenheit temperature and C is the Celsius temperature.

Your strategy

Your solution

Example 4

To find the total cost of production, an economist uses the formula $T = U \cdot N + F$, where T is the total cost, U is the cost per unit, N is the number of units made, and F is the fixed cost. Find the number of units made during a week when the total cost was $8000, the cost per unit was $16, and the fixed costs were $2000.

Strategy

To find the number of units made, replace the variables T, U, and F in the formula by the given values and solve for N.

Solution

$$T = U \cdot N + F$$
$$8000 = 16 \cdot N + 2000$$
$$8000 - 2000 = 16 \cdot N + 2000 - 2000$$
$$6000 = 16 \cdot N$$
$$\frac{6000}{16} = \frac{16 \cdot N}{16}$$
$$375 = N$$

The number of units made was 375.

You Try It 4

Find the cost per unit during a week when the total cost was $4500, the number of units produced was 250, and the fixed costs were $1500. Use the formula $T = U \cdot N + F$, where T is the total cost, U is the cost per unit, N is the number of units made, and F is the fixed cost.

Your strategy

Your solution

Solutions on p. S29

11.3 Exercises

Objective A   **To solve an equation of the form $ax + b = c$**

For Exercises 1 to 90, solve.

1. $3x + 5 = 14$

2. $5z + 6 = 31$

3. $2n - 3 = 7$

4. $4y - 4 = 20$

5. $5w + 8 = 3$

6. $3x + 10 = 1$

7. $3z - 4 = -16$

8. $6x - 1 = -13$

9. $5 + 2x = 7$

10. $12 + 7x = 33$

11. $6 - x = 3$

12. $4 - x = -2$

13. $3 - 4x = 11$

14. $2 - 3x = 11$

15. $5 - 4x = 17$

16. $8 - 6x = 14$

17. $3x + 6 = 0$

18. $5x - 20 = 0$

19. $-3x - 4 = -1$

20. $-7x - 22 = -1$

21. $12y - 30 = 6$

22. $9b - 7 = 2$

23. $3c + 7 = 4$

24. $8t + 13 = 5$

25. $-2x + 11 = -3$

26. $-4x + 15 = -1$

27. $14 - 5x = 4$

28. $7 - 3x = 4$

29. $-8x + 7 = -9$

30. $-7x + 13 = -8$

31. $9x + 13 = 13$

32. $-2x + 7 = 7$

33. $7d - 14 = 0$

34. $5z + 10 = 0$

35. $4n - 4 = -4$

36. $-13m - 1 = -1$

37. $3x + 5 = 7$

38. $4x + 6 = 9$

39. $6x - 1 = 16$

40. $12x - 3 = 7$

41. $2x - 3 = -8$ **42.** $5x - 3 = -12$ **43.** $-6x + 2 = -7$ **44.** $-3x + 9 = -1$

45. $-2x - 3 = -7$ **46.** $-5x - 7 = -4$ **47.** $3x + 8 = 2$ **48.** $2x - 9 = 8$

49. $3w - 7 = 0$ **50.** $7b - 2 = 0$ **51.** $-2d + 9 = 12$ **52.** $-7c + 3 = 1$

53. $\dfrac{1}{2}x - 2 = 3$ **54.** $\dfrac{1}{3}x + 1 = 4$ **55.** $\dfrac{3}{5}w - 1 = 2$ **56.** $\dfrac{2}{5}w + 5 = 6$

57. $\dfrac{2}{9}t - 3 = 5$ **58.** $\dfrac{5}{9}t - 3 = 2$ **59.** $\dfrac{y}{3} - 6 = -8$ **60.** $\dfrac{y}{2} - 2 = 3$

61. $\dfrac{x}{3} - 2 = -5$ **62.** $\dfrac{x}{4} - 3 = 5$ **63.** $\dfrac{5}{8}v + 6 = 3$ **64.** $\dfrac{2}{3}v - 4 = 3$

65. $\dfrac{4}{7}z + 10 = 5$ **66.** $\dfrac{3}{8}v - 3 = 4$ **67.** $\dfrac{2}{9}x - 3 = 5$ **68.** $\dfrac{1}{2}x + 3 = -8$

69. $\dfrac{3}{4}x - 5 = -4$ **70.** $\dfrac{2}{3}x - 5 = -8$ **71.** $1.5x - 0.5 = 2.5$

72. $2.5w - 1.3 = 3.7$ **73.** $0.8t + 1.1 = 4.3$ **74.** $0.3v + 2.4 = 1.5$

75. $0.4x - 2.3 = 1.3$ **76.** $1.2t + 6.5 = 2.9$ **77.** $3.5y - 3.5 = 10.5$

78. $1.9x - 1.9 = -1.9$ **79.** $0.32x + 4.2 = 3.2$ **80.** $5x - 3x + 2 = 8$

81. $6m + 2m - 3 = 5$

82. $4a - 7a - 8 = 4$

83. $3y - 8y - 9 = 6$

84. $x - 4x + 5 = 11$

85. $-2y + y - 3 = 6$

86. $-4y - y - 8 = 12$

87. $0.032x - 0.0194 = 0.139$

88. $-3.256x + 42.38 = -16.9$

89. $6.09x + 17.33 = 16.805$

90. $1.925x + 32.87 = -16.994$

Objective B   **To solve application problems using formulas**

Temperature Conversion   In Exercises 91 and 92, use the relationship between Fahrenheit temperature and Celsius temperature, which is given by the formula $F = 1.8C + 32$, where F is the Fahrenheit temperature and C is the Celsius temperature.

91. Find the Celsius temperature when the Fahrenheit temperature is $-40°$.

92. Find the Celsius temperature when the Fahrenheit temperature is $72°$. Round to the nearest tenth of a degree.

Physics   In Exercises 93 and 94, use the formula $V = V_0 + 32t$, where V is the final velocity of a falling object, V_0 is the starting velocity of a falling object, and t is the time for the object to fall.

93. Find the time required for an object to increase in velocity from 8 ft/s to 472 ft/s.

94. Find the time required for an object to increase in velocity from 16 ft/s to 128 ft/s.

Manufacturing   In Exercises 95 and 96, use the formula $T = U \cdot N + F$, where T is the total cost, U is the cost per unit, N is the number of units made, and F is the fixed cost.

95. Find the number of units made during a week when the total cost was $25,000, the cost per unit was $8, and the fixed costs were $5000.

96. Find the cost per unit during a week when the total cost was $80,000, the total number of units produced was 500, and the fixed costs were $15,000.

Taxes   In Exercises 97 and 98, use the formula $T = I \cdot R + B$, where T is the monthly tax, I is the monthly income, R is the income tax rate, and B is the base monthly tax.

97. The monthly tax that a clerk pays is $476. The clerk's monthly tax rate is 22%, and the base monthly tax is $80. Find the clerk's monthly income.

98. The monthly tax that Marcy, a teacher, pays is $770. Her monthly income is $3100, and the base monthly tax is $150. Find Marcy's income tax rate.

Compensation   In Exercises 99 to 102, use the formula $M = S \cdot R + B$, where M is the monthly earnings, S is the total sales, R is the commission rate, and B is the base monthly salary.

99. A book representative earns a base monthly salary of $600 plus a 9% commission on total sales. Find the total sales during a month in which the representative earned $3480.

100. A sales executive earns a base monthly salary of $1000 plus a 5% commission on total sales. Find the total sales during a month in which the executive earned $2800.

101. Miguel earns a base monthly salary of $750. Find his commission rate during a month in which total sales were $42,000 and he earned $2640.

102. Tina earns a base monthly salary of $500. Find her commission rate during a month when total sales were $42,500 and her earnings were $3560.

APPLYING THE CONCEPTS

103. Explain in your own words the steps you would take to solve the equation $\frac{2}{3}x - 4 = 10$. State the property of real numbers or the property of equations that is used at each step.

104. Make up an equation of the form $ax + b = c$ that has -3 as its solution.

105. Does the sentence "Solve $3x + 4(x - 3)$" make sense? Why or why not?

General Equations: Part II

To solve an equation of the form $ax + b = cx + d$

When a variable occurs on each side of an equation, the Addition Properties are used to rewrite the equation so that variable terms are on one side of the equation and constant terms are on the other side of the equation. Then the Multiplication Properties are used to simplify the equation to one of the form *variable = constant*.

HOW TO Solve: $4x - 6 = 8 - 3x$

$$4x - 6 = 8 - 3x$$

- The goal is to write the equation in the form *variable = constant.*

$$4x + 3x - 6 = 8 - 3x + 3x$$
$$7x - 6 = 8 + 0$$
$$7x - 6 = 8$$

- Add **3x** to each side of the equation. Then simplify (Addition Properties). Now only one variable term occurs in the equation.

$$7x - 6 + 6 = 8 + 6$$
$$7x + 0 = 14$$
$$7x = 14$$

- Add 6 to each side of the equation. Then simplify (Addition Properties). Now only one constant term occurs in the equation.

$$\frac{7x}{7} = \frac{14}{7}$$
$$1x = 2$$
$$x = 2$$

- Divide each side of the equation by the numerical coefficient of the variable term. Then simplify (Multiplication Properties).

The solution is 2.

- Write the solution.

Study Tip

Always check the solution of an equation. For the equation at the right:

$$\begin{array}{c|c} \multicolumn{2}{c}{4x - 6 = 8 - 3x} \\ \hline 4(2) - 6 & 8 - 3(2) \\ 8 - 6 & 8 - 6 \\ 2 & = 2 \end{array}$$

The solution checks.

Example 1

Solve: $\frac{2}{9}x - 3 = \frac{7}{9}x + 2$

Solution

$$\frac{2}{9}x - 3 = \frac{7}{9}x + 2$$

$$\frac{2}{9}x - \frac{7}{9}x - 3 = \frac{7}{9}x - \frac{7}{9}x + 2$$

- Subtract $\frac{7}{9}x$ from each side.

$$-\frac{5}{9}x - 3 = 2$$

$$-\frac{5}{9}x - 3 + 3 = 2 + 3$$

- Add 3 to each side.

$$-\frac{5}{9}x = 5$$

$$\left(-\frac{9}{5}\right)\left(-\frac{5}{9}\right)x = \left(-\frac{9}{5}\right)5$$

- Multiply each side by $-\frac{9}{5}$.

$$x = -9$$

The solution is -9.

You Try It 1

Solve: $\frac{1}{5}x - 2 = \frac{2}{5}x + 4$

Your solution

Solution on pp. S29–S30

Objective B   **To solve an equation containing parentheses**

When an equation contains parentheses, one of the steps in solving the equation requires use of the Distributive Property.

$$a(b + c) = ab + ac$$

The Distributive Property is used to rewrite a variable expression without parentheses.

HOW TO   Solve: $4(3 + x) - 2 = 2(x - 4)$

$4(3 + x) - 2 = 2(x - 4)$ — • The goal is to write the equation in the form *variable = constant*.

$12 + 4x - 2 = 2x - 8$ — • Use the Distributive Property to rewrite the equation without parentheses.

$10 + 4x = 2x - 8$ — • Combine like terms.

$10 + 4x - 2x = 2x - 2x - 8$ — • Use the Addition Property of Equations.

$10 + 2x = -8$ — Subtract $2x$ from each side of the equation.

$10 - 10 + 2x = -8 - 10$ — • Use the Addition Property of Equations.

$2x = -18$ — Subtract 10 from each side of the equation.

$$\dfrac{2x}{2} = \dfrac{-18}{2}$$ — • Use the Multiplication Property of Equations. Divide each side of the equation by the numerical coefficient of the variable term.

$x = -9$

Check: $4(3 + x) - 2 = 2(x - 4)$ — • Check the solution.

$4[3 + (-9)] - 2$	$2(-9 - 4)$
$4(-6) - 2$	$2(-13)$
$-24 - 2$	-26

$-26 = -26$ A true equation

The solution is -9. — • Write the solution.

The solution to this last equation illustrates the steps involved in solving first-degree equations.

Steps in Solving General First-Degree Equations

1. Use the Distributive Property to remove parentheses.
2. Combine like terms on each side of the equation.
3. Use the Addition Property of Equations to rewrite the equation with only one variable term.
4. Use the Addition Property of Equations to rewrite the equation with only one constant term.
5. Use the Multiplication Property of Equations to rewrite the equation so that the coefficient of the variable is 1.

Example 2

Solve: $3(x + 2) - x = 11$

Solution

$3(x + 2) - x = 11$

$3x + 6 - x = 11$ • Use the Distributive Property.

$2x + 6 = 11$ • Combine like terms on the left side.

$2x + 6 - 6 = 11 - 6$ • Use the Addition Property of Equations. Subtract 6 from each side.

$2x = 5$ • Combine like terms on each side.

$\dfrac{2x}{2} = \dfrac{5}{2}$ • Use the Multiplication Property. Divide both sides by 2.

$x = 2\dfrac{1}{2}$ • The solution checks.

The solution is $2\dfrac{1}{2}$.

You Try It 2

Solve: $4(x - 1) - x = 5$

Your solution

Example 3

Solve: $5x - 2(x - 3) = 6(x - 2)$

Solution

$5x - 2(x - 3) = 6(x - 2)$

$5x - 2x + 6 = 6x - 12$ • Distributive Property

$3x + 6 = 6x - 12$ • Combine like terms.

$3x - 6x + 6 = 6x - 6x - 12$ • Subtract $6x$ from each side.

$-3x + 6 = -12$ • Combine like terms.

$-3x + 6 - 6 = -12 - 6$ • Subtract 6 from each side.

$-3x = -18$ • Combine like terms.

$\dfrac{-3x}{-3} = \dfrac{-18}{-3}$ • Divide both sides by -3.

$x = 6$ • The solution checks.

The solution is 6.

You Try It 3

Solve: $2x - 7(3x + 1) = 5(5 - 3x)$

Your solution

Solutions on p. S30

11.4 Exercises

Objective A   **To solve an equation of the form $ax + b = cx + d$**

For Exercises 1 to 54, solve.

1. $6x + 3 = 2x + 5$

2. $7x + 1 = x + 19$

3. $3x + 3 = 2x + 2$

4. $6x + 3 = 3x + 6$

5. $5x + 4 = x - 12$

6. $3x - 12 = x - 8$

7. $7b - 2 = 3b - 6$

8. $2d - 9 = d - 8$

9. $9n - 4 = 5n - 20$

10. $8x - 7 = 5x + 8$

11. $2x + 1 = 16 - 3x$

12. $3x + 2 = -23 - 2x$

13. $5x - 2 = -10 - 3x$

14. $4x - 3 = 7 - x$

15. $2x + 7 = 4x + 3$

16. $7m - 6 = 10m - 15$

17. $c + 4 = 6c - 11$

18. $t - 6 = 4t - 21$

19. $3x - 7 = x - 7$

20. $2x + 6 = 7x + 6$

21. $3 - 4x = 5 - 3x$

22. $6 - 2x = 9 - x$

23. $7 + 3x = 9 + 5x$

24. $12 + 5x = 9 - 3x$

25. $5 + 2y = 7 + 5y$

26. $9 + z = 2 + 3z$

27. $8 - 5w = 4 - 6w$

28. $9 - 4x = 11 - 5x$

29. $6x + 1 = 3x + 2$

30. $7x + 5 = 4x + 7$

31. $5x + 8 = x + 5$

32. $9x + 1 = 3x - 4$

33. $2x - 3 = 6x - 4$

34. $4 - 3x = 4 - 5x$ **35.** $6 - 3x = 6 - 5x$ **36.** $2x + 7 = 4x - 3$

37. $6x - 2 = 2x - 9$ **38.** $4x - 7 = -3x + 2$ **39.** $6x - 3 = -5x + 8$

40. $7y - 5 = 3y + 9$ **41.** $-6t - 2 = -8t - 4$ **42.** $-7w + 2 = 3w - 8$

43. $-3 - 4x = 7 - 2x$ **44.** $-8 + 5x = 8 + 6x$ **45.** $3 - 7x = -2 + 5x$

46. $3x - 2 = 7 - 5x$ **47.** $5x + 8 = 4 - 2x$ **48.** $4 - 3x = 6x - 8$

49. $12z - 9 = 3z + 12$ **50.** $4c + 13 = -6c + 9$ **51.** $\dfrac{5}{7}m - 3 = \dfrac{2}{7}m + 6$

52. $\dfrac{4}{5}x - 1 = \dfrac{1}{5}x + 5$ **53.** $\dfrac{3}{7}x + 5 = \dfrac{5}{7}x - 1$ **54.** $\dfrac{3}{4}x + 2 = \dfrac{1}{4}x - 9$

Objective B   **To solve an equation containing parentheses**

For Exercises 55 to 102, solve.

55. $6x + 2(x - 1) = 14$ **56.** $3x + 2(x + 4) = 13$ **57.** $-3 + 4(x + 3) = 5$

58. $8b - 3(b - 5) = 30$ **59.** $6 - 2(d + 4) = 6$ **60.** $5 - 3(n + 2) = 8$

61. $5 + 7(x + 3) = 20$ **62.** $6 - 3(x - 4) = 12$ **63.** $2x + 3(x - 5) = 10$

64. $3x - 4(x + 3) = 9$ **65.** $3(x - 4) + 2x = 3$ **66.** $4 + 3(x - 9) = -12$

67. $2x - 3(x - 4) = 12$

68. $4x - 2(x - 5) = 10$

69. $2x + 3(x + 4) = 7$

70. $3(x + 2) + 7 = 12$

71. $3(x - 2) + 5 = 5$

72. $4(x - 5) + 7 = 7$

73. $3y + 7(y - 2) = 5$

74. $-3z - 3(z - 3) = 3$

75. $4b - 2(b + 9) = 8$

76. $3x - 6(x - 3) = 9$

77. $3x + 5(x - 2) = 10$

78. $3x - 5(x - 1) = -5$

79. $3x + 4(x + 2) = 2(x + 9)$

80. $5x + 3(x + 4) = 4(x + 2)$

81. $2d - 3(d - 4) = 2(d + 6)$

82. $3t - 4(t - 1) = 3(t - 2)$

83. $7 - 2(x - 3) = 3(x - 1)$

84. $4 - 3(x + 2) = 2(x - 4)$

85. $6x - 2(x - 3) = 11(x - 2)$

86. $9x - 5(x - 3) = 5(x + 4)$

87. $6c - 3(c + 1) = 5(c + 2)$

88. $2w - 7(w - 2) = 3(w - 4)$

89. $7 - (x + 1) = 3(x + 3)$

90. $12 + 2(x - 9) = 3(x - 12)$

91. $2x - 3(x + 4) = 2(x - 5)$

92. $3x + 2(x - 7) = 7(x - 1)$

93. $x + 5(x - 4) = 3(x - 8) - 5$

94. $2x - 2(x - 1) = 3(x - 2) + 7$

95. $9b - 3(b - 4) = 13 + 2(b - 3)$

96. $3y - 4(y - 2) = 15 - 3(y - 2)$

97. $3(x - 4) + 3x = 7 - 2(x - 1)$

98. $2(x - 6) + 7x = 5 - 3(x - 2)$

99. $3.67x - 5.3(x - 1.932) = 6.99$

100. $4.06x + 4.7(x + 3.22) = 1.774$

101. $8.45(z - 10) = 3(z - 3.854)$

102. $4(d - 1.99) - 3.92 = 3(d - 1.77)$

APPLYING THE CONCEPTS

103. If $2x - 2 = 4x + 6$, what is the value of $3x^2$?

104. If $3 + 2(4a - 3) = 4$ and $4 - 3(2 - 3b) = 11$, which is larger, a or b?

105. Explain what is wrong with the demonstration at the right, which suggests that $5 = 4$.

$$5x + 7 = 4x + 7$$
$$5x + 7 - 7 = 4x + 7 - 7 \quad \bullet \text{ Subtract 7 from each}$$
$$\text{side of the equation.}$$
$$5x = 4x$$
$$\frac{5x}{x} = \frac{4x}{x} \quad \bullet \text{ Divide each side of the}$$
$$\text{equation by } x.$$
$$5 = 4$$

106. The equation $x = x + 1$ has no solution, whereas the solution of the equation $2x + 3 = 3$ is zero. Is there a difference between no solution and a solution of zero? Explain.

11.5 Translating Verbal Expressions into Mathematical Expressions

Objective A **To translate a verbal expression into a mathematical expression given the variable**

One of the major skills required in applied mathematics is to translate a verbal expression into a mathematical expression. Doing so requires recognizing the verbal phrases that translate into mathematical operations. Following is a partial list of the verbal phrases used to indicate the different mathematical operations.

Addition	more than	5 more than x	$x + 5$
	the sum of	the sum of w and 3	$w + 3$
	the total of	the total of 6 and z	$6 + z$
	increased by	x increased by 7	$x + 7$
Subtraction	less than	5 less than y	$y - 5$
	the difference between	the difference between w and 3	$w - 3$
	decreased by	8 decreased by a	$8 - a$
Multiplication	times	3 times c	$3c$
	the product of	the product of 4 and t	$4t$
	of	two-thirds of v	$\dfrac{2}{3}v$
	twice	twice d	$2d$
Division	divided by	n divided by 3	$\dfrac{n}{3}$
	the quotient of	the quotient of z and 4	$\dfrac{z}{4}$
	the ratio of	the ratio of s to 6	$\dfrac{s}{6}$

Translating phrases that contain the words *sum, difference, product,* and *quotient* can sometimes cause a problem. In the examples at the right, note where the operation symbol is placed.

the *sum* of x *and* y $x + y$

the *difference* between x *and* y $x - y$

the *product* of x *and* y $x \cdot y$

the *quotient* of x *and* y $\dfrac{x}{y}$

Note where we place the fraction bar when translating the word *ratio.*

the *ratio* of x *to* y $\dfrac{x}{y}$

HOW TO Translate "the quotient of n and the sum of n and 6" into a mathematical expression.

the *quotient* of n *and* the *sum* of n *and* 6 $\dfrac{n}{n + 6}$

Example 1 Translate "the sum of 5 and the product of 4 and n" into a mathematical expression.

Solution $5 + 4n$

You Try It 1 Translate "the difference between 8 and twice t" into a mathematical expression.

Your solution

Example 2 Translate "the product of 3 and the difference between z and 4" into a mathematical expression.

Solution $3(z - 4)$

You Try It 2 Translate "the quotient of 5 and the product of 7 and x" into a mathematical expression.

Your solution

Solutions on p. S30

Objective B **To translate a verbal expression into a mathematical expression by assigning the variable**

In most applications that involve translating phrases into mathematical expressions, the variable to be used is not given. To translate these phrases, we must assign a variable to the unknown quantity before writing the mathematical expression.

HOW TO Translate "the difference between seven and twice a number" into a mathematical expression.

The difference between seven and twice a number

- Identify the phrases that indicate the mathematical operations.

The unknown number: n

- Assign a variable to one of the unknown quantities.

Twice the number: $2n$

- Use the assigned variable to write an expression for any other unknown quantity.

$7 - 2n$

- Use the identified operations to write the mathematical expression.

Example 3 Translate "the total of a number and the square of the number" into a mathematical expression.

Solution
The *total* of a number and the *square* of the number

The unknown number: x
The square of the number: x^2

$x + x^2$

You Try It 3 Translate "the product of a number and one-half of the number" into a mathematical expression.

Your solution

Solution on p. S30

11.5 Exercises

To translate a verbal expression into a mathematical expression given the variable

For Exercises 1 to 22, translate into a mathematical expression.

1. 9 less than y

2. w divided by 7

3. z increased by 3

4. the product of -2 and x

5. the sum of two-thirds of n and n

6. the difference between the square of r and r

7. the quotient of m and the difference between m and 3

8. v increased by twice v

9. the product of 9 and 4 more than x

10. the total of a and the quotient of a and 7

11. the difference between n and the product of -5 and n

12. x decreased by the quotient of x and 2

13. the product of c and one-fourth of c

14. the quotient of 3 less than z and z

15. the total of the square of m and twice the square of m

16. the product of y and the sum of y and 4

17. 2 times the sum of t and 6

18. the quotient of r and the difference between 8 and r

19. x divided by the total of 9 and x

20. the sum of z and the product of 6 and z

21. three times the sum of b and 6

22. the ratio of w to the sum of w and 8

To translate a verbal expression into a mathematical expression by assigning the variable

For Exercises 23 to 44, translate into a mathematical expression.

23. the square of a number

24. five less than some number

25. a number divided by twenty

26. the difference between a number and twelve

27. four times some number

28. the quotient of five and a number

29. three-fourths of a number

30. the sum of a number and seven

31. four increased by some number

32. the ratio of a number to nine

33. the difference between five times a number and the number

34. six less than the total of three and a number

35. the product of a number and two more than the number

36. the quotient of six and the sum of nine and a number

37. seven times the total of a number and eight

38. the difference between ten and the quotient of a number and two

39. the square of a number plus the product of three and the number

40. a number decreased by the product of five and the number

41. the sum of three more than a number and one-half of the number

42. eight more than twice the sum of a number and seven

43. the quotient of three times a number and the number

44. the square of a number divided by the sum of the number and twelve

APPLYING THE CONCEPTS

45. **a.** Translate the expression $2x + 3$ into a phrase.
b. Translate the expression $2(x + 3)$ into a phrase.

46. **a.** Translate the expression $\frac{2x}{7}$ into a phrase.

b. Translate the expression $\frac{2 + x}{7}$ into a phrase.

47. In your own words, explain how variables are used.

48. **Chemistry** The chemical formula for water is H_2O. This formula means that there are two hydrogen atoms and one oxygen atom in each molecule of water. If x represents the number of atoms of oxygen in a glass of pure water, express the number of hydrogen atoms in the glass of water.

49. **Chemistry** The chemical formula for one molecule of glucose (sugar) is $C_6H_{12}O_6$, where C is carbon, H is hydrogen, and O is oxygen. If x represents the number of atoms of hydrogen in a sample of pure sugar, express the number of carbon atoms and the number of oxygen atoms in the sample in terms of x.

11.6 Translating Sentences into Equations and Solving

Objective A   **To translate a sentence into an equation and solve**

An equation states that two mathematical expressions are equal. Therefore, to translate a sentence into an equation requires recognition of the words or phrases that mean "equals." Some of these phrases are

$$\left.\begin{array}{l} \text{equals} \\ \text{is} \\ \text{is equal to} \\ \text{amounts to} \\ \text{represents} \end{array}\right\} \text{translate to} =$$

Once the sentence is translated into an equation, the equation can be simplified to one of the form *variable = constant* and the solution can be found.

HOW TO   Translate "three more than twice a number is seventeen" into an equation and solve.

The unknown number: n

| Three more than twice a number | is | seventeen |

- Assign a variable to the unknown quantity.

- Find two verbal expressions for the same value.

$$2n + 3 = 17$$
$$2n + 3 - 3 = 17 - 3$$
$$2n = 14$$
$$\frac{2n}{2} = \frac{14}{2}$$
$$n = 7$$

- Write a mathematical expression for each verbal expression. Write the equals sign. Solve the resulting equation.

The number is 7.

Point of Interest

Number puzzle problems similar to the one on this page have appeared in textbooks for hundreds of years. Here is one from a 1st-century Chinese textbook: "When a number is divided by 3, the remainder is 2; when it is divided by 5, the remainder is 3; when it is divided by 7, the remainder is 2. Find the number." There are actually infinitely many solutions to this problem. See whether you can find one of them.

Example 1

Translate "a number decreased by six equals fifteen" into an equation and solve.

Solution
The unknown number: x

| A number decreased by six | equals | fifteen |

$$x - 6 = 15$$
$$x - 6 + 6 = 15 + 6$$
$$x = 21$$

The number is 21.

You Try It 1

Translate "a number increased by four equals twelve" into an equation and solve.

Your solution

Solution on p. S30

Example 2

The quotient of a number and six is five. Find the number.

Solution

The unknown number: z

The quotient of a number and six	is	five

$$\frac{z}{6} = 5$$

$$6 \cdot \frac{z}{6} = 6 \cdot 5$$

$$z = 30$$

The number is 30.

Example 3

Eight decreased by twice a number is four. Find the number.

Solution

The unknown number: t

Eight decreased by twice a number	is	four

$$8 - 2t = 4$$

$$8 - 8 - 2t = 4 - 8$$

$$-2t = -4$$

$$\frac{-2t}{-2} = \frac{-4}{-2}$$

$$t = 2$$

The number is 2.

Example 4

Three less than the ratio of a number to seven is one. Find the number.

Solution

The unknown number: x

Three less than the ratio of a number to seven	is	one

$$\frac{x}{7} - 3 = 1$$

$$\frac{x}{7} - 3 + 3 = 1 + 3$$

$$\frac{x}{7} = 4$$

$$7 \cdot \frac{x}{7} = 7 \cdot 4$$

$$x = 28$$

The number is 28.

You Try It 2

The product of two and a number is ten. Find the number.

Your solution

You Try It 3

The sum of three times a number and six equals four. Find the number.

Your solution

You Try It 4

Three more than one-half of a number is nine. Find the number.

Your solution

Solutions on pp. S30–S31

Objective B   **To solve application problems**

Example 5

The cost of a television with remote control is $649. This amount is $125 more than the cost of the same television without remote control. Find the cost of the television without remote control.

Strategy

To find the cost of the television without remote control, write and solve an equation using C to represent the cost of the television without remote control.

Solution

| $649 | is | $125 more than the television without remote control |

$$649 = C + 125$$
$$649 - 125 = C + 125 - 125$$
$$524 = C$$

The cost of the television without remote control is $524.

You Try It 5

The sale price of a pair of slacks is $38.95. This amount is $11 less than the regular price. Find the regular price.

Your strategy

Your solution

Example 6

By purchasing a fleet of cars, a company receives a discount of $1972 on each car purchased. This amount is 8% of the regular price. Find the regular price.

Strategy

To find the regular price, write and solve an equation using P to represent the regular price of the car.

Solution

| $1972 | is | 8% of the regular price |

$$1972 = 0.08 \cdot P$$
$$\frac{1972}{0.08} = \frac{0.08P}{0.08}$$
$$24,650 = P$$

The regular price is $24,650.

You Try It 6

At a certain speed, the engine rpm (revolutions per minute) of a car in fourth gear is 2500. This is two-thirds of the rpm of the engine in third gear. Find the rpm of the engine when it is in third gear.

Your strategy

Your solution

Solutions on p. S31

Example 7

Ron Sierra charged $1105 for plumbing repairs in an office building. This charge included $90 for parts and $35 per hour for labor. Find the number of hours he worked in the office building.

Strategy

To find the number of hours worked, write and solve an equation using N to represent the number of hours worked.

Solution

| $1105 | included | $90 for parts and $35 per hour for labor |

$$1105 = 90 + 35N$$
$$1105 - 90 = 90 - 90 + 35N$$
$$1015 = 35N$$
$$\frac{1015}{35} = \frac{35N}{35}$$
$$29 = N$$

Ron worked 29 h.

Example 8

The state income tax for Tim Fong last month was $256. This amount is $5 more than 8% of his monthly salary. Find Tim's monthly salary.

Strategy

To find Tim's monthly salary, write and solve an equation using S to represent his monthly salary.

Solution

| $256 | is | $5 more than 8% of the monthly salary |

$$256 = 0.08 \cdot S + 5$$
$$256 - 5 = 0.08S + 5 - 5$$
$$251 = 0.08S$$
$$\frac{251}{0.08} = \frac{0.08S}{0.08}$$
$$3137.50 = S$$

Tim's monthly salary is $3137.50.

You Try It 7

The total cost to make a model Z100 television is $300. The cost includes $100 for materials plus $12.50 per hour for labor. How many hours of labor are required to make a model Z100 television?

Your strategy

Your solution

You Try It 8

Natalie Adams earned $2500 last month for temporary work. This amount was the sum of a base monthly salary of $800 and an 8% commission on total sales. Find Natalie's total sales for the month.

Your strategy

Your solution

Solutions on p. S31

11.6 Exercises

Objective A   To translate a sentence into an equation and solve

For Exercises 1 to 26, write an equation and solve.

1. The sum of a number and seven is twelve. Find the number.

2. A number decreased by seven is five. Find the number.

3. The product of three and a number is eighteen. Find the number.

4. The quotient of a number and three is one. Find the number.

5. Five more than a number is three. Find the number.

6. A number divided by four is six. Find the number.

7. Six times a number is fourteen. Find the number.

8. Seven less than a number is three. Find the number.

9. Five-sixths of a number is fifteen. Find the number.

10. The total of twenty and a number is five. Find the number.

11. The sum of three times a number and four is eight. Find the number.

12. The sum of one-third of a number and seven is twelve. Find the number.

13. Seven less than one-fourth of a number is nine. Find the number.

14. The total of a number divided by four and nine is two. Find the number.

15. The ratio of a number to nine is fourteen. Find the number.

16. Five increased by the product of five and a number is equal to 30. Find the number.

17. Six less than the quotient of a number and four is equal to negative two. Find the number.

18. The product of a number plus three and two is eight. Find the number.

19. The difference between seven and twice a number is thirteen. Find the number.

20. Five more than the product of three and a number is eight. Find the number.

21. Nine decreased by the quotient of a number and two is five. Find the number.

22. The total of ten times a number and seven is twenty-seven. Find the number.

23. The sum of three-fifths of a number and eight is two. Find the number.

24. Five less than two-thirds of a number is three. Find the number.

25. [calculator] The difference between a number divided by 4.186 and 7.92 is 12.529. Find the number.

26. [calculator] The total of 5.68 times a number and 132.7 is the number minus 29.265. Find the number.

Objective B   **To solve application problems**

27. Consumerism   Sears has a pair of shoes on sale for $72.50. This amount is $4.25 less than the pair sells for at Target. Find the price at Target.

28. Compensation   As a restaurant manager, Uechi Kim is paid a salary of $832 a week. This is $58 more a week than the salary Uechi received last year. Find the weekly salary paid to Uechi last year.

29. Depreciation   The value of a sport utility vehicle this year is $16,000, which is four-fifths of what its value was last year. Find the value of the vehicle last year.

30. Real Estate   This year the value of a lakefront summer cottage is $175,000. This amount is twice the value of the cottage 6 years ago. What was its value 6 years ago?

31. ● **Bridges**   The length of the Akashi Kaikyo Bridge is 1991 m. This is 1505 m greater than the length of the Brooklyn Bridge. Find the length of the Brooklyn Bridge.

32. ● **Debt**   According to CardWeb.com, the average household credit card balance ten years ago was $3275, which is $5665 less than the average credit card balance today. Find the average credit card balance today.

Akashi Kaikyo Bridge

33. Finances   Each month the Manzanares family spends $1360 for their house payment and utilities, which amounts to one-fourth of the family's monthly income. Find the family's monthly income.

34. Consumerism   The cost of a graphing calculator is now three-fourths of what the calculator cost 5 years ago. The cost of the graphing calculator is now $72. Find the cost of the calculator 5 years ago.

35. Business   Assume that the Dell Computer Corp. has increased its output of computers by 400 computers per month. This amount represents an 8% increase over last year's production. Find the monthly output last year.

36. Sports   The average number of home runs per major league game today is 2.21. This represents 135% of the average number of home runs per game 40 years ago. (*Source:* Elias Sports Bureau) Find the average number of home runs per game 40 years ago. Round to the nearest hundredth.

37. Nutrition   The nutrition label on a bag of Baked Tostitos tortilla chips lists the sodium content of one serving as 200 mg, which is 8% of the recommended daily allowance of sodium. What is the recommended daily allowance of sodium? Express the answer in grams.

38. Markup   The price of a pair of skis at the Solitude Ski Shop is $340. This price includes the store's cost for the skis plus a markup at the rate of 25%. Find Solitude's cost for the skis.

39. Contractors   Budget Plumbing charged $400 for a water softener and installation. The charge included $310 for the water softener and $30 per hour for labor. How many hours of labor were required for the job?

40. Compensation   Sandy's monthly salary as a sales representative was $2580. This amount included her base monthly salary of $600 plus a 3% commission on total sales. Find her total sales for the month.

41. Conservation   In Central America and Mexico, 1184 plants and animals are known to be at risk of extinction. This represents approximately 10.7% of all the species known to be at risk of extinction on Earth. (*Source:* World Conservation Union) Approximately how many plants and animals are known to be at risk of extinction in the world?

42. Taxes   When you use your car for business, you are able to deduct the expense on your income tax return. In 2003 the deduction was 36 cents per mile driven. How many business-related miles did a taxpayer who deducted a total of $1728 drive?

43. Insecticides   Americans spend approximately $295 million a year on remedies for cockroaches. The table at the right shows the top U.S. cities for sales of roach insecticides. What percent of the total is spent in New York? Round to the nearest tenth of a percent.

City	Roach Insecticide Sales
Los Angeles	$16.8 million
New York	$9.8 million
Houston	$6.7 million

Source: IRI InfoScan for Combat

44. Consumerism   McPherson Cement sells cement for $75 plus $24 for each yard of cement. How many yards of cement can be purchased for $363?

45. Conservation A water flow restrictor has reduced the flow of water to 2 gal/min. This amount is 1 gal/min less than three-fifths the original flow rate. Find the original rate.

46. Temperature Conversion The Celsius temperature equals five-ninths times the difference between the Fahrenheit temperature and 32. Find the Fahrenheit temperature when the Celsius temperature is 40°.

47. Compensation Assume that a sales executive receives a base monthly salary of $600 plus an 8.25% commission on total sales per month. Find the executive's total sales during a month in which she receives total compensation of $4109.55.

Environment The graph at the right shows projected world carbon dioxide emissions, in billions of metric tons. Use the graph for Exercises 48 and 49. Round to the nearest hundredth of a billion.

48. The projected world carbon dioxide emissions in 2020 are equal to 160.4% of the emissions in 1998. Find the world carbon dioxide emissions in 1998.

49. The projected world carbon dioxide emissions in 2015 are equal to 152.1% of the emissions in 1990. Find the world carbon dioxide emissions in 1990.

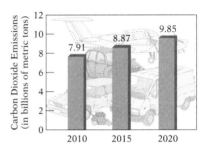

Projected World Carbon Dioxide Emissions

Source: U.S. Energy Information Administration

APPLYING THE CONCEPTS

50. A man's boyhood lasted $\frac{1}{6}$ of his life, he played football for the next $\frac{1}{8}$ of his life, and he married 5 years after quitting football. A daughter was born after he had been married $\frac{1}{12}$ of his life. The daughter lived $\frac{1}{2}$ as many years as her father. The man died 6 years after his daughter. How old was the man when he died? Use a number line to illustrate the time. Then write an equation and solve it.

51. It is always important to check the answer to an application problem to be sure the answer makes sense. Consider the following problem. "A 4-quart mixture of fruit juices is made from apple juice and cranberry juice. There are 6 more quarts of apple juice than of cranberry juice. Write and solve an equation for the number of quarts of each juice used." Does the answer to this question make sense? Explain.

52. A formula is an equation that relates variables in a known way. Find two examples of formulas that are used in your college major. Explain what each of the variables represents.

Focus on Problem Solving

From Concrete to Abstract

As you progress in your study of algebra, you will find that the problems become less concrete and more abstract. Problems that are concrete provide information pertaining to a specific instance. Abstract problems are theoretical; they are stated without reference to a specific instance. Let's look at an example of an abstract problem.

How many cents are in d dollars?

How can you solve this problem? Are you able to solve the same problem if the information given is concrete?

How many cents are in 5 dollars?

You know that there are 100 cents in 1 dollar. To find the number of cents in 5 dollars, multiply 5 by 100.

$100 \cdot 5 = 500$ There are 500 cents in 5 dollars.

Use the same procedure to find the number of cents in d dollars: multiply d by 100.

$100 \cdot d = 100d$ There are $100d$ cents in d dollars.

This problem might be taken a step further:

If one pen costs c cents, how many pens can be purchased with d dollars?

Consider the same problem using numbers in place of the variables.

If one pen costs 25 cents, how many pens can be purchased with 2 dollars?

To solve this problem, you need to calculate the number of cents in 2 dollars (multiply 2 by 100) and divide the result by the cost per pen (25 cents).

$\dfrac{100 \cdot 2}{25} = \dfrac{200}{25} = 8$ If one pen costs 25 cents, 8 pens can be purchased with 2 dollars.

Use the same procedure to solve the related abstract problem. Calculate the number of cents in d dollars (multiply d by 100) and divide the result by the cost per pen (c cents).

$\dfrac{100 \cdot d}{c} = \dfrac{100d}{c}$ If one pen costs c cents, $\dfrac{100d}{c}$ pens can be purchased with d dollars.

At the heart of the study of algebra is the use of variables. It is the variables in the problems above that make them abstract. But it is variables that enable us to generalize situations and state rules about mathematics.

Try the following problems.

1. How many nickels are in d dollars?

2. How long can you talk on a pay phone if you have only d dollars and the call costs c cents per minute?

3. If you travel m miles on one gallon of gasoline, how far can you travel on g gallons of gasoline?

4. If you walk a mile in x minutes, how far can you walk in h hours?

5. If one photocopy costs n nickels, how many photocopies can you make for q quarters?

Projects and Group Activities

Averages   We often discuss temperature in terms of average high or average low temperature. Temperatures collected over a period of time are analyzed to determine, for example, the average high temperature for a given month in your city or state. The following activity is planned to help you better understand the concept of "average."

1. Choose two cities in the United States. We will refer to them as City X and City Y. Over an 8-day period, record the daily high temperature each day in each city.

2. Determine the average high temperature for City X for the 8-day period. (Add the eight numbers, and then divide the sum by 8.) Do not round your answer.

3. Subtract the average high temperature for City X from each of the eight daily high temperatures for City X. You should have a list of eight numbers; the list should include positive numbers, negative numbers, and possibly zero.

4. Find the sum of the list of eight differences recorded in Step 3.

5. Repeat Steps 2 through 4 for City Y.

6. Compare the two sums found in Steps 4 and 5 for City X and City Y.

7. If you were to conduct this activity again, what would you expect the outcome to be? Use the results to explain what an average high temperature is. In your own words, explain what "average" means.

Chapter 11 Summary

Key Words	**Examples**
A *variable* is a letter of the alphabet used to stand for a quantity that is unknown or that can change. An expression that contains one or more variables is a *variable expression*. Replacing the variable or variables in a variable expression and then simplifying the resulting numerical expression is called *evaluating the variable expression*. [11.1A, p. 457]	Evaluate $5x^3 + 2y - 6$ when $x = -1$ and $y = 4$. $5x^3 + 2y - 6$ $5(-1)^3 + 2(4) - 6 = 5(-1) + 2(4) - 6$ $\qquad\qquad\qquad\quad = -5 + 8 - 6$ $\qquad\qquad\qquad\quad = 3 - 6$ $\qquad\qquad\qquad\quad = 3 + (-6) = -3$
The *terms of a variable expression* are the addends of the expression. A *variable term* consists of a *numerical coefficient* and a *variable part*. A *constant term* has no variable part. [11.1B, pp. 458–459]	The variable expression $-3x^2 + 2x - 5$ has three terms: $-3x^2$, $2x$, and -5. $-3x^2$ and $2x$ are variable terms. -5 is a constant term. For the term $-3x^2$, the coefficient is -3 and the variable part is x^2.
Like terms of a variable expression have the same variable part. Constant terms are also like terms. [11.1B, p. 459]	$-6a^3b^2$ and $4a^3b^2$ are like terms.
An *equation* expresses the equality of two mathematical expressions. [11.2A, p. 467]	$5x + 6 = 7x - 3$ $y = 4x - 10$ $3a^2 - 6a + 4 = 0$
A *solution of an equation* is a number that, when substituted for the variable, results in a true equation. [11.2A, p. 467]	6 is a solution of $x - 4 = 2$ because $6 - 4 = 2$ is a true equation.
Solving an equation means finding a solution of the equation. The goal is to rewrite the equation in the form *variable* = *constant*. [11.2B, p. 468]	$x = 5$ is in the form *variable* = *constant*. The solution of the equation $x = 5$ is the constant 5 because $5 = 5$ is a true equation.
A *formula* is an equation that expresses a relationship among variables. [11.2D, p. 472]	The relationship between Celsius temperatures and Fahrenheit temperatures is given by the formula $F = 1.8C + 32$, where F represents degrees Fahrenheit and C represents degrees Celsius.
Some of the words and phrases that translate to *equals* are *is, is equal to, amounts to,* and *represents*. [11.6A, p. 495]	"Eight plus a number is ten" translates to $8 + x = 10$.

Essential Rules and Procedures	**Examples**
Commutative Property of Addition [11.1B, p. 459] $a + b = b + a$	$-9 + 5 = 5 + (-9)$

Associative Property of Addition $[11.1B, p. 459]$

$(a + b) + c = a + (b + c)$

$(-6 + 4) + 2 = -6 + (4 + 2)$

Commutative Property of Multiplication $[11.1C, p. 461]$

$a \cdot b = b \cdot a$

$-5(10) = 10(-5)$

Associative Property of Multiplication $[11.1C, p. 461]$

$(a \cdot b) \cdot c = a \cdot (b \cdot c)$

$(-3 \cdot 4) \cdot 6 = -3 \cdot (4 \cdot 6)$

Distributive Property $[11.1C, p. 461]$

$a(b + c) = ab + ac$

$a(b - c) = ab - ac$

$2(x + 7) = 2(x) + 2(7) = 2x + 14$

$5(4x - 3) = 5(4x) - 5(3) = 20x - 15$

Addition Property of Zero $[11.2B, p. 468]$

The sum of a term and zero is the term.

$a + 0 = a$ or $0 + a = a$

$-16 + 0 = -16$

Addition Property of Equations $[11.2B, p. 468]$

If a, b, and c are algebraic expressions, then the equations $a = b$ and $a + c = b + c$ have the same solutions.

The same number or variable expression can be added to each side of an equation without changing the solution of the equation.

$$x + 7 = 20$$
$$x + 7 + (-7) = 20 + (-7)$$
$$x = 13$$

Multiplication Property of Reciprocals $[11.2C, p. 470]$

The product of a nonzero term and its reciprocal equals 1.

$8 \cdot \dfrac{1}{8} = 1$

Multiplication Property of One $[11.2C, p 470]$

The product of a term and 1 is the term.

$-7(1) = -7$

Multiplication Property of Equations $[11.2C, p. 470]$

If a, b, and c are algebraic expressions and $c \neq 0$, then the equation $a = b$ has the same solutions as the equation $ac = bc$.

Each side of an equation can be multiplied by the same nonzero number without changing the solution of the equation.

$$\frac{3}{4}x = 24$$
$$\frac{4}{3} \cdot \frac{3}{4}x = \frac{4}{3} \cdot 24$$
$$x = 32$$

Steps in Solving General First-Degree Equations
$[11.4B, p. 485]$

1. Use the Distributive Property to remove parentheses.

2. Combine like terms on each side of the equation.

3. Use the Addition Property of Equations to rewrite the equation with only one variable term.

4. Use the Addition Property of Equations to rewrite the equation with only one constant term.

5. Use the Multiplication Property of Equations to rewrite the equation so that the coefficient of the variable is 1.

$$8 - 4(2x + 3) = 2(1 - x)$$
$$8 - 8x - 12 = 2 - 2x$$
$$-8x - 4 = 2 - 2x$$
$$-8x + 2x - 4 = 2 - 2x + 2x$$
$$-6x - 4 = 2$$
$$-6x - 4 + 4 = 2 + 4$$
$$-6x = 6$$
$$\frac{-6x}{-6} = \frac{6}{-6}$$
$$x = -1$$

Chapter 11 Review Exercises

1. Simplify: $-2(a - b)$

2. Is -2 a solution of the equation $3x - 2 = -8$?

3. Solve: $x - 3 = -7$

4. Solve: $-2x + 5 = -9$

5. Evaluate $a^2 - 3b$ when $a = 2$ and $b = -3$.

6. Solve: $-3x = 27$

7. Solve: $\frac{2}{3}x + 3 = -9$

8. Simplify: $3x - 2(3x - 2)$

9. Solve: $6x - 9 = -3x + 36$

10. Solve: $x + 3 = -2$

11. Is 5 a solution of the equation $3x - 5 = -10$?

12. Evaluate $a^2 - (b \div c)$ when $a = -2$, $b = 8$, and $c = -4$.

13. Solve: $3(x - 2) + 2 = 11$

14. Solve: $35 - 3x = 5$

15. Simplify: $6bc - 7bc + 2bc - 5bc$

16. Solve: $7 - 3x = 2 - 5x$

17. Solve: $-\frac{3}{8}x = -\frac{15}{32}$

18. Simplify: $\frac{1}{2}x^2 - \frac{1}{3}x^2 + \frac{1}{5}x^2 + 2x^2$

19. Solve: $5x - 3(1 - 2x) = 4(2x - 1)$

20. Solve: $\frac{5}{6}x - 4 = 5$

21. **Fuel Efficiency**   A tourist drove a rental car 621 mi on 27 gal of gas. Find the number of miles per gallon of gas. Use the formula $D = M \cdot G$, where D is distance, M is miles per gallon, and G is the number of gallons.

22. **Temperature Conversion**   Find the Celsius temperature when the Fahrenheit temperature is 100°. Use the formula $F = 1.8C + 32$, where F is the Fahrenheit temperature and C is the Celsius temperature. Round to the nearest tenth.

23. Translate "the total of n and the quotient of n and five" into a mathematical expression.

24. Translate "the sum of five more than a number and one-third of the number" into a mathematical expression.

25. The difference between nine and twice a number is five. Find the number.

26. The product of five and a number is fifty. Find the number.

27. **Discount**   A compact disc player is now on sale for $228. This is 60% of the regular price. Find the regular price of the CD player.

28. **Agriculture**   A farmer harvested 28,336 bushels of corn. This amount represents a 12% increase over last year's crop. How many bushels of corn did the farmer harvest last year?

Chapter 11 Test

1. Solve: $\frac{x}{5} - 12 = 7$

2. Solve: $x - 12 = 14$

3. Simplify: $3y - 2x - 7y - 9x$

4. Solve: $8 - 3x = 2x - 8$

5. Solve: $3x - 12 = -18$

6. Evaluate $c^2 - (2a + b^2)$ when $a = 3$, $b = -6$, and $c = -2$.

7. Is 3 a solution of the equation $x^2 + 3x - 7 = 3x - 2$?

8. Simplify: $9 - 8ab - 6ab$

9. Solve: $-5x = 14$

10. Simplify: $3y + 5(y - 3) + 8$

11. Solve: $3x - 4(x - 2) = 8$

12. Solve: $5 = 3 - 4x$

13. Evaluate $\frac{x^2}{y} - \frac{y^2}{x}$ for $x = 3$ and $y = -2$.

14. Solve: $\frac{5}{8}x = -10$

15. Solve: $y - 4y + 3 = 12$

16. Solve: $2x + 4(x - 3) = 5x - 1$

17. **Finance**   A loan of $6600 is to be paid in 48 equal monthly installments. Find the monthly payment. Use the formula $L = P \cdot N$, where L is the loan amount, P is the monthly payment, and N is the number of months.

18. **Manufacturing**   A clock manufacturer's fixed costs per month are $5000. The unit cost for each clock is $15. Find the number of clocks made during a month in which the total cost was $65,000. Use the formula $T = U \cdot N + F$, where T is the total cost, U is the cost per unit, N is the number of units made, and F is the fixed costs.

19. **Physics**   Find the time required for a falling object to increase in velocity from 24 ft/s to 392 ft/s. Use the formula $V = V_0 + 32t$, where V is the final velocity of a falling object, V_0 is the starting velocity of a falling object, and t is the time for the object to fall.

20. Translate "the sum of x and one-third of x" into a mathematical expression.

21. Translate "five times the sum of a number and three" into a mathematical expression.

22. Translate "three less than two times a number is seven" into an equation and solve.

23. The total of five and three times a number is the number minus two. Find the number.

24. **Compensation**   Eduardo Santos earned $3600 last month. This salary is the sum of the base monthly salary of $1200 and a 6% commission on total sales. Find his total sales for the month.

25. **Consumerism**   Your mechanic charges you $278 for performing a 30,000-mile checkup on your car. This charge includes $152 for parts and $42 per hour for labor. Find the number of hours the mechanic worked on your car.

Cumulative Review Exercises

1. Simplify: $6^2 - (18 - 6) \div 4 + 8$

2. Subtract: $3\frac{1}{6} - 1\frac{7}{15}$

3. Simplify: $\left(\frac{3}{8} - \frac{1}{4}\right) \div \frac{3}{4} + \frac{4}{9}$

4. Multiply: 9.67×0.0049

5. Write "$84 earned in 20 hours" as a unit rate.

6. Solve the proportion $\frac{2}{3} = \frac{n}{40}$.
Round to the nearest hundredth.

7. Write $5\frac{1}{3}\%$ as a fraction.

8. What percent of 30 is 42?

9. 8 is 125% of what number?

10. Multiply: 3 ft 9 in. $\times 5$

11. Convert $1\frac{3}{8}$ lb to ounces.

12. Convert 282 mg to grams.

13. Add: $-2 + 5 + (-8) + 4$

14. Find -6 less than 13.

15. Simplify: $(-2)^2 - (-8) \div (3 - 5)^2$

16. Evaluate $3ab - 2ac$ when $a = -2$, $b = 6$, and $c = -3$.

17. Simplify: $3z - 2x + 5z - 8x$

18. Simplify: $6y - 3(y - 5) + 8$

19. Solve: $2x - 5 = -7$

20. Solve: $7x - 3(x - 5) = -10$

21. Solve: $-\frac{2}{3}x = 5$

22. Solve: $\frac{x}{3} - 5 = -12$

23. **Education**   In a mathematics class of 34 students, 6 received an A grade. Find the percent of the students in the mathematics class who received an A grade. Round to the nearest tenth of a percent.

24. **Markup**   The manager of a pottery store used a markup rate of 40%. Find the price of a piece of pottery that cost the store $28.50.

25. **Discount**   A department store has a suit regularly priced at $450 on sale for $369.
a. What is the discount?
b. What is the discount rate?

26. **Simple Interest**   A toy store borrowed $80,000 at a simple interest rate of 11% for 4 months. What is the simple interest due on the loan? Round to the nearest cent.

27. Translate "the sum of three times a number and 4" into a mathematical expression.

28. **Probability**   A tetrahedral die is one with four triangular sides numbered 1 to 4. If two tetrahedral dice are rolled, what is the probability that the sum of the upward faces is 7?

29. **Compensation**   Sunah Yee, a sales executive, receives a base salary of $800 plus an 8% commission on total sales. Find the total sales during a month in which Sunah earned $3400. Use the formula $M = S \cdot R + B$, where M is the monthly earnings, S is the total sales, R is the commission rate, and B is the base monthly salary.

30. Three less than eight times a number is three more than five times the number. Find the number.

12 Geometry

This is an aerial view of the house of William Paca, who was a Maryland Patriot and a signer of the Declaration of Independence. The house's large, formal garden has been restored to its original splendor. The best way to appreciate the shapes sculpted in the garden is to view it from above, like in this photo. Each geometric shape combines with the others to form the entire garden. **Exercise 35 on page 544** shows you how to use a geometric formula to first determine the size of an area, and then to calculate how much grass seed is needed for an area of that size.

OBJECTIVES

Section 12.1

A To define and describe lines and angles
B To define and describe geometric figures
C To solve problems involving angles formed by intersecting lines

Section 12.2

A To find the perimeter of plane geometric figures
B To find the perimeter of composite geometric figures
C To solve application problems

Section 12.3

A To find the area of geometric figures
B To find the area of composite geometric figures
C To solve application problems

Section 12.4

A To find the volume of geometric solids
B To find the volume of composite geometric solids
C To solve application problems

Section 12.6

A To solve similar and congruent triangles
B To solve application problems

Need help? For online student resources, such as section quizzes, visit this textbook's website at **math.college.hmco.com/students.**

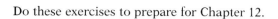

PREP TEST • • •

Do these exercises to prepare for Chapter 12.

1. Solve: $x + 47 = 90$

2. Solve: $32 + 97 + x = 180$

3. Simplify: $2(18) + 2(10)$

4. Evaluate abc when $a = 2$, $b = 3.14$, and $c = 9$.

5. Evaluate xyz^3 when $x = \frac{4}{3}$, $y = 3.14$, and $z = 3$.

6. Solve: $\frac{5}{12} = \frac{6}{x}$

GO FIGURE • • •

Draw the figure that would come next.

12.1 Angles, Lines, and Geometric Figures

To define and describe lines and angles

The word *geometry* comes from the Greek words for "earth" (*geo*) and "measure." The original purpose of geometry was to measure land. Today geometry is used in many sciences, such as physics, chemistry, and geology, and in applied fields such as mechanical drawing and astronomy. Geometric form is used in art and design.

Two basic geometric concepts are plane and space.

A **plane** is a flat surface, such as a table-top or a blackboard. Figures that can lie totally in a plane are called **plane figures.**

Plane

Space extends in all directions. Objects in space, such as trees, ice cubes, and doors, are called **solids.**

Space

A **line** extends indefinitely in two directions in a plane. A line has no width.

Line

Study Tip

A great many new vocabulary words are introduced in this chapter. There are eight new terms on this page alone: plane, plane figures, space, solids, line, line segment, parallel lines, and intersecting lines. All of these terms are in **bold type.** The bold type indicates that these are concepts you must know to learn the material. Be sure to study each new term as it is presented.

A **line segment** is part of a line and has two endpoints. The line segment *AB* is shown in the figure.

Line segment

The length of a line segment is the distance between the endpoints of the line segment. The length of a line segment may be expressed as the sum of two or more shorter line segments, as shown. For this example, $AB = 5$, $BC = 3$, and $AC = AB + BC = 5 + 3 = 8$.

HOW TO Given that $AB = 22$ and $AC = 31$, find the length of *BC*.

$$AC = AB + BC$$
$$31 = 22 + BC$$
$$31 - 22 = 22 - 22 + BC$$
$$9 = BC$$

• Substitute 22 for *AB* and 31 for *AC*, and solve for *BC*.

Lines in a plane can be parallel or intersecting. **Parallel lines** never meet; the distance between them is always the same. **Intersecting lines** cross at a point in the plane.

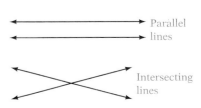

Parallel lines

Intersecting lines

The symbol ∥ means "is parallel to." In the accompanying figure, $AB \parallel CD$ and $p \parallel q$. Note that line p contains line segment AB and that line q contains line segment CD. Parallel lines contain parallel line segments.

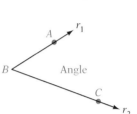

A **ray** starts at a point and extends indefinitely in one direction.

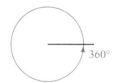

An **angle** is formed when two rays start from the same point. Rays r_1 and r_2 start from point B. The common endpoint is called the **vertex** of the angle.

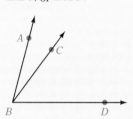
If A and C are points on rays r_1 and r_2 above, respectively, then the angle is called $\angle ABC$, $\angle CBA$, or $\angle B$, where $\angle$ is the symbol for angle. Note that an angle is named by giving three points, with the vertex as the second point listed, or by giving the point at the vertex.

An angle can also be named by writing a variable between the rays close to the vertex. In the figure, $\angle x = \angle QRS = \angle SRQ$ and $\angle y = \angle SRT = \angle TRS$. Note that in this figure, more than two rays meet at the vertex. In this case, the vertex cannot be used to name the angle.

A unit in which angles are measured is the **degree.** The symbol for degree is °. One complete revolution is 360° (360 degrees).

One-quarter of a revolution is 90°. A 90° angle is called a **right angle.** The symbol ∟ represents a right angle.

Perpendicular lines are intersecting lines that form right angles.

Point of Interest

The Babylonians knew that Earth is in approximately the same position in the sky every 365 days. Historians suggest that the reason one complete revolution of a circle is 360° is that 360 is the closest number to 365 that is divisible by many numbers.

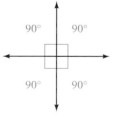

The symbol ⊥ means "is perpendicular to." In the accompanying figure, $AB \perp CD$ and $p \perp q$. Note that line p contains line segment AB and line q contains line segment CD. Perpendicular lines contain perpendicular line segments.

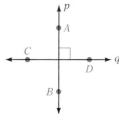

Complementary angles are two angles whose sum is 90°.

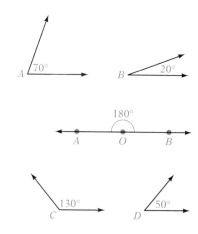

$\angle A + \angle B = 70° + 20° = 90°$
$\angle A$ and $\angle B$ are complementary angles.

One-half of a revolution is 180°. A 180° angle is called a **straight angle.** $\angle AOB$ in the figure is a straight angle.

Supplementary angles are two angles whose sum is 180°.

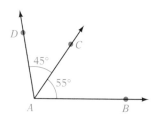

$\angle C + \angle D = 130° + 50° = 180°$
$\angle C$ and $\angle D$ are supplementary angles.

An **acute angle** is an angle whose measure is between 0° and 90°. $\angle D$ in the figure above is an acute angle. An **obtuse angle** is an angle whose measure is between 90° and 180°. $\angle C$ in the figure above is an obtuse angle.

In the accompanying figure, $\angle DAC = 45°$ and $\angle CAB = 55°$.

$\angle DAB = \angle DAC + \angle CAB$
$\qquad\quad = 45° + 55° = 100°$

Example 1

Given that $MN = 15$, $NO = 18$, and $MP = 48$, find the length of OP.

Solution
$\qquad MP = MN + NO + OP$
$\qquad 48 = 15 + 18 + OP$
$\qquad 48 = 33 + OP$
$48 - 33 = 33 - 33 + OP$
$\qquad 15 = OP$

You Try It 1

Given that $QR = 24$, $ST = 17$, and $QT = 62$, find the length of RS.

Your solution

Example 2

Find the complement of a 32° angle.

Solution
Let x represent the complement of 32°.

$\qquad\quad x + 32° = 90°$ ● The sum of
$x + 32° - 32° = 90° - 32°$ complementary
$\qquad\qquad\quad x = 58°$ angles is 90°.

58° is the complement of 32°.

You Try It 2

Find the supplement of a 32° angle.

Your solution

Solutions on p. S31

Example 3

Find the measure of $\angle x$.

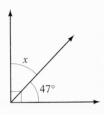

Solution

$$\angle x + 47° = 90°$$
$$\angle x + 47° - 47° = 90° - 47°$$
$$\angle x = 43°$$

You Try It 3

Find the measure of $\angle a$.

Your solution

Solution on p. S31

Objective B **To define and describe geometric figures**

TAKE NOTE

Any side of a triangle can be considered the base, but generally the **base of a triangle** refers to the side that the triangle rests on. The **height of a triangle** is a line segment drawn perpendicular to the base from the opposite vertex.

A **triangle** is a closed, three-sided plane figure. Figure ABC is a triangle. AB is called the **base.** The line CD, perpendicular to the base, is called the **height.**

The Angles in a Triangle

The sum of the three angles in a triangle is 180°.

$$\angle A + \angle B + \angle C = 180°$$

HOW TO In triangle DEF, $\angle D = 32°$ and $\angle E = 88°$. Find the measure of $\angle F$.

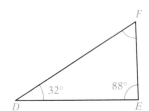

$$\angle D + \angle E + \angle F = 180°$$
$$32° + 88° + \angle F = 180°$$
$$120° + \angle F = 180°$$
$$120° - 120° + \angle F = 180° - 120°$$
$$\angle F = 60°$$

- The sum of the three angles in a triangle is 180°.
- $\angle D = 32°$ and $\angle E = 88°$
- Solve for $\angle F$.

A **right triangle** contains one right angle. The side opposite the right angle is called the **hypotenuse.** The **legs of a right triangle** are its other two sides. In a right triangle, the two acute angles are complementary.

$$\angle A + \angle B = 90°$$

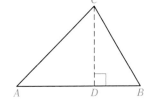

HOW TO In the right triangle at the left, $\angle A = 30°$. Find the measure of $\angle B$.

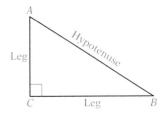

$$\angle A + \angle B = 90°$$
$$30° + \angle B = 90°$$
$$30° - 30° + \angle B = 90° - 30°$$
$$\angle B = 60°$$

- The two acute angles are complementary.
- $\angle A = 30°$
- Solve for $\angle B$.

A **quadrilateral** is a closed, four-sided plane figure. Three quadrilaterals with special characteristics are described here.

A **parallelogram** has opposite sides parallel and equal. The distance AE between the parallel sides is called the **height.**

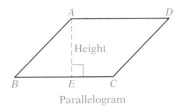

Parallelogram

A **rectangle** is a parallelogram that has four right angles.

A **square** is a rectangle that has four equal sides.

Rectangle   Square

A **circle** is a plane figure in which all points are the same distance from point O, which is called the **center** of the circle.

The **diameter of a circle** (d) is a line segment through the center of the circle with endpoints on the circle. AB is a diameter of the circle shown.

The **radius of a circle** (r) is a line segment from the center to a point on the circle. OC is a radius of the circle.

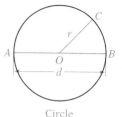

Circle

$$d = 2r \qquad \text{or} \qquad r = \frac{1}{2}d$$

HOW TO   The line segment AB is a diameter of the circle shown. Find the radius of the circle.

The radius is one-half the diameter. Therefore,

$$r = \frac{1}{2}d$$
$$= \frac{1}{2}(8 \text{ in.}) \qquad \bullet \ d = 8 \text{ in.}$$
$$= 4 \text{ in.}$$

8 in.

A **geometric solid** is a figure in space, or space figure. Four common space figures are the rectangular solid, cube, sphere, and cylinder.

A **rectangular solid** is a solid in which all six faces are rectangles.

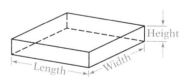

Height

Length   Width

Rectangular solid

A **cube** is a rectangular solid in which all six faces are squares.

Cube

A **sphere** is a solid in which all points on the surface are the same distance from point O, which is called the **center** of the sphere.

The **diameter of a sphere** is a line segment going through the center with endpoints on the sphere. AB is a diameter of the sphere shown.

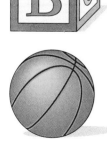

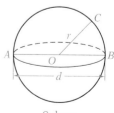

Sphere

The **radius of a sphere** is a line segment from the center to a point on the sphere. OC is a radius of the sphere.

$$d = 2r \qquad \text{or} \qquad r = \frac{1}{2}d$$

 The radius of the sphere shown at the right is 5 cm. Find the diameter of the sphere.

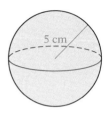

$d = 2r$ • **The diameter equals twice the radius.**
$\quad = 2(5 \text{ cm})$ • $r = 5 \text{ cm}$
$\quad = 10 \text{ cm}$

The diameter is 10 cm.

The most common **cylinder** is one in which the bases are circles and are perpendicular to the side.

Height

Base

Cylinder

Example 4

One angle in a right triangle is equal to 50°. Find the measure of the other angles.

Solution
In a right triangle, one angle measures 90° and the two acute angles are complementary.

$$\angle A + \angle B = 90°$$
$$\angle A + 50° = 90°$$
$$\angle A + 50° - 50° = 90° - 50°$$
$$\angle A = 40°$$

The other angles measure 90° and 40°.

Example 5

Two angles of a triangle measure 42° and 103°. Find the measure of the third angle.

Solution
The sum of the three angles of a triangle is 180°.

$$\angle A + \angle B + \angle C = 180°$$
$$\angle A + 42° + 103° = 180°$$
$$\angle A + 145° = 180°$$
$$\angle A + 145° - 145° = 180° - 145°$$
$$\angle A = 35°$$

The measure of the third angle is 35°.

Example 6

A circle has a radius of 8 cm. Find the diameter.

Solution
$d = 2r$
$\quad = 2 \cdot 8 \text{ cm} = 16 \text{ cm}$

The diameter is 16 cm.

You Try It 4

A right triangle has one angle equal to 7°. Find the measure of the other angles.

Your solution

You Try It 5

Two angles of a triangle measure 62° and 45°. Find the measure of the other angle.

Your solution

You Try It 6

A circle has a diameter of 8 in. Find the radius.

Your solution

Solutions on p. S32

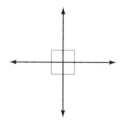

Objective C   **To solve problems involving angles formed by intersecting lines**

Four angles are formed by the intersection of two lines. If the two lines are perpendicular, then each of the four angles is a right angle. If the two lines are not perpendicular, then two of the angles formed are acute angles and two of the angles are obtuse angles. The two acute angles are always opposite each other, and the two obtuse angles are always opposite each other.

In the figure, $\angle w$ and $\angle y$ are acute angles. $\angle x$ and $\angle z$ are obtuse angles. Two angles that are on opposite sides of the intersection of two lines are called **vertical angles.** Vertical angles have the same measure. $\angle w$ and $\angle y$ are vertical angles. $\angle x$ and $\angle z$ are vertical angles.

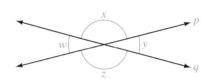

$\angle w = \angle y$
$\angle x = \angle z$

Two angles that share a common side are called **adjacent angles.** In the previous figure, $\angle x$ and $\angle y$ are adjacent angles, as are $\angle y$ and $\angle z$, $\angle z$ and $\angle w$, and $\angle w$ and $\angle x$. Adjacent angles of intersecting lines are supplementary angles.

$\angle x + \angle y = 180°$
$\angle y + \angle z = 180°$
$\angle z + \angle w = 180°$
$\angle w + \angle x = 180°$

HOW TO   In the figure at the left, $\angle c = 65°$. Find the measures of angles a, b, and d.

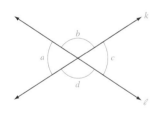

$\angle a = 65°$
● $\angle a = \angle c$ because $\angle c$ and $\angle a$ are vertical angles.

$\angle b + \angle c = 180°$
● $\angle c$ is supplementary to $\angle b$ because $\angle c$ and $\angle b$ are adjacent angles.
$\angle b + 65° = 180°$
● $\angle c = 65°$
$\angle b + 65° - 65° = 180° - 65°$
$\angle b = 115°$

$\angle d = 115°$
● $\angle d = \angle b$ because $\angle b$ and $\angle d$ are vertical angles.

A line intersecting two other lines at two different points is called a **transversal.**

If the lines cut by a transversal are parallel lines and the transversal is perpendicular to the parallel lines, then all eight angles formed are right angles.

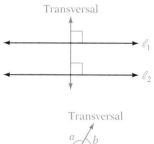

If the lines cut by a transversal are parallel lines and the transversal is not perpendicular to the parallel lines, then all four acute angles have the same measure and all four obtuse angles have the same measure. For the figure at the right,

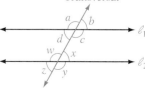

$\angle a = \angle c = \angle w = \angle y$ and $\angle b = \angle d = \angle x = \angle z$

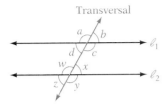

Alternate interior angles are two nonadjacent angles that are on opposite sides of the transversal and between the parallel lines. For the figure at the left, $\angle c$ and $\angle w$ are alternate interior angles. $\angle d$ and $\angle x$ are alternate interior angles. Alternate interior angles have the same measure.

Alternate exterior angles are two nonadjacent angles that are on opposite sides of the transversal and outside the parallel lines. For the figure at the left, $\angle a$ and $\angle y$ are alternate exterior angles. $\angle b$ and $\angle z$ are alternate exterior angles. Alternate exterior angles have the same measure.

Corresponding angles are two angles that are on the same side of the transversal and are both acute angles or are both obtuse angles. For the figure at the top left, the following pairs of angles are corresponding angles: $\angle a$ and $\angle w$, $\angle d$ and $\angle z$, $\angle b$ and $\angle x$, $\angle c$ and $\angle y$. Corresponding angles have the same measure.

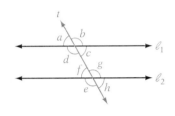

HOW TO In the figure at the left, $\ell_1 \parallel \ell_2$ and $\angle c = 58°$. Find the measures of $\angle f$, $\angle h$, and $\angle g$.

$\angle f = 58°$

* $\angle f = \angle c$ because $\angle f$ and $\angle c$ are alternate interior angles.

$\angle h = 58°$

* $\angle h = \angle c$ because $\angle c$ and $\angle h$ are corresponding angles.

$\angle g + \angle h = 180°$
$\angle g + 58° = 180°$
$\angle g = 122°$

* $\angle g$ is supplementary to $\angle h$.
* $\angle h = 58°$
* Subtract $58°$ from each side.

Example 7

In the figure, $\angle a = 75°$. Find $\angle b$.

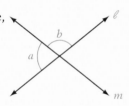

Solution

$\angle a + \angle b = 180°$

* $\angle a$ and $\angle b$ are supplementary.

$75° + \angle b = 180°$

* $\angle a = 75°$

$\angle b = 105°$

* Subtract $75°$ from each side.

You Try It 7

In the figure, $\angle a = 125°$. Find $\angle b$.

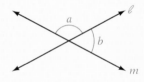

Your solution

Example 8

In the figure, $\ell_1 \parallel \ell_2$ and $\angle a = 70°$. Find $\angle b$.

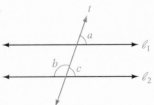

Solution

$\angle c = \angle a = 70°$

* Corresponding angles are equal.

$\angle b + \angle c = 180°$
$\angle b + 70° = 180°$
$\angle b = 110°$

* $\angle b$ and $\angle c$ are supplementary.
* $\angle c = 70°$
* Subtract $70°$ from each side.

You Try It 8

In the figure, $\ell_1 \parallel \ell_2$ and $\angle a = 120°$. Find $\angle b$.

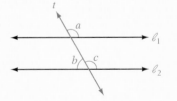

Your solution

Solutions on p. S32

12.1 Exercises

Objective A   To define and describe lines and angles

1. The measure of an acute angle is between ___ and ___.

2. The measure of an obtuse angle is between ___ and ___.

3. How many degrees are in a straight angle?

4. Two lines that intersect at right angles are ___ lines.

5. In the figure, $EF = 20$ and $FG = 10$. Find the length of EG.

6. In the figure, $EF = 18$ and $FG = 6$. Find the length of EG.

7. In the figure, it is given that $QR = 7$ and $QS = 28$. Find the length of RS.

8. In the figure, it is given that $QR = 15$ and $QS = 45$. Find the length of RS.

9. In the figure, it is given that $AB = 12$, $CD = 9$, and $AD = 35$. Find the length of BC.

10. In the figure, it is given that $AB = 21$, $BC = 14$, and $AD = 54$. Find the length of CD.

11. Find the complement of a 31° angle.

12. Find the complement of a 62° angle.

13. Find the supplement of a 72° angle.

14. Find the supplement of a 162° angle.

15. Find the complement of a 13° angle.

16. Find the complement of an 88° angle.

17. Find the supplement of a 127° angle.

18. Find the supplement of a 7° angle.

In Exercises 19 and 20, find the measure of angle AOB.

19.

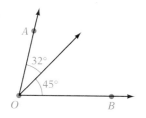

20.

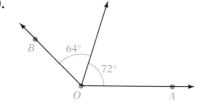

For Exercises 21 to 24, find the measure of angle a.

21.

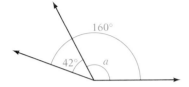

22.

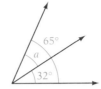

23.

24.

25. In the figure, it is given that $\angle LOM = 53°$ and $\angle LON = 139°$. Find the measure of $\angle MON$.

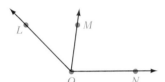

26. In the figure, it is given that $\angle MON = 38°$ and $\angle LON = 85°$. Find the measure of $\angle LOM$.

Objective B　To define and describe geometric figures

27. What is the sum of the three angles of a triangle?

28. Name the side opposite the right angle in a right triangle.

29. Name a parallelogram with four right angles.

30. Name the rectangle with four equal sides.

31. Name a rectangular solid in which all six faces are squares.

32. Name the solid in which all points are the same distance from the center.

33. Name a quadrilateral in which opposite sides are parallel and equal.

34. Name the plane figure in which all points are the same distance from the center.

35. Name the solid in which the bases are circular and perpendicular to the side.

36. Name a solid in which all the faces are rectangles.

37. A triangle has a 13° angle and a 65° angle. Find the measure of the other angle.

38. A triangle has a 105° angle and a 32° angle. Find the measure of the other angle.

39. A right triangle has a 45° angle. Find the measure of the other two angles.

40. A right triangle has a 62° angle. Find the measure of the other two angles.

41. A triangle has a 62° angle and a 104° angle. Find the measure of the other angle.

42. A triangle has a 30° angle and a 45° angle. Find the measure of the other angle.

43. A right triangle has a 25° angle. Find the measure of the other two angles.

44. Two angles of a triangle are 42° and 105°. Find the measure of the other angle.

45. Find the radius of a circle with a diameter of 16 in.

46. Find the radius of a circle with a diameter of 9 ft.

47. Find the diameter of a circle with a radius of $2\frac{1}{3}$ ft.

48. Find the diameter of a circle with a radius of 24 cm.

49. The radius of a sphere is 3.5 cm. Find the diameter.

50. The radius of a sphere is $1\frac{1}{2}$ ft. Find the diameter.

51. The diameter of a sphere is 4 ft 8 in. Find the radius.

52. The diameter of a sphere is 1.2 m. Find the radius.

Objective C **To solve problems involving angles formed by intersecting lines**

For Exercises 53 to 56, find the measures of angles *a* and *b*.

53.

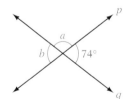

54.

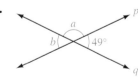

55.

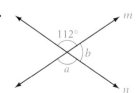

56.

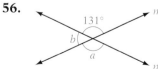

For Exercises 57 to 64, $\ell_1 \parallel \ell_2$. Find the measures of angles a and b.

57.

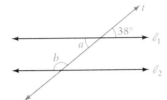

58.

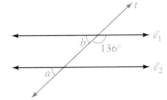

59.

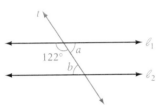

60.

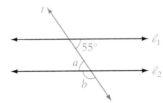

61.

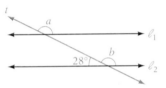

62.

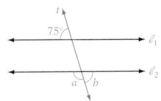

63.

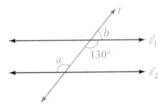

64.

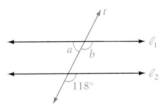

APPLYING THE CONCEPTS

65. **a.** What is the smallest possible whole number of degrees in an angle of a triangle?
   b. What is the largest possible whole number of degrees in an angle of a right triangle?

66. Determine whether the statement is always true, sometimes true, or never true.
   a. Two lines that are both parallel to a third line are parallel to each other.
   b. A triangle contains at least two acute angles.
   c. Vertical angles are complementary angles.

67. If AB and CD intersect at point O, and $\angle AOC = \angle BOC$, explain why AB is perpendicular to CD.

12.2 Plane Geometric Figures

To find the perimeter of plane geometric figures

A **polygon** is a closed figure determined by three or more line segments that lie in a plane. The **sides of a polygon** are the line segments that form the polygon. The figures below are examples of polygons.

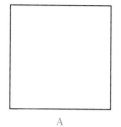

A

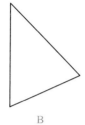

B

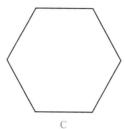

C

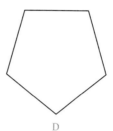

D

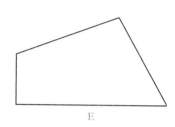

E

Point of Interest

Although a polygon is defined in terms of its *sides* (see the definition above), the word actually comes from the Latin word *polygonum*, which means having many *angles*. This is certainly the case for a polygon.

A **regular polygon** is one in which each side has the same length and each angle has the same measure. The polygons in Figures A, C, and D above are regular polygons.

The name of a polygon is based on the number of its sides. The table below lists the names of polygons that have from 3 to 10 sides.

Number of Sides	Name of the Polygon
3	Triangle
4	Quadrilateral
5	Pentagon
6	Hexagon
7	Heptagon
8	Octagon
9	Nonagon
10	Decagon

The Pentagon in Arlington, Virginia

Triangles and quadrilaterals are two of the most common types of polygons. Triangles are distinguished by the number of equal sides and also by the measures of their angles.

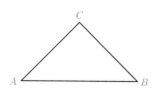

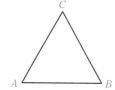

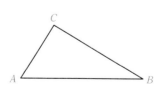

An **isosceles triangle** has two sides of equal length. The angles opposite the equal sides are of equal measure.

$AC = BC$
$\angle A = \angle B$

The three sides of an **equilateral triangle** are of equal length. The three angles are of equal measure.

$AB = BC = AC$
$\angle A = \angle B = \angle C$

A **scalene triangle** has no two sides of equal length. No two angles are of equal measure.

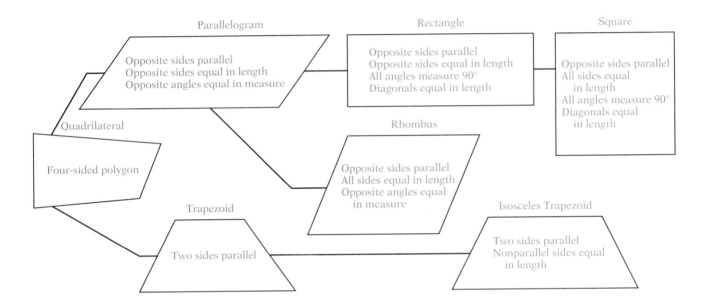

An **acute triangle** has three acute angles.

An **obtuse triangle** has one obtuse angle.

A **right triangle** has a right angle.

Quadrilaterals are also distinguished by their sides and angles, as shown below. Note that a rectangle, a square, and a rhombus are different forms of a parallelogram.

Parallelogram
Opposite sides parallel
Opposite sides equal in length
Opposite angles equal in measure

Rectangle
Opposite sides parallel
Opposite sides equal in length
All angles measure 90°
Diagonals equal in length

Square
Opposite sides parallel
All sides equal in length
All angles measure 90°
Diagonals equal in length

Quadrilateral
Four-sided polygon

Rhombus
Opposite sides parallel
All sides equal in length
Opposite angles equal in measure

Trapezoid
Two sides parallel

Isosceles Trapezoid
Two sides parallel
Nonparallel sides equal in length

The **perimeter** of a plane geometric figure is a measure of the distance around the figure. Perimeter is used in buying fencing for a lawn or determining how much baseboard is needed for a room.

The perimeter of a triangle is the sum of the lengths of the three sides.

Perimeter of a Triangle

$P = a + b + c$

HOW TO Find the perimeter of the triangle shown at the right.

$P = a + b + c$
$ = 3 \text{ cm} + 5 \text{ cm} + 6 \text{ cm}$
$ = 14 \text{ cm}$

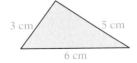

The perimeter of the triangle is 14 cm.

The perimeter of a quadrilateral is the sum of the lengths of the four sides. The perimeter of a square is the sum of the four equal sides.

> **Perimeter of a Square**
>
> $P = 4s$

HOW TO Find the perimeter of the square shown at the right.

$P = 4s$
   $= 4(3 \text{ ft})$ • $s = 3 \text{ ft}$
   $= 12 \text{ ft}$

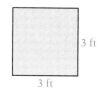

The perimeter of the square is 12 ft.

A rectangle is a quadrilateral with opposite sides of equal length. The length of a rectangle refers to the longer side, and the width refers to the length of the shorter side.

> **Perimeter of a Rectangle**
>
> $P = 2L + 2W$

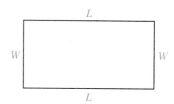

HOW TO Find the perimeter of the rectangle shown at the right.

$P = 2L + 2W$
   $= 2(6 \text{ m}) + 2(3 \text{ m})$ • $L = 6 \text{ m}, W = 3 \text{ m}$
   $= 12 \text{ m} + 6 \text{ m}$
   $= 18 \text{ m}$

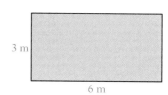

The perimeter of the rectangle is 18 m.

The distance around a circle is called the **circumference.** The circumference of a circle is equal to the product of π (pi) and the diameter.

> **Circumference of a Circle**
>
> $C = \pi d$
>   or
> $C = 2\pi r$ • Because diameter = $2r$

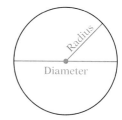

Point of Interest

Archimedes (c. 287–212 B.C.) was the mathematician who gave us the approximate value of π as $\frac{22}{7} = 3\frac{1}{7}$. He actually showed that π was between $3\frac{10}{71}$ and $3\frac{1}{7}$. The approximation $3\frac{10}{71}$ is closer to the exact value of π, but it is more difficult to use.

The formula for circumference uses the number π (pi). The value of π can be approximated by a decimal or a fraction.

$$\pi \approx 3.14 \qquad \pi \approx \frac{22}{7}$$

The π key on a calculator gives a closer approximation of π than 3.14.

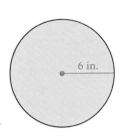

6 in.

HOW TO   Find the circumference of the circle shown at the right.

$C = 2\pi r$
$\approx 2 \cdot 3.14 \cdot 6$ in.   • $r = 6$ in.
$= 37.68$ in.

The circumference of the circle is approximately 37.68 in.

Example 1

Find the perimeter of a rectangle with a width of $\frac{2}{3}$ ft and a length of 2 ft.

Solution

$\frac{2}{3}$ ft

2 ft

$P = 2L + 2W$

$= 2(2 \text{ ft}) + 2\left(\frac{2}{3} \text{ ft}\right)$ • $L = 2$ ft, $W = \frac{2}{3}$ ft

$= 4 \text{ ft} + \frac{4}{3} \text{ ft}$

$= 5\frac{1}{3} \text{ ft}$

The perimeter of the rectangle is $5\frac{1}{3}$ ft.

You Try It 1

Find the perimeter of a rectangle with a length of 2 m and a width of 0.85 m.

Your solution

Example 2

Find the perimeter of a triangle with sides 5 in., 7 in., and 8 in.

Solution

5 in.   7 in.

8 in.

$P = a + b + c$
$= 5 \text{ in.} + 7 \text{ in.} + 8 \text{ in.}$
$= 20 \text{ in.}$

The perimeter of the triangle is 20 in.

You Try It 2

Find the perimeter of a triangle with sides 12 cm, 15 cm, and 18 cm.

Your solution

Example 3

Find the circumference of a circle with a radius of 18 cm. Use 3.14 for π.

Solution

18 cm

$C = 2\pi r$
$\approx 2 \cdot 3.14 \cdot 18 \text{ cm}$
$= 113.04 \text{ cm}$

The circumference is approximately 113.04 cm.

You Try It 3

Find the circumference of a circle with a diameter of 6 in. Use 3.14 for π.

Your solution

Solutions on p. S32

Objective B   **To find the perimeter of composite geometric figures**

A **composite geometric figure** is a figure made from two or more geometric figures. The following composite is made from part of a rectangle and part of a circle:

Perimeter of the composite figure = 3 sides of a rectangle + $\frac{1}{2}$ the circumference of a circle

Perimeter of the composite figure = $2L + W + \frac{1}{2}\pi d$

The perimeter of the composite figure below is found by adding the measures of twice the length plus the width plus one-half the circumference of the circle.

$P = 2L + W + \frac{1}{2}\pi d$

$\approx 2(12 \text{ m}) + 4 \text{ m} + \frac{1}{2}(3.14)(4 \text{ m})$ • $L = 12$ m, $W = 4$ m, $d = 4$ m. *Note:* The diameter of the circle is equal to the width of the rectangle.

$= 34.28 \text{ m}$

The perimeter is approximately 34.28 m.

Example 4

Find the perimeter of the composite figure. Use $\frac{22}{7}$ for π.

Solution

$$
\begin{array}{ccc}
\text{Perimeter} & \text{sum of} & \frac{1}{2} \text{ the cir-} \\
\text{of} & = \text{lengths} & + \text{cumference} \\
\text{composite} & \text{of the 4} & \text{of the circle} \\
\text{figure} & \text{sides} &
\end{array}
$$

$P = \quad 4s \quad + \quad \frac{1}{2}\pi d$

$\approx 4(5 \text{ cm}) + \frac{1}{2}\left(\frac{22}{7}\right)(7 \text{ cm})$

$= 20 \text{ cm} + 11 \text{ cm} = 31 \text{ cm}$

The perimeter is approximately 31 cm.

You Try It 4

Find the perimeter of the composite figure. Use 3.14 for π.

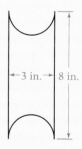

Your solution

Solution on p. S32

Objective C   **To solve application problems**

Example 5

The dimensions of a triangular sail are 18 ft, 11 ft, and 15 ft. What is the perimeter of the sail?

Strategy

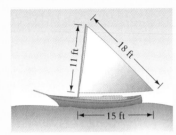

To find the perimeter, use the formula for the perimeter of a triangle.

Solution
$P = a + b + c$
    $= 18 \text{ ft} + 11 \text{ ft} + 15 \text{ ft}$
    $= 44 \text{ ft}$

The perimeter of the sail is 44 ft.

You Try It 5

What is the perimeter of a standard piece of computer paper that measures $8\frac{1}{2}$ in. by 11 in.?

Your strategy

Your solution

Example 6

If fencing costs $4.75 per foot, how much will it cost to fence a rectangular lot that is 108 ft wide and 240 ft long?

Strategy

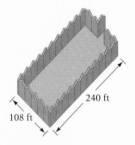

To find the cost of the fence:
- Find the perimeter of the lot.
- Multiply the perimeter by the per-foot cost of fencing.

Solution
$P = 2L + 2W$
    $= 2(240 \text{ ft}) + 2(108 \text{ ft})$
    $= 480 \text{ ft} + 216 \text{ ft}$
    $= 696 \text{ ft}$

Cost $= 696 \times 4.75 = 3306$

The cost is $3306.

You Try It 6

Metal stripping is being installed around a workbench that is 0.74 m wide and 3 m long. At $2.76 per meter, find the cost of the metal stripping. Round to the nearest cent.

Your strategy

Your solution

Solutions on p. S32

12.2 Exercises

Objective A   **To find the perimeter of plane geometric figures**

For Exercises 1 to 8, find the perimeter or circumference of the given figures. Use 3.14 for π.

1.

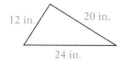

2.

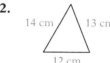

3.

4.

5.

14 cm

32 cm

6.

5 ft

18 ft

7.

15 cm

8.

9. Find the perimeter of a triangle with sides 2 ft 4 in., 3 ft, and 4 ft 6 in.

10. Find the perimeter of a rectangle with a length of 2 m and a width of 0.8 m.

11. Find the circumference of a circle with a radius of 8 cm. Use 3.14 for π.

12. Find the circumference of a circle with a diameter of 14 in. Use $\frac{22}{7}$ for π.

13. Find the perimeter of a square in which each side is equal to 60 m.

14. Find the perimeter of a triangle in which each side is $1\frac{2}{3}$ ft.

15. Find the perimeter of a five-sided figure with sides of 22 cm, 47 cm, 29 cm, 42 cm, and 17 cm.

16. Find the perimeter of a rectangular farm that is $\frac{1}{2}$ mi wide and $\frac{3}{4}$ mi long.

<u>Objective B</u>   **To find the perimeter of composite geometric figures**

For Exercises 17 to 24, find the perimeter. Use 3.14 for π.

17.

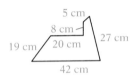

18.

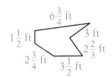

19.

20.

21.

22.

23.

24.

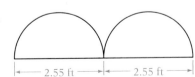

Objective C　**To solve application problems**

25. Landscaping　How many feet of fencing should be purchased for a rectangular garden that is 18 ft long and 12 ft wide?

26. Interior Design　Wall-to-wall carpeting is installed in a room that is 12 ft long and 10 ft wide. The edges of the carpet are nailed to the floor. Along how many feet must the carpet be nailed down?

27. Quilting　How many feet of binding are required to bind the edge of a rectangular quilt that measures 3.5 ft by 8.5 ft?

28. Carpentry　Find the length of molding needed to put around a circular table that is 3.8 ft in diameter. Use 3.14 for π.

29. Landscaping　The rectangular lot shown in the figure at the right is being fenced. The fencing along the road is to cost $6.20 per foot. The rest of the fencing costs $5.85 per foot. Find the total cost to fence the lot.

800 ft

1250 ft

30. Sewing　Bias binding is to be sewed around the edge of a rectangular tablecloth measuring 72 in. by 45 in. Each package of bias binding costs $3.50 and contains 15 ft of binding. How many packages of bias binding are needed for the tablecloth?

31. Travel　A bicycle tire has a diameter of 24 in. How many feet does the bicycle travel when the wheel makes 5 revolutions? Use 3.14 for π.

32. Travel　A tricycle tire has a diameter of 12 in. How many feet does the tricycle travel when the wheel makes 8 revolutions? Use 3.14 for π.

33. Architecture　The floor plan of a roller rink is shown in the figure at the right.
　a. Use estimation to determine whether the perimeter of the rink is more than 70 m or less than 70 m.
　b. Calculate the perimeter of the roller rink. Use 3.14 for π.

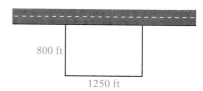

25 m

10 m

34. Home Improvement　A rain gutter is being installed on a home that has the dimensions shown in the figure at the right. At a cost of $11.30 per meter, how much will it cost to install the rain gutter?

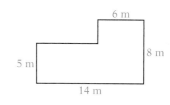

6 m

8 m

5 m

14 m

35. **Home Improvement** Find the length of weather stripping installed around the arched door shown in the figure at the right. Use 3.14 for π.

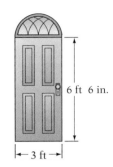

6 ft 6 in.

3 ft

36. 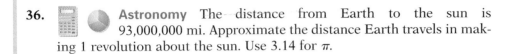 **Astronomy** The distance from Earth to the sun is 93,000,000 mi. Approximate the distance Earth travels in making 1 revolution about the sun. Use 3.14 for π.

37. **Earth Science** The distance from the surface to the center of Earth is 6356 km. Approximate the circumference of Earth. Use 3.14 for π.

APPLYING THE CONCEPTS

38. **a.** If the diameter of a circle is doubled, how many times larger is the resulting circumference?
b. If the radius of a circle is doubled, how many times larger is the resulting circumference?

39. **Geometry** In the pattern to the right, the length of one side of a square is 1 unit. Find the perimeter of the eighth figure in the pattern.

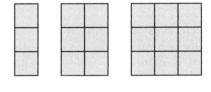

40. **Geometry** Remove six toothpicks from the figure at the right in such a way as to leave two squares.

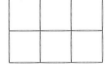

41. **Geometry** An equilateral triangle is placed inside an equilateral triangle as shown at the right. Now three more equilateral triangles are placed inside the unshaded equilateral triangles. The process is repeated again. Determine the perimeter of all the shaded triangles in Figure C.

2 cm
Figure A   Figure B   Figure C

42. **Metalwork** A wire whose length is given as x inches is bent into a square. Express the length of a side of the square in terms of x.

x

43. A forest ranger must determine the diameter of a redwood tree. Explain how the ranger could do this without cutting down the tree.

12.3 Area

Objective A **To find the area of geometric figures**

Area is a measure of the amount of surface in a region. Area can be used to describe the size of a rug, a parking lot, a farm, or a national park. Area is measured in square units.

A square that measures 1 in. on each side has an area of 1 square inch, which is written 1 in².

A square that measures 1 cm on each side has an area of 1 square centimeter, which is written 1 cm².

Larger areas can be measured in square feet (ft²), square meters (m²), square miles (mi²), acres (43,560 ft²), or any other square unit.

The area of a geometric figure is the number of squares that are necessary to cover the figure. In the figures below, two rectangles have been drawn and covered with squares. In the figure on the left, 12 squares, each of area 1 cm², were used to cover the rectangle. The area of the rectangle is 12 cm². In the figure on the right, 6 squares, each of area 1 in², were used to cover the rectangle. The area of the rectangle is 6 in².

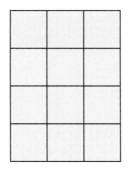

The area of the rectangle is 12 cm².

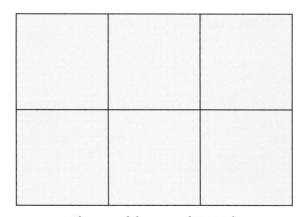

The area of the rectangle is 6 in².

Note from the above figures that the area of a rectangle can be found by multiplying the length of the rectangle by its width.

Area of a Rectangle

$A = LW$

HOW TO Find the area of the rectangle shown at the right.

$A = LW$
$\quad = (8\ \text{ft})(5\ \text{ft}) \qquad \bullet\ L = 8\ \text{ft}, W = 5\ \text{ft}$
$\quad = 40\ \text{ft}^2$

The area of the rectangle is 40 ft².

A square is a rectangle in which all sides are the same length. Therefore, both the length and the width can be represented by a side. Remember that $s \cdot s = s^2$.

> **Area of a Square**
>
> $A = s^2$

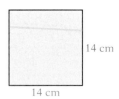

HOW TO Find the area of the square shown at the right.

$A = s^2$
$\quad = (14 \text{ cm})^2 \qquad \bullet \; s = 14 \text{ cm}$
$\quad = 196 \text{ cm}^2$

The area of the square is 196 cm².

The area of a circle is equal to the product of π and the square of the radius.

> **Area of a Circle**
>
> $A = \pi r^2$

Radius

HOW TO Find the area of the circle shown at the right.

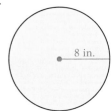

$A = \pi r^2$
$\quad = \pi (8 \text{ in.})^2 = 64\pi \text{ in}^2$
$\quad \approx 64 \cdot 3.14 \text{ in}^2 = 200.96 \text{ in}^2$

The area is exactly $64\pi \text{ in}^2$.
The area is approximately 200.96 in².

In the figure below, *AB* is the base of the triangle, and *CD*, which is perpendicular to the base, is the height. The area of a triangle is one-half the product of the base and the height.

> **Area of a Triangle**
>
> $A = \dfrac{1}{2}bh$

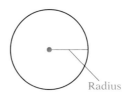

HOW TO Find the area of the triangle shown below.

$A = \dfrac{1}{2}bh$

$\quad = \dfrac{1}{2}(20 \text{ m})(5 \text{ m}) \qquad \bullet \; b = 20 \text{ m}, h = 5 \text{ m}$

$\quad = 50 \text{ m}^2$

The area of the triangle is 50 m².

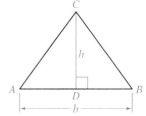

Integrating Technology

To calculate the area of the triangle shown at the right, you can enter

20 × 5 ÷ 2 =

or

.5 × 20 × 5 =

Example 1 Find the area of a circle with a diameter of 9 cm. Use 3.14 for π.

Solution $r = \dfrac{1}{2}d = \dfrac{1}{2}(9 \text{ cm}) = 4.5 \text{ cm}$

$A = \pi r^2$

$\quad \approx 3.14(4.5 \text{ cm})^2 = 63.585 \text{ cm}^2$

The area is approximately 63.585 cm².

You Try It 1 Find the area of a triangle with a base of 24 in. and a height of 14 in.

Your solution

Solution on p. S32

Objective B **To find the area of composite geometric figures**

The area of the composite figure shown below is found by calculating the area of the rectangle and then subtracting the area of the triangle.

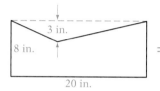

$A = LW - \dfrac{1}{2}bh$

$\quad = (20 \text{ in.})(8 \text{ in.}) - \dfrac{1}{2}(20 \text{ in.})(3 \text{ in.}) = 160 \text{ in}^2 - 30 \text{ in}^2 = 130 \text{ in}^2$

Example 2

Find the area of the shaded portion of the figure. Use 3.14 for π.

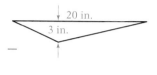

Solution

$\begin{array}{ccc} \text{Area of} \\ \text{shaded} = \\ \text{portion} \end{array} \underbrace{\begin{array}{c}\text{area of}\\\text{square}\end{array}}_{} - \underbrace{\begin{array}{c}\text{area of}\\\text{circle}\end{array}}_{}$

$\begin{aligned} A &= \quad s^2 \quad - \quad \pi r^2 \\ &= (8 \text{ m})^2 - \pi(4 \text{ m})^2 \\ &\approx 64 \text{ m}^2 - 3.14(16 \text{ m}^2) \\ &= 64 \text{ m}^2 - 50.24 \text{ m}^2 = 13.76 \text{ m}^2 \end{aligned}$

The area is approximately 13.76 m².

You Try It 2

Find the area of the composite figure.

Your solution

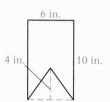

Solution on p. S33

Objective C **To solve application problems**

Example 3

A walkway 2 m wide is built along the front and along both sides of a building, as shown in the figure. Find the area of the walkway.

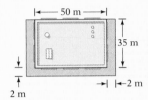

Strategy

To find the area of the walkway, add the area of the front section (54 m · 2 m) and the area of the two side sections (each 35 m · 2 m).

Solution

$$\text{Area of walkway} = \frac{\text{area of front section}}{} + \frac{2(\text{area of one side section})}{}$$

$$A = (54 \text{ m})(2 \text{ m}) + 2(35 \text{ m})(2 \text{ m})$$
$$= 108 \text{ m}^2 \qquad + 140 \text{ m}^2$$
$$= 248 \text{ m}^2$$

The area of the walkway is 248 m².

You Try It 3

New carpet is installed in a room measuring 9 ft by 12 ft. Find the area of the room in square yards. (9 ft² = 1 yd²)

Your strategy

Your solution

Solution on p. S33

12.3 Exercises

Objective A **To find the area of geometric figures**

For Exercises 1 to 8, find the area of the given figures. Use 3.14 for π.

1.

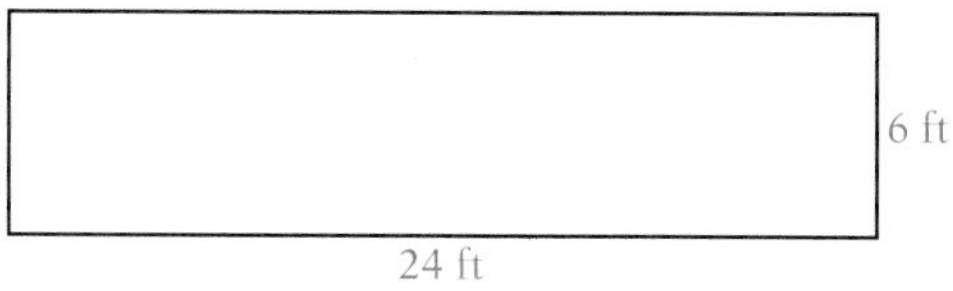

6 ft
24 ft

2.

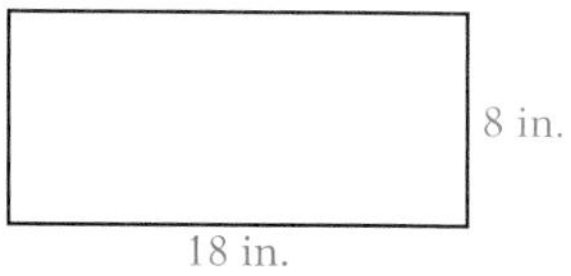

8 in.
18 in.

3.

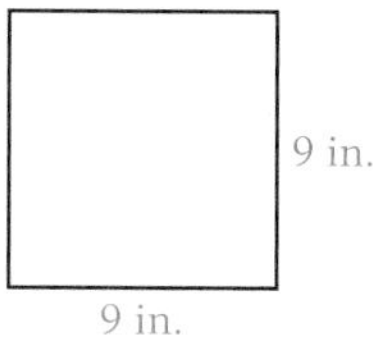

9 in.
9 in.

4.

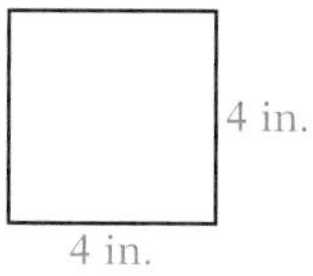

4 in.
4 in.

5.

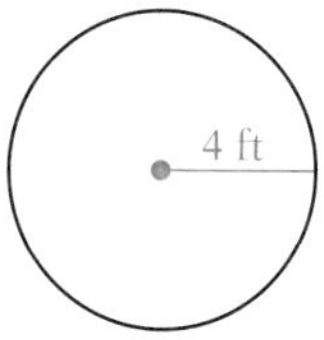

4 ft

6.

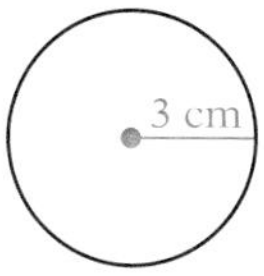

3 cm

7.

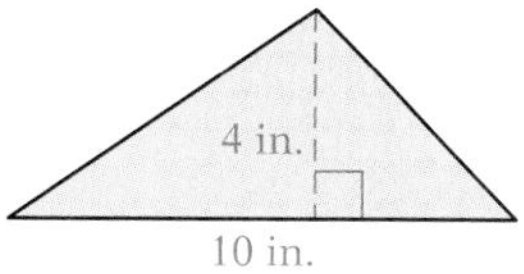

4 in.
10 in.

8.

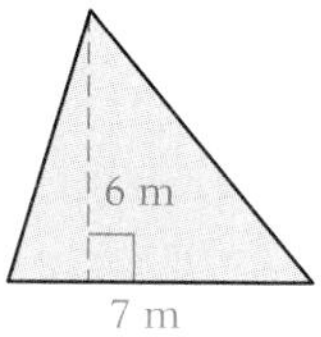

6 m
7 m

9. Find the area of a right triangle with a base of 3 cm and a height of 1.42 cm.

10. Find the area of a triangle with a base of 3 ft and a height of $\frac{2}{3}$ ft.

11. Find the area of a square with a side of 4 ft.

12. Find the area of a square with a side of 10 cm.

13. Find the area of a rectangle with a length of 43 in. and a width of 19 in.

14. Find the area of a rectangle with a length of 82 cm and a width of 20 cm.

15. Find the area of a circle with a radius of 7 in. Use $\frac{22}{7}$ for π.

16. Find the area of a circle with a diameter of 40 cm. Use 3.14 for π.

Objective B   **To find the area of composite geometric figures**

For Exercises 17 to 24, find the area. Use 3.14 for π.

17.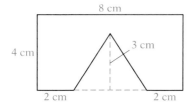

18.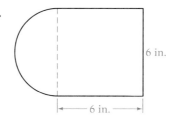

19.

20.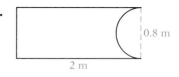

21.

22.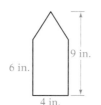

23.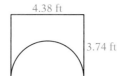

24.

Objective C   **To solve application problems**

25. **Sports**   Artificial turf is being used to cover a playing field. If the field is rectangular with a length of 100 yd and a width of 75 yd, how much artificial turf must be purchased to cover the field?

26.  **Telescopes**   The telescope lens of the Hale telescope at Mount Palomar, California, has a diameter of 200 in. Find the area of the lens. Leave the answer in terms of π.

27. **Agriculture**   An irrigation system waters a circular field that has a 50-foot radius. Find the area watered by the irrigation system. Use 3.14 for π.

28. **Interior Design**   A fabric wall hanging is to fill a space that measures 5 m by 3.5 m. Allowing for 0.1 m of the fabric to be folded back along each edge, how much fabric must be purchased for the wall hanging?

29. **Home Improvement**   You plan to stain the wooden deck attached to your house. The deck measures 10 ft by 8 ft. A quart of stain will cost $9.95 and will cover 50 ft². How many quarts of stain should you buy?

30. **Interior Design**   A carpet is to be installed in one room and a hallway, as shown in the diagram at the right. At a cost of $18.50 per square meter, how much will it cost to carpet the area?

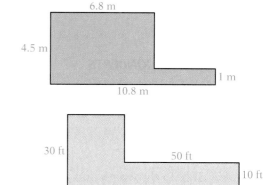

31. **Landscaping**   Find the area of a concrete driveway with the measurements shown in the figure.

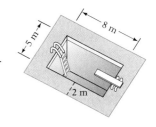

32. **Interior Design**   You want to tile your kitchen floor. The floor measures 12 ft by 9 ft. How many tiles, each a square with side $1\frac{1}{2}$ ft, should you purchase for the job?

33. **Interior Design**   You are wallpapering two walls of a child's room. One wall measures 9 ft by 8 ft, and the other measures 11 ft by 8 ft. The wallpaper costs $28.50 per roll, and each roll of the wallpaper will cover 40 ft². What is the cost to wallpaper the two walls?

34. **Construction**   Find the area of the 2-meter boundary around the swimming pool shown in the figure.

35. **Parks**   An urban renewal project involves reseeding a park that is in the shape of a square, 60 ft on each side. Each bag of grass seed costs \$5.75 and will seed 1200 ft². How much money should be budgeted for buying grass seed for the park?

36. **Architecture**   The roller rink shown in the figure at the right is to be covered with hardwood floor.

    a. Without doing the calculations, indicate whether the area of the rink is more than 8000 ft² or less than 8000 ft².

    b. Calculate how much hardwood floor is needed to cover the roller rink. Use 3.14 for π.

37. **Parks**   Find the total area of the national park with the dimensions shown in the figure. Use 3.14 for π.

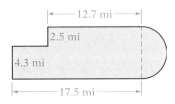

38. **Interior Design**   Find the cost of plastering the walls of a room 22 ft wide, 25 ft 6 in. long, and 8 ft high. Subtract 120 ft² for windows and doors. The cost is \$2.50 per square foot.

39. **a.** A circle has a radius of 8 in. Find the increase in area when the radius is increased by 2 in. Use 3.14 for π.

    b. A circle has a radius of 5 cm. Find the increase in area when the radius is doubled. Use 3.14 for π.

APPLYING THE CONCEPTS

40. **Geometry**   What fractional part of the area of the larger of the two squares is the shaded area? Write your answer as a fraction in simplest form. This problem appeared in *Math Teacher*, vol. 86, No. 3 (September 1993).

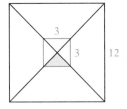

41. **a.** If both the length and the width of a rectangle are doubled, how many times larger is the area of the resulting rectangle?

    b. If the radius of a circle is doubled, what happens to the area?

    c. If the diameter of a circle is doubled, what happens to the area?

42.   The circles at the right are identical. Is the area in the circles to the left of the line equal to, less than, or greater than the area in the circles to the right of the line? Explain your answer.

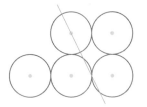

43. Determine whether the statement is always true, sometimes true, or never true.

    a. If two triangles have the same perimeter, then they have the same area.

    b. If two rectangles have the same area, then they have the same perimeter.

    c. If two squares have the same area, then the sides of the squares have the same length.

44. **Geometry**   All of the dots at the right are equally spaced, horizontally and vertically, 1 inch apart. What is the area of the triangle?

12.4 Volume

Objective A **To find the volume of geometric solids**

Volume is a measure of the amount of space inside a closed surface, or figure in space. Volume can be used to describe the amount of heating gas used for cooking, the amount of concrete delivered for the foundation of a house, or the amount of water in storage for a city's water supply.

A cube that is 1 ft on each side has a volume of 1 cubic foot, which is written 1 ft^3.

A cube that measures 1 cm on each side has a volume of 1 cubic centimeter, which is written 1 cm^3.

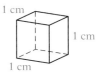

The volume of a solid is the number of cubes that are necessary to fill the solid exactly. The volume of the rectangular solid at the right is 24 cm^3 because it will hold exactly 24 cubes, each 1 cm on a side. Note that the volume can be found by multiplying the length times the width times the height.

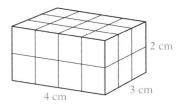

> **Volume of a Rectangular Solid**
>
> $V = LWH$

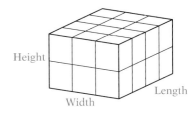

HOW TO   Find the volume of a rectangular solid with a length of 9 in., a width of 3 in., and a height of 4 in.

$V = LWH$
  $= (9 \text{ in.})(3 \text{ in.})(4 \text{ in.})$ • $L = 9$ **in.,** $W = 3$ **in.,**
  $= 108 \text{ in}^3$ $H = 4$ **in.**

The volume of the rectangular solid is 108 in^3.

The length, width, and height of a cube have the same measure. The volume of a cube is found by multiplying the side of the cube times itself three times (side cubed).

> **Volume of a Cube**
>
> $V = s^3$

HOW TO   Find the volume of the cube shown at the right.

$V = s^3$
$\quad = (3 \text{ ft})^3 \qquad \bullet \; s = 3 \text{ ft}$
$\quad = 27 \text{ ft}^3$

The volume of the cube is 27 ft³.

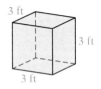

The volume of a sphere is found by multiplying four-thirds times pi (π) times the radius cubed.

> **Volume of a Sphere**
>
> $V = \dfrac{4}{3}\pi r^3$

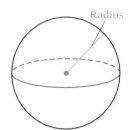

HOW TO   Find the volume of the sphere shown below. Use 3.14 for π. Round to the nearest hundredth.

$V = \dfrac{4}{3}\pi r^3$

$\quad \approx \dfrac{4}{3}(3.14)(2 \text{ in.})^3 \qquad \bullet \; r = 2 \text{ in}$

$\quad = \dfrac{4}{3}(3.14)(8 \text{ in}^3)$

$\quad \approx 33.49 \text{ in}^3$

The volume is approximately 33.49 in³.

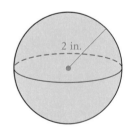

The volume of a cylinder is found by multiplying the area of the base of the cylinder (a circle) times the height.

> **Volume of a Cylinder**
>
> $V = \pi r^2 h$

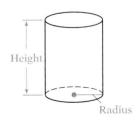

HOW TO   Find the volume of the cylinder shown below. Use 3.14 for π.

$V = \pi r^2 h$
$\approx 3.14(3 \text{ cm})^2(8 \text{ cm})$ • $r = 3$ cm, $h = 8$ cm
$= 3.14(9 \text{ cm}^2)(8 \text{ cm})$
$= 226.08 \text{ cm}^3$

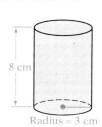
8 cm
Radius = 3 cm

The volume of the cylinder is approximately 226.08 cm³.

Example 1

Find the volume of a rectangular solid with a length of 3 ft, a width of 1.5 ft, and a height of 2 ft.

Solution
$V = LWH$
$= (3 \text{ ft})(1.5 \text{ ft})(2 \text{ ft})$
$= 9 \text{ ft}^3$

The volume is 9 ft³.

You Try It 1

Find the volume of a rectangular solid with a length of 8 cm, a width of 3.5 cm, and a height of 4 cm.

Your solution

Example 2

Find the volume of a cube that has a side measuring 2.5 in.

Solution
$V = s^3$
$= (2.5 \text{ in.})^3$
$= 15.625 \text{ in}^3$

The volume is 15.625 in³.

You Try It 2

Find the volume of a cube with a side of 5 cm.

Your solution

Example 3

Find the volume of a cylinder with a radius of 12 cm and a height of 65 cm. Use 3.14 for π.

Solution
$V = \pi r^2 h$
$\approx 3.14(12 \text{ cm})^2(65 \text{ cm})$
$= 3.14(144 \text{ cm}^2)(65 \text{ cm})$
$= 29{,}390.4 \text{ cm}^3$

The volume is approximately 29,390.4 cm³.

You Try It 3

Find the volume of a cylinder with a diameter of 14 in. and a height of 15 in. Use $\frac{22}{7}$ for π.

Your solution

Solutions on p. S33

Example 4

Find the volume of a sphere with a diameter of 12 in. Use 3.14 for π.

Solution

$r = \dfrac{1}{2}d = \dfrac{1}{2}(12 \text{ in.}) = 6 \text{ in.}$ • Find the radius.

$V = \dfrac{4}{3}\pi r^3$ • Use the formula for the volume of a sphere.

$\approx \dfrac{4}{3}(3.14)(6 \text{ in.})^3$

$= \dfrac{4}{3}(3.14)(216 \text{ in}^3)$

$= 904.32 \text{ in}^3$

The volume is approximately 904.32 in³.

You Try It 4

Find the volume of a sphere with a radius of 3 m. Use 3.14 for π.

Your solution

Solution on p. S33

Objective B   **To find the volume of composite geometric solids**

A **composite geometric solid** is a solid made from two or more geometric solids. The solid shown is made from a cylinder and one-half of a sphere.

Volume of the composite solid = volume of the cylinder + $\dfrac{1}{2}$ the volume of the sphere

> **HOW TO**   Find the volume of the composite solid shown above if the radius of the base of the cylinder is 3 in. and the height of the cylinder is 10 in. Use 3.14 for π.
>
> The volume equals the volume of a cylinder plus one-half the volume of a sphere. The radius of the sphere equals the radius of the base of the cylinder.
>
> $V = \pi r^2 h + \dfrac{1}{2}\left(\dfrac{4}{3}\pi r^3\right)$
>
> $\approx 3.14(3 \text{ in.})^2(10 \text{ in.}) + \dfrac{1}{2}\left(\dfrac{4}{3}\right)(3.14)(3 \text{ in.})^3$
>
> $= 3.14(9 \text{ in}^2)(10 \text{ in.}) + \dfrac{1}{2}\left(\dfrac{4}{3}\right)(3.14)(27 \text{ in}^3)$
>
> $= 282.6 \text{ in}^3 + 56.52 \text{ in}^3$
>
> $= 339.12 \text{ in}^3$
>
> The volume is approximately 339.12 in³.

Example 5

Find the volume of the solid in the figure. Use 3.14 for π.

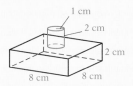

Solution

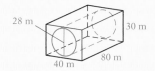

| Volume of the solid | = | volume of rectangu-lar solid | + | volume of cylinder |

$V = LWH + \pi r^2 h$
$\approx (8 \text{ cm})(8 \text{ cm})(2 \text{ cm}) + 3.14(1 \text{ cm})^2(2 \text{ cm})$
$= 128 \text{ cm}^3 + 6.28 \text{ cm}^3$
$= 134.28 \text{ cm}^3$

The volume is approximately 134.28 cm³.

You Try It 5

Find the volume of the solid in the figure. Use 3.14 for π.

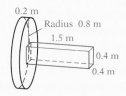

Your solution

Example 6

Find the volume of the solid in the figure. Use 3.14 for π.

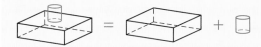

Solution

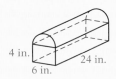

| Volume of the solid | = | volume of rectangu-lar solid | − | volume of cylinder |

$V = LWH - \pi r^2 h$
$\approx (80 \text{ m})(40 \text{ m})(30 \text{ m}) - 3.14(14 \text{ m})^2(80 \text{ m})$
$= 96,000 \text{ m}^3 - 49,235.2 \text{ m}^3$
$= 46,764.8 \text{ m}^3$

The volume is approximately 46,764.8 m³.

You Try It 6

Find the volume of the solid in the figure. Use 3.14 for π.

Your solution

Solutions on p. S33

To solve application problems

An aquarium is 28 in. long, 14 in. wide, and 16 in. high. Find the volume of the aquarium.

Strategy
To find the volume of the aquarium, use the formula for the volume of a rectangular solid.

Solution
$V = LWH$
$= (28 \text{ in.})(14 \text{ in.})(16 \text{ in.})$
$= 6272 \text{ in}^3$

The volume of the aquarium is 6272 in³.

Find the volume of a freezer that is 7 ft long, 3 ft high, and 2.5 ft wide.

Your strategy

Your solution

Find the volume of the bushing shown in the figure below. Use 3.14 for π.

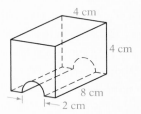

4 cm

4 cm

8 cm

2 cm

Strategy
To find the volume of the bushing, subtract the volume of the half-cylinder from the volume of the rectangular solid.

Solution

| Volume of the bushing | = | volume of rectangular solid | − | $\frac{1}{2}$ the volume of cylinder |

$V = LWH - \frac{1}{2}\pi r^2 h$

$\approx (8 \text{ cm})(4 \text{ cm})(4 \text{ cm}) - \frac{1}{2}(3.14)(1 \text{ cm})^2(8 \text{ cm})$

$= 128 \text{ cm}^3 - 12.56 \text{ cm}^3$

$= 115.44 \text{ cm}^3$

The volume of the bushing is approximately 115.44 cm³.

Find the volume of the channel iron shown in the figure below.

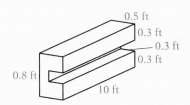

0.5 ft

0.3 ft

0.3 ft

0.3 ft

0.8 ft

10 ft

Your strategy

Your solution

Solutions on p. S33

12.4 Exercises

Objective A   **To find the volume of geometric solids**

For Exercises 1 to 8, find the volume. Round to the nearest hundredth. Use 3.14 for π.

1.

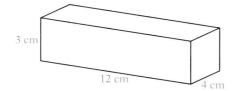

3 cm

12 cm

4 cm

2.

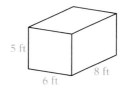

5 ft

6 ft

8 ft

3.

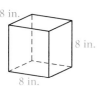

8 in.

8 in.

8 in.

4.

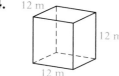

12 m

12 m

12 m

5.

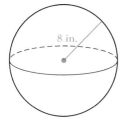

8 in.

6.

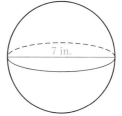

7 in.

7.

12 cm

2 cm

8.

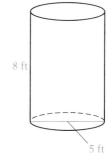

8 ft

5 ft

For Exercises 9 to 16, find the volume.

9. Find the volume, in cubic meters, of a rectangular solid with a length of 2 m, a width of 80 cm, and a height of 4 m.

10. Find the volume of a cylinder with a radius of 7 cm and a height of 14 cm. Use $\frac{22}{7}$ for π.

11. Find the volume of a sphere with an 11-millimeter radius. Use 3.14 for π. Round to the nearest hundredth.

12. Find the volume of a cube with a side of 2.14 m. Round to the nearest tenth.

13. Find the volume of a cylinder with a diameter of 12 ft and a height of 30 ft. Use 3.14 for π.

14. Find the volume of a sphere with a 6-foot diameter. Use 3.14 for π.

15. Find the volume of a cube with a side of $3\frac{1}{2}$ ft.

16. Find the volume, in cubic meters, of a rectangular solid with a length of 1.15 m, a width of 60 cm, and a height of 25 cm.

Objective B   **To find the volume of composite geometric solids**

For Exercises 17 to 22, find the volume. Use 3.14 for π.

17.

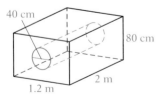

18.

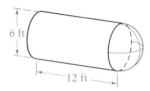

19.

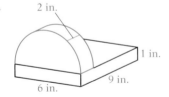

20.

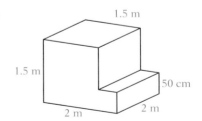

21.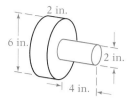

22.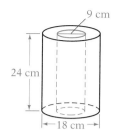

> **Objective C**   **To solve application problems**

For Exercises 23 to 35, solve. Use 3.14 for π.

23. Fish Hatchery   A rectangular tank at the fish hatchery is 9 m long, 3 m wide, and 1.5 m deep. Find the volume of the water in the tank when the tank is full.

24. Rocketry   A fuel tank in a booster rocket is a cylinder 10 ft in diameter and 52 ft high. Find the volume of the fuel tank.

25. Ballooning   A hot air balloon is in the shape of a sphere. Find the volume of a hot air balloon that is 32 ft in diameter. Round to the nearest hundredth.

26. Petroleum   A storage tank for propane is in the shape of a sphere that has a diameter of 9 m. Find the volume of the tank.

27. Petroleum   An oil tank, which is in the shape of a cylinder, is 4 m high and has a diameter of 6 m. The oil tank is two-thirds full. Find the number of cubic meters of oil in the tank. Round to the nearest hundredth.

28. Agriculture   A silo, which is in the shape of a cylinder, is 16 ft in diameter and has a height of 30 ft. The silo is three-fourths full. Find the volume of the portion of the silo that is not being used for storage.

29. Architecture   An architect is designing the heating system for an auditorium and needs to know the volume of the structure. Find the volume of the auditorium with the measurements shown in the figure.

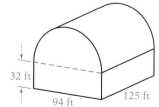

30. Pools   A swimming pool 50 ft long and 13 ft wide contains water to a depth of 10 ft. Find the total weight of the water in the swimming pool. (1 ft³ weighs 62.4 lb.)

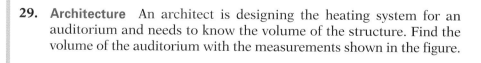

31. Metal Works Find the volume of the bushing shown at the right.

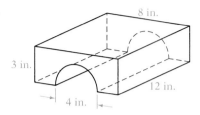

32. Aquariums How many gallons of water will fill an aquarium that is 12 in. wide, 18 in. long, and 16 in. high? Round to the nearest tenth. (1 gal = 231 in^3)

33. Aquariums How many gallons of water will fill a fish tank that is 12 in. long, 8 in. wide, and 9 in. high? Round to the nearest tenth. (1 gal = 231 in^3)

34. Petroleum A truck carrying an oil tank is shown in the figure at the right.
   a. Without doing the calculations, determine whether the volume of the oil tank is more than 240 ft^3 or less than 240 ft^3.
   b. If the tank is half full, how many cubic feet of oil is the truck carrying? Round to the nearest hundredth.

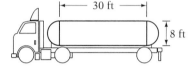

35. Construction The concrete floor of a building is shown in the figure at the right. At a cost of $5.85 per cubic foot, find the cost of having the floor poured. Round to the nearest cent.

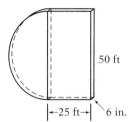

APPLYING THE CONCEPTS

36. Half a sphere is called a hemisphere. Derive a formula for the volume of a hemisphere.

37. a. If both the length and the width of a rectangular solid are doubled, how many times larger is the resulting rectangular solid?
   b. If the length, width, and height of a rectangular solid are all doubled, how many times larger is the resulting rectangular solid?
   c. If the side of a cube is doubled, how many times larger is the resulting cube?

 For Exercises 38 to 41, explain how you could cut through a cube so that the face of the resulting solid is the given geometric figure.

38. A square

39. An equilateral triangle

40. A trapezoid

41. A hexagon

42. Suppose a cylinder is cut into 16 equal pieces, which are then arranged as shown at the right. The figure resembles a rectangular solid. What variable expressions could be used to represent the length, width, and height of the rectangular solid? Explain how the formula for the volume of a cylinder is derived from this approach.

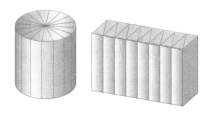

12.6 Similar and Congruent Triangles

Objective A   **To solve similar and congruent triangles**

Similar objects have the same shape but not necessarily the same size. A baseball is similar to a basketball. A model airplane is similar to an actual airplane.

Similar objects have corresponding parts; for example, the propellers on the model airplane correspond to the propellers on the actual airplane. The relationship between the sizes of each of the corresponding parts can be written as a ratio, and all such ratios will be the same. If the propellers on the model plane are $\frac{1}{50}$ the size of the propellers on the actual plane, then the model wing is $\frac{1}{50}$ the size of the actual wing, the model fuselage is $\frac{1}{50}$ the size of the actual fuselage, and so on.

The two triangles *ABC* and *DEF* shown are similar. The ratios of corresponding sides are equal.

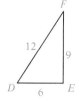

$$\frac{AB}{DE} = \frac{2}{6} = \frac{1}{3}, \frac{BC}{EF} = \frac{3}{9} = \frac{1}{3}, \text{ and } \frac{AC}{DF} = \frac{4}{12} = \frac{1}{3}$$

The ratio of corresponding sides $= \frac{1}{3}$.

Because the ratios of corresponding sides are equal, three proportions can be formed:

$$\frac{AB}{DE} = \frac{BC}{EF}, \frac{AB}{DE} = \frac{AC}{DF}, \text{ and } \frac{BC}{EF} = \frac{AC}{DF}$$

The ratio of corresponding heights equals the ratio of corresponding sides, as shown in the figure.

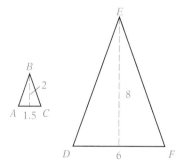

Ratio of corresponding sides $= \dfrac{1.5}{6} = \dfrac{1}{4}$

Ratio of heights $= \dfrac{2}{8} = \dfrac{1}{4}$

Congruent objects have the same shape *and* the same size.

The two triangles shown are congruent. They have exactly the same size.

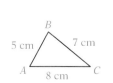

For triangles, *congruent* means that the corresponding sides *and* angles of the triangle are equal (this contrasts with similar triangles, in which corresponding angles, but not necessarily corresponding sides, are equal).

Here are two major rules that can be used to determine whether two triangles are congruent.

Side-Side-Side (SSS) Rule

Two triangles are congruent if three sides of one triangle equal the corresponding sides of the second triangle.

In the two triangles at the right, $AB = DE$, $AC = DF$, and $BC = EF$. The corresponding sides of triangles ABC and DEF are equal. The triangles are congruent by the SSS rule.

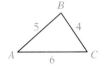

Side-Angle-Side (SAS) Rule

Two triangles are congruent if two sides and the included angle of one triangle equal the corresponding sides and included angle of the second triangle.

In the two triangles at the right, $AB = EF$, $AC = DE$, and $\angle CAB = \angle DEF$. The triangles are congruent by the SAS rule.

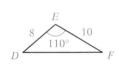

HOW TO   Determine whether the two triangles in the figure at the right are congruent.

Because $AC = DF$, $AB = FE$, and $BC = DE$, all three sides of one triangle equal the corresponding sides of the second triangle. The triangles are congruent by the SSS rule.

Example 1

Find the ratio of corresponding sides for the similar triangles ABC and DEF in the figure.

Solution

$$\frac{7 \text{ m}}{12 \text{ m}} = \frac{7}{12}$$

You Try It 1

Find the ratio of corresponding sides for the similar triangles ABC and DEF in the figure.

Your solution

Solution on p. S34

Example 2

Triangles *ABC* and *DEF* in the figure are similar. Find *x*, the length of side *EF*.

Solution

$$\frac{AB}{DE} = \frac{BC}{EF}$$ • The ratios of corresponding sides of similar triangles are equal.

$$\frac{8\ m}{12\ m} = \frac{6\ m}{x}$$

$$8x = 12 \cdot 6\ m$$
$$8x = 72\ m$$
$$\frac{8x}{8} = \frac{72\ m}{8}$$
$$x = 9\ m$$

Side *EF* is 9 m.

You Try It 2

Triangles *ABC* and *DEF* in the figure are similar. Find *x*, the length of side *DF*.

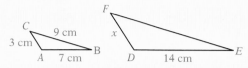

Your solution

Example 3

Determine whether triangle *ABC* in the figure is congruent to triangle *FDE*.

Solution
Because *AB = DF*, *AC = EF*, and angle *BAC* = angle *DFE*, the triangles are congruent by the SAS rule.

You Try It 3

Determine whether triangle *ABC* in the figure is congruent to triangle *DEF*.

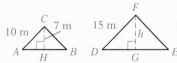

Your solution

Example 4

Triangles *ABC* and *DEF* in the figure are similar. Find *h*, the height of triangle *DEF*.

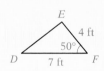

Solution

$$\frac{8\ cm}{12\ cm} = \frac{4\ cm}{h}$$ • The ratios of corresponding sides of similar triangles equal the ratio of corresponding heights:

$$8h = 12 \cdot 4\ cm$$
$$8h = 48\ cm$$
$$\frac{8h}{8} = \frac{48\ cm}{8}$$
$$\frac{AB}{DE} = \frac{CH}{FG}.$$
$$h = 6\ cm$$

The height of *DEF* is 6 cm.

You Try It 4

Triangles *ABC* and *DEF* in the figure are similar. Find *h*, the height of triangle *DEF*.

Your solution

Objective B   **To solve application problems**

| **Example 5** | **You Try It 5** |

Triangles *ABC* and *DEF* in the figure are similar. Find the area of triangle *DEF*.

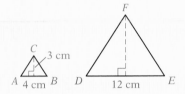

Triangles *ABC* and *DEF* in the figure are similar right triangles. Find the perimeter of triangle *ABC*.

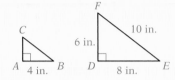

Strategy

To find the area of triangle *DEF*:

- Solve a proportion to find the height of triangle *DEF*. Let h = the height.

- Use the formula $A = \frac{1}{2}bh$.

Your strategy

Solution

$$\frac{AB}{DE} = \frac{\text{height of triangle } ABC}{\text{height of triangle } DEF}$$

$$\frac{4 \text{ cm}}{12 \text{ cm}} = \frac{3 \text{ cm}}{h}$$

$$4h = 12 \cdot 3 \text{ cm}$$

$$4h = 36 \text{ cm}$$

$$\frac{4h}{4} = \frac{36 \text{ cm}}{4}$$

$$h = 9 \text{ cm}$$

$$A = \frac{1}{2}bh$$

$$= \frac{1}{2}(12 \text{ cm})(9 \text{ cm})$$

$$= 54 \text{ cm}^2$$

The area is 54 cm².

Your solution

Solution on p. S34

12.6 Exercises

Objective A **To solve similar and congruent triangles**

Find the ratio of corresponding sides for the similar triangles in Exercises 1 to 4.

1.

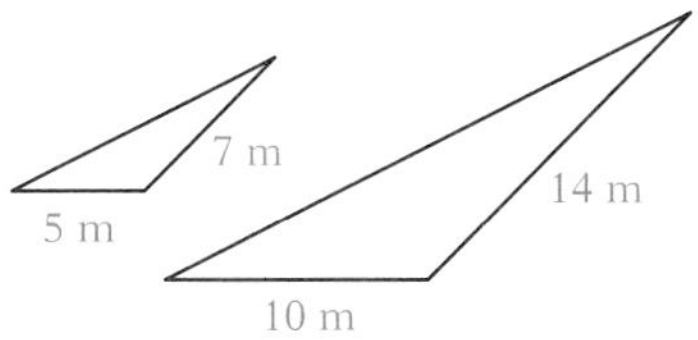

2.

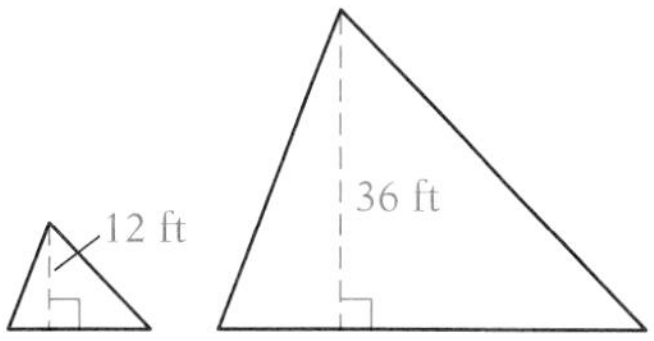

3.

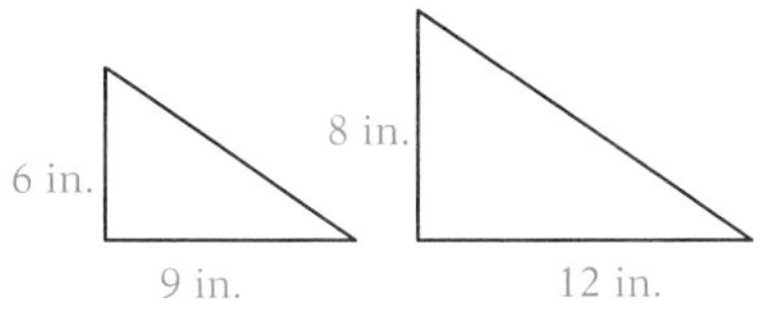

4.

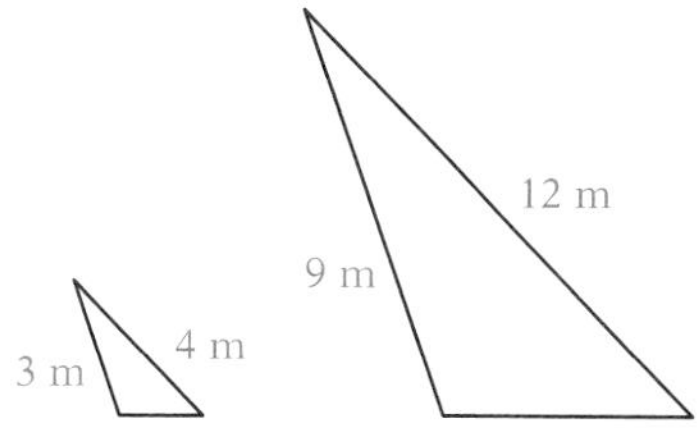

Determine whether the two triangles in Exercises 5 to 8 are congruent.

5.

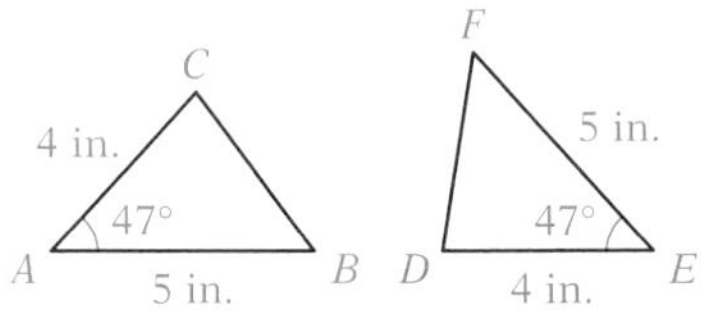

6.

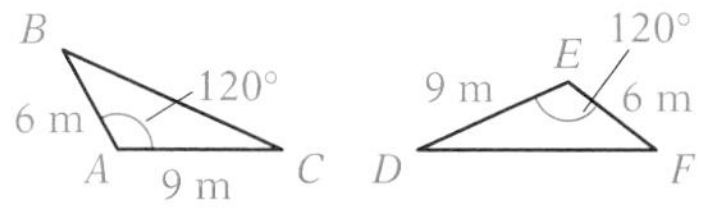

7.

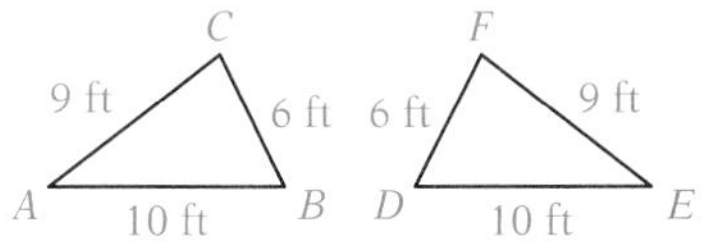

8.

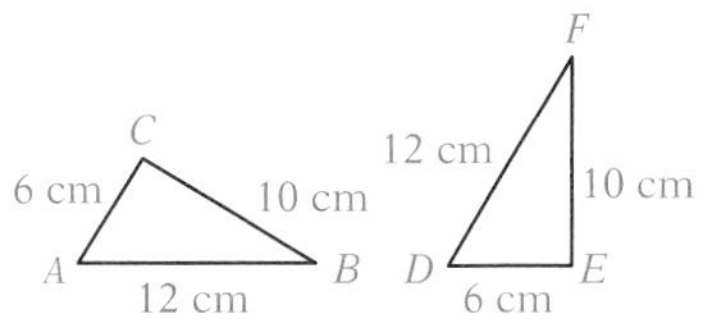

Triangles *ABC* and *DEF* in Exercises 9 to 12 are similar. Find the indicated distance. Round to the nearest tenth.

9. Find side *DE*.

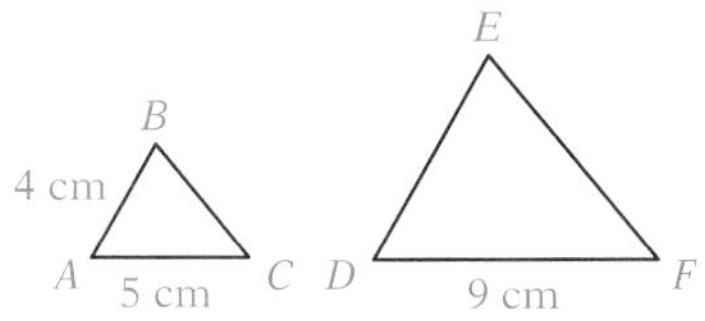

10. Find side *DE*.

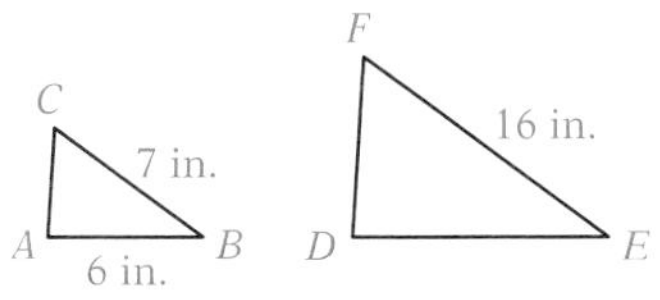

11. Find the height of triangle *DEF*.

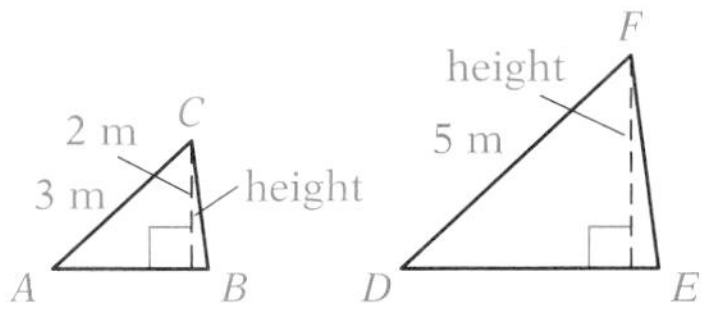

12. Find the height of triangle *ABC*.

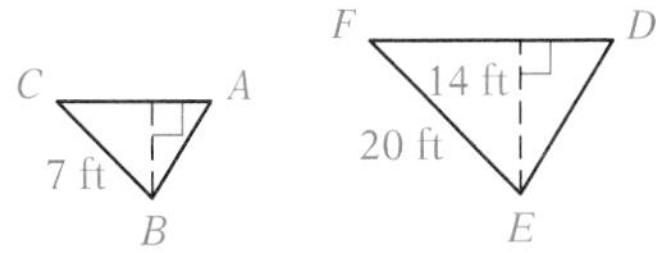

Objective B   **To solve application problems**

Measurement   The sun's rays, objects on Earth, and the shadows cast by those objects form similar triangles. For Exercises 13 and 14, find the height of the building.

13.

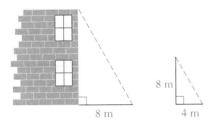

14.

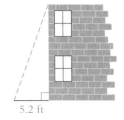

In Exercises 15 to 18, triangles *ABC* and *DEF* are similar.

15.   Find the perimeter of triangle *ABC*.

16.   Find the perimeter of triangle *DEF*.

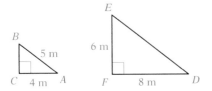

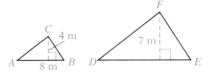

17.   Find the area of triangle *ABC*.

18.   Find the area of triangle *DEF*.

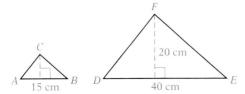

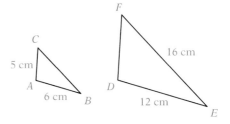

APPLYING THE CONCEPTS

19.   Determine whether the statement is always true, sometimes true, or never true.
   a. If two angles of one triangle are equal to two angles of a second triangle, then the triangles are similar triangles.
   b. Two isosceles triangles are similar triangles.
   c. Two equilateral triangles are similar triangles.

20.   Are all squares similar? Are all rectangles similar? Explain. Use a drawing in your explanation.

21.   Figure *ABC* is a right triangle and *DE* is parallel to *AB*. What is the perimeter of the trapezoid *ABED*?

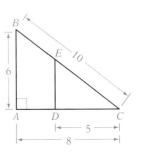

22.   Explain how, by using only a yardstick, you could determine the approximate height of a tree without climbing it.

Focus on Problem Solving

Trial and Error   Some problems in mathematics are solved by using **trial and error.** The trial-and-error method of arriving at a solution to a problem involves performing repeated tests or experiments until a satisfactory conclusion is reached.

Many of the Applying the Concepts exercises in this text require a trial-and-error method of solution. For example, an exercise in Section 12.4 reads as follows:

Explain how you could cut through a cube so that the face of the resulting solid is **(a)** a square, **(b)** an equilateral triangle, **(c)** a trapezoid, **(d)** a hexagon.

There is no formula to apply to this problem; there is no computation to perform. This problem requires picturing a cube and the results after it is cut through at different places on its surface and at different angles. For part a, cutting perpendicular to the top and bottom of the cube and parallel to two of its sides will result in a square. The other shapes may prove more difficult.

When solving problems of this type, keep an open mind. Sometimes when using the trial-and-error method, we are hampered by our narrowness of vision; we cannot expand our thinking to include other possibilities. Then when we see someone else's solution, it appears so obvious to us! For example, for the Applying the Concepts question above, it is necessary to conceive of cutting through the cube at places other than the top surface; we need to be open to the idea of beginning the cut at one of the corner points of the cube.

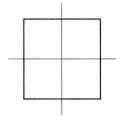

One topic of the Projects and Group Activities in this chapter is symmetry. Here again, the trial-and-error method is used to determine the lines of symmetry inherent in an object. For example, in determining lines of symmetry for a square, begin by drawing a square. The horizontal line of symmetry and the vertical line of symmetry may be immediately obvious to you.

But there are two others. Do you see that a line drawn through opposite corners of the square is also a line of symmetry?

Many of the questions in this text that require an answer of "always true, sometimes true, or never true" are best solved by the trial-and-error method. For example, consider the following statement, which is presented as this type of question in Section 12.3.

If two rectangles have the same area, then they have the same perimeter.

Try some numbers. Each of two rectangles, one measuring 6 units by 2 units and another measuring 4 units by 3 units, has an area of 12 square units, but the perimeter of the first is 16 units and the perimeter of the second is 14 units, so the answer "always true" has been eliminated. We still need to determine whether there is a case when it is true. After experimenting with a lot of numbers, you may come to realize that we are trying to determine whether it is possible for two different pairs of factors of a number to have the same sum. Is it?

Don't be afraid to make many experiments, and remember that *errors,* or tests that "don't work," are a part of the trial-and-*error* process.

Projects and Group Activities

Investigating Perimeter

The perimeter of the square at the right is 4 units.

If two squares are joined along one of the sides, the perimeter is 6 units. Note that it does not matter which sides are joined; the perimeter is still 6 units.

If three squares are joined, the perimeter of the resulting figure is 8 units for each possible placement of the squares.

Four squares can be joined in five different ways as shown. There are two possible perimeters: 10 units for A, B, C, and D, and 8 for E. ➤

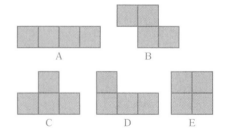

1. If five squares are joined, what is the maximum perimeter possible?

2. If five squares are joined, what is the minimum perimeter possible?

3. If six squares are joined, what is the maximum perimeter possible?

4. If six squares are joined, what is the minimum perimeter possible?

Symmetry Look at the letter A printed at the left. If the letter were folded along line ℓ, the two sides of the letter would match exactly. This letter has **symmetry** with respect to line ℓ. Line ℓ is called the **axis of symmetry.**

Now consider the letter H printed below at the left. Both lines ℓ_1 and ℓ_2 are axes of symmetry for this letter; the letter could be folded along either line and the two sides would match exactly.

1. Does the letter A have more than one axis of symmetry?

2. Find axes of symmetry for other capital letters of the alphabet.

3. Which lowercase letters have one axis of symmetry?

4. Do any of the lowercase letters have more than one axis of symmetry?

5. Find the number of axes of symmetry for each of the plane geometric figures presented in this chapter.

6. There are other types of symmetry. Look up the meaning of *point symmetry* and *rotational symmetry*. Which plane geometric figures provide examples of these types of symmetry?

7. Find examples of symmetry in nature, art, and architecture.

Chapter 12 Summary

Key Words	Examples
A *line* extends indefinitely in two directions. A *line segment* is part of a line and has two endpoints. The length of a line segment is the distance between the endpoints of the line segment. [12.1A, p. 515]	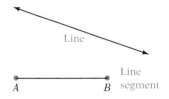
Parallel lines never meet; the distance between them is always the same. The symbol ∥ means "is parallel to." *Intersecting lines* cross at a point in the plane. *Perpendicular lines* are intersecting lines that form right angles. The symbol ⊥ means "is perpendicular to." [12.1A, pp. 515–516]	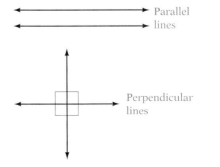

A *ray* starts at a point and extends indefinitely in one direction. An *angle* is formed when two rays start from the same point. The common point is called the *vertex* of the angle. An angle is measured in *degrees*. A 90° angle is a *right angle*. A 180° angle is a *straight angle*. *Complementary angles* are two angles whose measures have the sum 90°. *Supplementary angles* are two angles whose measures have the sum 180°. An *acute angle* is an angle whose measure is between 0° and 90°. An *obtuse angle* is an angle whose measure is between 90° and 180°. [12.1A, pp. 516–517]

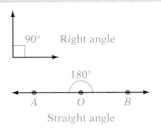

Two angles that are on opposite sides of the intersection of two lines are *vertical angles;* vertical angles have the same measure. Two angles that share a common side are *adjacent angles;* adjacent angles of intersecting lines are supplementary angles. [12.1C, p. 521]

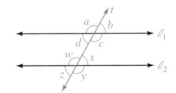

Angles w and y are vertical angles.
Angles x and y are adjacent angles.

A line that intersects two other lines at two different points is a *transversal*. If the lines cut by a transversal are parallel lines, equal angles are formed: *alternate interior angles, alternate exterior angles,* and *corresponding angles.* [12.1C, pp. 521–522]

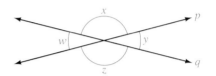

Parallel lines l_1 and l_2 are cut by transversal t. All four acute angles have the same measure. All four obtuse angles have the same measure.

A *quadrilateral* is a four-sided polygon. A *parallelogram*, a *rectangle*, and a *square* are quadrilaterals. [12.1B, pp. 518–519]

A *polygon* is a closed figure determined by three or more line segments. The line segments that form the polygon are its *sides*. A *regular polygon* is one in which each side has the same length and each angle has the same measure. Polygons are classified by the number of sides. [12.2A, p. 527]

Number of Sides	Name of the Polygon
3	Triangle
4	Quadrilateral
5	Pentagon
6	Hexagon
7	Heptagon
8	Octagon
9	Nonagon
10	Decagon

A *triangle* is a closed, three-sided plane figure. [12.1B, p. 518]

An *isosceles triangle* has two sides of equal length. The three sides of an *equilateral triangle* are of equal length. A *scalene triangle* has no two sides of equal length. An *acute triangle* has three actue angles. An *obtuse triangle* has one obtuse angle. [12.2A, pp. 527–528]

A *right triangle* contains a right angle. The side opposite the right angle is called the *hypotenuse*. The other two sides are called *legs*. [12.1B, p. 518]

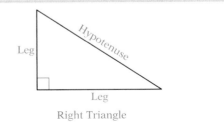

Right Triangle

A *circle* is a plane figure in which all points are the same distance from the center of the circle. A *diameter* of a circle is a line segment across the cricle through the center. A *radius* of a circle is a line segment from the center of the circle to a point on the circle. [12.1B, p. 519]

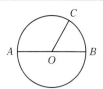

AB is a diameter of the circle.
OC is a radius.

Geometric solids are figures in space. Four common space figures are the rectangular solid, cube, sphere, and cylinder. A *rectangular solid* is a solid in which all six faces are rectangles. A *cube* is a rectangular solid in which all six faces are squares. A *sphere* is a solid in which all points on the sphere are the same distance from the center of the sphere. The most common *cylinder* is one in which the bases are circles and are perpendicular to the side. [12.1B, pp. 519–520]

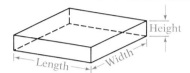

Rectangular Solid

The *square root* of a number is one of two identical factors of that number. The symbol for square root is $\sqrt{\ }$. A *perfect square* is the product of a whole number times itself. The square root of a perfect square is a whole number. [12.5A, p. 555]

$1^2 = 1, 2^2 = 4, 3^2 = 9, 4^2 = 16,$
$5^2 = 25, \ldots 1, 4, 9, 16, 25, \ldots$ are perfect squares.

$\sqrt{1} = 1, \sqrt{4} = 2, \sqrt{9} = 3, \sqrt{16} = 4, \ldots$

Similar triangles have the same shape but not necessarily the same size. The ratios of corresponding sides are equal. The ratio of corresponding heights is equal to the ratio of corresponding sides. *Congruent triangles* have the same shape and the same size. [12.6A, p. 561]

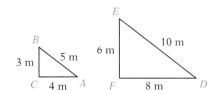

Triangles *ABC* and *DEF* are similar triangles. The ratio of corresponding sides is $\frac{1}{2}$.

Essential Rules and Procedures

Examples

Triangles [12.1B, p. 518]
Sum of three angles = 180°

Two angles of a triangle measure 32° and 48°. Find the measure of the third angle.

$\angle A + \angle B + \angle C = 180°$
$\angle A + 32° + 48° = 180°$
$\angle A + 80° = 180°$
$\angle A + 80° - 80° = 180° - 80°$
$\angle A = 100°$

The measure of the third angle is 100°.

Formulas for Perimeter (the distance around a figure)
[12.2A, pp. 528–529]
Triangle: $P = a + b + c$
Square: $P = 4s$
Rectangle: $P = 2L + 2W$
Circumference of a circle: $C = \pi d$ or $C = 2\pi r$

The length of a rectangle is 8 m. The width is 5.5 m. Find the perimeter of the rectangle.
$P = 2L + 2W$
$P = 2(8 \text{ m}) + 2(5.5 \text{ m})$
$P = 16 \text{ m} + 11 \text{ m}$
$P = 27 \text{ m}$
The perimeter is 27 m.

Formulas for Area (the amount of surface in a region)
[12.3A, pp. 537–538]

Triangle: $A = \frac{1}{2}bh$

Square: $A = s^2$
Rectangle: $A = LW$
Circle: $A = \pi r^2$

Find the area of a circle with a radius of 4 cm. Use 3.14 for π.
$A = \pi r^2$
$A \approx 3.14(4 \text{ cm})^2$
$A \approx 50.24 \text{ cm}^2$
The area is 50.24 cm².

Formulas for Volume (the amount of space inside a figure in space) [12.4A, pp. 545–546]
Rectangular solid: $V = LWH$
Cube: $V = s^3$

Sphere: $V = \frac{4}{3}\pi r^3$

Cylinder: $V = \pi r^2 h$

Find the volume of a cube that measures 3 in. on a side.
$V = s^3$
$V = 3^3$
$V = 27$
The volume is 27 in³.

Pythagorean Theorem [12.5B, p. 556]
The square of the hypotenuse of a right triangle is equal to the sum of the squares of the two legs.
If the length of one side of a triangle is unknown, one of the following formulas can be used to find it.
If the hypotenuse is unknown, use

$$\text{Hypotenuse} = \sqrt{(\text{leg})^2 + (\text{leg})^2}$$

If the length of a leg is unknown, use

$$\text{Leg} = \sqrt{(\text{hypotenuse})^2 - (\text{leg})^2}$$

Two legs of a right triangle measure 6 ft and 8 ft. Find the hypotenuse of the right triangle.

$$\begin{aligned}
\text{Hypotenuse} &= \sqrt{(\text{leg})^2 + (\text{leg})^2} \\
&= \sqrt{6^2 + 8^2} \\
&= \sqrt{36 + 64} \\
&= \sqrt{100} \\
&= 10
\end{aligned}$$

The length of the hypotenuse is 10 ft.

Side-Side-Side (SSS) Rule
Two triangles are congruent if three sides of one triangle equal the corresponding sides of the second triangle.

Side-Angle-Side (SAS) Rule
Two triangles are congruent if two sides and the included angle of one triangle equal the corresponding sides and included angle of the second triangle. [12.6A, p. 562]

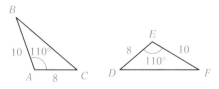

Triangles *ABC* and *DEF* are congruent by the SAS rule.

Chapter 12 Review Exercises

1. The diameter of a sphere is 1.5 m. Find the radius of the sphere.

2. Find the circumference of a circle with a radius of 5 cm. Use 3.14 for π.

3. Find the perimeter of the rectangle in the figure below.

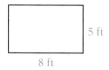

5 ft

8 ft

4. Given $AB = 15$, $CD = 6$, and $AD = 24$, find the length of BC.

5. Find the volume of the rectangular solid shown below.

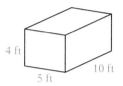

4 ft

5 ft

10 ft

6. Find the unknown side of the triangle in the figure below.

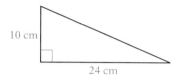

10 cm

24 cm

7. Find the supplement of a 105° angle.

8. Find the square root of 15. Round to the nearest thousandth.

9. Triangles ABC and DEF are similar. Find the height of triangle DEF.

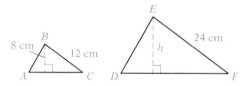

8 cm

B

12 cm

A

C

E

24 cm

h

D

F

10. Find the area of the circle shown below. Use 3.14 for π.

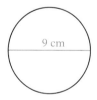

9 cm

11. Here $\ell_1 \parallel \ell_2$.
  a. Find the measure of angle b.
  b. Find the measure of angle a.

t

b

ℓ_1

45°

a

ℓ_2

12. Find the area of the rectangle shown below.

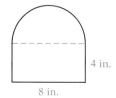

5 m

11 m

13. Find the volume of the composite figure shown below.

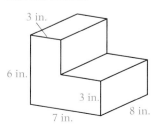

3 in.

6 in.

3 in.

7 in.

8 in.

14. Find the area of the composite figure shown below. Use 3.14 for π.

4 in.

8 in.

15. Find the volume of a sphere with a diameter of 8 ft. Use 3.14 for π. Round to the nearest tenth.

16. Triangles *ABC* and *DEF* are similar. Find the area of triangle *DEF*.

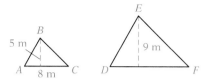

17. Find the perimeter of the composite figure shown below. Use 3.14 for π.

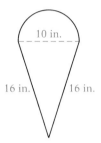

18. Here $\ell_1 \parallel \ell_2$.
  a. Find the measure of angle *b*.
  b. Find the measure of angle *a*.

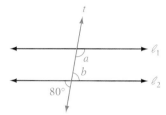

19. **Home Maintenance**   How high on a building will a 17-foot ladder reach when the bottom of the ladder is 8 ft from the building?

20. A right triangle has a 32° angle. Find the measures of the other two angles.

21. **Travel**   A bicycle tire has a diameter of 28 in. How many feet does the bicycle travel when the wheel makes 10 revolutions? Use 3.14 for π. Round to the nearest tenth of a foot.

22. **Interior Design**   New carpet is installed in a room measuring 18 ft by 14 ft. Find the area of the room in square yards. ($9 \text{ ft}^2 = 1 \text{ yd}^2$)

23. **Agriculture**   A silo, which is in the shape of a cylinder, is 9 ft in diameter and has a height of 18 ft. Find the volume of the silo. Use 3.14 for π.

24. Find the area of a right triangle with a base of 8 m and a height of 2.75 m.

25. **Travel**   If you travel 20 mi west and then 21 mi south, how far are you from your starting point?

Chapter 12 Test

1. Find the volume of a cylinder with a height of 6 m and a radius of 3 m. Use 3.14 for π.

2. Find the perimeter of a rectangle that has a length of 2 m and a width of 1.4 m.

3. Find the volume of the composite figure. Use 3.14 for π.

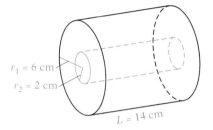

4. Triangles *ABC* and *FED* are congruent right triangles. Find the length of *FE*.

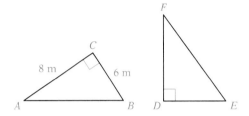

5. Find the complement of a 32° angle.

6. Find the area of a circle that has a diameter of 2 m. Use $\frac{22}{7}$ for π.

7. In the figure below, lines ℓ_1 and ℓ_2 are parallel. Angle x measures 30°. Find the measure of angle y.

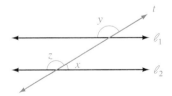

8. Find the perimeter of the composite figure. Use 3.14 for π.

9. Find the square root of 189. Round to the nearest thousandth.

10. Find the unknown side of the triangle shown below. Round to the nearest thousandth.

11. Find the area of the composite figure.

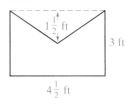

12. In the figure below, lines ℓ_1 and ℓ_2 are parallel. Angle x measures 45°. Find the measures of angles a and b.

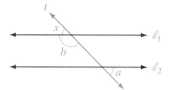

13. Triangles ABC and DEF are similar. Find side BC.

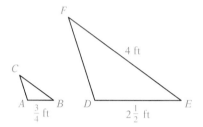

14. A right triangle has a 40° angle. Find the measures of the other two angles.

15. **Measurement** Use similar triangles to find the width of the canal shown in the figure at the right.

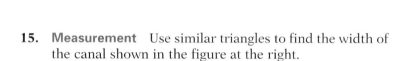

16. **Consumerism** How much more pizza is contained in a pizza with radius 10 in. than in one with radius 8 in.? Use 3.14 for π.

17. **Interior Design** A carpet is to be placed as shown in the diagram at the right. At $26.80 per square yard, how much will it cost to carpet the area? Round to the nearest cent. (9 ft² = 1 yd²)

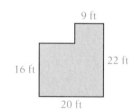

18. **Forestry** Find the cross-sectional area of a redwood tree that is 11 ft 6 in. in diameter. Use 3.14 for π. Round to the nearest hundredth.

19. **Construction** Find the length of the rafter needed for the roof shown in the figure.

20. **Measurement** A toolbox is 1 ft 2 in. long, 9 in. wide, and 8 in. high. The sides and bottom of the toolbox are $\frac{1}{2}$ in. thick. Find the volume of the interior of the toolbox in cubic inches.

Cumulative Review Exercises

1. Find the GCF of 96 and 144.

2. Add: $3\frac{5}{12} + 2\frac{9}{16} + 1\frac{7}{8}$

3. Find the quotient of $4\frac{1}{3}$ and $6\frac{2}{9}$.

4. Simplify: $\left(\frac{2}{3}\right)^2 \div \left(\frac{1}{3} + \frac{1}{2}\right) - \frac{2}{5}$

5. Simplify: $-\frac{2}{3} - \left(-\frac{5}{8}\right)$

6. Write "$348.80 earned in 40 hours" as a unit rate.

7. Solve the proportion $\frac{3}{8} = \frac{n}{100}$.

8. Write $37\frac{1}{2}\%$ as a fraction.

9. Evaluate $a^2 - (b^2 - c)$ when $a = 2$, $b = -2$, and $c = -4$.

10. 30.94 is 36.4% of what number?

11. Solve: $\frac{x}{3} + 3 = 1$

12. Solve: $2(x - 3) + 2 = 5x - 8$

13. Convert 32.5 km to meters.

14. Subtract: $32 \text{ m} - 42 \text{ cm}$

15. Solve: $\frac{2}{3}x = -10$

16. Solve: $2x - 4(x - 3) = 8$

17. **Finance** You bought a car for $26,488 and made a down payment of $1000. You paid the balance in 36 equal monthly installments. Find the monthly payment.

18. **Taxes** The sales tax on a jacket costing $175 is $6.75. At the same rate, find the sales tax on a stereo system costing $1220.

19. **Compensation**   A heavy-equipment operator receives an hourly wage of $16.06 an hour after receiving a 10% wage increase. Find the operator's hourly wage before the increase.

20. **Discount**   An after-Christmas sale has a discount rate of 55%. Find the sale price of a dress that had a regular price of $120.

21. **Investments**   An IRA pays 7% annual interest compounded daily. What would be the value of an investment of $25,000 after 20 years? Use the table in the Appendix.

22. **Shipping**   A square tile measuring 4 in. by 4 in. weighs 6 oz. Find the weight, in pounds, of a package of 144 such tiles.

23. **Metal Works**   Twenty-five rivets are used to fasten two steel plates together. The plates are 5.4 m long, and the rivets are equally spaced with a rivet at each end. Find the distance, in centimeters, between the rivets.

24. **Integer Problems**   The total of four times a number and two is negative six. Find the number.

25. The lines ℓ_1 and ℓ_2 in the figure below are parallel.
    a. Find angle a.
    b. Find angle b.

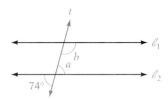

26. Find the perimeter of the composite figure. Use 3.14 for π.

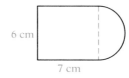

27. Find the area of the composite figure.

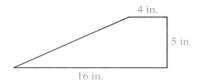

28. Find the volume of the composite figure. Use 3.14 for π.

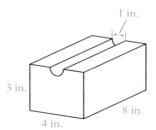

29. Find the unknown side of the triangle shown in the figure below. Round to the nearest hundredth.

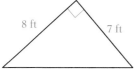

30. Triangles *ABC* and *FED* below are similar. Find the perimeter of *FED*.

Final Exam

1. Subtract: $100,914 - 97,655$

2. Find 34,821 divided by 657.

3. Find 90,001 decreased by 29,796.

4. Simplify: $3^2 \cdot (5 - 3)^2 \div 3 + 4$

5. Find the LCM of 9, 12, and 16.

6. Add: $\frac{3}{8} + \frac{5}{6} + \frac{1}{5}$

7. Subtract: $7\frac{5}{12} - 3\frac{13}{16}$

8. Find the product of $3\frac{5}{8}$ and $1\frac{5}{7}$.

9. Divide: $1\frac{2}{3} \div 3\frac{3}{4}$

10. Simplify: $\left(\frac{2}{3}\right)^3 \cdot \left(\frac{3}{4}\right)^2$

11. Simplify: $\left(\frac{2}{3}\right)^2 \div \left(\frac{3}{4} + \frac{1}{3}\right) - \frac{1}{3}$

12. Add: $\begin{array}{r} 4.972 \\ 28.6 \\ 1.88 \\ +\ 128.725 \end{array}$

13. Multiply: $\begin{array}{r} 2.97 \\ \times\ 0.0094 \end{array}$

14. Divide: $0.062\overline{)0.0426}$
    Round to the nearest hundredth.

15. Convert 0.45 to a fraction in simplest form.

16. Write "323.4 miles on 13.2 gallons of gas" as a unit rate.

17. Solve the proportion $\frac{12}{35} = \frac{n}{160}$.
    Round to the nearest tenth.

18. Write $22\frac{1}{2}\%$ as a fraction.

19. Write 1.35 as a percent.

20. Write $\frac{5}{4}$ as a percent.

21. Find 120% of 30.

22. 12 is what percent of 9?

23. 42 is 60% of what number?

24. Convert $1\frac{2}{3}$ ft to inches.

25. Subtract: 3 ft 2 in. − 1 ft 10 in.

26. Convert 40 oz to pounds.

27. Find the sum of 3 lb 12 oz and 2 lb 10 oz.

28. Convert 18 pt to gallons.

29. Divide: $3\overline{)5\text{ gal 1 qt}}$

30. Convert 2.48 m to centimeters.

31. Convert 4 m 62 cm to meters.

32. Convert 1 kg 614 g to kilograms.

33. Convert 2 L 67 ml to milliliters.

34. Convert 55 mi to kilometers. Round to the nearest hundredth. (1.61 km ≈ 1 mi)

35. **Consumerism** How much does it cost to run a 2400-watt air conditioner for 6 h at 8¢ per kilowatt-hour? Round to the nearest cent.

36. Write 0.0000000679 in scientific notation.

37. Find the perimeter of a rectangle with a length of 1.2 m and a width of 0.75 m.

38. Find the area of a rectangle with a length of 9 in. and a width of 5 in.

39. Find the volume of a box with a length of 20 cm, a width of 12 cm, and a height of 5 cm.

40. Add: $-2 + 8 + (-10)$

41. Subtract: $-30 - (-15)$

42. Multiply: $2\frac{1}{2} \times \left(-\frac{1}{5}\right)$

43. Find the quotient of $-1\frac{3}{8}$ and $5\frac{1}{2}$.

44. Simplify: $(-4)^2 \div (1 - 3)^2 - (-2)$

45. Simplify: $2x - 3(x - 4) + 5$

46. Solve: $\frac{2}{3}x = -12$

47. Solve: $3x - 5 = 10$

48. Solve: $8 - 3x = x + 4$

49. **Banking** You have $872.48 in your checking account. You write checks of $321.88 and $34.23 and then make a deposit of $443.56. Find your new checking account balance.

50. **Elections** On the basis of a pre-election survey, it is estimated that 5 out of 8 eligible voters will vote in an election. How many people will vote in an election with 102,000 eligible voters?

51. **Investments** This month a company is paying its stockholders a dividend of $1.60 per share. This is 80% of what the dividend per share was 1 year ago. What was the dividend per share 1 year ago?

52. **Compensation** A sales executive received commissions of $4320, $3572, $2864, and $4420 during a 4-month period. Find the mean monthly income from commissions for the 4 months.

53. **Simple Interest** A contractor borrows $120,000 for 9 months at an annual interest rate of 8%. What is the simple interest due on the loan?

54. **Probability** If two dice are tossed, what is the probability that the sum of the dots on the upward faces is divisible by 3?

55. 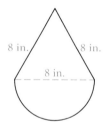 **Wars** The top four highest death counts, by country, in World War II are shown in the circle graph. Find what percent the death count of Chinese is of the total death count in all four countries. Round to the nearest tenth of a percent.

Top Four Highest Death
Counts in World War II
(in thousands)

Source: U.S. Department of Defense

56. **Discounts** A compact disc player that regularly sells for $314.00 is on sale for $226.08. What is the discount rate?

57. **Shipping** A square tile measuring 8 in. by 8 in. weighs 9 oz. Find the weight, in pounds, of a box containing 144 tiles.

58. Find the perimeter of the composite figure. Use 3.14 for π.

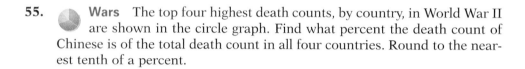

59. Find the area of the composite figure. Use 3.14 for π.

60. **Integer Problems** Five less than the quotient of a number and two is equal to three. Find the number.

Appendix

Table of Geometric Formulas

Pythagorean Theorem

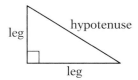

Hypotenuse $= \sqrt{(\text{leg})^2 + (\text{leg})^2}$

Leg $= \sqrt{(\text{hypotenuse})^2 - (\text{leg})^2}$

Perimeter and Area of a Triangle

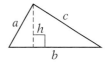

$P = a + b + c$

$A = \dfrac{1}{2}bh$

Perimeter and Area of a Rectangle

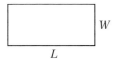

$P = 2L + 2W$

$A = LW$

Perimeter and Area of a Square

$P = 4s$

$A = s^2$

Circumference and Area of a Circle

$C = 2\pi r$ or $C = \pi d$

$A = \pi r^2$

Area of a Trapezoid

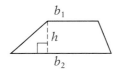

$A = \dfrac{1}{2}h(b_1 + b_2)$

Volume of a Rectangular Solid

$V = LWH$

Volume of a Cube

$V = s^3$

Volume of a Sphere

$V = \dfrac{4}{3}\pi r^3$

Volume of a Right Circular Cylinder

$V = \pi r^2 h$

Compound Interest Table

Compounded Annually

	4%	5%	6%	7%	8%	9%	10%
1 year	1.04000	1.05000	1.06000	1.07000	1.08000	1.09000	1.10000
5 years	1.21665	1.27628	1.33823	1.40255	1.46933	1.53862	1.61051
10 years	1.48024	1.62890	1.79085	1.96715	2.15893	2.36736	2.59374
15 years	1.80094	2.07893	2.39656	2.75903	3.17217	3.64248	4.17725
20 years	2.19112	2.65330	3.20714	3.86968	4.66095	5.60441	6.72750

Compounded Semiannually

	4%	5%	6%	7%	8%	9%	10%
1 year	1.04040	1.05062	1.06090	1.07123	1.08160	1.09203	1.10250
5 years	1.21899	1.28008	1.34392	1.41060	1.48024	1.55297	1.62890
10 years	1.48595	1.63862	1.80611	1.98979	2.19112	2.41171	2.65330
15 years	1.81136	2.09757	2.42726	2.80679	3.24340	3.74531	4.32194
20 years	2.20804	2.68506	3.26204	3.95926	4.80102	5.81634	7.03999

Compounded Quarterly

	4%	5%	6%	7%	8%	9%	10%
1 year	1.04060	1.05094	1.06136	1.07186	1.08243	1.09308	1.10381
5 years	1.22019	1.28204	1.34686	1.41478	1.48595	1.56051	1.63862
10 years	1.48886	1.64362	1.81402	2.00160	2.20804	2.43519	2.68506
15 years	1.81670	2.10718	2.44322	2.83182	3.28103	3.80013	4.39979
20 years	2.21672	2.70148	3.29066	4.00639	4.87544	5.93015	7.20957

Compounded Monthly

	4%	5%	6%	7%	8%	9%	10%
1 year	1.04074	1.051162	1.061678	1.072290	1.083000	1.093807	1.104713
5 years	1.220997	1.283359	1.348850	1.417625	1.489846	1.565681	1.645309
10 years	1.490833	1.647009	1.819397	2.009661	2.219640	2.451357	2.707041
15 years	1.820302	2.113704	2.454094	2.848947	3.306921	3.838043	4.453920
20 years	2.222582	2.712640	3.310204	4.038739	4.926803	6.009152	7.328074

Compounded Daily

	4%	5%	6%	7%	8%	9%	10%
1 year	1.04080	1.05127	1.06183	1.07250	1.08328	1.09416	1.10516
5 years	1.22139	1.28400	1.34983	1.41902	1.49176	1.56823	1.64861
10 years	1.49179	1.64866	1.82203	2.01362	2.22535	2.45933	2.71791
15 years	1.82206	2.11689	2.45942	2.85736	3.31968	3.85678	4.48077
20 years	2.22544	2.71810	3.31979	4.05466	4.95217	6.04830	7.38703

To use this table:
1. Locate the section that gives the desired compounding period.
2. Locate the interest rate in the top row of that section.
3. Locate the number of years in the left-hand column of that section.
4. Locate the number where the interest-rate column and the number-of-years row meet. This is the compound interest factor.

Example An investment yields an annual interest rate of 10% compounded quarterly for 5 years.
The compounding period is "compounded quarterly."
The interest rate is 10%.
The number of years is 5.
The number where the row and column meet is 1.63862. This is the compound interest factor.

Compound Interest Table

	Compounded Annually						
	11%	**12%**	**13%**	**14%**	**15%**	**16%**	**17%**
1 year	1.11000	1.12000	1.13000	1.14000	1.15000	1.16000	1.17000
5 years	1.68506	1.76234	1.84244	1.92542	2.01136	2.10034	2.19245
10 years	2.83942	3.10585	3.39457	3.70722	4.04556	4.41144	4.80683
15 years	4.78459	5.47357	6.25427	7.13794	8.13706	9.26552	10.53872
20 years	8.06239	9.64629	11.52309	13.74349	16.36654	19.46076	23.10560

	Compounded Semiannually						
	11%	**12%**	**13%**	**14%**	**15%**	**16%**	**17%**
1 year	1.11303	1.12360	1.13423	1.14490	1.15563	1.16640	1.17723
5 years	1.70814	1.79085	1.87714	1.96715	2.06103	2.15893	2.26098
10 years	2.91776	3.20714	3.52365	3.86968	4.24785	4.66096	5.11205
15 years	4.98395	5.74349	6.61437	7.61226	8.75496	10.06266	11.55825
20 years	8.51331	10.28572	12.41607	14.97446	18.04424	21.72452	26.13302

	Compounded Quarterly						
	11%	**12%**	**13%**	**14%**	**15%**	**16%**	**17%**
1 year	1.11462	1.12551	1.13648	1.14752	1.15865	1.16986	1.18115
5 years	1.72043	1.80611	1.89584	1.98979	2.08815	2.19112	2.29891
10 years	2.95987	3.26204	3.59420	3.95926	4.36038	4.80102	5.28497
15 years	5.09225	5.89160	6.81402	7.87809	9.10513	10.51963	12.14965
20 years	8.76085	10.64089	12.91828	15.67574	19.01290	23.04980	27.93091

	Compounded Monthly						
	11%	**12%**	**13%**	**14%**	**15%**	**16%**	**17%**
1 year	1.115719	1.126825	1.138032	1.149342	1.160755	1.172271	1.183892
5 years	1.728916	1.816697	1.908857	2.005610	2.107181	2.213807	2.325733
10 years	2.989150	3.300387	3.643733	4.022471	4.440213	4.900941	5.409036
15 years	5.167988	5.995802	6.955364	8.067507	9.356334	10.849737	12.579975
20 years	8.935015	10.892554	13.276792	16.180270	19.715494	24.019222	29.257669

	Compounded Daily						
	11%	**12%**	**13%**	**14%**	**15%**	**16%**	**17%**
1 year	1.11626	1.12747	1.13880	1.15024	1.16180	1.17347	1.18526
5 years	1.73311	1.82194	1.91532	2.01348	2.11667	2.22515	2.33918
10 years	3.00367	3.31946	3.66845	4.05411	4.48031	4.95130	5.47178
15 years	5.20569	6.04786	7.02625	8.16288	9.48335	11.01738	12.79950
20 years	9.02203	11.01883	13.45751	16.43582	20.07316	24.51534	29.94039

Monthly Payment Table

	4%	5%	6%	7%	8%	9%
1 year	0.0851499	0.0856075	0.0860664	0.0865267	0.0869884	0.0874515
2 years	0.0434249	0.0438714	0.0443206	0.0447726	0.0452273	0.0456847
3 years	0.0295240	0.0299709	0.0304219	0.0308771	0.0313364	0.0317997
4 years	0.0225791	0.0230293	0.0234850	0.0239462	0.0244129	0.0248850
5 years	0.0184165	0.0188712	0.0193328	0.0198012	0.0202764	0.0207584
15 years	0.0073969	0.0079079	0.0084386	0.0089883	0.0095565	0.0101427
20 years	0.0060598	0.0065996	0.0071643	0.0077530	0.0083644	0.0089973
25 years	0.0052784	0.0058459	0.0064430	0.0070678	0.0077182	0.0083920
30 years	0.0047742	0.0053682	0.0059955	0.0066530	0.0073376	0.0080462

	10%	11%	12%	13%
1 year	0.0879159	0.0883817	0.0888488	0.0893173
2 years	0.0461449	0.0466078	0.0470735	0.0475418
3 years	0.0322672	0.0327387	0.0332143	0.0336940
4 years	0.0253626	0.0258455	0.0263338	0.0268275
5 years	0.0212470	0.0217424	0.0222445	0.0227531
15 years	0.0107461	0.0113660	0.0120017	0.0126524
20 years	0.0096502	0.0103219	0.0110109	0.0117158
25 years	0.0090870	0.0098011	0.0105322	0.0112784
30 years	0.0087757	0.0095232	0.0102861	0.0110620

To use this table:
1. Locate the desired interest rate in the top row.
2. Locate the number of years in the left-hand column.
3. Locate the number where the interest-rate column and the number-of-years row meet. This is the monthly payment factor.

Example   A home has a 30-year mortgage at an annual interest rate of 12%.
The interest rate is 12%.
The number of years is 30.
The number where the row and column meet is 0.0102861. This is the monthly payment factor.

Table of Measurements

Prefixes in the Metric System of Measurement

kilo-	1000	deci-	0.1
hecto-	100	centi-	0.01
deca-	10	milli-	0.001

Measurement Abbreviations
U.S. Customary System

Length

in.   inches
ft   feet
yd   yards
mi   miles

Capacity

oz   fluid ounces
c   cups
qt   quarts
gal   gallons

Weight

oz   ounces
lb   pounds

Area

in^2 square inches
ft^2 square feet
yd^2 square yards
mi^2 square miles

Rate

ft/s   feet per second
mi/h   miles per hour

Time

h   hours
min   minutes
s   seconds

Metric System

Length

mm   millimeters
cm   centimeters
m   meters
km   kilometers

Capacity

ml   milliliters
cl   centiliters
L   liters
kl   kiloliters

Weight/Mass

mg   milligrams
cg   centigrams
g   grams
kg   kilograms

Area

cm^2 square centimeters
m^2 square meters
km^2 square kilometers

Rate

m/s   meters per second
km/s   kilometers per second
km/h   kilometers per hour

Time

h   hours
min   minutes
s   seconds

Table of Properties

Properties of Real Numbers

Commutative Property of Addition

If a and b are real numbers, then $a + b = b + a$.

Commutative Property of Multiplication

If a and b are real numbers, then $a \cdot b = b \cdot a$.

Associative Property of Addition

If a, b, and c are real numbers, then
$(a + b) + c = a + (b + c)$.

Associative Property of Multiplication

If a, b, and c are real numbers, then
$(a \cdot b) \cdot c = a \cdot (b \cdot c)$.

Addition Property of Zero

If a is a real number, then $a + 0 = 0 + a = a$.

Multiplication Property of Zero

If a is a real number, then $a \cdot 0 = 0 \cdot a = 0$.

Multiplication Property of One

If a is a real number, then $a \cdot 1 = 1 \cdot a = a$.

Inverse Property of Addition

If a is a real number, then $a + (-a) = (-a) + a = 0$.

Inverse Property of Multiplication

If a is a real number and $a \neq 0$, then
$a \cdot \dfrac{1}{a} = \dfrac{1}{a} \cdot a = 1$.

Distributive Property

If a, b, and c are real numbers, then
$a(b + c) = ab + ac$.

Properties of Zero and One in Division

Any number divided by 1 is the number.

Division by zero is not allowed.

Any number other than zero divided by itself is 1.

Zero divided by a number other than zero is zero.

Solutions to Chapter 1 "You Try It"

SECTION 1.1

You Try It 1

You Try It 2   **a.** $45 > 29$ **b.** $27 > 0$

You Try It 3   Thirty-six million four hundred sixty-two thousand seventy-five

You Try It 4   452,007

You Try It 5 $60,000 + 8000 + 200 + 80 + 1$

You Try It 6 $100,000 + 9000 + 200 + 7$

You Try It 7

```
          ┌──── Given place value
          │
  368,492
          │
          └── 8 > 5
```

368,492 rounded to the nearest ten-thousand is 370,000.

You Try It 8

```
          ┌──── Given place value
          │
  3962
          │
          └── 6 > 5
```

3962 rounded to the nearest hundred is 4000.

SECTION 1.2

You Try It 1

$$\begin{array}{r} \overset{1\ 1}{347} \\ +\ 12{,}453 \\ \hline 12{,}800 \end{array}$$

- $7 + 3 = 10$
  Write the 0 in the ones column. Carry the 1 to the tens column.
  $1 + 4 + 5 = 10$
  Write the 0 in the tens column. Carry the 1 to the hundreds column.
  $1 + 3 + 4 = 8$

347 increased by 12,453 is 12,800.

You Try It 2

$$\begin{array}{r} \overset{2}{95} \\ 88 \\ +\ 67 \\ \hline 250 \end{array}$$

- $5 + 8 + 7 = 20$
  Write the 0 in the ones column. Carry the 2 to the tens column.

You Try It 3

$$\begin{array}{r} \overset{1\ 1\ \ 21}{392} \\ 4{,}079 \\ 89{,}035 \\ +\ 4{,}992 \\ \hline 98{,}498 \end{array}$$

You Try It 4

Strategy   To find the total number of Wal-Mart stores outside of the United States, read the table to find the number of stores outside the United States in each of the four categories listed. Then add the four numbers.

Solution

$$\begin{array}{r} 942 \\ 238 \\ 71 \\ +\ \ 37 \\ \hline 1288 \end{array}$$

Wal-Mart has 1288 stores outside the United States.

SECTION 1.3

You Try It 1

$$\begin{array}{r} 8925 \\ -\ 6413 \\ \hline 2512 \end{array} \qquad \begin{array}{r} Check: \\ 6413 \\ +\ 2512 \\ \hline 8925 \end{array}$$

You Try It 2

$$\begin{array}{r} 17{,}504 \\ -\ \ 9{,}302 \\ \hline 8{,}202 \end{array} \qquad \begin{array}{r} Check: \\ 9{,}302 \\ +\ 8{,}202 \\ \hline 17{,}504 \end{array}$$

You Try It 3

$$\begin{array}{r} \overset{2\ \ 14\ \ 7\ \ 11}{\cancel{3}\ \cancel{4}\ \cancel{8}\ \cancel{1}} \\ -\ \ \ 8\ 6\ 5 \\ \hline 2\ 6\ 1\ 6 \end{array} \qquad \begin{array}{r} Check: \\ 865 \\ +\ 2616 \\ \hline 3481 \end{array}$$

You Try It 4

$$\begin{array}{r} \overset{\ \ \ \ \ \ \ 15}{\overset{4\ \ 5\ \ 12}{5\ 4{,}\cancel{3}\ \cancel{6}\ \cancel{2}}} \\ -\ 1\ 4{,}4\ 8\ 5 \\ \hline 4\ 0{,}0\ 7\ 7 \end{array} \qquad \begin{array}{r} Check: \\ 14{,}485 \\ +\ 40{,}077 \\ \hline 54{,}562 \end{array}$$

You Try It 5

$$\begin{array}{r} \overset{3\ \ 10}{6\ \cancel{4}{,}\cancel{0}\ 0\ 3} \\ -\ 5\ 4{,}9\ 3\ 6 \end{array}$$

- There are 2 zeros in the minuend.
  Borrow 1 thousand from the thousands column and write 10 in the hundreds column.

(Continued)

(Continued)

$$
\begin{array}{r}
9 \\
3 \ \ 10 \ \ 10 \\
6 \ 4,\emptyset \ \emptyset \ 3 \\
- \ 5 \ 4,9 \ 3 \ 6 \\
\end{array}
$$

- Borrow 1 hundred from the hundreds column and write 10 in the tens column.

$$
\begin{array}{r}
13 \ \ 9 \ \ 9 \\
5 \ \ 3 \ \ 10 \ \ 10 \ \ 13 \\
6 \ 4,\emptyset \ \emptyset \ 3 \\
- \ 5 \ 4,9 \ 3 \ 6 \\
\hline
9,0 \ 6 \ 7 \\
\end{array}
$$

- Borrow 1 ten from the tens column and add 10 to the 3 in the ones column.

Check:
$$
\begin{array}{r}
54,936 \\
+ \ \ 9,067 \\
\hline
64,003 \\
\end{array}
$$

You Try It 6

Strategy   To find the difference, subtract the number of personnel on active duty in the Air Force in 1945 (2,282,259) from the number of personnel on active duty in the Navy in 1945 (3,380,817).

Solution
$$
\begin{array}{r}
3,380,817 \\
- \ 2,282,259 \\
\hline
1,098,558 \\
\end{array}
$$

The difference was 1,098,558 personnel.

You Try It 7

Strategy   To find your take-home pay:
- Add to find the total of the deductions (127 + 18 + 35).
- Subtract the total of the deductions from your total salary (638).

Solution
$$
\begin{array}{r}
127 \\
18 \\
+ \ 35 \\
\hline
180 \ \text{in deductions} \\
\end{array}
\qquad
\begin{array}{r}
638 \\
- \ 180 \\
\hline
458 \\
\end{array}
$$

Your take-home pay is $458.

SECTION 1.4

You Try It 1

$$
\begin{array}{r}
3 \ 5 \\
648 \\
\times \ \ \ 7 \\
\hline
4536 \\
\end{array}
$$

- $7 \times 8 = 56$
  Write the 6 in the ones column.
  Carry the 5 to the tens column.
  $7 \times 4 = 28, 28 + 5 = 33$
  $7 \times 6 = 42, 42 + 3 = 45$

You Try It 2

$$
\begin{array}{r}
756 \\
\times \ 305 \\
\hline
3780 \\
22680 \\
\hline
230,580 \\
\end{array}
$$

- $5 \times 756 = 3780$
- Write a zero in the tens column for 0×756.
  $3 \times 756 = 2268$

You Try It 3

Strategy   To find the number of cars the dealer will receive in 12 months, multiply the number of months (12) by the number of cars received each month (37).

Solution
$$
\begin{array}{r}
37 \\
\times \ \ 12 \\
\hline
74 \\
37 \\
\hline
444 \\
\end{array}
$$

The dealer will receive 444 cars in 12 months.

You Try It 4

Strategy   To find the total cost of the order:
- Find the cost of the sports jackets by multiplying the number of jackets (25) by the cost for each jacket (23).
- Add the product to the cost for the suits (4800).

Solution
$$
\begin{array}{r}
23 \\
\times \ 25 \\
\hline
115 \\
46 \\
\hline
575 \\
\end{array}
\quad \text{cost for jackets}
\qquad
\begin{array}{r}
4800 \\
+ \ \ 575 \\
\hline
5375 \\
\end{array}
$$

The total cost of the order is $5375.

SECTION 1.5

You Try It 1

$$
\begin{array}{r}
7 \\
9 \overline{)63} \\
\end{array}
$$

Check: $7 \times 9 = 63$

You Try It 2

$$
\begin{array}{r}
453 \\
9 \overline{)\ 4077} \\
- 36 \\
\hline
47 \\
- 45 \\
\hline
27 \\
- 27 \\
\hline
0 \\
\end{array}
$$

Check: $453 \times 9 = 4077$

You Try It 3

```
        705
9)  6345
   −63
      04     • Think 9)4. Place 0 in quotient.
    − 0      • Subtract 0 × 9.
      45     • Bring down the 5.
    −45
       0
```

Check: 705 × 9 = 6345

You Try It 4

```
        870 r5
6)  5225
   −48
      42
    −42
      05     • Think 6)5. Place 0 in quotient.
    − 0      • Subtract 0 × 6.
       5
```

Check: (870 × 6) + 5 =
          5220 + 5 = 5225

You Try It 5

```
        3,058 r3
7)  21,409
   −21
      0 4    • Think 7)4. Place 0 in quotient.
    −  0     • Subtract 0 × 7.
      40
    −35
      59
    −56
       3
```

Check: (3058 × 7) + 3 =
          21,406 + 3 = 21,409

You Try It 6

```
        109
42)  4578
    −42
       37    • Think 42)37. Place 0 in
     − 0        quotient.
      378    • Subtract 0 × 42.
    −378
       0   Check: 109 × 42 = 4578
```

You Try It 7

```
         470 r29
39)  18,359      • Think 3)18. 6 × 39
    −15 6           is too large. Try 5.
      2 75         5 × 39 is too large.
    −2 73          Try 4.
        29
      − 0
        29
```

Check: (470 × 39) + 29 =
          18,330 + 29 = 18,359

You Try It 8

```
          62 r111
534)  33,219
     −32 04
       1 179
     −1 068
         111
```

Check: (62 × 534) + 111 =
          33,108 + 111 = 33,219

You Try It 9

```
          421 r33
515)  216,848
     −206 0
       10 84
     −10 30
         548
       −515
          33
```

Check: (421 × 515) + 33 =
          216,815 + 33 = 216,848

You Try It 10

Strategy To find the number of tires that can be stored on each shelf, divide the number of tires (270) by the number of shelves (15).

Solution
```
         18
15)  270
    −15
     120
    −120
       0
```

Each shelf can store 18 tires.

You Try It 11

Strategy To find the number of cases produced in 8 hours:
• Find the number of cases produced in 1 hour by dividing the number of cans produced (12,600) by the number of cans to a case (24).
• Multiply the number of cases produced in 1 hour by 8.

(Continued)

(Continued)

Solution

$$24)\overline{12,600} \quad \begin{matrix}525\end{matrix}$$ cases produced in 1 hour

$$\begin{array}{r} 525 \\ 24{\overline{\smash{\big)}\,12,600}} \\ \underline{-12\,0} \\ 60 \\ \underline{-48} \\ 120 \\ \underline{-120} \\ 0 \end{array}$$

$$\begin{array}{r} 525 \\ \times \quad 8 \\ \hline 4200 \end{array}$$

In 8 hours, 4200 cases are produced.

SECTION 1.6

You Try It 1 $2 \cdot 2 \cdot 2 \cdot 2 \cdot 3 \cdot 3 \cdot 3 = 2^4 \cdot 3^3$

You Try It 2 $10 \cdot 10 \cdot 10 \cdot 10 \cdot 10 \cdot 10 \cdot 10 = 10^7$

You Try It 3 $\begin{aligned} 2^3 \cdot 5^2 &= (2 \cdot 2 \cdot 2) \cdot (5 \cdot 5) = 8 \cdot 25 \\ &= 200 \end{aligned}$

You Try It 4

$$\begin{aligned} 5 \cdot (8 - 4)^2 &\div 4 - 2 \\ = 5 \cdot 4^2 \div 4 - 2 \quad &\bullet \text{ Parentheses} \\ = 5 \cdot 16 \div 4 - 2 \quad &\bullet \text{ Exponents} \\ = 80 \div 4 - 2 \quad &\bullet \text{ Multiplication} \\ &\quad \text{ and division} \\ = 20 - 2 \quad & \\ = 18 \quad &\bullet \text{ Subtraction} \end{aligned}$$

SECTION 1.7

You Try It 1

$$\begin{aligned} 40 \div 1 &= 40 \\ 40 \div 2 &= 20 \\ 40 \div 3 & \qquad \text{Will not divide evenly} \\ 40 \div 4 &= 10 \\ 40 \div 5 &= 8 \\ 40 \div 6 & \qquad \text{Will not divide evenly} \\ 40 \div 7 & \qquad \text{Will not divide evenly} \\ 40 \div 8 &= 5 \end{aligned}$$

1, 2, 4, 5, 8, 10, 20, and 40 are factors of 40.

You Try It 2

$$\begin{array}{r|l} & 44 \\ \hline 2 & 22 \\ 2 & 11 \\ 11 & 1 \end{array}$$

   • $44 \div 2 = 22$
   • $22 \div 2 = 11$
   • $11 \div 11 = 1$

$44 = 2 \cdot 2 \cdot 11$

You Try It 3

$$\begin{array}{r|l} & 177 \\ \hline 3 & 59 \\ 59 & 1 \end{array}$$

   • Try only 2, 3, 4, 7, and 11 because $11^2 > 59$.

$177 = 3 \cdot 59$

Solutions to Chapter 2 "You Try It"

SECTION 2.1

You Try It 1

	2	3	5
$12 =$	(2 · 2)	3	
$27 =$		(3 · 3 · 3)	
$50 =$	2		(5 · 5)

The LCM $= 2 \cdot 2 \cdot 3 \cdot 3 \cdot 3 \cdot 5 \cdot 5$
         $= 2700$

You Try It 2

	2	3	5
$36 =$	(2 · 2)	3 · 3	
$60 =$	2 · 2	(3)	5
$72 =$	2 · 2 · 2	3 · 3	

The GCF $= 2 \cdot 2 \cdot 3 = 12$.

You Try It 3

	2	3	5	11
$11 =$				11
$24 =$	2 · 2 · 2	3		
$30 =$	2	3	5	

Because no numbers are circled, the GCF $= 1$.

SECTION 2.2

You Try It 1 $4\dfrac{1}{4}$

You Try It 2 $\dfrac{17}{4}$

You Try It 3

$$\begin{array}{r} 4 \\ 5{\overline{\smash{\big)}\,22}} \\ \underline{-20} \\ 2 \end{array} \qquad \dfrac{22}{5} = 4\dfrac{2}{5}$$

You Try It 4

$$\begin{array}{r} 4 \\ 7{\overline{\smash{\big)}\,28}} \\ \underline{-28} \\ 0 \end{array} \qquad \dfrac{28}{7} = 4$$

You Try It 5 $14\dfrac{5}{8} = \dfrac{112 + 5}{8} = \dfrac{117}{8}$

SECTION 2.3

You Try It 1 $45 \div 5 = 9$ $\qquad \dfrac{3}{5} = \dfrac{3 \cdot 9}{5 \cdot 9} = \dfrac{27}{45}$

$\dfrac{27}{45}$ is equivalent to $\dfrac{3}{5}$.

You Try It 2 Write 6 as $\dfrac{6}{1}$.

$18 \div 1 = 18$ $\qquad 6 = \dfrac{6 \cdot 18}{1 \cdot 18} = \dfrac{108}{18}$

$\dfrac{108}{18}$ is equivalent to 6.

You Try It 3 $\dfrac{16}{24} = \dfrac{\overset{1}{\cancel{2}} \cdot \overset{1}{\cancel{2}} \cdot \overset{1}{\cancel{2}} \cdot 2}{\underset{1}{\cancel{2}} \cdot \underset{1}{\cancel{2}} \cdot \underset{1}{\cancel{2}} \cdot 3} = \dfrac{2}{3}$

You Try It 4 $\dfrac{8}{56} = \dfrac{\overset{1}{\cancel{2}} \cdot \overset{1}{\cancel{2}} \cdot \overset{1}{\cancel{2}}}{\underset{1}{\cancel{2}} \cdot \underset{1}{\cancel{2}} \cdot \underset{1}{\cancel{2}} \cdot 7} = \dfrac{1}{7}$

You Try It 5 $\dfrac{15}{32} = \dfrac{3 \cdot 5}{2 \cdot 2 \cdot 2 \cdot 2 \cdot 2} = \dfrac{15}{32}$

You Try It 6 $\dfrac{48}{36} = \dfrac{\overset{1}{\cancel{2}} \cdot \overset{1}{\cancel{2}} \cdot 2 \cdot 2 \cdot \overset{1}{\cancel{3}}}{\underset{1}{\cancel{2}} \cdot \underset{1}{\cancel{2}} \cdot \underset{1}{\cancel{3}} \cdot 3} = \dfrac{4}{3} = 1\dfrac{1}{3}$

SECTION 2.4

You Try It 1

$\begin{array}{r} \dfrac{3}{8} \\[2mm] + \dfrac{7}{8} \\[1mm] \hline \dfrac{10}{8} = \dfrac{5}{4} = 1\dfrac{1}{4} \end{array}$

• The denominators are the same. Add the numerators. Place the sum over the common denominator.

You Try It 2

$\begin{array}{r} \dfrac{5}{12} = \dfrac{20}{48} \\[2mm] + \dfrac{9}{16} = \dfrac{27}{48} \\[1mm] \hline \dfrac{47}{48} \end{array}$

• The LCM of 12 and 16 is 48.

You Try It 3

$\begin{array}{r} \dfrac{7}{8} = \dfrac{105}{120} \\[2mm] + \dfrac{11}{15} = \dfrac{88}{120} \\[1mm] \hline \dfrac{193}{120} = 1\dfrac{73}{120} \end{array}$

• The LCM of 8 and 15 is 120.

You Try It 4

$\begin{array}{r} \dfrac{3}{4} = \dfrac{30}{40} \\[2mm] \dfrac{4}{5} = \dfrac{32}{40} \\[2mm] + \dfrac{5}{8} = \dfrac{25}{40} \\[1mm] \hline \dfrac{87}{40} = 2\dfrac{7}{40} \end{array}$

• The LCM of 4, 5, and 8 is 40.

You Try It 5 $7 + \dfrac{6}{11} = 7\dfrac{6}{11}$

You Try It 6

$\begin{array}{r} 29 \\[1mm] + 17\dfrac{5}{12} \\[1mm] \hline 46\dfrac{5}{12} \end{array}$

You Try It 7

$\begin{array}{r} 7\dfrac{4}{5} = 7\dfrac{24}{30} \\[2mm] 6\dfrac{7}{10} = 6\dfrac{21}{30} \\[2mm] + 13\dfrac{11}{15} = 13\dfrac{22}{30} \\[1mm] \hline 26\dfrac{67}{30} = 28\dfrac{7}{30} \end{array}$

• LCM = 30

You Try It 8

$\begin{array}{r} 9\dfrac{3}{8} = 9\dfrac{45}{120} \\[2mm] 17\dfrac{7}{12} = 17\dfrac{70}{120} \\[2mm] + 10\dfrac{14}{15} = 10\dfrac{112}{120} \\[1mm] \hline 36\dfrac{227}{120} = 37\dfrac{107}{120} \end{array}$

• LCM = 120

You Try It 9

Strategy To find the total time spent on the activities, add the three times $\left(4\dfrac{1}{2}, 3\dfrac{3}{4}, 1\dfrac{1}{3}\right)$.

Solution

$\begin{array}{r} 4\dfrac{1}{2} = 4\dfrac{6}{12} \\[2mm] 3\dfrac{3}{4} = 3\dfrac{9}{12} \\[2mm] + 1\dfrac{1}{3} = 1\dfrac{4}{12} \\[1mm] \hline 8\dfrac{19}{12} = 9\dfrac{7}{12} \end{array}$

The total time spent on the three activities was $9\dfrac{7}{12}$ hours.

You Try It 10

Strategy   To find the overtime pay:
- Find the total number of overtime hours $\left(1\frac{2}{3} + 3\frac{1}{3} + 2\right)$.
- Multiply the total number of hours by the overtime hourly wage (36).

Solution

$$1\frac{2}{3}$$
$$3\frac{1}{3}$$
$$+\ 2$$
$$\overline{}$$
$$6\frac{3}{3} = 7 \text{ hours}$$

$$\begin{array}{r} 36 \\ \times\ \ 7 \\ \hline 252 \end{array}$$

Jeff earned \$252 in overtime pay.

SECTION 2.5

You Try It 1

$$\frac{16}{27}$$
$$-\ \frac{7}{27}$$
$$\overline{}$$
$$\frac{9}{27} = \frac{1}{3}$$

- The denominators are the same. Subtract the numerators. Place the difference over the common denominator.

You Try It 2

$$\frac{13}{18} = \frac{52}{72}$$
$$-\ \frac{7}{24} = \frac{21}{72}$$
$$\overline{}$$
$$\frac{31}{72}$$

- LCM = 72

You Try It 3

$$17\frac{5}{9} = 17\frac{20}{36}$$
$$-\ 11\frac{5}{12} = 11\frac{15}{36}$$
$$\overline{}$$
$$6\frac{5}{36}$$

- LCM = 36

You Try It 4

$$8\phantom{\frac{4}{13}} = 7\frac{13}{13}$$
$$-\ 2\frac{4}{13} = 2\frac{4}{13}$$
$$\overline{}$$
$$5\frac{9}{13}$$

- LCM = 13

You Try It 5

$$21\frac{7}{9} = 21\frac{28}{36} = 20\frac{64}{36}$$
$$-\ 7\frac{11}{12} = 7\frac{33}{36} = 7\frac{33}{36}$$
$$\overline{}$$
$$13\frac{31}{36}$$

- LCM = 36

You Try It 6

Strategy   To find the time remaining before the plane lands, subtract the number of hours already in the air $\left(2\frac{3}{4}\right)$ from the total time of the trip $\left(5\frac{1}{2}\right)$.

Solution

$$5\frac{1}{2} = 5\frac{2}{4} = 4\frac{6}{4}$$
$$-\ 2\frac{3}{4} = 2\frac{3}{4} = 2\frac{3}{4}$$
$$\overline{}$$
$$2\frac{3}{4} \text{ hours}$$

The plane will land in $2\frac{3}{4}$ hours.

You Try It 7

Strategy   To find the amount of weight to be lost during the third month:
- Find the total weight loss during the first two months $\left(7\frac{1}{2} + 5\frac{3}{4}\right)$.
- Subtract the total weight loss from the goal (24 pounds).

Solution

$$7\frac{1}{2} = 7\frac{2}{4}$$
$$+\ 5\frac{3}{4} = 5\frac{3}{4}$$
$$\overline{}$$
$$12\frac{5}{4} = 13\frac{1}{4} \text{ pounds lost}$$

$$24\phantom{\frac{4}{4}} = 23\frac{4}{4}$$
$$-\ 13\frac{1}{4} = 13\frac{1}{4}$$
$$\overline{}$$
$$10\frac{3}{4} \text{ pounds}$$

The patient must lose $10\frac{3}{4}$ pounds to achieve the goal.

SECTION 2.6

You Try It 1

$$\frac{4}{21} \times \frac{7}{44} = \frac{4 \cdot 7}{21 \cdot 44}$$

$$= \frac{\overset{1}{2} \cdot \overset{1}{2} \cdot \overset{1}{7}}{3 \cdot 7 \cdot 2 \cdot 2 \cdot 11} = \frac{1}{33}$$

You Try It 2

$$\frac{2}{21} \times \frac{10}{33} = \frac{2 \cdot 10}{21 \cdot 33}$$

$$= \frac{2 \cdot 2 \cdot 5}{3 \cdot 7 \cdot 3 \cdot 11} = \frac{20}{693}$$

You Try It 3
$$\frac{16}{5} \times \frac{15}{24} = \frac{16 \cdot 15}{5 \cdot 24}$$
$$= \frac{\cancel{2} \cdot \cancel{2} \cdot \cancel{2} \cdot 2 \cdot \cancel{3} \cdot \cancel{5}}{\cancel{5} \cdot \cancel{2} \cdot \cancel{2} \cdot \cancel{2} \cdot \cancel{3}} = \frac{2}{1} = 2$$

You Try It 4
$$5\frac{2}{5} \times \frac{5}{9} = \frac{27}{5} \times \frac{5}{9} = \frac{27 \cdot 5}{5 \cdot 9}$$
$$= \frac{\cancel{3} \cdot \cancel{3} \cdot 3 \cdot \cancel{5}}{\cancel{5} \cdot \cancel{3} \cdot \cancel{3}} = \frac{3}{1} = 3$$

You Try It 5
$$3\frac{2}{5} \times 6\frac{1}{4} = \frac{17}{5} \times \frac{25}{4} = \frac{17 \cdot 25}{5 \cdot 4}$$
$$= \frac{17 \cdot \cancel{5} \cdot 5}{\cancel{5} \cdot 2 \cdot 2} = \frac{85}{4} = 21\frac{1}{4}$$

You Try It 6
$$3\frac{2}{7} \times 6 = \frac{23}{7} \times \frac{6}{1} = \frac{23 \cdot 6}{7 \cdot 1}$$
$$= \frac{23 \cdot 2 \cdot 3}{7 \cdot 1} = \frac{138}{7} = 19\frac{5}{7}$$

You Try It 7

Strategy To find the value of the house today, multiply the old value of the house (170,000) by $2\frac{1}{2}$.

Solution
$$170,000 \times 2\frac{1}{2} = \frac{170,000}{1} \times \frac{5}{2}$$
$$= \frac{170,000 \cdot 5}{1 \cdot 2}$$
$$= 425,000$$

The value of the house today is $425,000.

You Try It 8

Strategy To find the cost of the air compressor:
• Multiply to find the value of the drying chamber $\left(\frac{4}{5} \times 160,000\right)$.
• Subtract the value of the drying chamber from the total value of the two items (160,000).

Solution
$$\frac{4}{5} \times \frac{160,000}{1} = \frac{640,000}{5}$$
$$= 128,000 \quad \bullet \text{ Value of the drying chamber}$$
$$160,000 - 128,000 = 32,000$$

The cost of the air compressor was $32,000.

SECTION 2.7

You Try It 1
$$\frac{3}{7} \div \frac{2}{3} = \frac{3}{7} \times \frac{3}{2} = \frac{3 \cdot 3}{7 \cdot 2} = \frac{9}{14}$$

You Try It 2
$$\frac{3}{4} \div \frac{9}{10} = \frac{3}{4} \times \frac{10}{9}$$
$$= \frac{3 \cdot 10}{4 \cdot 9} = \frac{\cancel{3} \cdot 2 \cdot \cancel{5}}{2 \cdot 2 \cdot \cancel{3} \cdot 3} = \frac{5}{6}$$

You Try It 3
$$\frac{5}{7} \div 6 = \frac{5}{7} \div \frac{6}{1} \qquad \bullet \ 6 = \frac{6}{1}. \text{ The}$$
$$= \frac{5}{7} \times \frac{1}{6} = \frac{5 \cdot 1}{7 \cdot 6} \qquad \text{reciprocal of } \frac{6}{1}$$
$$= \frac{5}{7 \cdot 2 \cdot 3} = \frac{5}{42} \qquad \text{is } \frac{1}{6}.$$

You Try It 4
$$12\frac{3}{5} \div 7 = \frac{63}{5} \div \frac{7}{1} = \frac{63}{5} \times \frac{1}{7}$$
$$= \frac{63 \cdot 1}{5 \cdot 7} = \frac{3 \cdot 3 \cdot \cancel{7}}{5 \cdot \cancel{7}} = \frac{9}{5} = 1\frac{4}{5}$$

You Try It 5
$$3\frac{2}{3} \div 2\frac{2}{5} = \frac{11}{3} \div \frac{12}{5}$$
$$= \frac{11}{3} \times \frac{5}{12} = \frac{11 \cdot 5}{3 \cdot 12}$$
$$= \frac{11 \cdot 5}{3 \cdot 2 \cdot 2 \cdot 3} = \frac{55}{36} = 1\frac{19}{36}$$

You Try it 6
$$2\frac{5}{6} \div 8\frac{1}{2} = \frac{17}{6} \div \frac{17}{2}$$
$$= \frac{17}{6} \times \frac{2}{17} = \frac{17 \cdot 2}{6 \cdot 17}$$
$$= \frac{\cancel{17} \cdot \cancel{2}}{2 \cdot 3 \cdot \cancel{17}} = \frac{1}{3}$$

You Try It 7
$$6\frac{2}{5} \div 4 = \frac{32}{5} \div \frac{4}{1}$$
$$= \frac{32}{5} \times \frac{1}{4} = \frac{32 \cdot 1}{5 \cdot 4}$$
$$= \frac{2 \cdot 2 \cdot 2 \cdot \cancel{2} \cdot \cancel{2}}{5 \cdot \cancel{2} \cdot \cancel{2}} = \frac{8}{5} = 1\frac{3}{5}$$

You Try It 8

Strategy To find the number of products, divide the number of minutes in 1 hour (60) by the time to assemble one product $\left(7\frac{1}{2}\right)$.

Solution
$$60 \div 7\frac{1}{2} = \frac{60}{1} \div \frac{15}{2} = \frac{60}{1} \cdot \frac{2}{15}$$
$$= \frac{60 \cdot 2}{1 \cdot 15} = 8$$

The factory worker can assemble eight products in 1 hour.

You Try It 9

Strategy   To find the length of the remaining piece:
- Divide the total length of the board (16) by the length of each shelf $\left(3\frac{1}{3}\right)$. This will give you the number of shelves cut, with a certain fraction of a shelf left over.
- Multiply the fractional part of the result in step 1 by the length of one shelf to determine the length of the remaining piece.

Solution

$$16 \div 3\frac{1}{3} = 16 \div \frac{10}{3}$$

$$= \frac{16}{1} \times \frac{3}{10} = \frac{16 \cdot 3}{1 \cdot 10}$$

$$= \frac{\overset{1}{\cancel{2}} \cdot 2 \cdot 2 \cdot 2 \cdot 3}{\underset{1}{\cancel{2}} \cdot 5} = \frac{24}{5}$$

$$= 4\frac{4}{5}$$

There are 4 pieces $3\frac{1}{3}$ feet long. There is 1 piece that is $\frac{4}{5}$ of $3\frac{1}{3}$ feet long.

$$\frac{4}{5} \times 3\frac{1}{3} = \frac{4}{5} \times \frac{10}{3}$$

$$= \frac{4 \cdot 10}{5 \cdot 3} = \frac{2 \cdot 2 \cdot 2 \cdot \overset{1}{\cancel{5}}}{\underset{1}{\cancel{5}} \cdot 3}$$

$$= \frac{8}{3} = 2\frac{2}{3}$$

The length of the piece remaining is $2\frac{2}{3}$ feet.

SECTION 2.8

You Try It 1 $\dfrac{9}{14} = \dfrac{27}{42}$ $\dfrac{13}{21} = \dfrac{26}{42}$ $\dfrac{9}{14} > \dfrac{13}{21}$

You Try It 2 $\left(\dfrac{7}{11}\right)^2 \cdot \left(\dfrac{2}{7}\right) = \left(\dfrac{7}{11} \cdot \dfrac{7}{11}\right) \cdot \left(\dfrac{2}{7}\right)$

$$= \frac{\overset{1}{\cancel{7}} \cdot 7 \cdot 2}{11 \cdot 11 \cdot \underset{1}{\cancel{7}}} = \frac{14}{121}$$

You Try It 3 $\left(\dfrac{1}{13}\right)^2 \cdot \left(\dfrac{1}{4} + \dfrac{1}{6}\right) \div \dfrac{5}{13} =$

$$\left(\frac{1}{13}\right)^2 \cdot \left(\frac{5}{12}\right) \div \frac{5}{13} =$$

$$\left(\frac{1}{169}\right) \cdot \left(\frac{5}{12}\right) \div \frac{5}{13} =$$

$$\left(\frac{1 \cdot 5}{13 \cdot 13 \cdot 12}\right) \div \frac{5}{13} =$$

$$\left(\frac{1 \cdot 5}{13 \cdot 13 \cdot 12}\right) \times \frac{13}{5} =$$

$$\frac{1 \cdot \overset{1}{\cancel{5}} \cdot \overset{1}{\cancel{13}}}{\underset{1}{\cancel{13}} \cdot 13 \cdot 12 \cdot \underset{1}{\cancel{5}}} = \frac{1}{156}$$

Solutions to Chapter 3 "You Try It"

SECTION 3.1

You Try It 1   The digit 4 is in the thousandths place.

You Try It 2 $\dfrac{501}{1000} = 0.501$
(five hundred one thousandths)

You Try It 3 $0.67 = \dfrac{67}{100}$ (sixty-seven hundredths)

You Try It 4   fifty-five and six thousand eighty-three ten-thousandths

You Try It 5   806.00491   • 1 is in the hundred-thousandths place.

You Try It 6

$$3.675849 \quad \text{┌── Given place value}$$
$$\text{└── } 4 < 5$$

3.675849 rounded to the nearest ten-thousandth is 3.6758.

You Try It 7

$$48.907 \quad \text{┌── Given place value}$$
$$\text{└── } 0 < 5$$

48.907 rounded to the nearest tenth is 48.9.

You Try It 8

————Given place value

31.8652

————8 > 5

31.8652 rounded to the nearest whole number is 32.

You Try It 9

2.65 rounded to the nearest whole number is 3.
To the nearest inch, the average annual precipitation in Yuma is 3 inch.

SECTION 3.2

You Try It 1

$$
\begin{array}{r}
{}^{1\,2} \\
4.62 \\
27.9 \\
+\ \ 0.62054 \\
\hline
33.14054
\end{array}
$$

• Place the decimal points on a vertical line.

You Try It 2

$$
\begin{array}{r}
{}^{1} \\
6.05 \\
12. \\
+\ \ 0.374 \\
\hline
18.424
\end{array}
$$

You Try It 3

Strategy   To determine the number, add the numbers of hearing-impaired Americans of ages 45 to 54, 55 to 64, and 65 to 74, and 75 and over.

Solution
$$
\begin{array}{r}
4.48 \\
4.31 \\
5.41 \\
+3.80 \\
\hline
18.00
\end{array}
$$

18 million Americans ages 45 and older are hearing-impaired.

You Try It 4

Strategy   To find the total income, add the four commissions (985.80, 791.46, 829.75, and 635.42) to the salary (875).

Solution   875 + 985.80 + 791.46 + 829.75
+ 635.42 = 4117.43

Anita's total income was $4117.43.

SECTION 3.3

You Try It 1

$$
\begin{array}{r}
{}^{11\ 9} \\
{}^{6\ 1\ 10\,13} \\
7\,2.\cancel{0}\,\cancel{3}\,9 \\
-\ \ 8.4\,7 \\
\hline
6\,3.5\,6\,9
\end{array}
$$

Check:
$$
\begin{array}{r}
{}^{1\ 1\ 1} \\
8.47 \\
+\ 63.569 \\
\hline
72.039
\end{array}
$$

You Try It 2

$$
\begin{array}{r}
{}^{14\ 9} \\
{}^{2\ 4\,10\,10} \\
3\,\cancel{5}.\cancel{0}\,\cancel{0} \\
-\ \ 9.6\,7 \\
\hline
2\,5.3\,3
\end{array}
$$

Check:
$$
\begin{array}{r}
{}^{1\ 1\ \ 1} \\
9.67 \\
+\ 25.33 \\
\hline
35.00
\end{array}
$$

You Try It 3

$$
\begin{array}{r}
{}^{16} \\
{}^{2\ 6\ 9\ 9\,10} \\
3.\cancel{7}\,\cancel{0}\,\cancel{0}\,\cancel{0} \\
-\ 1.9\,7\,1\,5 \\
\hline
1.7\,2\,8\,5
\end{array}
$$

Check:
$$
\begin{array}{r}
{}^{1\ 111} \\
1.9715 \\
+\ 1.7285 \\
\hline
3.7000
\end{array}
$$

You Try It 4

Strategy   To find the amount of change, subtract the amount paid (6.85) from 10.00.

Solution
$$
\begin{array}{r}
10.00 \\
-\ 6.85 \\
\hline
3.15
\end{array}
$$

Your change was $3.15.

You Try It 5

Strategy   To find the new balance:
• Add to find the total of the three checks (1025.60 + 79.85 + 162.47).
• Subtract the total from the previous balance (2472.69).

Solution
$$
\begin{array}{r}
1025.60 \\
79.85 \\
+\ 162.47 \\
\hline
1267.92
\end{array}
\qquad
\begin{array}{r}
2472.69 \\
-\ 1267.92 \\
\hline
1204.77
\end{array}
$$

The new balance is $1204.77.

SECTION 3.4

You Try It 1

$$
\begin{array}{r}
870 \\
\times\ \ 4.6 \\
\hline
522\ 0 \\
3480 \\
\hline
4002.0
\end{array}
$$

• 1 decimal place

• 1 decimal place

You Try It 2

$$
\begin{array}{r}
0.000086 \\
\times\ \ 0.057 \\
\hline
602 \\
430 \\
\hline
0.000004902
\end{array}
$$

• 6 decimal places
• 3 decimal places

• 9 decimal places

You Try It 3

$$
\begin{array}{r}
4.68 \\
\times\ 6.03 \\
\hline
1404 \\
28\ 080 \\
\hline
28.2204
\end{array}
$$

• 2 decimal places
• 2 decimal places

• 4 decimal places

You Try It 4 $6.9 \times 1000 = 6900$

You Try It 5 $4.0273 \times 10^2 = 402.73$

You Try It 6

Strategy   To find the total bill:
- Find the number of gallons of water used by multiplying the number of gallons used per day (5000) by the number of days (62).
- Find the cost of water by multiplying the cost per 1000 gallons (1.39) by the number of 1000-gallon units used.
- Add the cost of the water to the meter fee (133.70).

Solution

Number of gallons = $5000(62) = 310{,}000$

Cost of water $= \dfrac{310{,}000}{1000} \times 1.39 = 430.90$

Total cost $= 430.90 + 133.70 = 564.60$

The total bill is $564.60.

You Try It 7

Strategy   To find the cost of running the freezer for 210 hours, multiply the hourly cost (0.035) by the number of hours the freezer has run (210).

Solution
```
    0.035
 ×    210
    350
   7 0
   7.350
```

The cost of running the freezer for 210 hours is $7.35.

You Try It 8

Strategy   To find the total cost of the stereo:
- Multiply the monthly payment (37.18) by the number of months (18).
- Add that product to the down payment (175.00).

Solution
```
    37.18              175.00
  ×    18            + 669.24
    297 44            844.24
    371 8
    669.24
```

The total cost of the stereo is $844.24.

SECTION 3.5

You Try It 1
```
           2.7
0.052.)0.140.4
        −104
          36 4
        −36 4
             0
```
- Move the decimal point 3 places to the right in the divisor and the dividend. Write the decimal point in the quotient directly over the decimal point in the dividend.

You Try It 2
```
      0.4873 ≈ 0.487
76)37.0420
  −30 4
    6 64
   −6 08
      562
     −532
      300
     −228
```
- Write the decimal point in the quotient directly over the decimal point in the dividend.

You Try It 3
```
           72.73 ≈ 72.7
5.09.)370.20.00
     −356 3
       13 90
       10 18
        3 720
       −3 563
        1570
       −1527
```

You Try It 4 $309.21 \div 10{,}000 = 0.030921$

You Try It 5 $42.93 \div 10^4 = 0.004293$

You Try It 6

Strategy   To find how many times greater the average hourly earnings were, divide the 1990 average hourly earnings (10.02) by the 1970 average hourly earnings (3.23).

Solution $10.02 \div 3.23 \approx 3.1$

The average hourly earnings in 1990 were about 3.1 times greater than in 1970.

You Try It 7

Strategy   To find the average number of people watching TV:
- Add the number of people watching each day of the week.
- Divide the total number of people watching by 7.

Solution

$$91.9 + 89.8 + 90.6 + 93.9 + 78.0$$
$$+ 77.1 + 87.7 = 609$$

$$\frac{609}{7} = 87$$

An average of 87 million people watch television per day.

SECTION 3.6

You Try It 1

$$\begin{array}{r} 0.56 \approx 0.6 \\ 16\overline{)9.00} \end{array}$$

You Try It 2

$$4\frac{1}{6} = \frac{25}{6}$$

$$\begin{array}{r} 4.166 \approx 4.17 \\ 6\overline{)25.000} \end{array}$$

You Try It 3

$$0.56 = \frac{56}{100} = \frac{14}{25}$$

$$5.35 = 5\frac{35}{100} = 5\frac{7}{20}$$

You Try It 4

$$0.12\frac{7}{8} = \frac{12\frac{7}{8}}{100} = 12\frac{7}{8} \div 100$$

$$= \frac{103}{8} \times \frac{1}{100} = \frac{103}{800}$$

You Try It 5

$$\frac{5}{8} = 0.625$$ • Convert the fraction $\frac{5}{8}$ to a decimal.

$$0.630 > 0.625$$ • Compare the two decimals.

$$0.63 > \frac{5}{8}$$ • Convert 0.625 back to a fraction.

Solutions to Chapter 4 "You Try It"

SECTION 4.1

You Try It 1

$$\frac{20 \text{ pounds}}{24 \text{ pounds}} = \frac{20}{24} = \frac{5}{6}$$

20 pounds : 24 pounds = 20 : 24 = 5 : 6

20 pounds to 24 pounds = 20 to 24
= 5 to 6

You Try It 2

$$\frac{64 \text{ miles}}{8 \text{ miles}} = \frac{64}{8} = \frac{8}{1}$$

64 miles : 8 miles = 64 : 8 = 8 : 1

64 miles to 8 miles = 64 to 8 = 8 to 1

You Try It 3

Strategy   To find the ratio, write the ratio of board feet of cedar (12,000) to board feet of ash (18,000) in simplest form.

Solution

$$\frac{12,000}{18,000} = \frac{2}{3}$$

The ratio is $\frac{2}{3}$.

You Try It 4

Strategy   To find the ratio, write the ratio of the amount spent on radio advertising (45,000) to the amount spent on radio and television advertising (45,000 + 60,000) in simplest form.

Solution

$$\frac{\$45,000}{\$45,000 + \$60,000} = \frac{45,000}{105,000} = \frac{3}{7}$$

The ratio is $\frac{3}{7}$.

SECTION 4.2

You Try It 1

$$\frac{15 \text{ pounds}}{12 \text{ trees}} = \frac{5 \text{ pounds}}{4 \text{ trees}}$$

You Try It 2

$$\frac{260 \text{ miles}}{8 \text{ hours}}$$

$$\begin{array}{r} 32.5 \\ 8\overline{)260.0} \end{array}$$

32.5 miles/hour

You Try It 3

Strategy   To find Erik's profit per ounce:
• Find the total profit by subtracting the cost ($1625) from the selling price ($1720).
• Divide the total profit by the number of ounces (5).

Solution $1720 - 1625 = 95$

$95 \div 5 = 19$

The profit was $19/ounce.

SECTION 4.3

You Try It 1

$$\frac{6}{10} \diagdown \frac{9}{15}$$ $10 \times 9 = 90$
$6 \times 15 = 90$

The cross products are equal. The proportion is true.

You Try It 2

$$\frac{32}{6} \diagdown \frac{90}{8}$$ $6 \times 90 = 540$
$32 \times 8 = 256$

The cross products are not equal. The proportion is not true.

You Try It 3
$$\frac{n}{14} = \frac{3}{7}$$

• Find the cross products. Then solve for n.

$$n \times 7 = 14 \times 3$$
$$n \times 7 = 42$$
$$n = 42 \div 7$$
$$n = 6$$

Check:
$$\frac{6}{14} \asymp \frac{3}{7} \quad \begin{array}{l} 14 \times 3 = 42 \\ 6 \times 7 = 42 \end{array}$$

You Try It 4
$$\frac{5}{7} = \frac{n}{20}$$

• Find the cross products. Then solve for n.

$$5 \times 20 = 7 \times n$$
$$100 = 7 \times n$$
$$100 \div 7 = n$$
$$14.3 \approx n$$

You Try It 5
$$\frac{15}{20} = \frac{12}{n}$$

• Find the cross products. Then solve for n.

$$15 \times n = 20 \times 12$$
$$15 \times n = 240$$
$$n = 240 \div 15$$
$$n = 16$$

Check:
$$\frac{15}{20} \asymp \frac{12}{16} \quad \begin{array}{l} 20 \times 12 = 240 \\ 15 \times 16 = 240 \end{array}$$

You Try It 6
$$\frac{12}{n} = \frac{7}{4}$$

$$12 \times 4 = n \times 7$$
$$48 = n \times 7$$
$$48 \div 7 = n$$
$$6.86 \approx n$$

You Try It 7
$$\frac{n}{12} = \frac{4}{1}$$

$$n \times 1 = 12 \times 4$$
$$n \times 1 = 48$$
$$n = 48 \div 1$$
$$n = 48$$

Check:
$$\frac{48}{12} \asymp \frac{4}{1} \quad \begin{array}{l} 12 \times 4 = 48 \\ 48 \times 1 = 48 \end{array}$$

You Try It 8

Strategy   To find the number of tablespoons of fertilizer needed, write and solve a proportion using n to represent the number of tablespoons of fertilizer.

Solution
$$\frac{3 \text{ tablespoons}}{4 \text{ gallons}} = \frac{n \text{ tablespoons}}{10 \text{ gallons}}$$

• The unit "tablespoons" is in the numerator. The unit "gallons" is in the denominator.

$$3 \times 10 = 4 \times n$$
$$30 = 4 \times n$$
$$30 \div 4 = n$$
$$7.5 = n$$

For 10 gallons of water, 7.5 tablespoons of fertilizer are required.

You Try It 9

Strategy   To find the number of jars that can be packed in 15 boxes, write and solve a proportion using n to represent the number of jars.

Solution
$$\frac{24 \text{ jars}}{6 \text{ boxes}} = \frac{n \text{ jars}}{15 \text{ boxes}}$$

$$24 \times 15 = 6 \times n$$
$$360 = 6 \times n$$
$$360 \div 6 = n$$
$$60 = n$$

60 jars can be packed in 15 boxes.

Solutions to Chapter 5 "You Try It"

SECTION 5.1

You Try It 1   **a.** $125\% = 125 \times \dfrac{1}{100} = \dfrac{125}{100} = 1\dfrac{1}{4}$

b. $125\% = 125 \times 0.01 = 1.25$

You Try It 2
$$33\frac{1}{3}\% = 33\frac{1}{3} \times \frac{1}{100}$$
$$= \frac{100}{3} \times \frac{1}{100}$$
$$= \frac{100}{300} = \frac{1}{3}$$

You Try It 3 $0.25\% = 0.25 \times 0.01 = 0.0025$

You Try It 4 $0.048 = 0.048 \times 100\% = 4.8\%$

You Try It 5 $3.67 = 3.67 \times 100\% = 367\%$

You Try It 6 $0.62\dfrac{1}{2} = 0.62\dfrac{1}{2} \times 100\%$

$$= 62\dfrac{1}{2}\%$$

You Try It 7 $\dfrac{5}{6} = \dfrac{5}{6} \times 100\% = \dfrac{500}{6}\% = 83\dfrac{1}{3}\%$

You Try It 8 $1\dfrac{4}{9} = \dfrac{13}{9} = \dfrac{13}{9} \times 100\%$

$$= \dfrac{1300}{9}\% \approx 144.4\%$$

SECTION 5.2

You Try It 1   Percent × base = amount
$$0.063 \times 150 = n$$
$$9.45 = n$$

You Try It 2   Percent × base = amount
$$\dfrac{1}{6} \times 66 = n \qquad \bullet\ 16\dfrac{2}{3}\% = \dfrac{1}{6}$$
$$11 = n$$

You Try It 3

Strategy   To determine the amount that came from corporations, write and solve the basic percent equation using n to represent the amount. The percent is 4%. The base is $212 billion.

Solution   Percent × base = amount
$$4\% \times 212 = n$$
$$0.04 \times 212 = n$$
$$8.48 = n$$

Corporations gave $8.48 billion to charities.

You Try It 4

Strategy   To find the new hourly wage:
- Find the amount of the raise. Write and solve the basic percent equation using n to represent the amount of the raise (amount). The percent is 8%. The base is $33.50.
- Add the amount of the raise to the old wage (33.50).

Solution $8\% \times 33.50 = n$

$0.08 \times 33.50 = n$

$2.68 = n$

$$\begin{array}{r} 33.50 \\ +\ 2.68 \\ \hline 36.18 \end{array}$$

The new hourly wage is $36.18.

SECTION 5.3

You Try It 1   Percent × base = amount
$$n \times 32 = 16$$
$$n = 16 \div 32$$
$$n = 0.50$$
$$n = 50\%$$

You Try It 2   Percent × base = amount
$$n \times 15 = 48$$
$$n = 48 \div 15$$
$$n = 3.2$$
$$n = 320\%$$

You Try It 3   Percent × base = amount
$$n \times 45 = 30$$
$$n = 30 \div 45$$
$$n = \dfrac{2}{3} = 66\dfrac{2}{3}\%$$

You Try It 4

Strategy   To find what percent of the income the income tax is, write and solve the basic percent equation using n to represent the percent. The base is $33,500 and the amount is $5025.

Solution $n \times 33,500 = 5025$
$$n = 5025 \div 33,500$$
$$n = 0.15 = 15\%$$

The income tax is 15% of the income.

You Try It 5

Strategy   To find the percent who were women:
- Subtract to find the number of enlisted personnel who were women (518,921 − 512,370).
- Write and solve the basic percent equation using n to represent the percent. The base is 518,921, and the amount is the number of enlisted personnel who were women.

Solution $518,921 - 512,370 = 6551$

$n \times 518,921 = 6551$
$$n = 6551 \div 518,921$$
$$n \approx 0.013$$

In 1950, 1.3% of the enlisted personnel in the U.S. Army were women.

SECTION 5.4

You Try It 1

$$\text{Percent} \times \text{base} = \text{amount}$$
$$0.86 \times n = 215$$
$$n = 215 \div 0.86$$
$$n = 250$$

You Try It 2

$$\text{Percent} \times \text{base} = \text{amount}$$
$$0.025 \times n = 15$$
$$n = 15 \div 0.025$$
$$n = 600$$

You Try It 3

$$\text{Percent} \times \text{base} = \text{amount}$$
$$\frac{1}{6} \times n = 5 \qquad \bullet \ 16\frac{2}{3}\% = \frac{1}{6}$$
$$n = 5 \div \frac{1}{6}$$
$$n = 30$$

You Try It 4

Strategy To find the original value of the car, write and solve the basic percent equation using n to represent the original value (base). The percent is 42% and the amount is \$10,458.

Solution
$$42\% \times n = 10{,}458$$
$$0.42 \times n = 10{,}458$$
$$n = 10{,}458 \div 0.42$$
$$n = 24{,}900$$

The original value of the car was \$24,900.

You Try It 5

Strategy To find the difference between the original price and the sale price:
- Find the original price. Write and solve the basic percent equation using n to represent the original price (base). The percent is 80% and the amount is \$89.60.
- Subtract the sale price (89.60) from the original price.

Solution
$$80\% \times n = 89.60$$
$$0.80 \times n = 89.60$$
$$n = 89.60 \div 0.80$$
$$n = 112.00 \quad \text{(original price)}$$

$$112.00 - 89.60 = 22.40$$

The difference between the original price and the sale price is \$22.40.

SECTION 5.5

You Try It 1

$$\frac{26}{100} = \frac{22}{n}$$
$$26 \times n = 100 \times 22$$
$$26 \times n = 2200$$
$$n = 2200 \div 26$$
$$n \approx 84.62$$

You Try It 2

$$\frac{16}{100} = \frac{n}{132}$$
$$16 \times 132 = 100 \times n$$
$$2112 = 100 \times n$$
$$2112 \div 100 = n$$
$$21.12 = n$$

You Try It 3

Strategy To find the number of days it snowed, write and solve a proportion using n to represent the number of days it snowed (amount). The percent is 64% and the base is 150.

Solution
$$\frac{64}{100} = \frac{n}{150}$$
$$64 \times 150 = 100 \times n$$
$$9600 = 100 \times n$$
$$9600 \div 100 = n$$
$$96 = n$$

It snowed 96 days.

You Try It 4

Strategy To find the percent of pens that were not defective:
- Subtract to find the number of pens that were not defective $(200 - 5)$.
- Write and solve a proportion using n to represent the percent of pens that were not defective. The base is 200, and the amount is the number of pens not defective.

Solution
$$200 - 5 = 195 \quad \text{(number of pens not defective)}$$

$$\frac{n}{100} = \frac{195}{200}$$
$$n \times 200 = 100 \times 195$$
$$n \times 200 = 19{,}500$$
$$n = 19{,}500 \div 200$$
$$n = 97.5$$

97.5% of the pens were not defective.

Solutions to Chapter 6 "You Try It"

SECTION 6.1

You Try It 1

Strategy To find the unit cost, divide the total cost by the number of units.

Solution **a.** $7.67 \div 8 = 0.95875$
$.959$ per battery
b. $2.29 \div 15 \approx 0.153$
$.153$ per ounce

You Try It 2

Strategy To find the more economical purchase, compare the unit costs.

Solution $5.70 \div 6 = 0.95$
$3.96 \div 4 = 0.99$
$\$.95 < \$.99$

The more economical purchase is 6 cans for $5.70.

You Try It 3

Strategy To find the total cost, multiply the unit cost (9.96) by the number of units (7).

Solution

$$\boxed{\text{Unit cost}} \times \boxed{\text{number of units}} = \boxed{\text{total cost}}$$

$$9.96 \quad \times \quad 7 \quad = \quad 69.72$$

The total cost is $69.72.

SECTION 6.2

You Try It 1

Strategy To find the percent increase:
• Find the amount of the increase.
• Solve the basic percent equation for *percent*.

Solution

$$\boxed{\text{New value}} - \boxed{\text{original value}} = \boxed{\text{amount of increase}}$$

$$1.83 \quad - \quad 1.46 \quad = \quad 0.37$$

Percent $\times$ base $=$ amount
$n \quad \times 1.46 = \quad 0.37$
$n = 0.37 \div 1.46$
$n \approx 0.25 = 25\%$

The percent increase was 25%.

You Try It 2

Strategy To find the new hourly wage:
• Solve the basic percent equation for *amount*.
• Add the amount of the increase to the original wage.

Solution Percent $\times$ base $=$ amount
$0.14 \quad \times 12.50 = \quad n$
$1.75 = n$

$12.50 + 1.75 = 14.25$

The new hourly wage is $14.25.

You Try It 3

Strategy To find the markup, solve the basic percent equation for *amount*.

Solution Percent $\times$ base $=$ amount

$$\boxed{\begin{array}{c}\text{Markup} \\ \text{rate}\end{array}} \times \boxed{\text{cost}} = \boxed{\text{markup}}$$

$$0.20 \quad \times \quad 8 \quad = \quad n$$
$$1.60 = n$$

The markup is $1.60.

You Try It 4

Strategy To find the selling price:
• Find the markup by solving the basic percent equation for *amount*.
• Add the markup to the cost.

Solution Percent $\times$ base $=$ amount

$$\boxed{\begin{array}{c}\text{Markup} \\ \text{rate}\end{array}} \times \boxed{\text{cost}} = \boxed{\text{markup}}$$

$$0.55 \quad \times \quad 72 \quad = \quad n$$
$$39.60 = n$$

$$\boxed{\text{Cost}} + \boxed{\text{markup}} = \boxed{\text{selling price}}$$

$$72 \quad + \quad 39.60 \quad = \quad 111.60$$

The selling price is $111.60.

You Try It 5

Strategy To find the percent decrease:
• Find the amount of the decrease.
• Solve the basic percent equation for *percent*.

Solution

$$\boxed{\text{Original value}} - \boxed{\text{new value}} = \boxed{\text{amount of decrease}}$$

$$261{,}000 \quad - \quad 215{,}000 \quad = \quad 46{,}000$$

Percent $\times$ base $=$ amount
$n \quad \times 261{,}000 = 46{,}000$
$n = 46{,}000 \div 261{,}000$
$n \approx 0.176$

The percent decrease is 17.6%.

You Try It 6

Strategy   To find the visibility:
- Find the amount of decrease by solving the basic percent equation for *amount*.
- Subtract the amount of decrease from the original visibility.

Solution   Percent × base = amount

$$0.40 \times 5 = n$$
$$2 = n$$

$$5 - 2 = 3$$

The visibility was 3 miles.

You Try It 7

Strategy   To find the discount rate:
- Find the discount.
- Solve the basic percent equation for *percent*.

Solution

Regular price	−	sale price	=	discount

$$12.50 - 10.99 = 1.51$$

Percent × base = amount

Discount rate	×	regular price	=	discount

$$n \times 12.50 = 1.51$$
$$n = 1.51 \div 12.50$$
$$n = 0.1208$$

The discount rate is 12.1%.

You Try It 8

Strategy   To find the sale price:
- Find the discount by solving the basic percent equation for *amount*.
- Subtract to find the sale price.

Solution   Percent × base = amount

Discount rate	×	regular price	=	discount

$$0.15 \times 110 = n$$
$$16.5 = n$$

Regular price	−	discount	=	sale price

$$110 - 16.5 = 93.5$$

The sale price is $93.50.

SECTION 6.3

You Try It 1

Strategy   To find the simple interest due, multiply the principal (15,000) times the annual interest rate (8% = 0.08) times the time, in years
$$\left(18 \text{ months} = \frac{18}{12} \text{ years} = 1.5 \text{ years}\right).$$

Solution

Principal	×	annual interest rate	×	time (in years)	=	interest

$$15{,}000 \times 0.08 \times 1.5 = 1800$$

The interest due is $1800.

You Try It 2

Strategy   To find the maturity value:
- Use the simple interest formula to find the simple interest due.
- Find the maturity value by adding the principal and the interest.

Solution

Principal	×	annual interest rate	×	time (in years)	=	interest

$$3800 \times 0.06 \times \frac{90}{365} \approx 56.22$$

Principal	+	interest	=	maturity value

$$3800 + 56.22 = 3856.22$$

The maturity value is $3856.22.

You Try It 3

Strategy   To find the monthly payment:
- Find the maturity value by adding the principal and the interest.
- Divide the maturity value by the length of the loan in months (12).

Solution   Principal + interest = maturity value

$$1900 + 152 = 2052$$

Maturity value ÷ length of the loan = payment

$$2052 \div 12 = 171$$

The monthly payment is $171.

You Try It 4

Strategy   To find the finance charge, multiply the principal, or unpaid balance (1250), times the monthly interest rate (1.6%) times the number of months (1).

Solution

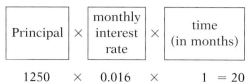

$$1250 \quad \times \quad 0.016 \quad \times \quad 1 \ = 20$$

The simple interest due is $20.

You Try It 5

Strategy   To find the interest earned:
- Find the new principal by multiplying the original principal (1000) by the factor found in the Compound Interest Table (3.29066).
- Subtract the original principal from the new principal.

Solution $1000 \times 3.29066 = 3290.66$

The new principal is $3290.66.

$3290.66 - 1000 = 2290.66$

The interest earned is $2290.66.

SECTION 6.4

You Try It 1

Strategy   To find the mortgage:
- Find the down payment by solving the basic percent equation for *amount*.
- Subtract the down payment from the purchase price.

Solution

Percent	$\times$	base	$=$	amount

Percent	$\times$	purchase price	$=$	down payment

$$0.25 \quad \times \quad 216{,}000 \quad = \quad n$$
$$54{,}000 = n$$

Purchase price	$-$	down payment	$=$	mortgage

$$216{,}000 \quad - \quad 54{,}000 \quad = \quad 162{,}000$$

The mortgage is $162,000.

You Try It 2

Strategy   To find the loan origination fee, solve the basic percent equation for *amount*.

Solution

Percent	$\times$	base	$=$	amount
Points	$\times$	mortgage	$=$	fee

$$0.045 \times \quad 80{,}000 \quad = \quad n$$
$$3600 = n$$

The loan origination fee was $3600.

You Try It 3

Strategy   To find the monthly mortgage payment:
- Subtract the down payment from the purchase price to find the mortgage.
- Multiply the mortgage by the factor found in the Monthly Payment Table.

Solution

Purchase price	$-$	down payment	$=$	mortgage

$$75{,}000 \quad - \quad 15{,}000 \quad = \quad 60{,}000$$

$$60{,}000 \quad \times\ 0.0089973 \quad = \quad 539.838$$
$$\uparrow$$
From the table

The monthly mortgage payment is $539.84.

You Try It 4

Strategy   To find the interest:
- Multiply the mortgage by the factor found in the Monthly Payment Table to find the monthly mortgage payment.
- Subtract the principal from the monthly mortgage payment.

Solution $125{,}000 \times 0.0083920 = 1049$
$$\qquad\qquad\quad \uparrow \qquad\qquad \uparrow$$
$$\qquad\quad \text{From the} \quad \text{Monthly mortgage}$$
$$\qquad\qquad \text{table} \qquad\qquad \text{payment}$$

Monthly mortgage payment	$-$	principal	$=$	interest

$$1049 \quad - \quad 492.65 \quad = \quad 556.35$$

The interest on the mortgage is $556.35.

You Try It 5

Strategy   To find the monthly payment:
- Divide the annual property tax by 12 to find the monthly property tax.
- Add the monthly property tax to the monthly mortgage payment.

(Continued)

(Continued)

Solution $744 \div 12 = 62$

The monthly property tax is $62.

$415.20 + 62 = 477.20$

The total monthly payment is
$477.20.

SECTION 6.5

You Try It 1

Strategy   To find the amount financed:
• Find the down payment by solving
the basic percent equation for
amount.
• Subtract the down payment from
the purchase price.

Solution   Percent $\times$ base = amount

$$\boxed{\text{Percent}} \times \boxed{\begin{array}{c}\text{purchase}\\\text{price}\end{array}} = \boxed{\begin{array}{c}\text{down}\\\text{payment}\end{array}}$$

$0.20 \times 19,200 = n$
$3840 = n$

The down payment is $3840.

$19,200 - 3840 = 15,360$

The amount financed is $15,360.

You Try It 2

Strategy   To find the license fee, solve the basic
percent equation for *amount*.

Solution   Percent $\times$ base = amount

$$\boxed{\text{Percent}} \times \boxed{\begin{array}{c}\text{purchase}\\\text{price}\end{array}} = \boxed{\text{sales tax}}$$

$0.015 \times 17,350 = n$
$260.25 = n$

The license fee is $260.25.

You Try It 3

Strategy   To find the cost, multiply the cost per
mile (0.31) by the number of miles
driven (23,000).

Solution $23,000 \times 0.31 = 7130$

The cost is $7130.

You Try It 4

Strategy   To find the cost per mile for car
insurance, divide the cost for
insurance (360) by the number of
miles driven (15,000).

Solution $360 \div 15,000 = 0.024$

The cost per mile for insurance is
$.024.

You Try It 5

Strategy   To find the monthly payment:
• Subtract the down payment from
the purchase price to find the
amount financed.
• Multiply the amount financed by
the factor found in the Monthly
Payment Table.

Solution $25,900 - 6475 = 19,425$

$19,425 \times 0.0244129 \approx 474.22$

The monthly payment is $474.22.

SECTION 6.6

You Try It 1

Strategy   To find the worker's earnings:
• Find the worker's overtime wage by
multiplying the hourly wage by 2.
• Multiply the number of overtime
hours worked by the overtime
wage.

Solution $18.50 \times 2 = 37$

The hourly wage for overtime is $37.

$37 \times 8 = 296$

The construction worker earns $296.

You Try It 2

Strategy   To find the salary per month, divide
the annual salary by the number of
months in a year (12).

Solution $48,228 \div 12 = 4019$

The contractor's monthly salary is
$4019.

You Try It 3

Strategy   To find the total earnings:
• Find the sales over $50,000.
• Multiply the commission rate by
sales over $50,000.
• Add the commission to the annual
salary.

Solution $175,000 - 50,000 = 125,000$

Sales over $50,000 totaled $125,000.

$125,000 \times 0.095 = 11,875$

Earnings from commissions totaled $11,875.

$27,000 + 11,875 = 38,875$

The insurance agent earned $38,875.

SECTION 6.7

You Try It 1

Strategy   To find the current balance:
- Subtract the amount of the check from the old balance.
- Add the amount of each deposit.

Solution

$$
\begin{array}{ll}
302.46 & \\
-\quad 20.59 & \text{check} \\
\hline
281.87 & \\
176.86 & \text{first deposit} \\
+\quad 94.73 & \text{second deposit} \\
\hline
553.46 &
\end{array}
$$

The current checking account balance is $553.46.

You Try It 2

Current checkbook

$$
\begin{array}{lr}
\text{balance:} & 623.41 \\
\text{Check: 237} & +\quad 78.73 \\
\hline
 & 702.14 \\
\text{Interest:} & +\quad 2.11 \\
\hline
 & 704.25 \\
\text{Deposit:} & -523.84 \\
\hline
 & 180.41
\end{array}
$$

Closing bank balance from bank statement: $180.41

Checkbook balance: $180.41

The bank statement and the checkbook balance.

Solutions to Chapter 7 "You Try It"

SECTION 7.1

You Try It 1

Strategy   To find what percent of the total number of cellular phones purchased the number purchased in March represents:
- Read the pictograph to determine the number of cellular phones purchased for each month.
- Find the total cellular phone purchases for the 4-month period.
- Solve the basic percent equation for percent (n). Amount = 3000; the base is the total sales for the 4-month period.

Solution

$$
\begin{array}{r}
4{,}500 \\
3{,}500 \\
3{,}000 \\
1{,}500 \\
\hline
12{,}500
\end{array}
$$

$$
\begin{array}{l}
\text{Percent} \times \text{base} = \text{amount} \\
\quad n \quad \times 12{,}500 = 3000 \\
\qquad\qquad\qquad n = 3000 \div 12{,}500 \\
\qquad\qquad\qquad n = 0.24
\end{array}
$$

The number of cellular phones purchased in March represents 24% of the total number of cellular phones purchased.

You Try It 2

Strategy   To find the ratio of the annual cost of fuel to the annual cost of maintenance:
- Locate the annual fuel cost and the annual maintenance cost in the circle graph.
- Write the ratio of the annual fuel cost to the annual maintenance cost in simplest form.

Solution   Annual fuel cost: $700
Annual maintenance cost: $500

$$\frac{700}{500} = \frac{7}{5}$$

The ratio is $\frac{7}{5}$.

You Try It 3

Strategy To find the amount paid for medical/dental insurance:
- Locate the percent of the distribution that is medical/dental insurance.
- Solve the basic percent equation for amount.

Solution The percent of the distribution that is medical/dental insurance: 6%

Percent × base = amount
0.06   × 2900 = n
             174 = n

The amount paid for medical/dental insurance is $174.

SECTION 7.2

You Try It 1

Strategy To write the ratio:
- Read the graph to find the lung capacity of an inactive female and of an athletic female.
- Write the ratio in simplest form.

Solution Lung capacity of an inactive female: 25
Lung capacity of an athletic female: 55

$$\frac{25}{55} = \frac{5}{11}$$

The ratio is $\frac{5}{11}$.

You Try It 2

Strategy To determine between which two years the net income of Math Associates increased the most:
- Read the line graph to determine the net income of Math Associates for each of the years shown.
- Subtract to find the difference between each two years.
- Find the greatest difference.

Solution 2000: $1 million
2001: $3 million
2002: $5 million
2003: $8 million
2004: $12 million

Between 2000 and 2001: 3 − 1 = 2
Between 2001 and 2002: 5 − 3 = 2
Between 2002 and 2003: 8 − 5 = 3
Between 2003 and 2004: 12 − 8 = 4

4 > 3 > 2

The net income of Math Associates increased the most between 2003 and 2004.

SECTION 7.3

You Try It 1

Strategy To find the number of employees:
- Read the histogram to find the number of employees whose hourly wage is between $10 and $12 and the number whose hourly wage is between $12 and $14.
- Add the two numbers.

Solution Number whose wage is between $10 and $12: 7
Number whose wage is between $12 and $14: 15

7 + 15 = 22

22 employees earn between $10 and $14.

You Try It 2

Strategy To write the ratio:
- Read the graph to find the number of states with a per capita income between $28,000 and $32,000 and the number with a per capita income between $32,000 and $36,000.
- Write the ratio in simplest form.

Solution Number of states with a per capita income between $28,000 and $32,000: 18
Number of states with a per capita income between $32,000 and $36,000: 9

$$\frac{18}{9} = \frac{2}{1}$$

The ratio is $\frac{2}{1}$.

SECTION 7.4

You Try It 1

Strategy To find the mean amount spent by the 12 customers:

- Find the sum of the numbers.
- Divide the sum by the number of customers (12).

Solution $6.26 + 8.23 + 5.09 + 8.11 + 7.50 +$
$6.69 + 5.66 + 4.89 + 5.25 +$
$9.36 + 6.75 + 7.05 = 80.84$

$$\bar{x} = \frac{80.84}{12} \approx 6.74$$

The mean amount spent by the 12 customers was $6.74.

You Try It 2

Strategy   To find the median weight loss:
- Arrange the weight losses from smallest to largest.
- Because there is an even number of values, the median is the mean of the middle two numbers.

Solution   10, 14, 16, 16, 22, 27, 29, 31, 31, 40

$$\text{Median} = \frac{22 + 27}{2} = \frac{49}{2} = 24.5$$

The median weight loss was 24.5 pounds.

You Try It 3

Strategy   To draw the box-and-whiskers plot:
- Find the median, Q_1, and Q_3.
- Use the smallest value, Q_1, the median, Q_3, and the largest value to draw the box-and-whiskers plot.

Solution

4   7   7   8   8   9   13

Q_1 ... Median ... Q_3

a.

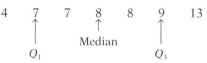

b. Answers about the spread of the data will vary. For example, in You Try It 3, the values in the interquartile range are all very close to the median. They are not

so close to the median in Example 3. The whiskers are long with respect to the box in You Try It 3, whereas they are short with respect to the box in Example 3. This shows that the data values outside the interquartile range are closer together in Example 3 than in You Try It 3.

SECTION 7.5

You Try It 1

Strategy   To find the probability:
- List the outcomes of the experiment in a systematic way. We will use a table.
- Use the table to count the number of possible outcomes of the experiment.
- Count the number of outcomes of the experiment that are favorable to the event of 2 true questions and 1 false question.
- Use the probability formula.

Solution

Question 1	Question 2	Question 3
T	T	T
T	T	F
T	F	T
T	F	F
F	T	T
F	T	F
F	F	T
F	F	F

There are 8 possible outcomes:

$S = \{\text{TTT, TTF, TFT, TFF, FTT, FTF, FFT, FFF}\}$

There are 3 outcomes favorable to the event:

$\{\text{TTF, TFT, FTT}\}$

Probability of an event
$$= \frac{\text{number of favorable outcomes}}{\text{number of possible outcomes}} = \frac{3}{8}$$

The probability of 2 true questions and 1 false question is $\frac{3}{8}$.

Solutions to Chapter 8 "You Try It"

SECTION 8.1

You Try It 1 $14 \text{ ft} = 14 \text{ ft} \times \dfrac{1 \text{ yd}}{3 \text{ ft}} = \dfrac{14 \text{ yd}}{3} = 4\dfrac{2}{3} \text{ yd}$

You Try It 2 $9240 \text{ ft} = 9240 \text{ ft} \times \dfrac{1 \text{ mi}}{5280 \text{ ft}}$

$= \dfrac{9240 \text{ mi}}{5280} = 1\dfrac{3}{4} \text{ mi}$

You Try It 3

$$\begin{array}{r} 3 \text{ ft } 6 \text{ in.} \\ 12\overline{)\ 42} \\ -36 \\ \hline 6 \end{array}$$

• 12 in. = 1 ft

42 in. = 3 ft 6 in.

You Try It 4

$$\begin{array}{r} 4 \text{ yd } 2 \text{ ft} \\ 3\overline{)\ 14} \\ -12 \\ \hline 2 \end{array}$$

• 3 ft = 1 yd

14 ft = 4 yd 2 ft

You Try It 5

$$\begin{array}{r} 3 \text{ ft }\ \ 5 \text{ in.} \\ +\ 4 \text{ ft }\ \ 9 \text{ in.} \\ \hline 7 \text{ ft } 14 \text{ in.} \end{array}$$

• 14 in. = 1 ft 2 in.

7 ft 14 in. = 8 ft 2 in.

You Try It 6

$$\begin{array}{r} {\scriptstyle 3 \text{ ft}}\ \ {\scriptstyle 14 \text{ in.}} \\ \cancel{4 \text{ ft } 2 \text{ in.}} \\ -\ 1 \text{ ft } 8 \text{ in.} \\ \hline 2 \text{ ft } 6 \text{ in.} \end{array}$$

• Borrow 1 ft (12 in.) from 4 ft and add it to 2 in.

You Try It 7

$$\begin{array}{r} 4 \text{ yd } 1 \text{ ft} \\ \times\ \ \ \ \ \ \ 8 \\ \hline 32 \text{ yd } 8 \text{ ft} \end{array}$$

• 8 ft = 2 yd 2 ft

32 yd 8 ft = 34 yd 2 ft

You Try It 8

$$\begin{array}{r} 3 \text{ yd }\ \ \ 2 \text{ ft} \\ 2\overline{)\ 7 \text{ yd }\ \ \ 1 \text{ ft}} \\ -6 \text{ yd} \\ \hline 1 \text{ yd} = \underline{3 \text{ ft}} \\ 4 \text{ ft} \\ -4 \text{ ft} \\ \hline 0 \end{array}$$

You Try It 9 $6\dfrac{1}{4} \text{ ft} = 6\dfrac{3}{12} \text{ ft} = 5\dfrac{15}{12} \text{ ft}$

$\underline{-3\dfrac{2}{3} \text{ ft} = 3\dfrac{8}{12} \text{ ft} = 3\dfrac{8}{12} \text{ ft}}$

$2\dfrac{7}{12} \text{ ft}$

You Try It 10

Strategy   To find the width of the storage room:
• Multiply the number of tiles (8) by the width of each tile (9 in.).
• Divide the result by the number of inches in 1 foot (12) to find the width in feet.

Solution   9 in. × 8 = 72 in.

72 ÷ 12 = 6

The width is 6 ft.

You Try It 11

Strategy   To find the length of each piece, divide the total length (9 ft 8 in.) by the number of pieces (4).

Solution

$$\begin{array}{r} 2 \text{ ft }\ \ \ \ 5 \text{ in.} \\ 4\overline{)\ 9 \text{ ft }\ \ \ \ 8 \text{ in.}} \\ -8 \text{ ft} \\ \hline 1 \text{ ft} = \underline{12 \text{ in.}} \\ 20 \text{ in.} \\ -20 \text{ in.} \\ \hline 0 \text{ in.} \end{array}$$

Each piece is 2 ft 5 in. long.

SECTION 8.2

You Try It 1 $3 \text{ lb} = 3 \text{ lb} \times \dfrac{16 \text{ oz}}{1 \text{ lb}} = 48 \text{ oz}$

You Try It 2 $4200 \text{ lb} = 4200 \text{ lb} \times \dfrac{1 \text{ ton}}{2000 \text{ lb}}$

$= \dfrac{4200 \text{ tons}}{2000} = 2\dfrac{1}{10} \text{ tons}$

You Try It 3

$$\begin{array}{r} {\scriptstyle 6 \text{ lb}}\ \ {\scriptstyle 17 \text{ oz}} \\ \cancel{7 \text{ lb } 1 \text{ oz}} \\ -\ 3 \text{ lb }\ \ 4 \text{ oz} \\ \hline 3 \text{ lb } 13 \text{ oz} \end{array}$$

• Borrow 1 lb (16 oz) from 7 lb and add it to 1 oz.

You Try It 4

$$3 \text{ lb } 6 \text{ oz}$$
$$\underline{\times \qquad 4}$$
$$12 \text{ lb } 24 \text{ oz} = 13 \text{ lb } 8 \text{ oz}$$

You Try It 5

Strategy   To find the weight of 12 bars of soap:
- Multiply the number of bars (12) by the weight of each bar (7 oz).
- Convert the number of ounces to pounds.

Solution

$$\begin{array}{r} 12 \\ \times \ 7 \text{ oz} \\ \hline 84 \text{ oz} \end{array}$$

$$84 \ \cancel{oz} \times \frac{1 \text{ lb}}{16 \ \cancel{oz}} = 5\frac{1}{4} \text{ lb}$$

The 12 bars of soap weigh $5\frac{1}{4}$ lb.

SECTION 8.3

You Try It 1

$$18 \text{ pt} = 18 \ \cancel{pt} \times \frac{1 \ \cancel{qt}}{2 \ \cancel{pt}} \times \frac{1 \text{ gal}}{4 \ \cancel{qt}}$$
$$= \frac{18 \text{ gal}}{8} = 2\frac{1}{4} \text{ gal}$$

You Try It 2

$$\begin{array}{r} 1 \text{ gal} \quad 2 \text{ qt} \\ 3\overline{)\ 4 \text{ gal} \quad 2 \text{ qt}} \\ \underline{-3 \text{ gal}} \\ 1 \text{ gal} = 4 \text{ qt} \\ 6 \text{ qt} \\ \underline{-6 \text{ qt}} \\ 0 \end{array}$$

You Try It 3

Strategy   To find the number of gallons of water needed:
- Find the number of quarts required by multiplying the number of quarts one student needs per day (5) by the number of students (5) by the number of days (3).

- Convert the number of quarts to gallons.

Solution $5 \times 5 \times 3 = 75$ qt

$$75 \ \cancel{qt} \cdot \frac{1 \text{ gal}}{4 \ \cancel{qt}} = \frac{75 \text{ gal}}{4} = 18\frac{3}{4} \text{ gal}$$

The students should take $18\frac{3}{4}$ gal of water.

SECTION 8.4

Your Try It 1

$$18{,}000 \text{ s} = 18{,}000 \ \cancel{s} \times \frac{1 \ \cancel{min}}{60 \ \cancel{s}} \times \frac{1 \text{ h}}{60 \ \cancel{min}}$$
$$= \frac{18{,}000 \text{ h}}{3600} = 5 \text{ h}$$

SECTION 8.5

You Try It 1

$$4.5 \text{ Btu} = 4.5 \ \cancel{Btu} \times \frac{778 \text{ ft} \cdot \text{lb}}{1 \ \cancel{Btu}}$$
$$= 3501 \text{ ft} \cdot \text{lb}$$

You Try It 2

$$\text{Energy} = 800 \text{ lb} \times 16 \text{ ft} = 12{,}800 \text{ ft} \cdot \text{lb}$$

You Try It 3   56,000 Btu =

$$56{,}000 \ \cancel{Btu} \times \frac{778 \text{ ft} \cdot \text{lb}}{1 \ \cancel{Btu}} =$$
$$43{,}568{,}000 \text{ ft} \cdot \text{lb}$$

You Try It 4 $\text{Power} = \dfrac{90 \text{ ft} \times 1200 \text{ lb}}{24 \text{ s}}$
$$= 4500 \ \frac{\text{ft} \cdot \text{lb}}{\text{s}}$$

You Try It 5 $\dfrac{3300}{550} = 6 \text{ hp}$

Solutions to Chapter 9 "You Try It"

SECTION 9.1

You Try It 1 $3.07 \text{ m} = 307 \text{ cm}$

You Try It 2 $750 \text{ m} = 0.750 \text{ km}$

$$3 \text{ km } 750 \text{ m} = 3 \text{ km} + 0.750 \text{ km}$$
$$= 3.750 \text{ km}$$

You Try It 3

Strategy   To find the cost of the shelves:
- Multiply the length of the bookcase (175 cm) by the number of shelves (4).
- Convert centimeters to meters.
- Multiply the number of meters by the cost per meter ($15.75).

(Continued)

(Continued)

Solution

$$175 \text{ cm}$$
$$\underline{\times \quad 4}$$
$$700 \text{ cm}$$

$$700 \text{ cm} = 7 \text{ m}$$

$$15.75$$
$$\underline{\times \quad 7}$$
$$110.25$$

The cost of the shelves is $110.25.

SECTION 9.2

You Try It 1   42.3 mg = 0.0423 g

You Try It 2   54 mg = 0.054 g

$$3 \text{ g } 54 \text{ mg} = 3 \text{ g} + 0.054 \text{ g}$$
$$= 3.054 \text{ g}$$

You Try It 3

Strategy   To find how much fertilizer is required:
• Convert 300 g to kilograms.
• Multiply the number of kilograms by the number of trees (400).

Solution   300 g = 0.3 kg

$$400$$
$$\underline{\times \quad 0.3 \text{ kg}}$$
$$120.0 \text{ kg}$$

To fertilize the trees, 120 kg of fertilizer are required.

SECTION 9.3

You Try It 1   2 kl = 2000 L

$$2 \text{ kl } 167 \text{ L} = 2000 \text{ L} + 167 \text{ L}$$
$$= 2167 \text{ L}$$

You Try It 2 $325 \text{ cm}^3 = 325 \text{ ml} = 0.325 \text{ L}$

You Try It 3

Strategy   To find the profit:
• Convert 5 L to milliliters.
• Find the number of jars by dividing the number of milliliters by the number of milliliters in each jar (125).
• Multiply the number of jars by the cost per jar ($.85).
• Find the total cost by adding the cost of the jars to the cost for the moisturizer ($299.50).

• Find the income by multiplying the number of jars by the selling price per jar ($29.95).
• Subtract the total cost from the income.

Solution   5 L = 5000 ml

$$5000 \div 125 = 40 \quad \text{This is the number of jars.}$$

$$0.85$$
$$\underline{\times \quad 40}$$
$$34.00 \quad \text{This is the cost of the jars.}$$

$$299.50$$
$$\underline{+ \quad 34.00}$$
$$333.50 \quad \text{This is the total cost.}$$

$$29.95$$
$$\underline{\times \quad 40}$$
$$1198.00 \quad \text{This is the income from sales.}$$

$$1198.00$$
$$\underline{- \quad 333.50}$$
$$864.50$$

The profit on the 5 L of moisturizer is $864.50.

SECTION 9.4

You Try It 1

Strategy   To find the number of Calories burned off, multiply the number of hours spent doing housework $\left(4\frac{1}{2}\right)$ by the Calories used per hour (240).

Solution $4\frac{1}{2} \times 240 = \frac{9}{2} \times 240 = 1080$

Doing $4\frac{1}{2}$ h of housework burns off 1080 Calories.

You Try It 2

Strategy   To find the number of kilowatt-hours used:
• Find the number of watt-hours used.
• Convert watt-hours to kilowatt-hours.

Solution $150 \times 200 = 30,000$
30,000 Wh = 30 kWh

30 kWh of energy are used.

You Try It 3

Strategy To find the cost:
- Convert 20 min to hours.
- Multiply to find the total number of hours the oven is used.
- Multiply the number of hours used by the number of watts to find the watt-hours.
- Convert watt-hours to kilowatt-hours.
- Multiply the number of kilowatt-hours by the cost per kilowatt-hour.

Solution $20 \text{ min} = 20 \text{ min} \times \dfrac{1 \text{ h}}{60 \text{ min}}$

$= \dfrac{20}{60} \text{ h} = \dfrac{1}{3} \text{ h}$

$\dfrac{1}{3} \text{ h} \times 30 = 10 \text{ h}$

$10 \text{ h} \times 500 \text{ W} = 5000 \text{ Wh}$

$5000 \text{ Wh} = 5 \text{ kWh}$

$5 \times 8.7\cent = 43.5\cent$

The cost is 43.5¢.

You Try It 2 $\dfrac{\$2.69}{\text{gal}} \approx \dfrac{\$2.69}{\text{gal}} \times \dfrac{1 \text{ gal}}{3.79 \text{ L}}$

$= \dfrac{\$2.69}{3.79 \text{ L}} \approx \dfrac{\$.71}{\text{L}}$

$\$2.69/\text{gal} \approx \$.71/\text{L}$

You Try It 3 $45 \text{ cm} = \dfrac{45 \text{ cm}}{1} \times \dfrac{1 \text{ in.}}{2.54 \text{ cm}}$

$= \dfrac{45 \text{ in.}}{2.54} \approx 17.72 \text{ in.}$

$45 \text{ cm} \approx 17.72 \text{ in.}$

You Try It 4 $\dfrac{75 \text{ km}}{\text{h}} \approx \dfrac{75 \text{ km}}{\text{h}} \times \dfrac{1 \text{ mi}}{1.61 \text{ km}}$

$= \dfrac{75 \text{ mi}}{1.61 \text{ h}} \approx 46.58 \text{ mi/h}$

$75 \text{ km/h} \approx 46.58 \text{ mi/h}$

You Try It 5 $\dfrac{\$1.75}{\text{L}} \approx \dfrac{\$1.75}{\text{L}} \times \dfrac{3.79 \text{ L}}{1 \text{ gal}}$

$= \dfrac{\$6.6325}{1 \text{ gal}} \approx \$6.63/\text{gal}$

$\$1.75/\text{L} \approx \$6.63/\text{gal}$

SECTION 9.5

You Try It 1

$\dfrac{60 \text{ ft}}{\text{s}} \approx \dfrac{60 \text{ ft}}{\text{s}} \times \dfrac{1 \text{ m}}{3.28 \text{ ft}}$

$= \dfrac{60 \text{ m}}{3.28 \text{ s}} \approx 18.29 \text{ m/s}$

$60 \text{ ft/s} \approx 18.29 \text{ m/s}$

- The conversion rate is $\dfrac{1 \text{ m}}{3.28 \text{ ft}}$ with m in the numerator and ft in the denominator.

Solutions to Chapter 10 "You Try It"

SECTION 10.1

You Try It 1 -232 ft

You Try It 2

You Try It 3 $-12 < -8$ • -12 is to the left of -8 on the number line.

You Try It 4 $|-7| = 7; |21| = 21$

You Try It 5 $|2| = 2; |-9| = 9$

You Try It 6 $-|-12| = -12$

SECTION 10.2

You Try It 1 $-154 + (-37) = -191$ • The signs of the addends are the same.

You Try It 2 $-5 + (-2) + 9 + (-3)$
$= -7 + 9 + (-3)$
$= 2 + (-3)$
$= -1$

You Try It 3 $-8 - 14$
$= -8 + (-14)$ • Rewrite "−" as "+"; the opposite of 14 is −14.
$= -22$

You Try It 4 $3 - (-15)$
$$= 3 + 15 \quad \bullet \text{ Rewrite "}-\text{" as "}+\text{";}$$
$$= 18 \qquad \text{the opposite of } -15 \text{ is } 15.$$

You Try It 5 $4 - (-3) - 12 - (-7) - 20$
$$= 4 + 3 + (-12) + 7 + (-20)$$
$$= 7 + (-12) + 7 + (-20)$$
$$= -5 + 7 + (-20)$$
$$= 2 + (-20)$$
$$= -18$$

You Try It 6

Strategy   To find the temperature, add the increase ($12°C$) to the previous temperature ($-10°C$).

Solution $-10 + 12 = 2$

After an increase of $12°C$, the temperature is $2°C$.

SECTION 10.3

You Try It 1 $(-3)(-5) = 15$ $\bullet$ The signs are the same. The product is positive.

You Try It 2   The signs are different. The product is negative.
$$-38 \cdot 51 = -1938$$

You Try It 3 $-7(-8)(9)(-2) = 56(9)(-2)$
$$= 504(-2)$$
$$= -1008$$

You Try It 4 $(-135) \div (-9) = 15$ $\bullet$ The signs are the same. The quotient is positive.

You Try It 5 $84 \div (-6) = -14$ $\bullet$ The signs are different. The quotient is negative.

You Try It 6 $-72 \div 4 = -18$

You Try It 7   Division by zero is undefined.
$-39 \div 0$ is undefined.

You Try It 8

Strategy   To find the melting point of argon, multiply the melting point of mercury ($-38°C$) by 5.

Solution $5(-38) = -190$

The melting point of argon is $-190°C$.

You Try It 9

Strategy   To find the average daily low temperature:
- Add the seven temperature readings.
- Divide by 7.

Solution
$$-6 + (-7) + 1 + 0 + (-5) + (-10) + (-1)$$
$$= -13 + 1 + 0 + (-5) + (-10) + (-1)$$
$$= -12 + 0 + (-5) + (-10) + (-1)$$
$$= -12 + (-5) + (-10) + (-1)$$
$$= -17 + (-10) + (-1)$$
$$= -27 + (-1)$$
$$= -28$$

$-28 \div 7 = -4$

The average daily low temperature was $-4°F$.

SECTION 10.4

You Try It 1   The LCM of 9 and 12 is 36.
$$\frac{5}{9} - \frac{11}{12} = \frac{20}{36} - \frac{33}{36} = \frac{20}{36} + \frac{-33}{36}$$
$$= \frac{20 + (-33)}{36} = \frac{-13}{36}$$
$$= -\frac{13}{36}$$

You Try It 2   The LCM of 8, 6, and 3 is 24.
$$-\frac{7}{8} - \frac{5}{6} + \frac{2}{3}$$
$$= -\frac{21}{24} - \frac{20}{24} + \frac{16}{24}$$
$$= \frac{-21}{24} + \frac{-20}{24} + \frac{16}{24}$$
$$= \frac{-21 + (-20) + 16}{24} = \frac{-25}{24}$$
$$= -\frac{25}{24} = -1\frac{1}{24}$$

You Try It 3 $16.127 - 67.91 = 16.127 + (-67.91)$
$$\begin{array}{r} 67.910 \\ -16.127 \\ \hline 51.783 \end{array}$$

$16.127 - 67.91 = -51.783$

You Try It 4 $2.7 + (-9.44) + 6.2$
$$= -6.74 + 6.2$$
$$= -0.54$$

You Try It 5   The product is positive.
$$\left(-\frac{2}{3}\right)\left(-\frac{9}{10}\right) = \frac{2 \cdot 9}{3 \cdot 10}$$
$$= \frac{3}{5}$$

You Try It 6 The quotient is negative.

$$-\frac{5}{8} \div \frac{5}{40} = -\left(\frac{5}{8} \div \frac{5}{40}\right)$$

$$= -\left(\frac{5}{8} \times \frac{40}{5}\right)$$

$$= -\left(\frac{5 \cdot 40}{8 \cdot 5}\right)$$

$$= -5$$

You Try It 7 The product is negative.

$$\begin{array}{r} 5.44 \\ \times\ 3.8 \\ \hline 4352 \\ 1632\ \ \\ \hline 20.672 \end{array}$$

$$-5.44 \times 3.8 = -20.672$$

You Try It 8 $3.44 \times (-1.7) \times 0.6$
$$= (-5.848) \times 0.6$$
$$= -3.5088$$

You Try It 9

$$\begin{array}{r} 0.231 \\ 1.7\overline{)0.3.940} \\ \underline{-3\ 4}\ \ \ \\ 54\ \ \\ \underline{-51}\ \ \\ 30\ \\ \underline{-17}\ \\ 13 \end{array}$$

$$-0.394 \div 1.7 \approx -0.23$$

You Try It 10

Strategy To find how many degrees the temperature fell, subtract the lower temperature ($-13.33°C$) from the higher temperature ($12.78°C$).

Solution $12.78 - (-13.33) = 12.78 + 13.33$
$$= 26.11$$

The temperature fell $26.11°C$ in the 15-min period.

SECTION 10.5

You Try It 1 The number is less than 1. Move the decimal point 7 places to the right. The exponent on 10 is -7.

$$0.000000961 = 9.61 \times 10^{-7}$$

You Try It 2 The exponent on 10 is positive. Move the decimal point 6 places to the right.

$$7.329 \times 10^6 = 7,329,000$$

You Try It 3 $9 - 9 \div (-3)$
$$= 9 - (-3) \quad \bullet \text{ Do the division.}$$
$$= 9 + 3 \quad \bullet \text{ Rewrite as addition. Add.}$$
$$= 12$$

You Try It 4 $8 \div 4 \cdot 4 - (-2)^2$
$$= 8 \div 4 \cdot 4 - 4 \quad \bullet \text{ Exponents}$$
$$= 2 \cdot 4 - 4 \quad \bullet \text{ Division}$$
$$= 8 - 4 \quad \bullet \text{ Multiplication}$$
$$= 8 + (-4) \quad \bullet \text{ Subtraction}$$
$$= 4$$

You Try It 5 $8 - (-15) \div (2 - 7)$
$$= 8 - (-15) \div (-5)$$
$$= 8 - 3$$
$$= 8 + (-3)$$
$$= 5$$

You Try It 6 $(-2)^2 \times (3 - 7)^2 - (-16) \div (-4)$
$$= (-2)^2 \times (-4)^2 - (-16) \div (-4)$$
$$= 4 \times 16 - (-16) \div (-4)$$
$$= 64 - (-16) \div (-4)$$
$$= 64 - 4$$
$$= 64 + (-4)$$
$$= 60$$

You Try It 7 $7 \div \left(\frac{1}{7} - \frac{3}{14}\right) - 9$

$$= 7 \div \left(-\frac{1}{14}\right) - 9$$

$$= 7(-14) - 9$$
$$= -98 - 9$$
$$= -98 + (-9)$$
$$= -107$$

Solutions to Chapter 11 "You Try It"

SECTION 11.1

You Try It 1

$6a - 5b$

$6(-3) - 5(4) = -18 - 20$
$= -18 + (-20)$
$= -38$

You Try It 2

$-3s^2 - 12 \div t$

$-3(-2)^2 - 12 \div 4 = -3(4) - 12 \div 4$
$= -12 - 12 \div 4$
$= -12 - 3$
$= -12 + (-3)$
$= -15$

You Try It 3

$-\dfrac{2}{3}m + \dfrac{3}{4}n^3$

$-\dfrac{2}{3}(6) + \dfrac{3}{4}(2)^3 = -\dfrac{2}{3}(6) + \dfrac{3}{4}(8)$
$= -4 + 6$
$= 2$

You Try It 4

$-3yz - z^2 + y^2$

$-3\left(-\dfrac{2}{3}\right)\left(\dfrac{1}{3}\right) - \left(\dfrac{1}{3}\right)^2 + \left(-\dfrac{2}{3}\right)^2$

$= -3\left(-\dfrac{2}{3}\right)\left(\dfrac{1}{3}\right) - \dfrac{1}{9} + \dfrac{4}{9}$

$= \dfrac{2}{3} - \dfrac{1}{9} + \dfrac{4}{9} = \dfrac{6}{9} - \dfrac{1}{9} + \dfrac{4}{9} = \dfrac{9}{9}$

$= 1$

You Try It 5

$5a^2 - 6b^2 + 7a^2 - 9b^2$
$= 5a^2 + (-6)b^2 + 7a^2 + (-9)b^2$
$= 5a^2 + 7a^2 + (-6)b^2 + (-9)b^2$
$= 12a^2 + (-15)b^2$
$= 12a^2 - 15b^2$

You Try It 6

$-6x + 7 + 9x - 10$
$= (-6)x + 7 + 9x + (-10)$
$= (-6)x + 9x + 7 + (-10)$
$= 3x + (-3)$
$= 3x - 3$

You Try It 7

$\dfrac{3}{8}w + \dfrac{1}{2} - \dfrac{1}{4}w - \dfrac{2}{3}$

$= \dfrac{3}{8}w + \dfrac{1}{2} + \left(-\dfrac{1}{4}\right)w + \left(-\dfrac{2}{3}\right)$

$= \dfrac{3}{8}w + \left(-\dfrac{1}{4}\right)w + \dfrac{1}{2} + \left(-\dfrac{2}{3}\right)$

$= \dfrac{3}{8}w + \left(-\dfrac{2}{8}\right)w + \dfrac{3}{6} + \left(-\dfrac{4}{6}\right)$

$= \dfrac{1}{8}w + \left(-\dfrac{1}{6}\right)$

$= \dfrac{1}{8}w - \dfrac{1}{6}$

You Try It 8

$5(a - 2) = 5a - 5(2)$
$= 5a - 10$

You Try It 9

$8s - 2(3s - 5)$
$= 8s - 2(3s) - (-2)(5)$
$= 8s - 6s + 10$
$= 2s + 10$

You Try It 10

$4(x - 3) - 2(x + 1)$
$= 4x - 4(3) - 2x - 2(1)$
$= 4x - 12 - 2x - 2$
$= 4x - 2x - 12 - 2$
$= 2x - 14$

SECTION 11.2

You Try It 1

$$\begin{array}{c|c} x(x + 3) = 4x + 6 \\ \hline (-2)(-2 + 3) & 4(-2) + 6 \\ (-2)(1) & (-8) + 6 \\ \hline -2 = -2 \end{array}$$

Yes, -2 is a solution.

You Try It 2

$$\begin{array}{c|c} x^2 - x = 3x + 7 \\ \hline (-3)^2 - (-3) & 3(-3) + 7 \\ 9 + 3 & -9 + 7 \\ \hline 12 \neq -2 \end{array}$$

No, -3 is not a solution.

You Try It 3

$-2 + y = -5$
$-2 + 2 + y = -5 + 2$ • **Add 2 to each side.**
$0 + y = -3$
$y = -3$

The solution is -3.

You Try It 4

$7 = y + 8$
$7 - 8 = y + 8 - 8$ • **Subtract 8 from each side.**
$-1 = y + 0$
$-1 = y$

The solution is -1.

You Try It 5

$\dfrac{1}{5} = z + \dfrac{4}{5}$

$\dfrac{1}{5} - \dfrac{4}{5} = z + \dfrac{4}{5} - \dfrac{4}{5}$ • **Subtract $\dfrac{4}{5}$ from each side.**

$-\dfrac{3}{5} = z + 0$

$-\dfrac{3}{5} = z$

The solution is $-\dfrac{3}{5}$.

You Try It 6

$$4z = -20$$

$$\frac{4z}{4} = \frac{-20}{4}$$ • Divide each side by 4.

$$1z = -5$$

$$z = -5$$

The solution is -5.

$$\frac{5x}{5} = \frac{-2}{5}$$ • Divide each side by 5.

$$x = -\frac{2}{5}$$

The solution is $-\frac{2}{5}$.

You Try It 7

$$8 = \frac{2}{5}n$$

$$\left(\frac{5}{2}\right)(8) = \left(\frac{5}{2}\right)\frac{2}{5}n$$ • Multiply each side by $\frac{5}{2}$.

$$20 = 1n$$

$$20 = n$$

The solution is 20.

You Try It 2

$$7 - x = 3$$

$$7 - 7 - x = 3 - 7$$ • Subtract 7 from each side.

$$-x = -4$$

$$(-1)(-x) = (-1)(-4)$$ • Multiply each side by -1.

$$x = 4$$

The solution is 4.

You Try It 8

$$\frac{2}{3}t - \frac{1}{3}t = -2$$

$$\frac{1}{3}t = -2$$ • Combine like terms.

$$\left(\frac{3}{1}\right)\frac{1}{3}t = \left(\frac{3}{1}\right)(-2)$$ • Multiply each side by 3.

$$1t = -6$$

$$t = -6$$

The solution is -6.

You Try It 3

Strategy To find the Celsius temperature, replace the variable F in the formula by the given value and solve for C.

Solution

$$F = 1.8C + 32$$

$$-22 = 1.8C + 32$$ • Substitute -22 for F.

$$-22 - 32 = 1.8C + 32 - 32$$ • Subtract 32 from each side.

$$-54 = 1.8C$$ • Combine like terms.

$$\frac{-54}{1.8} = \frac{1.8C}{1.8}$$ • Divide each side by 1.8.

$$-30 = C$$

The temperature is $-30°C$.

You Try It 9

Strategy To find the regular price, replace the variables S and D in the formula by the given values and solve for R.

Solution

$$S = R - D$$

$$44 = R - 16$$

$$44 + 16 = R - 16 + 16$$

$$60 = R$$

The regular price is $60.

You Try It 4

Strategy To find the cost per unit, replace the variables T, N, and F in the formula by the given values and solve for U.

Solution

$$T = U \cdot N + F$$

$$4500 = U \cdot 250 + 1500$$

$$4500 = 250U + 1500$$

$$4500 - 1500 = 250U + 1500 - 1500$$

$$3000 = 250U$$

$$\frac{3000}{250} = \frac{250U}{250}$$

$$12 = U$$

The cost per unit is $12.

You Try It 10

Strategy To find the monthly payment, replace the variables A and N in the formula by the given values and solve for M.

Solution

$$A = MN$$

$$6840 = M \cdot 24$$

$$6840 = 24M$$

$$\frac{6840}{24} = \frac{24M}{24}$$

$$285 = M$$

The monthly payment is $285.

SECTION 11.3

You Try It 1

$$5x + 8 = 6$$

$$5x + 8 - 8 = 6 - 8$$ • Subtract 8 from each side.

$$5x = -2$$

SECTION 11.4

You Try It 1

$$\frac{1}{5}x - 2 = \frac{2}{5}x + 4$$

$$\frac{1}{5}x - \frac{2}{5}x - 2 = \frac{2}{5}x - \frac{2}{5}x + 4$$ • Subtract $\frac{2}{5}x$ from each side.

$$-\frac{1}{5}x - 2 = 4$$

$$-\frac{1}{5}x - 2 + 2 = 4 + 2 \qquad \bullet \text{ Add 2 to each side.}$$

$$-\frac{1}{5}x = 6$$

$$(-5)\left(-\frac{1}{5}x\right) = (-5)6 \qquad \bullet \text{ Multiply each side by } -5.$$

$$x = -30$$

The solution is -30.

You Try It 2
$$4(x - 1) - x = 5$$
$$4x - 4 - x = 5$$
$$3x - 4 = 5$$
$$3x - 4 + 4 = 5 + 4$$
$$3x = 9$$
$$\frac{3x}{3} = \frac{9}{3}$$
$$x = 3$$

The solution is 3.

You Try It 3
$$2x - 7(3x + 1) = 5(5 - 3x)$$
$$2x - 21x - 7 = 25 - 15x \qquad \bullet \text{ Distributive Property}$$
$$-19x - 7 = 25 - 15x \qquad \bullet \text{ Combine like terms.}$$
$$-19x + 15x - 7 = 25 - 15x + 15x \qquad \bullet \text{ Add } 15x \text{ to both sides.}$$
$$-4x - 7 = 25 \qquad \bullet \text{ Combine like terms.}$$
$$-4x - 7 + 7 = 25 + 7 \qquad \bullet \text{ Add 7 to both sides.}$$
$$-4x = 32 \qquad \bullet \text{ Combine like terms.}$$
$$\frac{-4x}{-4} = \frac{32}{-4} \qquad \bullet \text{ Divide each side by } -4.$$
$$x = -8$$

The solution is -8.

SECTION 11.5

You Try It 1 $\quad 8 - 2t$

You Try It 2 $\quad \dfrac{5}{7x}$

You Try It 3 $\quad$ The product of a number and one-half of the number
The unknown number: x

One-half the number: $\dfrac{1}{2}x$

$$(x)\left(\frac{1}{2}x\right)$$

SECTION 11.6

You Try It 1 $\quad$ The unknown number: x

A number increased by four	equals	twelve

$$x + 4 = 12$$
$$x + 4 - 4 = 12 - 4$$
$$x = 8$$

The number is 8.

You Try It 2 $\quad$ The unknown number: x

The product of two and a number	is	ten

$$2x = 10$$
$$\frac{2x}{2} = \frac{10}{2}$$
$$x = 5$$

The number is 5.

You Try It 3 $\quad$ The unknown number: x

The sum of three times a number and six	equals	four

$$3x + 6 = 4$$
$$3x + 6 - 6 = 4 - 6$$
$$3x = -2$$
$$\frac{3x}{3} = \frac{-2}{3}$$
$$x = -\frac{2}{3}$$

The number is $-\dfrac{2}{3}$.

You Try It 4 $\quad$ The unknown number: x

Three more than one-half of a number	is	nine

$$\frac{1}{2}x + 3 = 9$$
$$\frac{1}{2}x + 3 - 3 = 9 - 3$$
$$\frac{1}{2}x = 6$$
$$2 \cdot \frac{1}{2}x = 2 \cdot 6$$
$$x = 12$$

The number is 12.

You Try It 5

Strategy   To find the regular price, write and solve an equation using R to represent the regular price of the slacks.

Solution

$38.95	is	$11 less than the regular price

$$38.95 = R - 11$$
$$38.95 + 11 = R - 11 + 11$$
$$49.95 = R$$

The regular price of the slacks is $49.95.

You Try It 6

Strategy   To find the rpm of the engine when it is in third gear, write and solve an equation using R to represent the rpm of the engine in third gear.

Solution

2500	is	two-thirds of the rpm of the engine in third gear

$$2500 = \frac{2}{3}R$$
$$\frac{3}{2}(2500) = \left(\frac{3}{2}\right)\frac{2}{3}R$$
$$3750 = R$$

The rpm of the engine when in third gear is 3750 rpm.

You Try It 7

Strategy   To find the number of hours of labor, write and solve an equation using H to represent the number of hours of labor required.

Solution

$300	includes	$100 for materials plus $12.50 per hour of labor

$$300 = 100 + 12.50H$$
$$300 - 100 = 100 - 100 + 12.50H$$
$$200 = 12.50H$$
$$\frac{200}{12.50} = \frac{12.50H}{12.50}$$
$$16 = H$$

16 h of labor are required.

You Try It 8

Strategy   To find the total sales, write and solve an equation using S to represent the total sales.

Solution

$2500	is	the sum of $800 and an 8% commission on total sales

$$2500 = 800 + 0.08S$$
$$2500 - 800 = 800 - 800 + 0.08S$$
$$1700 = 0.08S$$
$$\frac{1700}{0.08} = \frac{0.08S}{0.08}$$
$$21{,}250 = S$$

Natalie's total sales for the month were $21,250.

Solutions to Chapter 12 "You Try It"

SECTION 12.1

You Try It 1
$$QT = QR + RS + ST$$
$$62 = 24 + RS + 17$$
$$62 = 41 + RS$$
$$62 - 41 = 41 - 41 + RS$$
$$21 = RS$$

You Try It 2   Let x represent the supplement of a $32°$ angle. The sum of supplementary angles is $180°$.

$$x + 32° = 180°$$
$$x + 32° - 32° = 180° - 32°$$
$$x = 148°$$

$148°$ is the supplement of $32°$.

You Try It 3
$$\angle a + 68° = 118°$$
$$\angle a + 68° - 68° = 118° - 68°$$
$$\angle a = 50°$$

You Try It 4 In a right triangle, one angle measures 90° and the two acute angles are complementary.

$$\angle A + \angle B = 90°$$
$$\angle A + 7° = 90°$$
$$\angle A + 7° - 7° = 90° - 7°$$
$$\angle A = 83°$$

The other angles measure 90° and 83°.

You Try It 5 The sum of the three angles of a triangle is 180°.

$$\angle A + \angle B + \angle C = 180°$$
$$\angle A + 62° + 45° = 180°$$
$$\angle A + 107° = 180°$$
$$\angle A + 107° - 107° = 180° - 107°$$
$$\angle A = 73°$$

The measure of the other angle is 73°.

You Try It 6 $r = \dfrac{1}{2}d$

$r = \dfrac{1}{2}(8 \text{ in.}) = 4 \text{ in.}$

The radius is 4 in.

You Try It 7 Angles a and b are supplementary angles.

$$\angle a + \angle b = 180°$$
$$125° + \angle b = 180°$$
$$125° - 125° + \angle b = 180° - 125°$$
$$\angle b = 55°$$

You Try It 8 $\angle c$ and $\angle a$ are corresponding angles. Corresponding angles are equal.

$$\angle c = \angle a = 120°$$

$\angle b$ and $\angle c$ are supplementary angles.

$$\angle b + \angle c = 180°$$
$$\angle b + 120° = 180°$$
$$\angle b + 120° - 120° = 180° - 120°$$
$$\angle b = 60°$$

SECTION 12.2

You Try It 1 $P = 2L + 2W$
$= 2(2 \text{ m}) + 2(0.85 \text{ m})$
$= 4 \text{ m} + 1.7 \text{ m}$
$= 5.7 \text{ m}$

The perimeter of the rectangle is 5.7 m.

You Try It 2 $P = a + b + c$
$= 12 \text{ cm} + 15 \text{ cm} + 18 \text{ cm}$
$= 45 \text{ cm}$

The perimeter of the triangle is 45 cm.

You Try It 3 $C = \pi d$
$\approx 3.14 \cdot 6 \text{ in.}$
$= 18.84 \text{ in.}$

The circumference is approximately 18.84 in.

You Try It 4

$$\begin{array}{c} \text{Perimeter} \\ \text{of} \\ \text{composite} \\ \text{figure} \end{array} = \begin{array}{c} \text{two} \\ \text{lengths} \\ \text{of a} \\ \text{rectangle} \end{array} + \begin{array}{c} \text{the} \\ \text{circumference} \\ \text{of a} \\ \text{circle} \end{array}$$

$P = 2L + \pi d$
$\approx 2(8 \text{ in.}) + 3.14(3 \text{ in.})$
$= 16 \text{ in.} + 9.42 \text{ in.}$
$= 25.42 \text{ in.}$

The perimeter is approximately 25.42 in.

You Try It 5

Strategy To find the perimeter, use the formula for the perimeter of a rectangle.

Solution $P = 2L + 2W$
$= 2(11 \text{ in.}) + 2\left(8\dfrac{1}{2} \text{ in.}\right)$
$= 22 \text{ in.} + 17 \text{ in.}$
$= 39 \text{ in.}$

The perimeter of the computer paper is 39 in.

You Try It 6

Strategy To find the cost:
- Find the perimeter of the workbench.
- Multiply the perimeter by the perimeter cost of the stripping.

Solution $P = 2L + 2W$
$= 2(3 \text{ m}) + 2(0.74 \text{ m})$
$= 6 \text{ m} + 1.48 \text{ m}$
$= 7.48 \text{ m}$

$\$2.76 \times 7.48 = \$20.6448$

The cost is $20.64.

SECTION 12.3

You Try It 1 $A = \dfrac{1}{2}bh = \dfrac{1}{2}(24 \text{ in.})(14 \text{ in.}) = 168 \text{ in}^2$

The area is 168 in².

You Try It 2

$$A = \text{area of rectangle} - \text{area of triangle}$$
$$A = LW - \frac{1}{2}bh$$
$$= (10 \text{ in.} \times 6 \text{ in.}) - \left(\frac{1}{2} \times 6 \text{ in.} \times 4 \text{ in.}\right)$$
$$= 60 \text{ in}^2 - 12 \text{ in}^2$$
$$= 48 \text{ in}^2$$

The area is 48 in².

You Try It 3

Strategy   To find the area of the room:
• Find the area in square feet.
• Convert to square yards.

Solution
$$A = LW$$
$$= 12 \text{ ft} \cdot 9 \text{ ft}$$
$$= 108 \text{ ft}^2$$

$$108 \text{ ft}^2 \times \frac{1 \text{ yd}^2}{9 \text{ ft}^2} = \frac{108}{9} \text{ yd}^2$$
$$= 12 \text{ yd}^2$$

The area of the room is 12 yd².

SECTION 12.4

You Try It 1
$$V = LWH$$
$$= (8 \text{ cm})(3.5 \text{ cm})(4 \text{ cm})$$
$$= 112 \text{ cm}^3$$

The volume is 112 cm³.

You Try It 2
$$V = s^3$$
$$= (5 \text{ cm})^3$$
$$= 125 \text{ cm}^3$$

The volume is 125 cm³.

You Try It 3 $r = \frac{1}{2}d = \frac{1}{2}(14 \text{ in.}) = 7 \text{ in.}$

$$V = \pi r^2 h$$
$$\approx \frac{22}{7}(7 \text{ in.})^2(15 \text{ in.})$$
$$= 2310 \text{ in}^3$$

The volume is approximately 2310 in³.

You Try It 4 $V = \frac{4}{3}\pi r^3$

$$\approx \frac{4}{3}(3.14)(3 \text{ m})^3$$
$$= 113.04 \text{ m}^3$$

The volume is approximately 113.04 m³.

You Try It 5
$$V = \text{volume of rectangular solid}$$
$$+ \text{ volume of cylinder}$$

$$V = LWH + \pi r^2 h$$
$$\approx (1.5 \text{ m})(0.4 \text{ m})(0.4 \text{ m}) + 3.14(0.8 \text{ m})^2(0.2 \text{ m})$$
$$= 0.24 \text{ m}^3 + 0.40192 \text{ m}^3$$
$$= 0.64192 \text{ m}^3$$

The volume is approximately 0.64192 m³.

You Try It 6
$$V = \text{volume of rectangular solid}$$
$$+ \frac{1}{2} \text{ the volume of cylinder}$$

$$V = LWH + \frac{1}{2}\pi r^2 h$$

$$\approx (24 \text{ in.})(6 \text{ in.})(4 \text{ in.}) + \frac{1}{2}(3.14)(3 \text{ in.})^2(24 \text{ in.})$$
$$= 576 \text{ in}^3 + 339.12 \text{ in}^3$$
$$= 915.12 \text{ in}^3$$

The volume is approximately 915.12 in³.

You Try It 7

Strategy   To find the volume of the freezer, use the formula for the volume of a rectangular solid.

Solution $V = LWH$
$$= (7 \text{ ft})(2.5 \text{ ft})(3 \text{ ft})$$
$$= 52.5 \text{ ft}^3$$

The volume of the freezer is 52.5 ft³.

You Try It 8

Strategy
To find the volume of the channel iron, subtract the volume of the cut-out rectangular solid from the large rectangular solid.

Solution

$$V = LWH - LWH$$
$$= (10 \text{ ft})(0.5 \text{ ft})(0.8 \text{ ft}) - (10 \text{ ft})(0.3 \text{ ft})(0.2 \text{ ft})$$
$$= 4 \text{ ft}^3 - 0.6 \text{ ft}^3$$
$$= 3.4 \text{ ft}^3$$

The volume of the channel iron is 3.4 ft³.

SECTION 12.5

You Try It 1   **a.** $\sqrt{16} = 4$
$\sqrt{169} = 13$

b. $\sqrt{32} \approx 5.657$
$\sqrt{162} \approx 12.728$

You Try It 2   Hypotenuse $= \sqrt{(\text{leg})^2 + (\text{leg})^2}$
$$= \sqrt{8^2 + 11^2}$$
$$= \sqrt{64 + 121}$$
$$= \sqrt{185}$$
$$\approx 13.601$$

The hypotenuse is approximately 13.601 in.

You Try It 3   Leg $= \sqrt{(\text{hypotenuse})^2 - (\text{leg})^2}$
$$= \sqrt{12^2 - 5^2}$$
$$= \sqrt{144 - 25}$$
$$= \sqrt{119}$$
$$\approx 10.909$$

The length of the leg is approximately 10.909 ft.

You Try It 4

Strategy   To find the distance between the holes, use the Pythagorean Theorem. The hypotenuse is the distance between the holes. The length of each leg is given (3 cm and 8 cm).

Solution   Hypotenuse $= \sqrt{(\text{leg})^2 + (\text{leg})^2}$
$$= \sqrt{3^2 + 8^2}$$
$$= \sqrt{9 + 64}$$
$$= \sqrt{73}$$
$$\approx 8.544$$

The distance is approximately 8.544 cm.

SECTION 12.6

You Try It 1 $\dfrac{4 \text{ cm}}{7 \text{ cm}} = \dfrac{4}{7}$

You Try It 2 $\dfrac{AB}{DE} = \dfrac{AC}{DF}$

$$\frac{7 \text{ cm}}{14 \text{ cm}} = \frac{3 \text{ cm}}{x}$$
$$7x = 14 \cdot 3 \text{ cm}$$
$$7x = 42 \text{ cm}$$
$$\frac{7x}{7} = \frac{42 \text{ cm}}{7}$$
$$x = 6 \text{ cm}$$

Side *DF* is 6 cm.

You Try It 3 $AC = DF$, $\angle ACB = \angle DFE$, but $BC \ne EF$ because $\angle CAB \ne \angle FDE$. Therefore, the triangles are not congruent.

You Try It 4 $\dfrac{AC}{DF} = \dfrac{\text{height } CH}{\text{height } FG}$

$$\frac{10 \text{ m}}{15 \text{ m}} = \frac{7 \text{ m}}{h}$$
$$10h = 15 \cdot 7 \text{ m}$$
$$10h = 105 \text{ m}$$
$$\frac{10h}{10} = \frac{105 \text{ m}}{10}$$
$$h = 10.5 \text{ m}$$

The height *FG* is 10.5 m.

You Try It 5

Strategy   To find the perimeter of triangle *ABC*:
• Solve a proportion to find the lengths of sides *BC* and *AC*.
• Use the formula $P = a + b + c$.

Solution $\dfrac{BC}{EF} = \dfrac{AB}{DE}$

$$\frac{BC}{10 \text{ in.}} = \frac{4 \text{ in.}}{8 \text{ in.}}$$
$$8(BC) = 10 \text{ in.}(4)$$
$$8(BC) = 40 \text{ in.}$$
$$\frac{8(BC)}{8} = \frac{40 \text{ in.}}{8}$$
$$BC = 5 \text{ in.}$$

$$\frac{AC}{DF} = \frac{AB}{DE}$$
$$\frac{AC}{6 \text{ in.}} = \frac{4 \text{ in.}}{8 \text{ in.}}$$
$$8(AC) = 6 \text{ in.}(4)$$
$$8(AC) = 24 \text{ in.}$$
$$\frac{8(AC)}{8} = \frac{24 \text{ in.}}{8}$$
$$AC = 3 \text{ in.}$$

Perimeter $= 4 \text{ in.} + 5 \text{ in.} + 3 \text{ in.}$
$$= 12 \text{ in.}$$

The perimeter of triangle *ABC* is 12 in.

Answers to Chapter 1 Selected Exercises

PREP TEST

1. 8   **2.** 1 2 3 4 5 6 7 8 9 10   **3.** a and D; b and E; c and A; d and B; e and F; f and C

SECTION 1.1

1. (number line 0–12 with point at 3)   **3.** (number line 0–12 with point at 9)   **5.** $37 < 49$ **7.** $101 > 87$
9. $245 > 158$ **11.** $0 < 45$ **13.** $815 < 928$ **15.** Millions   **17.** Hundred-thousands   **19.** Three thousand seven hundred ninety   **21.** Fifty-eight thousand four hundred seventy-three   **23.** Four hundred ninety-eight thousand five hundred twelve   **25.** Six million eight hundred forty-two thousand seven hundred fifteen   **27.** 357   **29.** 63,780
31. 7,024,709   **33.** $6000 + 200 + 90 + 5$ **35.** $400,000 + 50,000 + 3000 + 900 + 20 + 1$
37. $300,000 + 1000 + 800 + 9$ **39.** $3,000,000 + 600 + 40 + 2$ **41.** 850   **43.** 4000   **45.** 53,000   **47.** 630,000
49. 250,000   **51.** 72,000,000   **53.** 999; 10,000

SECTION 1.2

1. 28   **3.** 125   **5.** 102   **7.** 154   **9.** 1489   **11.** 828   **13.** 1584   **15.** 1219   **17.** 102,317   **19.** 79,326
21. 1804   **23.** 1579   **25.** 19,740   **27.** 7420   **29.** 120,570   **31.** 207,453   **33.** 24,218   **35.** 11,974
37. 9323   **39.** 77,139   **41.** 14,383   **43.** 9473   **45.** 33,247   **47.** 5058   **49.** 1992   **51.** 68,263
53. Cal.: 17,754 Est.: 17,700   **55.** Cal.: 2872 Est.: 2900   **57.** Cal.: 101,712 Est.: 101,000   **59.** Cal.: 158,763 Est.: 158,000   **61.** Cal.: 261,595 Est.: 260,000   **63.** Cal.: 946,718 Est.: 940,000
65. Cal.: 32,691,621 Est.: 33,000,000   **67.** Cal.: 34,420,922 Est.: 34,000,000   **69.** There were 118,295 multiple births during the year.
71. The estimated income from the four *Star Wars* movies was $1,500,000,000.   **73. a.** The income from the two movies with the lowest box-office returns is $599,300,000.   **b.** Yes, this income exceeds the income from the 1977 *Star Wars* production.   **75. a.** During the three days, 1285 miles will be driven.   **b.** At the end of the trip, the odometer will read 69,977 miles.   **77.** Americans ages 16 to 34 have invested $1796 in these three investments.   **79.** The sum of the average amounts invested in home equity and retirement for all Americans is greater than the sum of all categories for Americans aged 16 and 34.   **81.** 11 different sums   **83.** No. $0 + 0 = 0$ **85.** 10 numbers

SECTION 1.3

1. 4   **3.** 4   **5.** 10   **7.** 4   **9.** 9   **11.** 22   **13.** 60   **15.** 66   **17.** 31   **19.** 901   **21.** 791   **23.** 1125
25. 3131   **27.** 47   **29.** 925   **31.** 4561   **33.** 3205   **35.** 1222   **37.** 3021   **39.** 3022   **41.** 3040
43. 212   **45.** 60,245   **47.** 65   **49.** 17   **51.** 23   **53.** 456   **55.** 57   **57.** 375   **59.** 3139   **61.** 3621
63. 738   **65.** 3545   **67.** 749   **69.** 5343   **71.** 66,463   **73.** 16,590   **75.** 52,404   **77.** 38,777   **79.** 4638
81. 3612   **83.** 2913   **85.** 2583   **87.** 5268   **89.** 71,767   **91.** 11,239   **93.** 8482   **95.** 625   **97.** 76,725
99. 23   **101.** 4648   **103.** Cal.: 29,837 Est.: 30,000   **105.** Cal.: 36,668 Est.: 40,000   **107.** Cal.: 101,998 Est.: 100,000
109. There was an increase of 75,621 complaints from 2001 to 2002.   **111.** The amount that remains to be paid is $10,275.   **113.** The Giant erupts 25 feet higher than Old Faithful.   **115.** The expected increase over 10 years is 106,000.   **117.** The amount remaining is $436.   **119. a.** True   **b.** False   **c.** False

SECTION 1.4

1. 6×2 or $6 \cdot 2$ **3.** 4×7 or $4 \cdot 7$ **5.** 12   **7.** 35   **9.** 25   **11.** 0   **13.** 72   **15.** 198   **17.** 335
19. 2492   **21.** 5463   **23.** 4200   **25.** 6327   **27.** 1896   **29.** 5056   **31.** 1685   **33.** 46,963   **35.** 59,976
37. 19,120   **39.** 19,790   **41.** 108   **43.** 3664   **45.** 20,036   **47.** 71,656   **49.** 432   **51.** 1944   **53.** 41,832
55. 43,620   **57.** 335,195   **59.** 594,625   **61.** 321,696   **63.** 342,171   **65.** 279,220   **67.** 191,800
69. 463,712   **71.** 180,621   **73.** 478,800   **75.** 158,422   **77.** 4,696,714   **79.** 5,542,452   **81.** 198,423
83. 18,834   **85.** 260,178   **87.** 315,109,895   **89.** Cal.: 440,076 Est.: 450,000   **91.** Cal.: 6,491,166 Est.: 6,300,000   **93.** Cal.: 18,728,744 Est.: 18,000,000

95. Cal.: 57,691,192   **97.** The plane used 5190 gallons of fuel on a 6-hour flight.   **99.** The area is 256 square miles.
Est.: 54,000,000
101. Company A offers the lower total price.   **103.** The estimated cost of the electricians' labor is $5100.   **105.** The total cost is $2138.   **107.** There are 12 accidental deaths each hour; 288 deaths each day; and 105,120 deaths each year.

SECTION 1.5

1. 2   **3.** 6   **5.** 7   **7.** 16   **9.** 210   **11.** 44   **13.** 703   **15.** 910   **17.** 21,560   **19.** 3580   **21.** 482
23. 1075   **25.** 52   **27.** 34   **29.** 2 r1   **31.** 5 r2   **33.** 13 r1   **35.** 10 r3   **37.** 90 r2   **39.** 230 r1
41. 204 r3   **43.** 1347 r3   **45.** 1720 r2   **47.** 409 r2   **49.** 6214 r2   **51.** 8708 r2   **53.** 1080 r2   **55.** 4200
57. 19,600   **59.** 1 r38   **61.** 1 r26   **63.** 21 r21   **65.** 30 r22   **67.** 5 r40   **69.** 9 r17   **71.** 200 r21
73. 303 r1   **75.** 67 r13   **77.** 176 r13   **79.** 1086 r7   **81.** 403   **83.** 12 r456   **85.** 4 r160   **87.** 160 r27
89. 1669 r14   **91.** 7950   **93.** Cal.: 2225   **95.** Cal.: 11,016   **97.** Cal.: 26,656   **99.** Cal.: 504   **101.** Cal.: 541
Est.: 2000   Est.: 10,000   Est.: 30,000   Est.: 500   Est.: 500
103. Cal.: 20,621   **105.** The average monthly expense for housing is $976.   **107.** The average monthly claim for theft
Est.: 20,000
is $25,000.   **109.** The average number of hours worked by employees in Britain is 35 hours.   **111.** 380 pennies are in circulation for each person.   **113.** 198,400,000 cases of eggs are produced during the year.   **115.** The average U.S. household will spend $130 on gasoline each month.   **117.** The average starting salary of an accounting major is $13,092 greater than that of a psychology major.   **119.** The difference is $10,848.   **121.** The total pay is $491.   **123.** 212

SECTION 1.6

1. 2^3 **3.** $6^3 \cdot 7^4$ **5.** $2^3 \cdot 3^3$ **7.** $5 \cdot 7^5$ **9.** $3^3 \cdot 6^4$ **11.** $3^3 \cdot 5 \cdot 9^3$ **13.** 8   **15.** 400   **17.** 900   **19.** 972
21. 120   **23.** 360   **25.** 0   **27.** 90,000   **29.** 540   **31.** 4050   **33.** 11,025   **35.** 25,920   **37.** 4,320,000
39. 5   **41.** 10   **43.** 47   **45.** 8   **47.** 5   **49.** 8   **51.** 6   **53.** 53   **55.** 44   **57.** 19   **59.** 67   **61.** 168
63. 27   **65.** 14   **67.** 10   **69.** 9   **71.** 12   **73.** 32   **75.** 39   **77.** 1024

SECTION 1.7

1. 1, 2, 4   **3.** 1, 2, 5, 10   **5.** 1, 7   **7.** 1, 3, 9   **9.** 1, 13   **11.** 1, 2, 3, 6, 9, 18   **13.** 1, 2, 4, 7, 8, 14, 28, 56
15. 1, 3, 5, 9, 15, 45   **17.** 1, 29   **19.** 1, 2, 11, 22   **21.** 1, 2, 4, 13, 26, 52   **23.** 1, 2, 41, 82   **25.** 1, 3, 19, 57
27. 1, 2, 3, 4, 6, 8, 12, 16, 24, 48   **29.** 1, 5, 19, 95   **31.** 1, 2, 3, 6, 9, 18, 27, 54   **33.** 1, 2, 3, 6, 11, 22, 33, 66
35. 1, 2, 4, 5, 8, 10, 16, 20, 40, 80   **37.** 1, 2, 3, 4, 6, 8, 12, 16, 24, 32, 48, 96   **39.** 1, 2, 3, 5, 6, 9, 10, 15, 18, 30, 45, 90
41. $2 \cdot 3$ **43.** Prime   **45.** $2 \cdot 2 \cdot 2 \cdot 3$ **47.** $3 \cdot 3 \cdot 3$ **49.** $2 \cdot 2 \cdot 3 \cdot 3$ **51.** Prime   **53.** $2 \cdot 3 \cdot 3 \cdot 5$
55. $5 \cdot 23$ **57.** $2 \cdot 3 \cdot 3$ **59.** $2 \cdot 2 \cdot 7$ **61.** Prime   **63.** $2 \cdot 31$ **65.** $2 \cdot 11$ **67.** Prime   **69.** $2 \cdot 3 \cdot 11$
71. $2 \cdot 37$ **73.** Prime   **75.** $5 \cdot 11$ **77.** $2 \cdot 2 \cdot 2 \cdot 3 \cdot 5$ **79.** $2 \cdot 2 \cdot 2 \cdot 2 \cdot 2 \cdot 5$ **81.** $2 \cdot 2 \cdot 2 \cdot 3 \cdot 3 \cdot 3$
83. $5 \cdot 5 \cdot 5 \cdot 5$ **85.** 3, 5; 5, 7; 11, 13; 41, 43; 71, 73; and 17, 19 are all the twin primes less than 100.

CHAPTER 1 REVIEW EXERCISES*

1. 600 [1.6A]   **2.** 10,000 + 300 + 20 + 7 [1.1C]   **3.** 1, 2, 3, 6, 9, 18 [1.7A]   **4.** 12,493 [1.2A]
5. 1749 [1.3B]   **6.** 2135 [1.5A]   **7.** 101 > 87 [1.1A]   **8.** $5^2 \cdot 7^5$ [1.6A]   **9.** 619,833 [1.4B]
10. 5409 [1.3B]   **11.** 1081 [1.2A]   **12.** 2 [1.6B]   **13.** 45,700 [1.1D]   **14.** Two hundred seventy-six thousand fifty-seven [1.1B]   **15.** 1306 r59 [1.5C]   **16.** 2,011,044 [1.1B]   **17.** 488 r2 [1.5B]   **18.** 17 [1.6B]
19. 32 [1.6B]   **20.** $2 \cdot 2 \cdot 2 \cdot 3 \cdot 3$ [1.7B]   **21.** 2133 [1.3A]   **22.** 22,761 [1.4B]   **23.** The total pay for last week's work is $768. [1.4C]   **24.** He drove 27 miles per gallon of gasoline. [1.5D]   **25.** Each monthly car payment is $310. [1.5D]   **26.** The total income from commissions is $2567. [1.2B]   **27.** The total amount deposited is $301.

*Note: The numbers in brackets following the answers in the Chapter Review are a reference to the objective that corresponds to that problem. For example, the reference [1.2A] stands for Section 1.2, Objective A. This notation will be used for all Prep Tests, Chapter Reviews, Chapter Tests, and Cumulative Reviews throughout the text.

The new checking account balance is $817. [1.2B]   **28.** The total of the car payments is $2952. [1.4C]
29. More males were involved in college sports in 2001 than in 1972. [1.1A]   **30.** The difference between the numbers of male and female athletes in 1972 was 140,407 students. [1.3C]   **31.** The number of female athletes increased by 120,939 students from 1972 to 2001. [1.3C]   **32.** 159,421 more students were involved in ahtletics in 2001 than in 1972. [1.3C]

CHAPTER 1 TEST

1. 432 [1.6A]   **2.** Two hundred seven thousand sixty-eight [1.1B]   **3.** 9333 [1.3B]   **4.** 1, 2, 4, 5, 10, 20 [1.7A]
5. 6,854,144 [1.4B]   **6.** 9 [1.6B]   **7.** $900,000 + 6000 + 300 + 70 + 8$ [1.1C]   **8.** 75,000 [1.1D]
9. 1121 r27 [1.5C]   **10.** $3^3 \cdot 7^2$ [1.6A]   **11.** 54,915 [1.2A]   **12.** $2 \cdot 2 \cdot 3 \cdot 7$ [1.7B]   **13.** 4 [1.6B]
14. 726,104 [1.4A]   **15.** 1,204,006 [1.1B]   **16.** 8710 r2 [1.5B]   **17.** $21 > 19$ [1.1A]   **18.** 703 [1.5A]
19. 96,798 [1.2A]   **20.** 19,922 [1.3B]   **21.** The difference in projected total enrollment between 2012 and 2009 is 154,000 students. [1.3C]   **22.** The average enrollment in each of the grades 9 through 12 in 2012 is 3,858,500 students. [1.5D]   **23.** 3000 boxes were needed to pack the lemons. [1.5D]   **24.** The investor receives $2844 over the 12-month period. [1.4C]   **25. a.** 855 miles were driven during the 3 days. [1.2B]   **b.** The odometer reading at the end of the 3 days is 48,481 miles. [1.2B]

Answers to Chapter 2 Selected Exercises

PREP TEST

1. 20 [1.4A]   **2.** 120 [1.4A]   **3.** 9 [1.4A]   **4.** 10 [1.2A]   **5.** 7 [1.3A]   **6.** 2 r3 [1.5C]   **7.** 1, 2, 3, 4, 6, 12 [1.5B]   **8.** 59 [1.6B]   **9.** 7 [1.3A]   **10.** $44 < 48$ [1.1A]

SECTION 2.1

1. 40   **3.** 24   **5.** 30   **7.** 12   **9.** 24   **11.** 60   **13.** 56   **15.** 9   **17.** 32   **19.** 36   **21.** 660
23. 9384   **25.** 24   **27.** 30   **29.** 24   **31.** 576   **33.** 1680   **35.** 1   **37.** 3   **39.** 5   **41.** 25   **43.** 1
45. 4   **47.** 4   **49.** 6   **51.** 4   **53.** 1   **55.** 7   **57.** 5   **59.** 8   **61.** 1   **63.** 25   **65.** 7   **67.** 8
69. Two composite numbers are relatively prime if they do not have any common factor except the factor 1. Examples: 4 and 5, 8 and 9, and 16 and 21.

SECTION 2.2

1. Improper fraction   **3.** Proper fraction   **5.** $\frac{3}{4}$ **7.** $\frac{7}{8}$ **9.** $1\frac{1}{2}$ **11.** $2\frac{5}{8}$ **13.** $3\frac{3}{5}$ **15.** $\frac{5}{4}$ **17.** $\frac{8}{3}$
19. $\frac{28}{8}$ **21.**   **23.**   **25.**   **27.** $2\frac{3}{4}$ **29.** 5   **31.** $1\frac{1}{8}$ **33.** $2\frac{3}{10}$ **35.** 3
37. $1\frac{1}{7}$ **39.** $2\frac{1}{3}$ **41.** 16   **43.** $2\frac{1}{8}$ **45.** $2\frac{2}{5}$ **47.** 1   **49.** 9   **51.** $\frac{7}{3}$ **53.** $\frac{13}{2}$ **55.** $\frac{41}{6}$ **57.** $\frac{37}{4}$
59. $\frac{21}{2}$ **61.** $\frac{73}{9}$ **63.** $\frac{58}{11}$ **65.** $\frac{21}{8}$ **67.** $\frac{13}{8}$ **69.** $\frac{100}{9}$ **71.** $\frac{27}{8}$ **73.** $\frac{85}{13}$

SECTION 2.3

1. $\frac{5}{10}$ **3.** $\frac{9}{48}$ **5.** $\frac{12}{32}$ **7.** $\frac{9}{51}$ **9.** $\frac{12}{16}$ **11.** $\frac{27}{9}$ **13.** $\frac{20}{60}$ **15.** $\frac{44}{60}$ **17.** $\frac{12}{18}$ **19.** $\frac{35}{49}$ **21.** $\frac{10}{18}$
23. $\frac{21}{3}$ **25.** $\frac{35}{45}$ **27.** $\frac{60}{64}$ **29.** $\frac{21}{98}$ **31.** $\frac{30}{48}$ **33.** $\frac{15}{42}$ **35.** $\frac{102}{144}$ **37.** $\frac{153}{408}$ **39.** $\frac{340}{800}$ **41.** $\frac{1}{3}$ **43.** $\frac{1}{2}$
45. $\frac{1}{6}$ **47.** $1\frac{1}{9}$ **49.** 0   **51.** $\frac{9}{22}$ **53.** 3   **55.** $\frac{4}{21}$ **57.** $\frac{12}{35}$ **59.** $\frac{7}{11}$ **61.** $1\frac{1}{3}$ **63.** $\frac{3}{5}$ **65.** $\frac{1}{11}$

67. 4   **69.** $\frac{1}{3}$ **71.** $\frac{3}{5}$ **73.** $2\frac{1}{4}$ **75.** $\frac{1}{5}$ **77.** $\frac{3}{1}, \frac{6}{2}, \frac{9}{3}, \frac{12}{4}, \frac{15}{5}$ are fractions that are equal to 3.   **79. a.** $\frac{4}{25}$

b. $\frac{4}{25}$

SECTION 2.4

1. $\frac{3}{7}$ **3.** 1   **5.** $1\frac{4}{11}$ **7.** $3\frac{2}{5}$ **9.** $2\frac{4}{5}$ **11.** $2\frac{1}{4}$ **13.** $1\frac{3}{8}$ **15.** $1\frac{7}{15}$ **17.** $\frac{15}{16}$ **19.** $1\frac{4}{11}$ **21.** 1

23. $1\frac{7}{8}$ **25.** $1\frac{1}{6}$ **27.** $\frac{13}{14}$ **29.** $\frac{53}{60}$ **31.** $1\frac{1}{56}$ **33.** $\frac{23}{60}$ **35.** $\frac{56}{57}$ **37.** $1\frac{17}{18}$ **39.** $1\frac{11}{48}$ **41.** $1\frac{9}{20}$

43. $1\frac{109}{180}$ **45.** $1\frac{91}{144}$ **47.** $2\frac{5}{72}$ **49.** $\frac{39}{40}$ **51.** $1\frac{19}{24}$ **53.** $1\frac{65}{72}$ **55.** $3\frac{2}{3}$ **57.** $10\frac{1}{12}$ **59.** $9\frac{2}{7}$ **61.** $6\frac{7}{40}$

63. $9\frac{47}{48}$ **65.** $8\frac{3}{13}$ **67.** $16\frac{29}{120}$ **69.** $24\frac{29}{40}$ **71.** $33\frac{7}{24}$ **73.** $10\frac{5}{36}$ **75.** $10\frac{5}{12}$ **77.** $14\frac{73}{90}$ **79.** $10\frac{13}{48}$

81. $42\frac{13}{54}$ **83.** $8\frac{1}{36}$ **85.** $14\frac{1}{12}$ **87.** $8\frac{61}{72}$ **89.** The length of the shaft is $1\frac{5}{16}$ inches.   **91.** The total thickness

is $1\frac{5}{16}$ inches.   **93. a.** A total of 20 hours was worked.   **b.** Your total salary for the week is $220.   **95.** The total

length of wood needed is $55\frac{3}{4}$ feet.   **97.** Those who changed homes outside the county were $\frac{1}{3}$ of the people who

changed homes.

SECTION 2.5

1. $\frac{2}{17}$ **3.** $\frac{1}{3}$ **5.** $\frac{1}{10}$ **7.** $\frac{5}{13}$ **9.** $\frac{1}{3}$ **11.** $\frac{4}{7}$ **13.** $\frac{1}{4}$ **15.** $\frac{9}{23}$ **17.** $\frac{1}{4}$ **19.** $\frac{1}{2}$ **21.** $\frac{19}{56}$ **23.** $\frac{1}{2}$

25. $\frac{11}{60}$ **27.** $\frac{15}{56}$ **29.** $\frac{37}{51}$ **31.** $\frac{17}{70}$ **33.** $\frac{49}{120}$ **35.** $\frac{8}{45}$ **37.** $\frac{11}{21}$ **39.** $\frac{23}{60}$ **41.** $\frac{1}{18}$ **43.** $5\frac{1}{5}$ **45.** $10\frac{9}{17}$

47. $4\frac{7}{8}$ **49.** $\frac{16}{21}$ **51.** $5\frac{1}{2}$ **53.** $5\frac{4}{7}$ **55.** $7\frac{5}{24}$ **57.** $48\frac{31}{70}$ **59.** $85\frac{2}{9}$ **61.** $9\frac{5}{13}$ **63.** $15\frac{11}{20}$ **65.** $4\frac{23}{24}$

67. $2\frac{11}{15}$ **69.** The missing dimension is $9\frac{1}{2}$ inches.   **71.** The difference between Meyfarth's distance and Coachman's

distance was $9\frac{3}{8}$ inches. The difference between Kostadinova's distance and Meyfarth's distance was $5\frac{1}{4}$ inches.

73. a. The distance from the starting point to the second checkpoint is $7\frac{17}{24}$ miles.   **b.** The distance from the second

checkpoint to the finish line is $4\frac{7}{24}$ miles.   **75. a.** Yes   **b.** The wrestler needs to lose $3\frac{1}{4}$ pounds to reach the desired

weight.   **77.** $2\frac{5}{6}$ **79.**

$\frac{3}{8}$	$\frac{3}{4}$	$\frac{3}{4}$
1	$\frac{5}{8}$	$\frac{1}{4}$
$\frac{1}{2}$	$\frac{1}{2}$	$\frac{7}{8}$

SECTION 2.6

1. $\frac{7}{12}$ **3.** $\frac{7}{48}$ **5.** $\frac{1}{48}$ **7.** $\frac{11}{14}$ **9.** $\frac{1}{7}$ **11.** $\frac{1}{8}$ **13.** 6   **15.** $\frac{5}{12}$ **17.** 6   **19.** $\frac{2}{3}$ **21.** $\frac{3}{16}$ **23.** $\frac{3}{80}$

25. 10   **27.** $\frac{1}{15}$ **29.** $\frac{2}{3}$ **31.** $\frac{7}{26}$ **33.** 4   **35.** $\frac{100}{357}$ **37.** $\frac{5}{24}$ **39.** $\frac{1}{12}$ **41.** $\frac{4}{15}$ **43.** $1\frac{1}{2}$ **45.** 4

47. $\frac{4}{9}$ **49.** $\frac{1}{2}$ **51.** $16\frac{1}{2}$ **53.** 10   **55.** $6\frac{3}{7}$ **57.** $18\frac{1}{3}$ **59.** $1\frac{5}{7}$ **61.** $3\frac{1}{2}$ **63.** $25\frac{5}{8}$ **65.** $1\frac{11}{16}$ **67.** 16

69. 3   **71.** $8\frac{37}{40}$ **73.** $6\frac{19}{28}$ **75.** $7\frac{2}{5}$ **77.** 16   **79.** $32\frac{4}{5}$ **81.** $28\frac{1}{2}$ **83.** 9   **85.** $\frac{5}{8}$ **87.** $3\frac{1}{40}$

89. The salmon costs $11.   **91. a.** No. $\frac{1}{3}$ of 9 feet is approximately 3 ft.   **b.** The length of the board cut off is $3\frac{1}{12}$ feet.

93. The area of the square is $27\frac{9}{16}$ square feet.   **95. a.** The amount budgeted for housing and utilities is $1680.

b. The amount remaining for other than housing and utilities is $2520. **97.** The total cost is $363. **99.** The weight of the $12\frac{7}{12}$-foot steel rod is $54\frac{19}{36}$ pounds. **101.** $\frac{3}{16}$ of the total portfolio is invested in corporate bonds. **105.** *A*

SECTION 2.7

1. $\frac{5}{6}$ **3.** 1 **5.** 0 **7.** $\frac{1}{2}$ **9.** $2\frac{73}{256}$ **11.** $1\frac{1}{9}$ **13.** $\frac{1}{6}$ **15.** $\frac{7}{10}$ **17.** 2 **19.** 2 **21.** $\frac{1}{6}$ **23.** 6

25. $\frac{1}{15}$ **27.** 2 **29.** $2\frac{1}{2}$ **31.** 3 **33.** $1\frac{1}{6}$ **35.** $3\frac{1}{3}$ **37.** 6 **39.** $\frac{1}{2}$ **41.** $\frac{1}{30}$ **43.** $1\frac{4}{5}$ **45.** 13

47. $\frac{25}{288}$ **49.** 3 **51.** $\frac{1}{5}$ **53.** $\frac{11}{28}$ **55.** $\frac{5}{86}$ **57.** 120 **59.** $\frac{11}{40}$ **61.** $\frac{33}{40}$ **63.** $4\frac{4}{9}$ **65.** $\frac{13}{32}$ **67.** $10\frac{2}{3}$

69. $9\frac{39}{40}$ **71.** $\frac{12}{53}$ **73.** $4\frac{62}{191}$ **75.** 68 **77.** $8\frac{2}{7}$ **79.** $3\frac{13}{49}$ **81.** 4 **83.** $1\frac{3}{5}$ **85.** $\frac{9}{34}$ **87.** There are

12 servings in 16 ounces of cereal. **89.** Each acre costs $24,000. **91.** The nut will make 12 turns in moving $1\frac{7}{8}$ inches.

93. a. The total weight of the fat and bone is $1\frac{5}{12}$ pounds. **b.** The chef can cut 28 servings from the roast.

95. The actual length of wall a is $12\frac{1}{2}$ feet. The actual length of wall b is 18 feet. The actual length of wall c is $15\frac{3}{4}$ feet.

97. $\frac{17}{50}$ of the money borrowed is spent on home improvement, cars and tuition. **99.** The capacity of the music center is

1800 people. **101.** $\frac{1}{6}$ of the puzzle is left to complete. **103.** Your total earnings for last week's work are $111.

105. The average teenage boy consumes 3500 calories each week in soda. **107.** 740 miles **109. a.** $\frac{2}{3}$ **b.** $2\frac{5}{8}$

111. The quotient

SECTION 2.8

1. $\frac{11}{40} < \frac{19}{40}$ **3.** $\frac{2}{3} < \frac{5}{7}$ **5.** $\frac{5}{8} > \frac{7}{12}$ **7.** $\frac{7}{9} < \frac{11}{12}$ **9.** $\frac{13}{14} > \frac{19}{21}$ **11.** $\frac{7}{24} < \frac{11}{30}$ **13.** $\frac{9}{64}$ **15.** $\frac{8}{729}$ **17.** $\frac{1}{24}$

19. $\frac{8}{245}$ **21.** $\frac{1}{121}$ **23.** $\frac{81}{625}$ **25.** $\frac{7}{36}$ **27.** $\frac{27}{49}$ **29.** $\frac{5}{6}$ **31.** $1\frac{5}{12}$ **33.** $\frac{7}{48}$ **35.** $\frac{29}{36}$ **37.** $\frac{55}{72}$ **39.** $\frac{35}{54}$

41. 2 **43.** $\frac{9}{19}$ **45.** $\frac{7}{32}$ **47.** $\frac{64}{75}$

CHAPTER 2 REVIEW EXERCISES

1. $\frac{2}{3}$ [2.3B] **2.** $\frac{5}{16}$ [2.8B] **3.** $\frac{13}{4}$ [2.2A] **4.** $1\frac{13}{18}$ [2.4B] **5.** $\frac{11}{18} < \frac{17}{24}$ [2.8A] **6.** $14\frac{19}{42}$ [2.5C]

7. $\frac{5}{36}$ [2.8C] **8.** $9\frac{1}{24}$ [2.6B] **9.** 2 [2.7B] **10.** $\frac{25}{48}$ [2.5B] **11.** $3\frac{1}{3}$ [2.7B] **12.** 4 [2.1B]

13. $\frac{24}{36}$ [2.3A] **14.** $\frac{3}{4}$ [2.7A] **15.** $\frac{32}{44}$ [2.3A] **16.** $16\frac{1}{2}$ [2.6B] **17.** 36 [2.1A] **18.** $\frac{4}{11}$ [2.3B]

19. $1\frac{1}{8}$ [2.4A] **20.** $10\frac{1}{8}$ [2.5C] **21.** $18\frac{13}{54}$ [2.4C] **22.** 5 [2.1B] **23.** $3\frac{2}{5}$ [2.2B] **24.** $\frac{1}{15}$ [2.8C]

25. $5\frac{7}{8}$ [2.4C] **26.** 54 [2.1A] **27.** $\frac{1}{3}$ [2.5A] **28.** $\frac{19}{7}$ [2.2B] **29.** 2 [2.7A] **30.** $\frac{1}{15}$ [2.6A]

31. $\frac{1}{8}$ [2.6A] **32.** $1\frac{7}{8}$ [2.2A] **33.** The total rainfall for the 3 months was $21\frac{7}{24}$ inches. [2.4D] **34.** The cost per

acre was $36,000. [2.7C] **35.** The second checkpoint is $4\frac{3}{4}$ miles from the finish line. [2.5D] **36.** The car can travel

243 miles. [2.6C]

CHAPTER 2 TEST

1. $\frac{4}{9}$ [2.6A] **2.** 8 [2.1B] **3.** $1\frac{3}{7}$ [2.7A] **4.** $\frac{7}{24}$ [2.8C] **5.** $\frac{49}{5}$ [2.2B] **6.** 8 [2.6B] **7.** $\frac{5}{8}$ [2.3B]

8. $\frac{3}{8} < \frac{5}{12}$ [2.8A]   **9.** $\frac{5}{6}$ [2.8C]   **10.** 120 [2.1A]   **11.** $\frac{1}{4}$ [2.5A]   **12.** $3\frac{3}{5}$ [2.2B]   **13.** $2\frac{2}{19}$ [2.7B]

14. $\frac{45}{72}$ [2.3A]   **15.** $1\frac{61}{90}$ [2.4B]   **16.** $13\frac{81}{88}$ [2.5C]   **17.** $\frac{7}{48}$ [2.5B]   **18.** $\frac{1}{6}$ [2.8B]   **19.** $1\frac{11}{12}$ [2.4A]

20. $22\frac{4}{15}$ [2.4C]   **21.** $\frac{11}{4}$ [2.2A]   **22.** The electrician earns \$840. [2.6C]   **23.** 11 lots were available for sale.
[2.7C]   **24.** The developer plans to build 30 houses on the property. [2.7C]   **25.** The total rainfall for the 3-month

period was $21\frac{11}{24}$ inches. [2.4D]

CUMULATIVE REVIEW EXERCISES

1. 290,000 [1.1D]   **2.** 291,278 [1.3B]   **3.** 73,154 [1.4B]   **4.** 540 r12 [1.5C]   **5.** 1 [1.6B]

6. $2 \cdot 2 \cdot 11$ [1.7B]   **7.** 210 [2.1A]   **8.** 20 [2.1B]   **9.** $\frac{23}{3}$ [2.2B]   **10.** $6\frac{1}{4}$ [2.2B]   **11.** $\frac{15}{48}$ [2.3A]

12. $\frac{2}{5}$ [2.3B]   **13.** $1\frac{7}{48}$ [2.4B]   **14.** $14\frac{11}{48}$ [2.4C]   **15.** $\frac{13}{24}$ [2.5B]   **16.** $1\frac{7}{9}$ [2.5C]   **17.** $\frac{7}{20}$ [2.6A]

18. $7\frac{1}{2}$ [2.6B]   **19.** $1\frac{1}{20}$ [2.7A]   **20.** $2\frac{5}{8}$ [2.7B]   **21.** $\frac{1}{9}$ [2.8B]   **22.** $5\frac{5}{24}$ [2.8C]

23. The amount in the checkbook account at the end of the week was \$862. [1.3C]   **24.** The total income from the
tickets was \$1410. [1.4C]   **25.** The total weight is $12\frac{1}{24}$ pounds. [2.4D]   **26.** The length of the remaining piece is

$4\frac{17}{24}$ feet. [2.5D]   **27.** The car travels 225 miles on $8\frac{1}{3}$ gallons of gas. [2.6C]   **28.** 25 parcels can be sold from the
remaining land. [2.7C]

Answers to Chapter 3 Selected Exercises

PREP TEST

1. $\frac{3}{10}$ [2.2A]   **2.** 36,900 [1.1D]   **3.** Four thousand seven hundred ninety-one [1.1B]   **4.** 6842 [1.1B]

5. 9394 [1.2A]   **6.** 1638 [1.3B]   **7.** 76,804 [1.4B]   **8.** 278 r18 [1.5C]

SECTION 3.1

1. Thousandths   **3.** Ten-thousandths   **5.** Hundredths   **7.** 0.3   **9.** 0.21   **11.** 0.461   **13.** 0.093   **15.** $\frac{1}{10}$

17. $\frac{47}{100}$ **19.** $\frac{289}{1000}$ **21.** $\frac{9}{100}$ **23.** Thirty-seven hundredths   **25.** Nine and four tenths   **27.** Fifty-three
ten-thousandths   **29.** Forty-five thousandths   **31.** Twenty-six and four hundredths   **33.** 3.0806   **35.** 407.03
37. 246.024   **39.** 73.02684   **41.** 5.4   **43.** 30.0   **45.** 413.60   **47.** 6.062   **49.** 97   **51.** 5440   **53.** 0.0236
55. 0.18 ounce   **57.** 26.2 miles   **59.** For example, **a.** 0.15   **b.** 1.05   **c.** 0.001

SECTION 3.2

1. 150.1065   **3.** 95.8446   **5.** 69.644   **7.** 92.883   **9.** 113.205   **11.** 0.69   **13.** 16.305   **15.** 110.7666
17. 104.4959   **19.** Cal.: 234.192   **21.** Cal.: 781.943   **23.** The total length of the shaft is 5.65 inches.
　　　　　　　　　Est.: 234   　　　　　　　Est.: 782
25. The amount in the checking account is \$3664.20.   **27.** The combined populations of Asia and Africa in 2050 are
expected to be 7.1 billion people.   **29.** The number of self-employed people who earn more than \$5000 is 6.5 million.
31. No, \$10 is not enough.   **33.** No, a 4-foot rope cannot be wrapped around the box.

SECTION 3.3

1. 5.627   **3.** 113.6427   **5.** 6.7098   **7.** 215.697   **9.** 53.8776   **11.** 72.7091   **13.** 0.3142   **15.** 1.023
17. 261.166   **19.** 655.32   **21.** 342.9268   **23.** 8.628   **25.** 4.685   **27.** 10.383
29. Cal.: 2.74506   **31.** Cal.: 7.14925   **33.** The missing dimension is 7.55 inches.   **35. a.** The total amount of
　　　Est.: 3   　　　　　Est.: 7

the checks is $607.36. **b.** Your new balance is $422.38. **37.** The increase is 0.39 million births. **39.** The growth in online shopping from 2000 to 2003 is 22.6 million households. **41. a.** 0.1 **b.** 0.01 **c.** 0.001

SECTION 3.4

1. 0.36 **3.** 0.30 **5.** 0.25 **7.** 0.45 **9.** 6.93 **11.** 1.84 **13.** 4.32 **15.** 0.74 **17.** 39.5 **19.** 2.72
21. 0.603 **23.** 0.096 **25.** 13.50 **27.** 79.80 **29.** 4.316 **31.** 1.794 **33.** 0.06 **35.** 0.072 **37.** 0.1323
39. 0.03568 **41.** 0.0784 **43.** 0.076 **45.** 34.48 **47.** 580.5 **49.** 20.148 **51.** 0.04255 **53.** 0.17686
55. 0.19803 **57.** 14.8657 **59.** 0.0006608 **61.** 53.9961 **63.** 0.536335 **65.** 0.429 **67.** 2.116 **69.** 0.476
71. 1.022 **73.** 37.96 **75.** 2.318 **77.** 3.2 **79.** 6.5 **81.** 6285.6 **83.** 3200 **85.** 35,700 **87.** 6.3
89. 3.9 **91.** 49,000 **93.** 6.7 **95.** 0.012075 **97.** 0.0117796 **99.** 0.31004 **101.** 0.082845 **103.** 5.175
105. Cal.: 91.2 **107.** Cal.: 1.0472 **109.** Cal.: 3.897 **111.** Cal.: 11.2406 **113.** Cal.: 0.371096
 Est.: 90   Est.: 0.8   Est.: 4.5   Est.: 12   Est.: 0.32
115. Cal.: 31.8528 **117.** Cal.: 1941.069459 **119.** Cal.: 0.00004351152 **121.** The motor costs $1.51 to operate.
 Est.: 30   Est.: 2000   Est.: 0.00005
123. a. The estimated amount received is $25.00. **b.** The amount received was $23.40. **125.** The area is 23.625 square feet. **127. a.** The amount of overtime pay is $650.25. **b.** The nurse's total income is $1806.25.
129. The cost is $341.25. **131. a.** The total cost for grade 1 is $21.12. **b.** The total cost for grade 2 is $29.84.
c. The total cost for grade 3 is $201.66. **d.** The total cost is $252.62. **133.** Cars 2 and 5 would fail the test.

137. $1\dfrac{3}{10} \times 2\dfrac{31}{100} = \dfrac{13}{10} \times \dfrac{231}{100} = \dfrac{3003}{1000} = 3\dfrac{3}{1000} = 3.003$

SECTION 3.5

1. 0.82 **3.** 4.8 **5.** 89 **7.** 60 **9.** 84.3 **11.** 32.3 **13.** 5.06 **15.** 1.3 **17.** 0.11 **19.** 3.8 **21.** 6.3
23. 0.6 **25.** 2.5 **27.** 1.1 **29.** 130.6 **31.** 0.81 **33.** 0.09 **35.** 40.70 **37.** 0.46 **39.** 0.019
41. 0.087 **43.** 0.360 **45.** 0.103 **47.** 0.009 **49.** 1 **51.** 3 **53.** 1 **55.** 57 **57.** 0.407 **59.** 4.267
61. 0.01037 **63.** 0.008295 **65.** 0.82537 **67.** 0.032 **69.** 0.23627 **71.** 0.000053 **73.** 0.0018932
75. 18.42 **77.** 16.07 **79.** 0.0135 **81.** 0.023678 **83.** 0.112 **85.** Cal.: 11.1632 **87.** Cal.: 884.0909
 Est.: 10   Est.: 1000
89. Cal.: 1.8269 **91.** Cal.: 58.8095 **93.** Cal.: 72.3053 **95.** Cal.: 0.0023 **97.** 6.23 yards are gained per carry.
 Est.: 1.5   Est.: 50   Est.: 100   Est.: 0.0025
99. The cost per can is $.28. **101.** The cost per mile is $.04. **103.** The monthly payment is $58.65.
105. 2.9 million more women are expected to be attending institutions of higher learning in 2010. **107.** The Army's budget was 4.2 times greater than the Navy's advertising budget. **109.** The population of this segment is expected to be 2.1 times greater in 2030 than in 2000. **111.** The cigarette consumption in 2000 was 2.5 times greater than in 1960.
113. A total of 9.7 million acres was burned. **119.** × **121.** × **123.** ÷ **125.** 2.53

SECTION 3.6

1. 0.625 **3.** 0.667 **5.** 0.167 **7.** 0.417 **9.** 1.750 **11.** 1.500 **13.** 4.000 **15.** 0.003 **17.** 7.080
19. 37.500 **21.** 0.160 **23.** 8.400 **25.** $\dfrac{4}{5}$ **27.** $\dfrac{8}{25}$ **29.** $\dfrac{1}{8}$ **31.** $1\dfrac{1}{4}$ **33.** $16\dfrac{9}{10}$ **35.** $8\dfrac{2}{5}$ **37.** $8\dfrac{437}{1000}$
39. $2\dfrac{1}{4}$ **41.** $\dfrac{23}{150}$ **43.** $\dfrac{703}{800}$ **45.** $7\dfrac{19}{50}$ **47.** $\dfrac{57}{100}$ **49.** $\dfrac{2}{3}$ **51.** $0.6 > 0.45$ **53.** $3.89 < 3.98$
55. $0.025 < 0.105$ **57.** $\dfrac{4}{5} < 0.802$ **59.** $0.85 < \dfrac{7}{8}$ **61.** $\dfrac{7}{12} > 0.58$ **63.** $\dfrac{11}{12} < 0.92$ **65.** $0.623 > 0.6023$
67. $0.87 > 0.087$ **69.** $0.033 < 0.3$ **71.** The population ages 0 to 19 is more than $\dfrac{1}{4}$ of the total population.
73. Yes, the digits 538461 repeat.

CHAPTER 3 REVIEW EXERCISES

1. 54.5 [3.5A] **2.** 833.958 [3.2A] **3.** $0.055 < 0.1$ [3.6C] **4.** Twenty-two and ninety-two ten-thousandths [3.1A]
5. 0.05678 [3.1B] **6.** 2.33 [3.6A] **7.** $\dfrac{3}{8}$ [3.6B] **8.** 36.714 [3.2A] **9.** 34.025 [3.1A] **10.** $\dfrac{5}{8} > 0.62$ [3.6C]

11. 0.778   [3.6A]   **12.** $\frac{2}{3}$ [3.6B]   **13.** 22.8635   [3.3A]   **14.** 7.94   [3.1B]   **15.** 8.932   [3.4A]

16. Three hundred forty-two and thirty-seven hundredths   [3.1A]   **17.** 3.06753   [3.1A]   **18.** 25.7446   [3.4A]

19. 6.594   [3.5A]   **20.** 4.8785   [3.3A]   **21.** The new balance in your account is $661.51.   [3.3B]   **22.** There are 53.466 million children in grades K–12.   [3.2B]   **23.** There are 40.49 million more children in public school than in private school.   [3.3B]   **24.** During a 5-day school week, 9.5 million gallons of milk are served.   [3.4B]   **25.** The number who drove is 6.4 times greater than the number who flew.   [3.5B]

CHAPTER 3 TEST

1. 0.66 < 0.666   [3.6C]   **2.** 4.087   [3.3A]   **3.** Forty-five and three hundred two ten-thousandths   [3.1A]

4. 0.692   [3.6A]   **5.** $\frac{33}{40}$ [3.6B]   **6.** 0.0740   [3.1B]   **7.** 1.538   [3.5A]   **8.** 27.76626   [3.3A]   **9.** 7.095   [3.1B]

10. 232   [3.5A]   **11.** 458.581   [3.2A]   **12.** The missing dimension is 1.37 inches.   [3.3B]   **13.** 0.00548   [3.4A]

14. 255.957   [3.2A]   **15.** 209.07086   [3.1A]   **16.** Each payment is $395.40.   [3.5B]   **17.** Your total income is $3087.14.   [3.2B]   **18.** The cost of the call is $4.63.   [3.4B]   **19.** The yearly average computer use by a 10th-grade student is 348.4 hours.   [3.4B]   **20.** On average a 2nd-grade student uses the computer 36.4 hours more per year than a 5th-grade student.   [3.4B]

CUMULATIVE REVIEW EXERCISES

1. 235 r17   [1.5C]   **2.** 128   [1.6A]   **3.** 3   [1.6B]   **4.** 72   [2.1A]   **5.** $4\frac{2}{5}$ [2.2B]   **6.** $\frac{37}{8}$ [2.2B]

7. $\frac{25}{60}$ [2.3A]   **8.** $1\frac{17}{48}$ [2.4B]   **9.** $8\frac{35}{36}$ [2.4C]   **10.** $5\frac{23}{36}$ [2.5C]   **11.** $\frac{1}{12}$ [2.6A]   **12.** $9\frac{1}{8}$ [2.6B]

13. $1\frac{2}{9}$ [2.7A]   **14.** $\frac{19}{20}$ [2.7B]   **15.** $\frac{3}{16}$ [2.8B]   **16.** $2\frac{5}{18}$ [2.8C]   **17.** Sixty-five and three hundred nine ten-thousandths   [3.1A]   **18.** 504.6991   [3.2A]   **19.** 21.0764   [3.3A]   **20.** 55.26066   [3.4A]   **21.** 2.154   [3.5A]

22. 0.733   [3.6A]   **23.** $\frac{1}{6}$ [3.6B]   **24.** $\frac{8}{9} < 0.98$ [3.6C]   **25.** Sweden mandates 14 days more vacation than Germany.   [1.3C]   **26.** The patient must lose $7\frac{3}{4}$ pounds the third month to achieve the goal.   [2.5D]

27. Your checking account balance is $617.38.   [3.3B]   **28.** The resulting thickness is 1.395 inches.   [3.3B]   **29.** You paid $6008.80 in income tax last year.   [3.4B]   **30.** The amount of each payment is $23.87.   [3.5B]

Answers to Chapter 4 Selected Exercises

PREP TEST

1. $\frac{4}{5}$ [2.3B]   **2.** $\frac{1}{2}$ [2.3B]   **3.** 24.8   [3.6A]   **4.** 4 × 33   [1.4A]   **5.** 4   [1.5A]

SECTION 4.1

1. $\frac{1}{5}$ 1:5   1 to 5   **3.** $\frac{2}{1}$ 2:1   2 to 1   **5.** $\frac{3}{8}$ 3:8   3 to 8   **7.** $\frac{37}{24}$ 37:24   37 to 24   **9.** $\frac{1}{1}$ 1:1   1 to 1

11. $\frac{7}{10}$ 7:10   7 to 10   **13.** $\frac{1}{2}$ 1:2   1 to 2   **15.** $\frac{2}{1}$ 2:1   2 to 1   **17.** $\frac{3}{4}$ 3:4   3 to 4   **19.** $\frac{5}{3}$ 5:3   5 to 3

21. $\frac{2}{3}$ 2:3   2 to 3   **23.** $\frac{2}{1}$ 2:1   2 to 1   **25.** The ratio is $\frac{1}{3}$.   **27.** The ratio is $\frac{3}{8}$.   **29.** The ratio is $\frac{2}{77}$.

31. The ratio is $\frac{1}{12}$.   **33. a.** The amount of increase is $20,000.   **b.** The ratio is $\frac{2}{9}$.   **35.** The ratio is $\frac{11}{31}$.

37. No, the ratio $= \frac{830}{1389} \approx 0.5976$ is greater than $\frac{2}{5}$ (0.4).

SECTION 4.2

1. $\dfrac{3 \text{ pounds}}{4 \text{ people}}$ **3.** $\dfrac{\$20}{3 \text{ boards}}$ **5.** $\dfrac{20 \text{ miles}}{1 \text{ gallon}}$ **7.** $\dfrac{5 \text{ children}}{2 \text{ families}}$ **9.** $\dfrac{8 \text{ gallons}}{1 \text{ hour}}$ **11.** 2.5 feet/second   **13.** $975/week
15. 110 trees/acre   **17.** $18.84/hour   **19.** 52.4 miles/hour   **21.** 28 miles/gallon   **23.** $1.65/pound   **25.** The gas mileage was 28.4 miles/gallon.   **27.** The rocket uses 213,600 gallons/minute.   **29. a.** 175 pounds of beef was packaged.   **b.** The beef cost $2.09/pound.   **31. a.** The camera goes through film at the rate of 336 feet/minute.
b. The camera uses the film at a rate of 89 seconds/roll.   **33. a.** The price of the computer hardware would be 109,236 euros.   **b.** The cost of the car would be 3,978,000 yen.

SECTION 4.3

1. True   **3.** Not true   **5.** Not true   **7.** True   **9.** True   **11.** Not true   **13.** True   **15.** True   **17.** True
19. Not true   **21.** True   **23.** Not true   **25.** 3   **27.** 6   **29.** 9   **31.** 5.67   **33.** 4   **35.** 4.38   **37.** 88
39. 3.33   **41.** 26.25   **43.** 96   **45.** 9.78   **47.** 3.43   **49.** 1.34   **51.** 50.4   **53.** A 0.5-ounce serving contains 50 calories.   **55.** Ron used 70 pounds of fertilizer.   **57.** There were 375 wooden bats produced.
59. The distance is 16 miles.   **61.** 1.25 ounces are required.   **63.** 160,000 people would vote.   **65.** The monthly payment is $176.75.   **67.** You will own 400 shares.   **69.** A bowling ball would weigh 2.67 pounds on the moon.
71. The dividend would be $1071.

CHAPTER 4 REVIEW EXERCISES

1. True [4.3A]   **2.** $\dfrac{2}{5}$ 2:5   2 to 5   [4.1A]   **3.** 62.5 miles/hour [4.2B]   **4.** True [4.3A]   **5.** 68 [4.3B]

6. $7.50/hour [4.2B]   **7.** $1.75/pound [4.2B]   **8.** $\dfrac{2}{7}$ 2:7   2 to 7 [4.1A]   **9.** 36 [4.3B]   **10.** 19.44 [4.3B]

11. $\dfrac{2}{5}$ 2:5   2 to 5 [4.1A]   **12.** Not true [4.3A]   **13.** $\dfrac{\$15}{4 \text{ hours}}$ [4.2A]   **14.** 27.2 miles/gallon [4.2B]

15. $\dfrac{1}{1}$ 1:1   1 to 1 [4.1A]   **16.** True [4.3A]   **17.** 65.45 [4.3B]   **18.** $\dfrac{100 \text{ miles}}{3 \text{ hours}}$ [4.2A]   **19.** The ratio

is $\dfrac{2}{5}$. [4.1B]   **20.** The property tax is $6400. [4.3C]   **21.** The ratio is $\dfrac{2}{1}$. [4.1B]   **22.** The cost per phone

is $37.50. [4.2C]   **23.** 1344 blocks would be needed. [4.3C]   **24.** The ratio is $\dfrac{5}{2}$. [4.1B]   **25.** The turkey costs $.93/pound. [4.2C]   **26.** The average was 56.8 miles/hour. [4.2C]   **27.** The cost is $493.50. [4.3C]   **28.** The cost is $44.75/share. [4.2C]   **29.** 22.5 pounds of fertilizer will be used. [4.3C]   **30.** The ratio is $\dfrac{1}{2}$. [4.1B]

CHAPTER 4 TEST

1. $3836.40/month [4.2B]   **2.** $\dfrac{1}{6}$ 1:6   1 to 6 [4.1A]   **3.** $\dfrac{9 \text{ supports}}{4 \text{ feet}}$ [4.2A]   **4.** Not true [4.3A]

5. $\dfrac{3}{2}$ 3:2   3 to 2 [4.1A]   **6.** 144 [4.3B]   **7.** 30.5 miles/gallon [4.2B]   **8.** $\dfrac{1}{3}$ 1:3   1 to 3 [4.1A]

9. True [4.3A]   **10.** 40.5 [4.3B]   **11.** $\dfrac{\$27}{4 \text{ boards}}$ [4.2A]   **12.** $\dfrac{3}{5}$ 3:5   3 to 5 [4.1A]   **13.** The dividend is

$625. [4.3C]   **14.** The ratio is $\dfrac{43}{56}$. [4.1B]   **15.** The plane's speed is 538 miles/hour. [4.2C]   **16.** The college

student's body contains 132 pounds of water. [4.3C]   **17.** The cost of the lumber is $1.73/foot. [4.2C]   **18.** The amount

of medication required is 0.875 ounce. [4.3C]   **19.** The ratio is $\dfrac{4}{5}$. [4.1B]   **20.** 36 defective hard drives are expected

to be found in the production of 1200 hard drives. [4.3C]

CUMULATIVE REVIEW EXERCISES

1. 9158 [1.3B]   **2.** $2^4 \cdot 3^3$ [1.6A]   **3.** 3 [1.6B]   **4.** $2 \cdot 2 \cdot 2 \cdot 2 \cdot 2 \cdot 5$ [1.7B]   **5.** 36 [2.1A]   **6.** 14 [2.1B]

7. $\dfrac{5}{8}$ [2.3B]   **8.** $8\dfrac{3}{10}$ [2.4C]   **9.** $5\dfrac{11}{18}$ [2.5C]   **10.** $2\dfrac{5}{6}$ [2.6B]   **11.** $4\dfrac{2}{3}$ [2.7B]   **12.** $\dfrac{23}{30}$ [2.8C]

13. Four and seven hundred nine ten-thousandths [3.1A]   **14.** 2.10 [3.1B]   **15.** 1.990 [3.5A]   **16.** $\frac{1}{15}$ [3.6B]

17. $\frac{1}{8}$ [4.1A]   **18.** $\frac{29¢}{2\ \text{pencils}}$ [4.2A]   **19.** 33.4 miles/gallon [4.2B]   **20.** 4.25 [4.3B]   **21.** The car's speed is 57.2 miles/hour. [4.2C]   **22.** 36 [4.3B]   **23.** Your new balance is $744. [1.3C]   **24.** The monthly payment is $570. [1.5D]   **25.** 105 pages remain to be read. [2.6C]   **26.** The cost per acre was $36,000. [2.7C]   **27.** The change was $17.62. [3.3B]   **28.** Your monthly salary is $3468.25. [3.5B]   **29.** 25 inches will erode in 50 months. [4.3C]   **30.** 1.6 ounces are required. [4.3C]

Answers to Chapter 5 Selected Exercises

PREP TEST

1. $\frac{19}{100}$ [2.6B]   **2.** 0.23 [3.4A]   **3.** 47 [3.4A]   **4.** 2850 [3.4A]   **5.** 4000 [3.5A]   **6.** 32 [2.7B]

7. 62.5 [3.6A]   **8.** $66\frac{2}{3}$ [2.2B]   **9.** 1.75 [3.5A]

SECTION 5.1

1. $\frac{1}{4}$, 0.25   **3.** $1\frac{3}{10}$, 1.30   **5.** 1, 1.00   **7.** $\frac{73}{100}$, 0.73   **9.** $3\frac{83}{100}$, 3.83   **11.** $\frac{7}{10}$, 0.70   **13.** $\frac{22}{25}$, 0.88

15. $\frac{8}{25}$, 0.32   **17.** $\frac{2}{3}$ **19.** $\frac{5}{6}$ **21.** $\frac{1}{9}$ **23.** $\frac{5}{11}$ **25.** $\frac{3}{70}$ **27.** $\frac{1}{15}$ **29.** 0.065   **31.** 0.123   **33.** 0.0055

35. 0.0825   **37.** 0.0505   **39.** 0.02   **41.** 0.804   **43.** 0.049   **45.** 73%   **47.** 1%   **49.** 294%   **51.** 0.6%

53. 310.6%   **55.** 70%   **57.** 37%   **59.** 40%   **61.** 12.5%   **63.** 150%   **65.** 166.7%   **67.** 87.5%   **69.** 48%

71. $33\frac{1}{3}\%$ **73.** $166\frac{2}{3}\%$ **75.** $87\frac{1}{2}\%$ **77.** 6% of those surveyed named something other than corn on the cob, cole slaw, corn bread, or fries.   **79.** This represents $\frac{1}{2}$ off the regular price.   **81. a.** False   **b.** For example, $200\% \times 4 = 2 \times 4 = 8$

SECTION 5.2

1. 8   **3.** 10.8   **5.** 0.075   **7.** 80   **9.** 51.895   **11.** 7.5   **13.** 13   **15.** 3.75   **17.** 20   **19.** 210

21. 5% of 95   **23.** 79% of 16   **25.** 72% of 40   **27.** 25,805.0324   **29.** About 13.2 million people aged 18 to 24 do not have health insurance.   **31.** 12,151 more faculty members described their political views as liberal than described their views as far left.   **33. a.** The sales tax is $1770.   **b.** The total cost of the car is $31,270.   **35.** 6232 respondents did not answer yes to the question.   **37.** Employees spend 48.2 hours with family and friends.   **39.** There are approximately 3.4 hours difference between the actual and preferred amounts of time the employees spent on self.

SECTION 5.3

1. 32%   **3.** $16\frac{2}{3}\%$ **5.** 200%   **7.** 37.5%   **9.** 18%   **11.** 0.25%   **13.** 20%   **15.** 400%   **17.** 2.5%

19. 37.5%   **21.** 0.25%   **23.** 2.4%   **25.** 9.6%   **27.** 70% of couples disagree about financial matters.   **29.** Approximately 25.4% of the vegetables were wasted.   **31.** The typical American household spends 6% of the total amount spent on energy utilities on lighting.   **33.** 27% of the food produced in the United States is wasted.   **35.** Approximately 27.4% of the total expenses is spent for food.   **37.** 91.8% of the total is spent on all categories except training.

SECTION 5.4

1. 75   **3.** 50   **5.** 100   **7.** 85   **9.** 1200   **11.** 19.2   **13.** 7.5   **15.** 32   **17.** 200   **19.** 80   **21.** 9

23. 504   **25.** 108   **27.** There were 15.8 million travelers who allowed their children to miss school to go along on a trip.   **29.** 3364 people responded to the survey.   **31. a.** 3000 boards were tested.   **b.** 2976 boards tested were not defective.   **33.** 200,935,308 people in the United States were age 20 and older in 2000.   **35.** The recommended daily allowance of copper for an adult is 2 milligrams.

SECTION 5.5

1. 65   **3.** 25%   **5.** 75   **7.** 12.5%   **9.** 400   **11.** 19.5   **13.** 14.8%   **15.** 62.62   **17.** 5   **19.** 45
21. 15   **23.** The total amount collected was $24,500.   **25.** The world's total land area is 58,750,000 square miles.
27. 22,577 hotels in the United States are located along highways.   **29.** 14,000,000 ounces of gold were mined in the United States that year.   **31.** 46.8% of the deaths were due to traffic accidents.   **33.** The 108th House of Representatives had the larger percent of Republicans.

CHAPTER 5 REVIEW EXERCISES

1. 60 [5.2A]   **2.** 20% [5.3A]   **3.** 175% [5.1B]   **4.** 75 [5.4A]   **5.** $\frac{3}{25}$ [5.1A]   **6.** 19.36 [5.2A]

7. 150% [5.3A]   **8.** 504 [5.4A]   **9.** 0.42 [5.1A]   **10.** 5.4 [5.2A]   **11.** 157.5 [5.4A]   **12.** 0.076 [5.1A]

13. 77.5 [5.2A]   **14.** $\frac{1}{6}$ [5.1A]   **15.** 160% [5.5A]   **16.** 75 [5.5A]   **17.** 38% [5.1B]   **18.** 10.9 [5.4A]

19. 7.3% [5.3A]   **20.** 613.3% [5.3A]   **21.** The student answered 85% of the questions correctly. [5.5B]
22. The company spent $4500 for newspaper advertising. [5.2B]   **23.** 31.7% of the cost is for electricity. [5.3B]
24. The total cost of the video camera is $1041.25. [5.2B]   **25.** Approximately 78.6% of the women wore sunscreen often. [5.3B]   **26.** The world's population in 2000 was approximately 6,100,000,000 people. [5.4B]   **27.** The cost of the computer 4 years ago was $3000. [5.5B]   **28.** The dollar value of all the online transactions made that year was $52 billion. [5.4B]

CHAPTER 5 TEST

1. 0.973 [5.1A]   **2.** $\frac{5}{6}$ [5.1A]   **3.** 30% [5.1B]   **4.** 163% [5.1B]   **5.** 150% [5.1B]   **6.** $66\frac{2}{3}\%$ [5.1B]

7. 50.05 [5.2A]   **8.** 61.36 [5.2A]   **9.** 76% of 13 [5.2A]   **10.** 212% of 12 [5.2A]   **11.** The amount spent for for advertising is $4500. [5.2B]   **12.** 1170 pounds of vegetables were not spoiled. [5.2B]   **13.** 14.7% of the daily recommended amount of potassium is provided. [5.3B]   **14.** 9.1% of the daily recommended number of calories is provided. [5.3B]   **15.** 16% of the permanent employees are hired. [5.3B]   **16.** The student answered approximately 91.3% of the questions correctly. [5.3B]   **17.** 80 [5.4A]   **18.** 28.3 [5.4A]   **19.** 32,000 PDAs were tested. [5.4B]
20. The increase was 60% of the original price. [5.3B]   **21.** 143.0 [5.5A]   **22.** 1000% [5.5A]   **23.** The dollar increase is $1.74. [5.5B]   **24.** The population now is 220% of what it was 10 years ago. [5.5B]   **25.** The value of the car is $12,500. [5.5B]

CUMULATIVE REVIEW EXERCISES

1. 4 [1.6B]   **2.** 240 [2.1A]   **3.** $10\frac{11}{24}$ [2.4C]   **4.** $12\frac{41}{48}$ [2.5C]   **5.** $12\frac{4}{7}$ [2.6B]   **6.** $\frac{7}{24}$ [2.7B]

7. $\frac{1}{3}$ [2.8B]   **8.** $\frac{13}{36}$ [2.8C]   **9.** 3.08 [3.1B]   **10.** 1.1196 [3.3A]   **11.** 34.2813 [3.5A]   **12.** 3.625 [3.6A]

13. $1\frac{3}{4}$ [3.6B]   **14.** $\frac{3}{8} < 0.87$ [3.6C]   **15.** 53.3 [4.3B]   **16.** $9.60/hour [4.2B]   **17.** $\frac{11}{60}$ [5.1A]

18. $83\frac{1}{3}\%$ [5.1B]   **19.** 19.56 [5.2A/5.5A]   **20.** $133\frac{1}{3}\%$ [5.3A/5.5A]   **21.** 9.92 [5.4A/5.5A]

22. 342.9% [5.3A/5.5A]   **23.** Sergio's take-home pay is $592. [2.6C]   **24.** Each monthly payment is $204.25. [3.5B]
25. 420 gallons were used during the month. [3.5B]   **26.** The real estate tax is $5000. [4.3C]   **27.** The sales tax is 6% of the purchase price. [5.3B/5.5B]   **28.** 45% of the people did not favor the candidate. [5.3B/5.5B]   **29.** The approximate average number of hours spent watching TV in a week is 61.3 hours. [5.2B/5.5B]   **30.** 18% of the children tested had levels of lead that exceeded federal standards. [5.3B/5.5B]

Answers to Chapter 6 Selected Exercises

PREP TEST

1. 0.75 [3.5A] **2.** 52.05 [3.4A] **3.** 504.51 [3.3A] **4.** 9750 [3.4A] **5.** 45 [3.4A] **6.** 1417.24 [3.2A]
7. 3.33 [3.5A] **8.** 0.605 [3.5A] **9.** $0.379 < 0.397$ [3.6C]

SECTION 6.1

1. The unit cost is $.055 per ounce. **3.** The unit cost is $.374 per ounce. **5.** The unit cost is $.080 per tablet.
7. The unit price is $6.975 per clamp. **9.** The unit cost is $.199 per ounce. **11.** The unit cost is $.119 per screw.
13. The Sutter Home pasta sauce is the more economical purchase. **15.** 20 ounces is the more economical purchase.
17. 400 tablets is the more economical purchase. **19.** Land O' Lakes cheddar cheese is the more economical purchase.
21. Maxwell House coffee is the more economical purchase. **23.** Friskies Chef's Blend is the more economical purchase.
25. The total cost is $13.77. **27.** The total cost is $1.84. **29.** The total cost is $6.37. **31.** The total cost is $2.71.
33. The total cost is $5.96.

SECTION 6.2

1. The percent increase is 19.6%. **3.** The percent increase is 117.6%. **5.** The percent increase is 457.1%.
7. The population 8 years later was 157,861 people. **9.** The average age of American mothers giving birth in 2000 was
24.9 years. **11.** The markup is $35.70. **13.** The markup rate is 30%. **15. a.** The markup is $77.76. **b.** The
selling price is $239.76. **17. a.** The markup is $1.10. **b.** The selling price is $3.10. **19.** The selling price is $74.
21. The amount represents a decrease of 40%. **23.** There is a decrease of 540 employees. **25. a.** The amount of
decrease is 13 minutes. **b.** The amount represents a decrease of 25%. **27. a.** The amount of decrease is $.60.
b. The new dividend is $1.00. **29.** The amount represents a decrease of 6.6%. **31.** The discount rate is $33\frac{1}{3}$%.
33. The discount is $68. **35.** The discount rate is 30%. **37. a.** The discount is $.25 per pound. **b.** The sale price
is $1.00 per pound. **39. a.** The amount of the discount is $4. **b.** The discount rate is 20%. **41.** Yes

SECTION 6.3

1. a. $10,000 **b.** $850 **c.** 4.25% **d.** 2 years **3.** The simple interest owed is $960. **5.** The simple interest
due is $3375. **7.** The simple interest due is $1320. **9.** The simple interest due is $92.47. **11.** The simple interest
due is $84.76. **13.** The maturity value is $5120. **15.** The maturity value is $164,250. **17.** The total amount due
on the loan is $12,875. **19.** The maturity value is $14,543.70. **21.** The monthly payment is $6187.50.
23. a. The interest charged is $1080. **b.** The monthly payment is $545. **25.** The monthly payment is $1332.50.
27. The finance charge is $1.48. **29.** The finance charge is $185.53. **31.** The difference in finance charges is $10.07.
33. The value of the investment after 1 year is $780.60. **35.** The value of the investment after 15 years is $7281.78.
37. a. The value of the investment in 5 years will be $111,446.25. **b.** The amount of interest earned will be $36,446.25.
39. The amount of interest earned is $5799.48. **41.** The interest owed is $16.

SECTION 6.4

1. The mortgage is $82,450. **3.** The down payment is $7500. **5.** The down payment is $212,500. **7.** The loan
origination fee is $3750. **9. a.** The down payment is $7500. **b.** The mortgage is $142,500. **11.** The mortgage is
$189,000. **13.** The monthly mortgage payment is $1157.73. **15.** No, the couple cannot afford to buy the house.
17. The monthly property tax is $112.35. **19. a.** The monthly mortgage payment is $1678.40. **b.** The interest
payment is $736.68. **21.** The total monthly payment for the mortgage and property tax is $982.70. **23.** The monthly
mortgage payment is $1645.53. **25.** By using the 20-year loan, the couple will save $63,408.

SECTION 6.5

1. No, Amanda does not have enough money for the down payment.   **3.** The sales tax is $1192.50.   **5.** The license fee is $450.   **7. a.** The sales tax is $1120.   **b.** The total cost of the sales tax and the license fee is $1395.
9. a. The down payment is $4050.   **b.** The amount financed is $12,150.   **11.** The amount financed is $28,000.
13. The monthly truck payment is $552.70.   **15.** The cost is $5120.   **17.** The cost is about $.11 per mile.
19. The amount of interest is $74.75.   **21. a.** The amount financed is $153,200.   **b.** The monthly payment is $2961.78.   **23.** The monthly payment is $649.63.   **25.** The 7% loan has the lesser loan cost.

SECTION 6.6

1. Lewis earns $380.   **3.** The real estate agent's commission is $3930.   **5.** The stockbroker's commission is $84.
7. The teacher's monthly salary is $3244.   **9.** The overtime wage is $51.60/hour.   **11.** The golf pro's commission was $112.50.   **13.** The typist earns $618.75.   **15.** Maxine's hourly wage is $85.   **17. a.** Mark's hourly wage on Saturday is $23.85.   **b.** Mark earns $190.80.   **19. a.** The nurse's increase in hourly pay is $2.15.   **b.** The nurse's hourly pay is $23.65.   **21.** Nicole's earnings were $475.   **23.** The starting salary for a chemical engineer increased $922 over that of the previous year.   **25.** The starting salary for a political science major decreased $4115 from that of the previous year.

SECTION 6.7

1. Your current checking account balance is $486.32.   **3.** The real estate firm's current checking account balance is $1222.47.   **5.** The nutritionist's current balance is $825.27.   **7.** The current checking account balance is $3000.82.
9. Yes, there is enough money in the carpenter's account to purchase the refrigerator.   **11.** Yes, there is enough money in the account to make the two purchases.   **13.** The bank statement and checkbook balance.   **15.** The bank statement and checkbook balance.   **17.** added   **19.** subtract

CHAPTER 6 REVIEW EXERCISES

1. The unit cost is $.195 per ounce or 19.5¢ per ounce.   [6.1A]   **2.** The cost is $.164 or 16.4¢ per mile.   [6.5B]
3. The percent increase is 30.4%.   [6.2A]   **4.** The markup is $72.   [6.2B]   **5.** The simple interest due is $3000.
[6.3A]   **6.** The value of the investment after 10 years is $45,550.75.   [6.3C]   **7.** The percent increase is 15%.   [6.2A]
8. The total monthly payment for the mortgage and property tax is $578.53.   [6.4B]   **9.** The monthly payment is $518.02.   [6.5B]   **10.** The value of the investment will be $53,593.   [6.3C]   **11.** The down payment is $18,750.
[6.4A]   **12.** The total cost of the sales tax and license fee is $1471.25.   [6.5A]   **13.** The selling price is $2079.   [6.2B]
14. The interest paid is $97.33.   [6.5B]   **15.** The commission was $3240.   [6.6A]   **16.** The sale price is $141.   [6.2D]
17. The current checkbook balance is $943.68.   [6.7A]   **18.** The maturity value is $31,200.   [6.3A]
19. The origination fee is $1875.   [6.4A]   **20.** The more economical purchase is 33 ounces for $6.99.   [6.1B]
21. The monthly mortgage payment is $934.08.   [6.4B]   **22.** The total income was $655.20.   [6.6A]   **23.** The donut shop's checkbook balance is $8866.58.   [6.7A]   **24.** The monthly payment is $14,093.75.   [6.3A]   **25.** The finance charge is $7.20.   [6.3B]

CHAPTER 6 TEST

1. The cost per foot is $6.92.   [6.1A]   **2.** The more economical purchase is 3 pounds for $7.49.   [6.1B]
3. The total cost is $14.53.   [6.1C]   **4.** The percent increase in the cost of the exercise bicycle is 20%.   [6.2A]
5. The selling price of the compact disc player is $301.   [6.2B]   **6.** The percent decrease is 7.7%.   [6.2C]
7. The percent decrease is 20%.   [6.2C]   **8.** The sale price of the corner hutch is $209.30.   [6.2D]   **9.** The discount rate is 40%.   [6.2D]   **10.** The simple interest due is $2000.   [6.3A]   **11.** The maturity value is $26,725.   [6.3A]
12. The finance charge is $4.50.   [6.3B]   **13.** The amount of interest earned in 10 years will be $24,420.60.   [6.3C]
14. The loan origination fee is $3350.   [6.4A]   **15.** The monthly mortgage payment is $1713.44.   [6.4B]
16. The amount financed is $19,000.   [6.5A]   **17.** The monthly truck payment is $482.68.   [6.5B]   **18.** Shaney earns $1071.   [6.6A]   **19.** The current checkbook balance is $6612.25.   [6.7A]   **20.** The bank statement and the checkbook balance.   [6.7B]

CUMULATIVE REVIEW EXERCISES

1. 13 [1.6B]   **2.** $8\frac{13}{24}$ [2.4C]   **3.** $2\frac{37}{48}$ [2.5C]   **4.** 9 [2.6B]   **5.** 2 [2.7B]   **6.** 5 [2.8C]   **7.** 52.2 [3.5A]

8. 1.417 [3.6A]   **9.** $51.25/hour [4.2B]   **10.** 10.94 [4.3B]   **11.** 62.5% [5.1B]   **12.** 27.3 [5.2A]

13. 0.182 [5.1A]   **14.** 42% [5.3A]   **15.** 250 [5.4A]   **16.** 154.76 [5.4A/5.5A]   **17.** The total rainfall is $13\frac{11}{12}$

inches. [2.4D]   **18.** The amount paid in taxes is $970. [2.6C]   **19.** The ratio is $\frac{3}{5}$. [4.1B]   **20.** 33.4 miles are

driven per gallon. [4.2C]   **21.** The cost is $.93 per pound. [4.2C]   **22.** The dividend is $280. [4.3C]   **23.** The

sale price is $720. [6.2D]   **24.** The selling price of the disc player is $119. [6.2B]   **25.** The percent increase in Sook

Kim's salary is 8%. [6.2A]   **26.** The simple interest due is $2700. [6.3A]   **27.** The monthly car payment is $791.81.

[6.5B]   **28.** The family's new checking account balance is $2243.77. [6.7A]   **29.** The cost per mile is $.20. [6.5B]

30. The monthly mortgage payment is $1232.26. [6.4B]

Answers to Chapter 7 Selected Exercises

PREP TEST

1. 48.0% was bill-related mail. [5.3B]   **2. a.** The greatest cost increase is between 2009 and 2010.   **b.** Between those

years, there was an increase of $5318. [1.3C]   **3. a.** The ratio is $\frac{5}{3}$.   **b.** The ratio is 1 : 1. [4.1B]

4. a. 3.9, 3.9, 4.2, 4.5, 5.2, 5.5, 7.1 [3.6C]   **b.** The average is 4.9 million viewers per night. [3.5B]

5. a. 4500 women are in the Marine Corps. [5.2B]   **b.** $\frac{1}{20}$ of the women in the military are in the Marine Corps. [5.1A]

SECTION 7.1

1. The gross revenue is $750 million.   **3.** The percent is 40%.   **5.** 50 more people agreed that humanity should

explore space than agreed that space exploration impacts daily life.   **7.** 150 children said they hid their vegetables under

a napkin.   **11.** The ratio is $\frac{1}{3}$.   **13.** The percent is 9.4%.   **15.** The number of people surveyed is 150 people.

17. The percent is 28%.   **19.** Americans spent $279,000,000 on portable game machines.   **21.** Yes.

23. The number of homeless aged 25 to 34 is more than twice the number of homeless under the age of 25.

25. Out of every 100,000 homeless people, there are 8000 people over age 54.   **27.** North America is 2,550,000 square

miles larger than South America.   **29.** Australia is 5.2% of the total land area.   **31.** $2027.50 is spent on health care.

33. No, the amount spent on housing is not more than twice the amount spent on transporation.

SECTION 7.2

1. 39 million passenger cars were produced worldwide.   **3.** The percent is 28%.   **5.** The Mini Cooper gets

approximately 10 more miles per gallon while traveling on the highway.   **7.** The maximum salary of police officers in the

suburbs is $16,000 higher than the maximum salary of police officers in the city.   **9.** The greatest difference in salaries is

in Philadelphia.   **11.** The average snowfall during January is 20 inches.   **13.** The snowfall during March and April

was 25 inches.   **15.** The difference is 800 Calories.   **17.** The ratio is $\frac{7}{6}$.

19.

Year	Difference Between the Amount Spent for Foreign and for Domestic Aid (in billions of dollars)
1991	$1.3
1992	$1.1
1993	$1.0
1994	$0.9
1995	$0.8
1996	$0.8
1997	$1.1
1998	$0.9
1999	$1.0

SECTION 7.3

1. 44 students have a tuition that is between $3000 and $6000.   **3.** 18 students paid more than $12,000.   **5.** There are 410 cars between 6 and 12 years old.   **7.** 230 cars are more than 12 years old.   **9.** 54 adults spend between 1 and 2 hours at the mall.   **11.** The percent is 22%.   **13.** There were 24 entrants in the discus finals.   **15.** 37.5% of the entrants had distances between 160 feet and 170 feet.   **17.** The percent is 10.8%.   **21.** The percent is 32.4%.
23. 900,000 students scored above 800.

SECTION 7.4

1. a. Median   **b.** Mean   **c.** Mode   **d.** Median   **e.** Mode   **f.** Mean   **3.** The mean number of seats filled is 381.5625 seats. The median number of seats filled is 394.5 seats. Since each number occurs only once, there is no mode.
5. The mean cost is $45.615. The median cost is $45.855.   **7.** The mean monthly rate is $403.625. The median monthly rate is $404.50.   **9.** The mean life expectancy is 70.8 years. The median life expectancy is 72 years.   **13. a.** 25%
b. 75%   **c.** 75%   **d.** 25%   **15.** Lowest is $46,596. Highest is $82,879. Q_1 = $56,067. Q_3 = $66,507.
Median = $61,036. Range = $36,283. Interquartile range = $10,440.   **17. a.** There were 40 adults who had cholesterol levels above 217.   **b.** There were 60 adults who had cholesterol levels below 254.   **c.** There are 20 cholesterol levels in each quartile.   **d.** 25% of the adults had cholesterol levels not more than 198.   **19. a.** Range = 4.39 million metric tons. Q_1 = 0.56 million metric tons. Q_3 = 2.10 million metric tons. Interquartile range = 1.54 million metric tons
b.

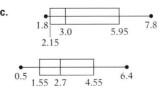

c. 4.80   **21. a.** No, the difference in the means is not greater than 1 inch.

b. The difference in medians is 0.3 inch.   **c.**

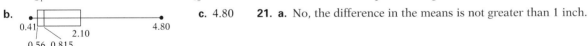

23. Answers will vary. For example, 55, 55, 55, 55, 55, or 50, 55, 55, 55, 60

SECTION 7.5

1. {(HHHH), (HHHT), (HHTT), (HHTH), (HTTT), (HTHH), (HTTH), (HTHT), (TTTT), (TTTH), (TTHH), (THHH), (TTHT), (THHT), (THTT), (THTH)}   **3.** {(1, 1), (1, 2), (1, 3), (1, 4), (2, 1), (2, 2), (2, 3), (2, 4), (3, 1), (3, 2), (3, 3), (3, 4), (4, 1), (4, 2), (4, 3), (4, 4)}   **5. a.** {1, 2, 3, 4, 5, 6, 7, 8}   **b.** {1, 2, 3}   **7. a.** The probability that the sum is 5 is $\frac{1}{9}$.
b. The probability that the sum is 15 is 0.   **c.** The probablity that the sum is less than 15 is 1.   **d.** The probability that the sum is 2 is $\frac{1}{36}$.   **9. a.** The probability that the number is divisible by 4 is $\frac{1}{4}$.   **b.** The probability that the number

is a multiple of 3 is $\frac{1}{3}$. **11.** The probability of throwing a sum of 5 is greater. **13. a.** The probability is $\frac{4}{11}$ that the letter I is drawn. **b.** The probability of choosing an S is greater. **15. a.** The probability is $\frac{1}{3}$ that the marble chosen is green. **b.** The probability of choosing a red marble is greater. **17.** The probability is $\frac{8}{47}$ that the paper has a B grade. **19.** The probability is 0.81 that an employee has a group health insurance plan.

CHAPTER 7 REVIEW EXERCISES

1. The agencies spent $349 million on maintaining websites. [7.1B] **2.** The ratio is $\frac{9}{8}$. [7.1B] **3.** 8.9% of the total amount of money was spent by NASA. [7.1B] **4.** Texas had the larger population. [7.2B] **5.** The population of California is 12.5 million people more than the population of Texas. [7.2B] **6.** The Texas population increased the least from 1925 to 1950. [7.2B] **7.** There were 54 games in which the Knicks scored fewer than 100 points. [7.3B] **8.** The ratio is $\frac{31}{8}$. [7.3B] **9.** The percent is 11.3%. [7.3B] **10.** From the pictograph, O'Hare airport has 10 million more passengers than Los Angeles airport. [7.1A] **11.** The ratio is $2:3$. [7.1A] **12.** The difference was 50 days. [7.2A] **13.** The percent is 50%. [7.2A] **14. a.** The Southeast had the lowest number of days of full operation. **b.** This region had 30 days of full operation. [7.2A] **15.** The probability of one tail and three heads is $\frac{1}{4}$. [7.5A] **16.** There were 15 people who slept 8 or more hours. [7.3A] **17.** The percent is 28.3%. [7.3A] **18. a.** The mean heart rate is 91.6 heartbeats per minute. The median heart rate is 93.5 heartbeats per minute. The mode is 96 heartbeats per minute. [7.4A] **b.** The range is 36 heartbeats per minute. The interquartile range is 15 heartbeats per minute. [7.4B]

CHAPTER 7 TEST

1. 19 students spent between $15 and $25 each week. [7.3B] **2.** The ratio is $\frac{2}{3}$. [7.3B] **3.** The percent is 45%. [7.3B] **4.** There were 36 people that were surveyed for the Gallup poll. [7.1A] **5.** The ratio is $\frac{5}{2}$. [7.1A] **6.** The percent is 58.3%. [7.1A] **7.** During 1995 and 1996, the number of fatalities was the same. [7.2A] **8.** There were 32 fatal accidents from 1991 to 1999. [7.2A] **9.** There were 4 more fatalities from 1995 to 1998. [7.2A] **10.** There were 355 more films rated R. [7.1B] **11.** There were 16 times more films rated PG-13. [7.1B] **12.** The percent of films rated G was 5.6%. [7.1B] **13.** There are 24 states that have a median income between $40,000 and $60,000. [7.3A] **14.** The percent is 72%. [7.3A] **15.** The percent is 18%. [7.3A] **16.** The probability is $\frac{3}{10}$ that the ball chosen is red. [7.5A] **17.** The student enrollment increased the least during the 1990s. [7.2B] **18.** The increase in the enrollment was 11 million students. [7.2B] **19. a.** The mean time is 2.53 days. [7.4A] **b.** The median time is 2.55 days. [7.4A] **c.** [7.4B]

CUMULATIVE REVIEW EXERCISES

1. 540 [1.6A] **2.** 14 [1.6B] **3.** 120 [2.1A] **4.** $\frac{5}{12}$ [2.3B] **5.** $12\frac{3}{40}$ [2.4C] **6.** $4\frac{17}{24}$ [2.5C]

7. 2 [2.6B] **8.** $\frac{64}{85}$ [2.7B] **9.** $8\frac{1}{4}$ [2.8C] **10.** 209.305 [3.1A] **11.** 2.82348 [3.4A] **12.** 16.67 [3.6A]

13. 26.4 miles/gallon [4.2B] **14.** 3.2 [4.3B] **15.** 80% [5.1B] **16.** 80 [5.4A] **17.** 16.34 [5.2A] **18.** 40% [5.3A] **19.** The salesperson's income for the week was $650. [6.6A] **20.** The cost is $407.50. [4.3C] **21.** The interest due is $3750. [6.3A] **22.** The markup rate is 55%. [6.2B] **23.** The amount budgeted for food is $570. [7.1B] **24.** The difference in the number answered correctly is 12 problems. [7.2B] **25.** The mean high temperature is 69.6°F. [7.4A] **26.** The probability is $\frac{5}{36}$ that the sum of the dots on the two dice is 8. [7.5A]

Answers to Chapter 8 Selected Exercises

PREP TEST

1. 702 [1.2A]   **2.** 58 [1.3B]   **3.** 4 [2.6B]   **4.** 10 [2.6B]   **5.** 25 [2.6B]   **6.** 46 [2.6B]   **7.** 238 [1.5A]
8. 1.5 [3.5A]

SECTION 8.1

1. 72 in.   **3.** $2\frac{1}{2}$ ft   **5.** 39 ft   **7.** $5\frac{1}{3}$ yd   **9.** 84 in.   **11.** $3\frac{1}{3}$ yd   **13.** 10,560 ft   **15.** $\frac{5}{8}$ ft   **17.** 1 mi 1120 ft

19. 9 ft 11 in.   **21.** 2 ft 9 in.   **23.** 14 ft 6 in.   **25.** 2 ft 8 in.   **27.** $11\frac{1}{6}$ ft   **29.** 4 mi 2520 ft   **31.** 14 tiles can

be placed along one row.   **33.** The missing dimension is $1\frac{5}{6}$ ft.   **35.** The length of material needed is $7\frac{1}{2}$ in.

37. The length of each piece is $1\frac{2}{3}$ ft.   **39.** The length of framing needed is 6 ft 6 in.   **41.** The total length of the wall

is $33\frac{3}{4}$ ft.   **43.** Yes.

SECTION 8.2

1. 4 lb   **3.** 128 oz   **5.** $1\frac{3}{5}$ tons   **7.** 12,000 lb   **9.** $4\frac{1}{8}$ lb   **11.** 24 oz   **13.** 2600 lb   **15.** $\frac{1}{4}$ ton

17. $11\frac{1}{4}$ lb   **19.** 4 tons 1000 lb   **21.** 2 lb 8 oz   **23.** 5 tons 400 lb   **25.** 1 ton 1700 lb   **27.** 33 lb

29. 14 lb   **31.** 9 oz   **33.** 1 lb 7 oz   **35.** The load of bricks weighs 2000 lb.   **37.** The package of tiles weighs 63 lb.
39. The weight of the case of soft drinks is 9 lb.   **41.** Each container holds 1 lb 5 oz of shampoo.   **43.** The ham roast
costs $27.   **45.** The cost of mailing the manuscript is $8.75.   **47.** Answers will vary.

SECTION 8.3

1. $7\frac{1}{2}$ c   **3.** 24 fl oz   **5.** 4 pt   **7.** 7 c   **9.** $5\frac{1}{2}$ gal   **11.** 9 qt   **13.** $3\frac{3}{4}$ qt   **15.** $1\frac{1}{4}$ pt   **17.** $4\frac{1}{4}$ qt

19. 3 gal 2 qt   **21.** 2 qt 1 pt   **23.** 7 qt   **25.** 6 fl oz   **27.** $17\frac{1}{2}$ pt   **29.** $\frac{7}{8}$ gal   **31.** 5 gal 1 qt

33. 1 gal 2 qt   **35.** $2\frac{3}{4}$ gal   **37.** $7\frac{1}{2}$ gal of coffee should be prepared.   **39.** There are $4\frac{1}{4}$ qt of final solution.

41. The farmer used $8\frac{3}{4}$ gal of oil.   **43.** The more economical purchase is $1.59 for 1 qt.   **45.** The profit made was

$83.50.   **47.** 1 grain = 0.002286 oz; 1 dram = 0.0625 oz; 1 furlong = $\frac{1}{8}$ mi; 1 rod = 16.5 ft

SECTION 8.4

1. 14 weeks   **3.** 150 h   **5.** $9\frac{1}{4}$ h   **7.** 1110 s   **9.** $3\frac{1}{2}$ h   **11.** 23,400 s   **13.** $3\frac{1}{2}$ days   **15.** 3600 min

17. 4 weeks   **19.** 504 h   **21.** 2 days   **23.** 259,200 s   **25.** Yes   **27.** Yes   **29.** 7 years   **31.** 2190 days

33. 30,660 h

SECTION 8.5

1. 19,450 ft · lb   **3.** 19,450,000 ft · lb   **5.** 1500 ft · lb   **7.** 29,700 ft · lb   **9.** 30,000 ft · lb   **11.** 25,500 ft · lb

13. 35,010,000 ft · lb   **15.** 9,336,000 ft · lb   **17.** 2 hp   **19.** 8 hp   **21.** $4950 \frac{\text{ft} \cdot \text{lb}}{\text{s}}$ **23.** $3850 \frac{\text{ft} \cdot \text{lb}}{\text{s}}$

25. $500 \frac{\text{ft} \cdot \text{lb}}{\text{s}}$ **27.** $4800 \frac{\text{ft} \cdot \text{lb}}{\text{s}}$ **29.** $1440 \frac{\text{ft} \cdot \text{lb}}{\text{s}}$ **31.** 9 hp   **33.** 12 hp

CHAPTER 8 REVIEW EXERCISES

1. 48 in. [8.1A]   **2.** 2 ft 6 in. [8.1B]   **3.** 1600 ft · lb [8.5A]   **4.** 40 fl oz [8.3A]   **5.** $4\frac{2}{3}$ yd [8.1A]

6. $1\frac{1}{5}$ tons [8.2A]   **7.** 2 lb 7 oz [8.2B]   **8.** 54 oz [8.2A]   **9.** 9 ft 3 in. [8.1B]   **10.** 1 ton 1000 lb [8.2B]

11. 7 c 2 fl oz [8.3B]   **12.** 1 yd 2 ft [8.1B]   **13.** 3 qt [8.3A]   **14.** $6\frac{1}{4}$ h [8.4A]   **15.** $1375 \frac{\text{ft} \cdot \text{lb}}{\text{s}}$ [8.5B]

16. 44 lb [8.2B]   **17.** 38,900 ft · lb [8.5A]   **18.** 7 hp [8.5B]   **19.** The length of the remaining piece is 3 ft 6 in.

[8.1C]   **20.** The cost of mailing the book is $8.40. [8.2C]   **21.** There are $13\frac{1}{2}$ qt in a case. [8.3C]

22. 16 gal of milk were sold that day. [8.3C]   **23.** 27,230,000 ft · lb [8.5A]   **24.** $480\frac{\text{ft} \cdot \text{lb}}{\text{s}}$ [8.5B]

CHAPTER 8 TEST

1. 30 in. [8.1A]   **2.** 2 ft 5 in. [8.1B]   **3.** $1\frac{1}{3}$ ft [8.1C]   **4.** The wall is 48 ft long. [8.1C]   **5.** 46 oz [8.2A]

6. 2 lb 8 oz [8.2B]   **7.** 17 lb 1 oz [8.2B]   **8.** 1 lb 11oz [8.2B]   **9.** The total weight of the workbooks is 750 lb.

[8.2C]   **10.** The amount the class received for recycling was $28.13. [8.2C]   **11.** $3\frac{1}{4}$ gal [8.3A]   **12.** 28 pt [8.3A]

13. $12\frac{1}{4}$ gal [8.3B]   **14.** 8 gal 1 qt [8.3B]   **15.** $4\frac{1}{2}$ weeks [8.4A]   **16.** 4680 min [8.4A]   **17.** There are 60 c in

a case. [8.3C]   **18.** Nick's profit is $144. [8.3C]   **19.** 3750 ft · lb [8.5A]   **20.** 31,120,000 ft · lb [8.5A]

21. $160 \frac{\text{ft} \cdot \text{lb}}{\text{s}}$ [8.5B]   **22.** 4 hp [8.5B]

CUMULATIVE REVIEW EXERCISES

1. 180 [2.1A]   **2.** $5\frac{3}{8}$ [2.2B]   **3.** $3\frac{7}{24}$ [2.5C]   **4.** 2 [2.7B]   **5.** $4\frac{3}{8}$ [2.8C]   **6.** 2.10 [3.1B]

7. 0.038808 [3.4A]   **8.** 8.8 [4.3B]   **9.** 1.25 [5.2A]   **10.** 42.86 [5.4A]   **11.** The unit cost is $5.15/lb. [6.1A]

12. $8\frac{11}{15}$ in. [8.1B]   **13.** 1 lb 8 oz [8.2B]   **14.** 31 lb 8 oz [8.2B]   **15.** $2\frac{1}{2}$ qt [8.3B]   **16.** 1 lb 12 oz [8.2B]

17. The dividend would be $280. [4.3C]   **18.** Anna's balance is $642.79. [6.7A]   **19.** The executive's monthly

income is $4100. [6.6A]   **20.** The amount of carrots that could be sold is 2425 lb. [5.2B]   **21.** The percent is 18%.

[7.3A]   **22.** The selling price of a compact disc player is $308. [6.2B]   **23.** The interest paid on the loan is $8000.

[6.3A]   **24.** Each student received $633. [8.2C]   **25.** The cost of mailing the books is $20.16. [8.2C]   **26.** The

better buy is 36 oz for $2.98. [6.1B]   **27.** The probability is $\frac{1}{9}$ that the sum of the dots on the two dice is 9. [7.5A]

28. 3200 ft · lb [8.5A]   **29.** $400 \frac{\text{ft} \cdot \text{lb}}{\text{s}}$ [8.5B]

Answers to Chapter 9 Selected Exercises

PREP TEST

1. 37,320 [3.4A]   **2.** 659,000 [3.4A]   **3.** 0.04107 [3.5A]   **4.** 28.496 [3.5A]   **5.** 5.125 [3.3A]
6. 5.96 [3.2A]   **7.** 0.13 [3.4A]   **8.** 56.35 [2.6A, 3.4A]   **9.** 0.5 [2.6B, 3.5A]   **10.** 675 [2.6B]

SECTION 9.1

1. 420 mm   **3.** 8.1 cm   **5.** 6.804 km   **7.** 2109 m   **9.** 4.32 m   **11.** 88 cm   **13.** 7.038 km   **15.** 3500 m
17. 2.60 m   **19.** 168.5 cm   **21.** 148 mm   **23.** 62.07 m   **25.** 31.9 cm   **27.** 8.075 km   **29.** The missing
dimension is 7.8 cm.   **31.** The distance between the rivets is 17.9 cm.   **33.** The amount of fencing left on the roll is
15.6 m.   **35.** It takes 500 s for light to travel from the sun to Earth.   **37.** Light travels 25,920,000,000 km in 1 day.

SECTION 9.2

1. 0.420 kg   **3.** 0.127 g   **5.** 4200 g   **7.** 450 mg   **9.** 1.856 kg   **11.** 4.057 g   **13.** 1370 g   **15.** 45.6 mg
17. 18.000 kg   **19.** 3.922 kg   **21.** 7.891 g   **23.** 4.063 kg   **25.** There are 40 g in 1 serving.   **27. a.** There are
3.288 g of cholesterol in 12 eggs.   **b.** There are 0.132 g of cholesterol in four glasses of milk.   **29. a.** There is 0.186 kg
of mix in the package.   **b.** There is 0.42 g of sodium in two servings.   **31.** The amount of seed needed is 1.6 kg.
33. The profit from repackaging the nuts is $117.50.   **35.** Corn was 50.3% of the total exports.

SECTION 9.3

1. 4.2 L   **3.** 3420 ml   **5.** 423 cm^3 **7.** 642 ml   **9.** 0.042 L   **11.** 435 cm^3 **13.** 4620 L   **15.** 1.423 kl
17. 1267 cm^3 **19.** 3.042 L   **21.** 3.004 kl   **23.** 8.200 L   **25. a.** There is less than 25 L of oxygen in 50 L of air.
b. There are 10.5 L of oxygen in 50 L of air.   **27.** 24 L of chlorine were used in a month.   **29.** 4000 patients can be
immunized.   **31.** The 12 one-liter bottles are the better buy.   **33.** The profit on the gasoline was $8465.   **35.** 2.72 L;
2720 ml; 2L 720 ml

SECTION 9.4

1. 3300 Calories can be omitted from your diet.   **3. a.** There are 90 Calories in $1\frac{1}{2}$ servings.   **b.** There are 30 fat
Calories in 6 slices of bread.   **5.** 2025 Calories would be needed.   **7.** You burn 10,125 Calories.   **9.** You would have
to hike for 2.6 h.   **11.** 1250 Wh are used.   **13.** The fax machine used 0.567 kWh.   **15.** The cost of running an air
conditioner is $1.58.   **17. a.** 400 lumens is less than half the output of Soft White bulb.   **b.** The energy saver bulb
costs $.42 less to operate.   **19.** The cost of using the welder is $109.98.   **21.** Answers will vary.

SECTION 9.5

1. 91.74 m   **3.** 1.73 m   **5.** 6.82 kg   **7.** 235.85 ml   **9.** 104.65 km/h   **11.** $7.68/kg   **13.** $.39/L
15. 40,068.07 km   **17.** 328 ft   **19.** 1.58 gal   **21.** 4920 ft   **23.** 6.33 gal   **25.** 49.69 mi/h   **27.** $1.46/gal
29. 4.62 lb   **31.** Gary will lose 1 lb.   **33.** 186,335.40 mi/s   **35. a.** False   **b.** False   **c.** True   **d.** True
e. False

CHAPTER 9 REVIEW EXERCISES

1. 1250 m [9.1A]   **2.** 450 mg [9.2A]   **3.** 5.6 ml [9.3A]   **4.** 1090 yd [9.5B]   **5.** 7.9 cm [9.1A]
6. 5.34 m [9.1A]   **7.** 0.990 kg [9.2A]   **8.** 2.550 L [9.3A]   **9.** 4.870 km [9.1A]   **10.** 3.7 mm [9.1A]
11. 6.829 g [9.2A]   **12.** 1200 cm^3 [9.3A]   **13.** 4050 g [9.2A]   **14.** 870 cm [9.1A]   **15.** 192 cm^3 [9.3A]
16. 0.356 g [9.2A]   **17.** 3.72 m [9.1A]   **18.** 8300 L [9.3A]   **19.** 2.089 L [9.3A]   **20.** 5.410 L [9.3A]
21. 3.792 kl [9.3A]   **22.** 468 ml [9.3A]   **23.** There are 37.2 m of wire left on the roll. [9.1B]   **24.** The total cost
of the chicken is $12.72. [9.2B]   **25.** $7.48/kg [9.5A]   **26.** The amount of coffee that should be prepared is 50 L.
[9.3B]   **27.** You can eliminate 2700 Calories. [9.4A]   **28.** The cost of running the TV set is $3.42. [9.4A]

29. 4.18 lb   [9.5B]   **30.** 8.75 h of cycling are needed.   [9.4A]   **31.** The profit was $52.80.   [9.3B]

32. The color TV used 1.120 kWh of electricity.   [9.4A]   **33.** The amount of fertilizer used was 125 kg.   [9.2B]

CHAPTER 9 TEST

1. 2960 m   [9.1A]   **2.** 378 mg   [9.2A]   **3.** 46 ml   [9.3A]   **4.** 919 ml   [9.3A]   **5.** 4.26 cm   [9.1A]

6. 7.96 m   [9.1A]   **7.** 0.847 kg   [9.2A]   **8.** 3.920 L   [9.3A]   **9.** 5.885 km   [9.1A]   **10.** 15 mm   [9.1A]

11. 3.089 g   [9.2A]   **12.** 1600 cm^3 [9.3A]   **13.** 3290 g   [9.2A]   **14.** 420 cm   [9.1A]   **15.** 96 cm^3 [9.3A]

16. 1.375 g   [9.2A]   **17.** 4.02 m   [9.1A]   **18.** 8920 L   [9.3A]   **19.** A 140-pound sedentary person should consume

2100 Calories per day to maintain that weight.   [9.4A]   **20.** 3.15 kWh of energy is used during the week for operating

the television.   [9.4A]   **21.** The total length of the rafters is 114 m.   [9.1B]   **22.** The weight of the box is 36 kg.   [9.2B]

23. The amount of vaccine needed is 5.2 L.   [9.3B]   **24.** 56.4 km/h   [9.5A]   **25.** The distance between the rivets is

17.5 cm.   [9.1B]   **26.** The cost to fertilize the trees is $660.   [9.2B]   **27.** The total cost is $16.32.   [9.4A]   **28.** The

assistant should order 11 L of acid.   [9.3B]   **29.** The measure of the large hill is 393.6 ft.   [9.5B]

30. 4.8 in. is approximately 12.2 cm.   [9.5A]

CUMULATIVE REVIEW EXERCISES

1. 6   [1.6B]   **2.** $12\frac{13}{36}$ [2.4C]   **3.** $\frac{29}{36}$ [2.5C]   **4.** $3\frac{1}{14}$ [2.7B]   **5.** 1   [2.8B]   **6.** 2.0702   [3.3A]

7. 31.3   [4.3B]   **8.** 175%   [5.1B]   **9.** 145   [5.4A]   **10.** 2.25 gal   [8.3A]   **11.** 8.75 m   [9.1A]

12. 3.420 km   [9.1A]   **13.** 5050 g   [9.2A]   **14.** 3.672 g   [9.2A]   **15.** 6000 ml   [9.3A]   **16.** 2400 L   [9.3A]

17. $3933 is left after the rent is paid.   [2.6C]   **18.** The business paid $7207.20 in income tax.   [3.4B]   **19.** The

property tax is $5500.   [4.3C]   **20.** The car buyer will receive a rebate of $2820.   [5.2B]   **21.** The percent is 6.5%.

[5.3B]   **22.** Your mean grade is 76.   [7.4A]   **23.** Karla's salary next year will be $25,200.   [5.2B]   **24.** The discount

rate is 22%.   [6.2D]   **25.** The length of the wall is 36 ft.   [8.1C]   **26.** There are 12 qt of apple juice in the case.

[8.3C]   **27.** The profit was $123.20.   [8.3C]   **28.** 24 L of chlorine was used.   [9.3B]   **29.** The total cost of

operating the hair dryer is $1.89.   [9.4A]   **30.** 96.6 km/h   [9.5A]

Answers to Chapter 10 Selected Exercises

PREP TEST

1. 54 > 45   [1.1A]   **2.** 4 [1.3A]   **3.** 15,847   [1.2A]   **4.** 3779   [1.3B]   **5.** 26,432   [1.4B]   **6.** 6   [2.3B]

7. $1\frac{4}{15}$ [2.4B]   **8.** $\frac{7}{16}$ [2.5B]   **9.** 11.058   [3.2A]   **10.** 3.781   [3.3A]   **11.** $\frac{2}{5}$ [2.6A]   **12.** $\frac{5}{9}$ [2.7A]

13. 9.4   [3.4A]   **14.** 0.4   [3.5A]   **15.** 31   [1.6B]

SECTION 10.1

1. −120 ft   **3.** +2 dollars   **5.**   **7.**

9. 1   **11.** −1   **13.** 3   **15. a.** A is −4.   **b.** C is −2.   **17. a.** A is −7.   **b.** D is −4.   **19.** −2 > −5

21. −16 < 1   **23.** 3 > −7   **25.** −11 < −8   **27.** 35 > 28   **29.** −42 < 27   **31.** 21 > −34   **33.** −27 > −39

35. −87 < 63   **37.** 86 > −79   **39.** −62 > −84   **41.** −131 < 101   **43.** −7, −2, 0, 3   **45.** −5, −3, 1, 4

47. −4, 0, 5, 9   **49.** −10, −7, −5, 4, 12   **51.** −11, −7, −2, 5, 10   **53.** −16   **55.** 3   **57.** −45   **59.** 59

61. 88   **63.** 4   **65.** 9   **67.** 11   **69.** 12   **71.** 2   **73.** 6   **75.** 5   **77.** 1   **79.** −5   **81.** 16   **83.** 12

85. −29   **87.** −14   **89.** 15   **91.** −33   **93.** 32   **95.** −42   **97.** 61   **99.** −52   **101.** $|-12| > |8|$

103. $|6| < |13|$ **105.** $|-1| < |-17|$ **107.** $|17| = |-17|$ **109.** −9, −|6|, −4, |−7| **111.** −9, −|−7|, |4|, 5

113. −|10|, −|−8|, −3, |5| **115. a.** 8 and −2 are 5 units from 3.   **b.** 2 and −4 are 3 units from −1.   **117.** −12 min

and counting is closer to blastoff.   **119.** The loss was greater during the first quarter.   **121.** 11, −11

SECTION 10.2

1. $-14, -364$ **3.** -2 **5.** 20   **7.** -11 **9.** -9 **11.** -3 **13.** 1   **15.** -5 **17.** -30 **19.** 9   **21.** 1
23. -10 **25.** -28 **27.** -41 **29.** -392 **31.** -20 **33.** -23 **35.** -2 **37.** -6 **39.** -6
41. Negative six minus positive four   **43.** Positive six minus negative four   **45.** $9 + 5$ **47.** $1 + (-8)$ **49.** 8
51. -7 **53.** -9 **55.** 36   **57.** -3 **59.** 18   **61.** -9 **63.** 11   **65.** 0   **67.** 11   **69.** 2   **71.** -138
73. 86   **75.** -337 **77.** 4   **79.** -12 **81.** -12 **83.** 3   **85.** The temperature is -1°C.   **87.** Nick's score
was -15 points after his opponent shot the moon.   **89.** The change in the price of the stock is -9 dollars.   **91.** The
temperature is 115°F.   **93.** The difference in elevation is 7046 m.   **95.** The difference is 82°C.   **97.** The difference in
temperature is 13°C.   **99.**

-3	2	1
4	0	-4
-1	-2	3

SECTION 10.3

1. Subtraction   **3.** Multiplication   **5.** 42   **7.** -24 **9.** 6   **11.** 18   **13.** -20 **15.** -16 **17.** 25   **19.** 0
21. -72 **23.** -102 **25.** 140   **27.** -228 **29.** -320 **31.** -156 **33.** -70 **35.** 162   **37.** 120
39. 36   **41.** 192   **43.** -108 **45.** -2100 **47.** 20   **49.** -48 **51.** 140   **53.** $3(-12) = -36$
55. $-5(11) = -55$ **57.** -2 **59.** 8   **61.** 0   **63.** -9 **65.** -9 **67.** 9   **69.** -24 **71.** -12 **73.** 31
75. 17   **77.** 15   **79.** -13 **81.** -18 **83.** 19   **85.** 13   **87.** -19 **89.** 17   **91.** 26   **93.** 23   **95.** 25
97. -34 **99.** 11   **101.** -13 **103.** 13   **105.** 12   **107.** -14 **109.** -14 **111.** -6 **113.** -4
115. The average high temperature was -4°F.   **117.** The average score was -2.   **119.** The wind chill factor is -45°F.
121. a. 25   **b.** -17 **123. a.** True   **b.** True

SECTION 10.4

1. $-\dfrac{5}{24}$ **3.** $-\dfrac{19}{24}$ **5.** $\dfrac{5}{26}$ **7.** $\dfrac{7}{24}$ **9.** $-\dfrac{19}{60}$ **11.** $-1\dfrac{3}{8}$ **13.** $\dfrac{3}{4}$ **15.** $-\dfrac{47}{48}$ **17.** $\dfrac{3}{8}$ **19.** $-\dfrac{7}{60}$ **21.** $\dfrac{13}{24}$
23. -3.4 **25.** -8.89 **27.** -8.0 **29.** -0.68 **31.** -181.51 **33.** 2.7   **35.** -20.7 **37.** -37.19
39. -34.99 **41.** 6.778   **43.** -8.4 **45.** $\dfrac{1}{21}$ **47.** $\dfrac{2}{9}$ **49.** $-\dfrac{2}{9}$ **51.** $-\dfrac{45}{328}$ **53.** $\dfrac{2}{3}$ **55.** $\dfrac{15}{64}$ **57.** $-\dfrac{3}{7}$
59. $-1\dfrac{1}{9}$ **61.** $\dfrac{5}{6}$ **63.** $-2\dfrac{2}{7}$ **65.** $-13\dfrac{1}{2}$ **67.** 31.15   **69.** -112.97 **71.** 0.0363   **73.** 97   **75.** 2.2
77. -4.14 **79.** -3.8 **81.** -22.70 **83.** 0.07   **85.** 0.55   **87.** The temperature fell 32.22°C in 27 min.
89. The difference between the boiling point and the melting point of oxygen is 35.438°C.   **91. a.** The closing price was
\$19.39.   **b.** The closing price was \$72.46.   **93.** Answers will vary. $-\dfrac{17}{24}$ is one example.

SECTION 10.5

1. 2.37×10^6 **3.** 4.5×10^{-4} **5.** 3.09×10^5 **7.** 6.01×10^{-7} **9.** 5.7×10^{10} **11.** 1.7×10^{-8} **13.** 710,000
15. 0.000043   **17.** 671,000,000   **19.** 0.00000713   **21.** 5,000,000,000,000   **23.** 0.00801   **25.** 1.6×10^{10} mi
27. $\$3.1 \times 10^{12}$ **29.** 3.7×10^{-6} m   **31.** 4   **33.** 0   **35.** 12   **37.** -6 **39.** -5 **41.** 2   **43.** -3 **45.** 1
47. 2   **49.** -3 **51.** 14   **53.** -4 **55.** 33   **57.** -13 **59.** -12 **61.** 17   **63.** 0   **65.** 30   **67.** 94
69. -8 **71.** 39   **73.** 22   **75.** 0.21   **77.** -0.96 **79.** -0.29 **81.** -1.76 **83.** 2.1   **85.** $\dfrac{3}{16}$ **87.** $\dfrac{7}{16}$
89. $-\dfrac{5}{16}$ **91.** $-\dfrac{5}{8}$ **93. a.** $3.45 \times 10^{-14} > 3.45 \times 10^{-15}$ **b.** $5.23 \times 10^{18} > 5.23 \times 10^{17}$
c. $3.12 \times 10^{12} > 3.12 \times 10^{11}$ **95. a.** 100   **b.** -100 **c.** 225   **d.** -225 **99. a.** 1.99×10^{30} kg
b. 1.67×10^{-27} kg

CHAPTER 10 REVIEW EXERCISES

1. -22 [10.1B] **2.** 1 [10.2B] **3.** $-\dfrac{5}{24}$ [10.4A] **4.** 0.21 [10.4A] **5.** $\dfrac{8}{25}$ [10.4B] **6.** -1.28 [10.4B]

7. 10 [10.5B] **8.** $-\dfrac{7}{18}$ [10.5B] **9.** 4 [10.1B] **10.** $0 > -3$ [10.1A] **11.** -6 [10.1B] **12.** 6 [10.3B]

13. $\dfrac{17}{24}$ [10.4A] **14.** $-\dfrac{1}{4}$ [10.4B] **15.** $1\dfrac{5}{8}$ [10.4B] **16.** 24 [10.5B] **17.** -26 [10.2A] **18.** 2 [10.5B]

19. 3.97×10^{-5} [10.5A] **20.** -0.08 [10.4B] **21.** $\dfrac{1}{36}$ [10.4A] **22.** $\dfrac{3}{40}$ [10.4B] **23.** -0.042 [10.4B]

24. $\dfrac{1}{3}$ [10.5B] **25.** 5 [10.1B] **26.** $-2 > -40$ [10.1A] **27.** -26 [10.3A] **28.** 1.33 [10.5B]

29. $-\dfrac{1}{4}$ [10.4A] **30.** -7.4 [10.4A] **31.** $\dfrac{15}{32}$ [10.4B] **32.** 240,000 [10.5A] **33.** $-4°$ [10.2C]

34. The student's score was 98. [10.3C] **35.** The difference between the boiling and melting points is 395.45°C. [10.4C]

CHAPTER 10 TEST

1. 3 [10.2B] **2.** -2 [10.1B] **3.** $\dfrac{1}{15}$ [10.4A] **4.** -0.0608 [10.4B] **5.** $-8 > -10$ [10.1A]

6. -1.88 [10.4A] **7.** -26 [10.5B] **8.** 90 [10.3A] **9.** -4.014 [10.4A] **10.** -9 [10.3B] **11.** -7 [10.2A]

12. $\dfrac{7}{24}$ [10.4A] **13.** 8.76×10^{10} [10.5A] **14.** -48 [10.3A] **15.** 0 [10.3B] **16.** 10 [10.2B]

17. $-\dfrac{4}{5}$ [10.4B] **18.** $0 > -4$ [10.1A] **19.** -14 [10.2A] **20.** -4 [10.5B] **21.** $\dfrac{3}{10}$ [10.4A]

22. 0.00000009601 [10.5A] **23.** 3.4 [10.4B] **24.** $\dfrac{1}{12}$ [10.4A] **25.** $\dfrac{1}{12}$ [10.4B] **26.** 3.213 [10.4A]

27. The temperature is 7°C. [10.2C] **28.** The melting point of oxygen is -213°C. [10.3C] **29.** The temperature fell 46.62°C. [10.4C] **30.** The average low temperature was -2°F. [10.3C]

CUMULATIVE REVIEW EXERCISES

1. 0 [1.6B] **2.** $4\dfrac{13}{14}$ [2.5C] **3.** $2\dfrac{7}{12}$ [2.7B] **4.** $1\dfrac{2}{7}$ [2.8C] **5.** 1.80939 [3.3A] **6.** 18.67 [4.3B]

7. 13.75 [5.4A] **8.** 1 gal 3 qt [8.3A] **9.** 6.692 L [9.3A] **10.** 1.28 m [9.5A] **11.** 57.6 [5.2A]

12. 340% [5.1B] **13.** -3 [10.2A] **14.** $-3\dfrac{3}{8}$ [10.4A] **15.** $-10\dfrac{13}{24}$ [10.4A] **16.** 19 [10.5B]

17. 3.488 [10.4B] **18.** $31\dfrac{1}{2}$ [10.4B] **19.** -7 [10.3B] **20.** $\dfrac{25}{42}$ [10.4B] **21.** -4 [10.5B] **22.** -4 [10.5B]

23. The length remaining is $2\dfrac{1}{3}$ ft. [2.5D] **24.** Nimisha's new balance is $803.31. [6.7A] **25.** The percent decrease is 27.3%. [6.2C] **26.** The amount of coffee that should be prepared is 10 gal. [8.3C] **27.** The dividend per share after the increase was $1.68. [6.2A] **28.** The median hourly pay is $11.40. [7.4A] **29.** 600,000 people would vote. [4.3C] **30.** The average high temperature is $-4°$. [10.3C]

Answers to Chapter 11 Selected Exercises

PREP TEST

1. -7 [10.2B] **2.** -20 [10.3A] **3.** 0 [10.2A] **4.** 1 [10.3B] **5.** 1 [10.4B] **6.** $\dfrac{1}{15}$ [2.8B]

7. $\dfrac{19}{24}$ [2.8C] **8.** 4 [10.5B] **9.** -21 [10.5B]

SECTION 11.1

1. -33 **3.** -12 **5.** -4 **7.** -3 **9.** -22 **11.** -40 **13.** -1 **15.** 14 **17.** 32 **19.** 6 **21.** 7

23. 49 **25.** -24 **27.** 63 **29.** 9 **31.** 4 **33.** $-\dfrac{2}{3}$ **35.** 0 **37.** $-3\dfrac{1}{4}$ **39.** 8.5023

41. -18.950658 **43.** $2x^2, 3x, \underline{-4}$ **45.** $3a^2, -4a, \underline{8}$ **47.** $\underline{3x^2}, -4x$ **49.** $\underline{1y^2}, 6a$ **51.** $16z$ **53.** $9m$ **55.** $12at$

57. $3yt$ **59.** Unlike terms   **61.** $-2t^2$ **63.** $13c - 5$ **65.** $-2t$ **67.** $3y^2 - 2$ **69.** $14w - 8u$

71. $-23xy + 10$ **73.** $-11v^2$ **75.** $-8ab - 3a$ **77.** $4y^2 - y$ **79.** $-3a - 2b^2$ **81.** $7x^2 - 8x$ **83.** $-3s + 6t$

85. $-3m + 10n$ **87.** $5ab + 4ac$ **89.** $\dfrac{2}{3}a^2 + \dfrac{3}{5}b^2$ **91.** $6.994x$ **93.** $1.56m - 3.77n$ **95.** $5x + 20$ **97.** $4y - 12$

99. $-2a - 8$ **101.** $15x + 30$ **103.** $15c - 25$ **105.** $-3y + 18$ **107.** $7x + 14$ **109.** $4y - 8$ **111.** $5x + 24$

113. $y - 6$ **115.** $6n - 3$ **117.** $6y + 20$ **119.** $10x + 4$ **121.** $-6t - 6$ **123.** $z - 2$ **125.** $y + 6$

127. $9t + 15$ **129.** $5t + 24$ **131. a.** | 1 | 1 | 1 | x | x | **b.** | x | x | x | x | 1 | 1 | 1 | 1 | 1 | 1 |

c. | x | x | x | 1 | 1 | **d.** | x | x | 1 | 1 | 1 | 1 | **e.** | x | x | x | 1 | 1 | 1 | **f.** $3x + 3$

133. Answers will vary.

SECTION 11.2

1. Yes   **3.** No   **5.** Yes   **7.** Yes   **9.** Yes   **11.** Yes   **13.** Yes   **15.** Yes   **17.** No   **19.** No   **21.** Yes

23. -2 **25.** 14 **27.** 2 **29.** -4 **31.** -5 **33.** 0 **35.** 2 **37.** -3 **39.** 10 **41.** -5 **43.** -12

45. -7 **47.** $\dfrac{2}{3}$ **49.** -1 **51.** $\dfrac{1}{3}$ **53.** $-\dfrac{1}{8}$ **55.** $-\dfrac{3}{4}$ **57.** $-1\dfrac{1}{12}$ **59.** 6 **61.** -9 **63.** -5 **65.** 14

67. 8 **69.** -3 **71.** 20 **73.** -21 **75.** -15 **77.** 16 **79.** -42 **81.** 15 **83.** $-38\dfrac{2}{5}$ **85.** $9\dfrac{3}{5}$

87. $-10\dfrac{4}{5}$ **89.** $1\dfrac{17}{18}$ **91.** $-2\dfrac{2}{3}$ **93.** 3 **95.** The original investment was \$23,610.   **97.** The value of the fund increased by \$1190.   **99.** 18.5 gal of gasoline was used.   **101.** The car gets 34.2 mi/gal.   **103.** The markup on each stuffed animal is \$16.30.   **105.** The compact disc costs \$14.50.   **109.** Answers will vary. For example, $x + 5 = 1$.

SECTION 11.3

1. 3 **3.** 5 **5.** -1 **7.** -4 **9.** 1 **11.** 3 **13.** -2 **15.** -3 **17.** -2 **19.** -1 **21.** 3 **23.** -1

25. 7 **27.** 2 **29.** 2 **31.** 0 **33.** 2 **35.** 0 **37.** $\dfrac{2}{3}$ **39.** $2\dfrac{5}{6}$ **41.** $-2\dfrac{1}{2}$ **43.** $1\dfrac{1}{2}$ **45.** 2 **47.** -2

49. $2\dfrac{1}{3}$ **51.** $-1\dfrac{1}{2}$ **53.** 10 **55.** 5 **57.** 36 **59.** -6 **61.** -9 **63.** $-4\dfrac{4}{5}$ **65.** $-8\dfrac{3}{4}$ **67.** 36 **69.** $1\dfrac{1}{3}$

71. 2 **73.** 4 **75.** 9 **77.** 4 **79.** -3.125 **81.** 1 **83.** -3 **85.** -9 **87.** 4.95 **89.** -0.0862069

91. The temperature is $-40°$C.   **93.** The time is 14.5 s.   **95.** 2500 units were made.   **97.** The clerk's monthly income is \$1800.   **99.** The total sales were \$32,000.   **101.** Miguel's commission rate was 4.5%.

SECTION 11.4

1. $\dfrac{1}{2}$ **3.** -1 **5.** -4 **7.** -1 **9.** -4 **11.** 3 **13.** -1 **15.** 2 **17.** 3 **19.** 0 **21.** -2 **23.** -1

25. $-\dfrac{2}{3}$ **27.** -4 **29.** $\dfrac{1}{3}$ **31.** $-\dfrac{3}{4}$ **33.** $\dfrac{1}{4}$ **35.** 0 **37.** $-1\dfrac{3}{4}$ **39.** 1 **41.** -1 **43.** -5 **45.** $\dfrac{5}{12}$

47. $-\dfrac{4}{7}$ **49.** $2\dfrac{1}{3}$ **51.** 21 **53.** 21 **55.** 2 **57.** -1 **59.** -4 **61.** $-\dfrac{6}{7}$ **63.** 5 **65.** 3 **67.** 0

69. -1 **71.** 2 **73.** $1\dfrac{9}{10}$ **75.** 13 **77.** $2\dfrac{1}{2}$ **79.** 2 **81.** 0 **83.** $3\dfrac{1}{5}$ **85.** 4 **87.** $-6\dfrac{1}{2}$ **89.** $-\dfrac{3}{4}$

91. $-\dfrac{2}{3}$ **93.** -3 **95.** $-1\dfrac{1}{4}$ **97.** $2\dfrac{5}{8}$ **99.** 1.9936196 **101.** 13.383119 **103.** 48

SECTION 11.5

1. $y - 9$ **3.** $z + 3$ **5.** $\frac{2}{3}n + n$ **7.** $\frac{m}{m-3}$ **9.** $9(x + 4)$ **11.** $n - (-5)n$ **13.** $c\left(\frac{1}{4}c\right)$ **15.** $m^2 + 2m^2$

17. $2(t + 6)$ **19.** $\frac{x}{9+x}$ **21.** $3(b + 6)$ **23.** x^2 **25.** $\frac{x}{20}$ **27.** $4x$ **29.** $\frac{3}{4}x$ **31.** $4 + x$ **33.** $5x - x$

35. $x(x + 2)$ **37.** $7(x + 8)$ **39.** $x^2 + 3x$ **41.** $(x + 3) + \frac{1}{2}x$ **43.** $\frac{3x}{x}$ **45. a.** Answers will vary. For example,

the sum of twice x and 3.   **b.** Answers will vary. For example, twice the sum of x and 3.   **49.** carbon: $\frac{1}{2}x$; oxygen: $\frac{1}{2}x$

SECTION 11.6

1. $x + 7 = 12$; 5   **3.** $3x = 18$; 6   **5.** $x + 5 = 3$; -2 **7.** $6x = 14$; $2\frac{1}{3}$ **9.** $\frac{5}{6}x = 15$; 18   **11.** $3x + 4 = 8$; $1\frac{1}{3}$

13. $\frac{1}{4}x - 7 = 9$; 64   **15.** $\frac{x}{9} = 14$; 126   **17.** $\frac{x}{4} - 6 = -2$; 16   **19.** $7 - 2x = 13$; -3 **21.** $9 - \frac{x}{2} = 5$; 8

23. $\frac{3}{5}x + 8 = 2$; -10 **25.** $\frac{x}{4.186} - 7.92 = 12.529$; 85.599514   **27.** The price at Target is $76.75.   **29.** The value of
the SUV last year was $20,000.   **31.** The length of the Brooklyn Bridge is 486 m.   **33.** The family's monthly income is
$5440.   **35.** The monthly output a year ago was 5000 computers.   **37.** The recommended daily allowance of sodium
is 2.5 g.   **39.** It took 3 h to install the water softener.   **41.** About 11,065 plants and animals are known to be at risk of
extinction in the world.   **43.** The percent is 3.3%.   **45.** The original water flow rate was 5 gal/min.   **47.** The total
sales for the month were $42,540.   **49.** The world carbon dioxide emissions in 1990 were 5.83 billion metric tons.

CHAPTER 11 REVIEW EXERCISES

1. $-2a + 2b$ [11.1C]   **2.** Yes [11.2A]   **3.** -4 [11.2B]   **4.** 7 [11.3A]   **5.** 13 [11.1A]   **6.** -9 [11.2C]
7. -18 [11.3A]   **8.** $-3x + 4$ [11.1C]   **9.** 5 [11.4A]   **10.** -5 [11.2B]   **11.** No [11.2A]   **12.** 6 [11.1A]

13. 5 [11.4B]   **14.** 10 [11.3A]   **15.** $-4bc$ [11.1B]   **16.** $-2\frac{1}{2}$ [11.4A]   **17.** $1\frac{1}{4}$ [11.2C]   **18.** $\frac{71}{30}x^2$ [11.1B]

19. $-\frac{1}{3}$ [11.4B]   **20.** $10\frac{4}{5}$ [11.3A]   **21.** The car averaged 23 mi/gal. [11.2D]   **22.** The temperature

is 37.8°C. [11.3B]   **23.** $n + \frac{n}{5}$ [11.5A]   **24.** $(n + 5) + \frac{1}{3}n$ [11.5B]   **25.** The number is 2. [11.6A]   **26.** The

number is 10. [11.6A]   **27.** The regular price of the CD player is $380. [11.6B]   **28.** Last year's crop was 25,300
bushels. [11.6B]

CHAPTER 11 TEST

1. 95 [11.3A]   **2.** 26 [11.2B]   **3.** $-11x - 4y$ [11.1B]   **4.** $3\frac{1}{5}$ [11.4A]   **5.** -2 [11.3A]   **6.** -38 [11.1A]

7. No [11.2A]   **8.** $-14ab + 9$ [11.1B]   **9.** $-2\frac{4}{5}$ [11.2C]   **10.** $8y - 7$ [11.1C]   **11.** 0 [11.4B]

12. $-\frac{1}{2}$ [11.3A]   **13.** $-5\frac{5}{6}$ [11.1A]   **14.** -16 [11.2C]   **15.** -3 [11.3A]   **16.** 11 [11.4B]   **17.** The monthly
payment is $137.50. [11.2D]   **18.** 4000 clocks were made during the month. [11.3B]   **19.** The time required is
11.5 s. [11.3B]   **20.** $x + \frac{1}{3}x$ [11.5A]   **21.** $5(x + 3)$ [11.5B]   **22.** $2x - 3 = 7$; 5 [11.6A]

23. The number is $-3\frac{1}{2}$. [11.6A]   **24.** Santos's total sales for the month were $40,000. [11.6B]   **25.** The mechanic
worked for 3 h. [11.6B]

CUMULATIVE REVIEW EXERCISES

1. 41 [1.6B]   **2.** $1\frac{7}{10}$ [2.5C]   **3.** $\frac{11}{18}$ [2.8C]   **4.** 0.047383 [3.4A]   **5.** \$4.20/h [4.2B]   **6.** 26.67 [4.3B]

7. $\frac{4}{75}$ [5.1A]   **8.** 140% [5.3A]   **9.** 6.4 [5.4A]   **10.** 18 ft 9 in. [8.1B]   **11.** 22 oz [8.2A]

12. 0.282 g [9.2A]   **13.** -1 [10.2A]   **14.** 19 [10.2B]   **15.** 6 [10.5B]   **16.** -48 [11.1A]

17. $-10x + 8z$ [11.1B]   **18.** $3y + 23$ [11.1C]   **19.** -1 [11.3A]   **20.** $-6\frac{1}{4}$ [11.4B]   **21.** $-7\frac{1}{2}$ [11.2C]

22. -21 [11.3A]   **23.** The percent is 17.6%. [5.3B]   **24.** The price of the piece of pottery is \$39.90. [6.2B]

25. a. The discount is \$81.   **b.** The discount rate is 18%. [6.2D]   **26.** The simple interest due on the loan is

\$2933.33. [6.3A]   **27.** $3n + 4$ [11.5B]   **28.** The probability is $\frac{1}{8}$ that the sum of the upward faces on the two dice

is 7. [7.5A]   **29.** The total sales were \$32,500. [11.3B]   **30.** The number is 2. [11.6A]

Answers to Chapter 12 Selected Exercises

PREP TEST

1. 43 [11.2B]   **2.** 51 [11.2B]   **3.** 56 [1.6B]   **4.** 56.52 [11.1A]   **5.** 113.04 [11.1A]   **6.** 14.4 [4.3B]

SECTION 12.1

1. 0°; 90°   **3.** 180°   **5.** 30   **7.** 21   **9.** 14   **11.** 59°   **13.** 108°   **15.** 77°   **17.** 53°   **19.** 77°   **21.** 118°
23. 133°   **25.** 86°   **27.** 180°   **29.** Rectangle or square   **31.** Cube   **33.** Parallelogram, rectangle, or square

35. Cylinder   **37.** 102°   **39.** 90° and 45°   **41.** 14°   **43.** 90° and 65°   **45.** 8 in.   **47.** $4\frac{2}{3}$ ft   **49.** 7 cm

51. 2 ft 4 in.   **53.** $\angle a = 106°$, $\angle b = 74°$ **55.** $\angle a = 112°$, $\angle b = 68°$ **57.** $\angle a = 38°$, $\angle b = 142°$
59. $\angle a = 58°$, $\angle b = 58°$ **61.** $\angle a = 152°$, $\angle b = 152°$ **63.** $\angle a = 130°$, $\angle b = 50°$ **65. a.** 1°   **b.** 90°

SECTION 12.2

1. 56 in.   **3.** 20 ft   **5.** 92 cm   **7.** 47.1 cm   **9.** 9 ft 10 in.   **11.** 50.24 cm   **13.** 240 m   **15.** 157 cm
17. 121 cm   **19.** 50.56 m   **21.** 3.57 ft   **23.** 139.3 m   **25.** The amount of fencing needed is 60 ft.   **27.** The
amount of binding needed is 24 ft.   **29.** The total cost of the fence is \$24,422.50.   **31.** The bicycle travels 31.4 ft.
33. a. The perimeter of the rink is larger than the perimeter of the rectangle. The perimeter of the rink is more than 70 m.
b. The perimeter of the rink is 81.4 m.   **35.** Approximately 20.71 ft of weather stripping are installed.   **37.** The

circumference of Earth is approximately 39,915.68 km.   **39.** 22 units   **41.** $14\frac{1}{4}$ cm

SECTION 12.3

1. 144 ft²   **3.** 81 in²   **5.** 50.24 ft²   **7.** 20 in²   **9.** 2.13 cm²   **11.** 16 ft²   **13.** 817 in²   **15.** 154 in²
17. 26 cm²   **19.** 2220 cm²   **21.** 150.72 in²   **23.** 8.851323 ft²   **25.** The area of the playing field is 7500 yd².
27. The area watered by the irrigation system is approximately 7850 ft².   **29.** You should buy 2 qt.   **31.** The area of
the driveway is 1250 ft².   **33.** The cost to wallpaper the two walls is \$114.   **35.** \$17.25 should be budgeted for grass
seed.   **37.** The total area of the park is 125.1492 mi².   **39. a.** The amount of the increase is about 113.04 in².
b. The amount of the increase is about 235.5 cm².   **41. a.** If the length and width are doubled, the area is increased
4 times.   **b.** If the radius is doubled, the area is quadrupled.   **c.** If the diameter is doubled, the area is quadrupled.
43. a. Sometimes true   **b.** Sometimes true   **c.** Always true

SECTION 12.4

1. 144 cm³ **3.** 512 in³ **5.** 2143.57 in³ **7.** 150.72 cm³ **9.** 6.4 m³ **11.** 5572.45 mm³ **13.** 3391.2 ft³

15. $42\frac{7}{8}$ ft³ **17.** 82.26 in³ **19.** 1.6688 m³ **21.** 69.08 in³ **23.** The volume of the water in the tank is 40.5 m³.

25. The volume is approximately 17,148.59 ft³. **27.** The amount of oil is approximately 75.36 m³. **29.** The volume of the auditorium is approximately 809,516.25 ft³. **31.** The volume of the bushing is approximately 212.64 in³. **33.** The tank will hold 3.7 gal. **35.** The cost is approximately $6526.41. **37. a.** 4 times larger **b.** 8 times larger **c.** 8 times larger

SECTION 12.5

1. 2.646 **3.** 6.481 **5.** 12.845 **7.** 13.748 **9.** 5 in. **11.** 8.602 cm **13.** 11.180 ft **15.** 4.472 cm

17. 12.728 yd **19.** 10.392 ft **21.** 21.213 cm **23.** 8.944 m **25.** 7.879 yd **27.** The ramp is 9.66 ft long.

29. The distance is 21.6 mi. **31.** The length of the diagonal is 12.1 mi. **33.** The ladder is 7.4 m high on the building.

35. The perimeter is 27.7 in. **37.** The distance is 250 ft. **39.** The distance is 4.243 in. **41. a.** Always true

b. Always true **45.** 8 m

SECTION 12.6

1. $\frac{1}{2}$ **3.** $\frac{3}{4}$ **5.** congruent **7.** congruent **9.** 7.2 cm **11.** 3.3 m **13.** The height of the building is 16 m.

15. The perimeter is 12 m. **17.** The area is 56.25 cm². **19. a.** Always true **b.** Sometimes true **c.** Always true

21. 16.5 units

CHAPTER 12 REVIEW EXERCISES

1. 0.75 m [12.1B] **2.** 31.4 cm [12.2A] **3.** 26 ft [12.2A] **4.** 3 [12.1A] **5.** 200 ft³ [12.4A]

6. 26 cm [12.5B] **7.** 75° [12.1A] **8.** 3.873 [12.5A] **9.** 16 cm [12.6A] **10.** 63.585 cm² [12.3A]

11. a. 45° **b.** 135° [12.1C] **12.** 55 m² [12.3A] **13.** 240 in³ [12.4B] **14.** 57.12 in² [12.3B]

15. 267.9 ft³ [12.4A] **16.** 64.8 m² [12.6B] **17.** 47.7 in. [12.2B] **18. a.** 80° **b.** 100° [12.1C]

19. The ladder will reach 15 ft up the building. [12.5C] **20.** The other angles of the triangle are 90° and 58°. [12.1B]

21. The bicycle travels approximately 73.3 ft in 10 revolutions. [12.2C] **22.** The area of the room is 28 yd². [12.3C]

23. The volume of the silo is approximately 1144.53 ft³. [12.4C] **24.** The area is 11 m². [12.3A]

25. The distance from the starting point is 29 mi. [12.5C]

CHAPTER 12 TEST

1. 169.56 m³ [12.4A] **2.** 6.8 m [12.2A] **3.** 1406.72 cm³ [12.4B] **4.** 10 m [12.6A] **5.** 58° [12.1A]

6. $3\frac{1}{7}$ m² [12.3A] **7.** 150° [12.1C] **8.** 15.85 ft [12.2B] **9.** 13.748 [12.5A] **10.** 9.747 ft [12.5B]

11. 10.125 ft² [12.3B] **12.** $\angle a = 45°$; $\angle b = 135°$ [12.1C] **13.** $1\frac{1}{5}$ ft [12.6A] **14.** 90° and 50° [12.1B]

15. The width of the canal is 25 ft. [12.6B] **16.** The amount of extra pizza is 113.04 in². [12.3C] **17.** It will cost $1113.69 to carpet the area. [12.3C] **18.** The area is 103.82 ft². [12.3C] **19.** The length of the rafter is 15 ft. [12.5C] **20.** The volume of the interior of the toolbox is 780 in³. [12.4C]

CUMULATIVE REVIEW EXERCISES

1. 48 [2.1B] **2.** $7\frac{41}{48}$ [2.4C] **3.** $\frac{39}{56}$ [2.7B] **4.** $\frac{2}{15}$ [2.8C] **5.** $-\frac{1}{24}$ [10.4A] **6.** $8.72/h [4.2B]

7. 37.5 [4.3B] **8.** $\frac{3}{8}$ [5.1A] **9.** −4 [11.1A] **10.** 85 [5.4A] **11.** −6 [11.3A] **12.** $\frac{4}{3}$ [11.4B]

13. 32,500 m [9.1A] **14.** 31.58 m [9.1A] **15.** −15 [11.2C] **16.** 2 [11.4B] **17.** The monthly payment

is $708.   [1.5D]   **18.** The sales tax on the stereo is $47.06.   [4.3C]   **19.** The original wage was $14.60.   [5.4B]
20. The sale price of the dress is $54.   [6.2D]   **21.** The value of the investment after 20 years would be $101,366.50.
[6.3C]   **22.** The weight of the package is 54 lb.   [8.2C]   **23.** The distance between the rivets is 22.5 cm.   [9.1B]
24. The number is −2.   [11.6A]   **25. a.** 74°   **b.** 106°   [12.1C]   **26.** 29.42 cm   [12.2B]   **27.** 50 in²   [12.3B]
28. 92.86 in³   [12.4B]   **29.** 10.63 ft   [12.5B]   **30.** 36 cm   [12.6B]

FINAL EXAM

1. 3259   [1.3B]   **2.** 53   [1.5C]   **3.** 60,205   [1.3B]   **4.** 16   [1.6B]   **5.** 144   [2.1A]   **6.** $1\frac{49}{120}$ [2.4B]

7. $3\frac{29}{48}$ [2.5C]   **8.** $6\frac{3}{14}$ [2.6B]   **9.** $\frac{4}{9}$ [2.7B]   **10.** $\frac{1}{6}$ [2.8B]   **11.** $\frac{1}{13}$ [2.8C]   **12.** 164.177   [3.2A]

13. 0.027918   [3.4A]   **14.** 0.69   [3.5A]   **15.** $\frac{9}{20}$ [3.6B]   **16.** 24.5 mi/gal   [4.2B]   **17.** 54.9   [4.3B]

18. $\frac{9}{40}$ [5.1A]   **19.** 135%   [5.1B]   **20.** 125%   [5.1B]   **21.** 36   [5.2A]   **22.** $133\frac{1}{3}$%   [5.3A]   **23.** 70   [5.4A]

24. 20 in.   [8.1A]   **25.** 1 ft 4 in.   [8.1B]   **26.** 2.5 lb   [8.2A]   **27.** 6 lb 6 oz   [8.2B]   **28.** 2.25 gal   [8.3A]
29. 1 gal 3 qt   [8.3B]   **30.** 248 cm   [9.1A]   **31.** 4.62 m   [9.1A]   **32.** 1.614 kg   [9.2A]   **33.** 2067 ml   [9.3A]
34. 88.55 km   [9.5A]   **35.** The cost is $1.15.   [9.4A]   **36.** 6.79×10^{-8} [10.5A]   **37.** 3.9 m   [12.2A]

38. 45 in²   [12.3A]   **39.** 1200 cm³   [12.4A]   **40.** −4   [10.2A]   **41.** −15   [10.2B]   **42.** $-\frac{1}{2}$ [10.4B]

43. $-\frac{1}{4}$ [10.4B]   **44.** 6   [10.5B]   **45.** $-x + 17$ [11.1C]   **46.** −18   [11.2C]   **47.** 5   [11.3A]   **48.** 1   [11.4A]
49. Your new balance is $959.93.   [6.7A]   **50.** 63,750 people will vote.   [4.3C]   **51.** One year ago the dividend
per share was $2.00.   [5.4B]   **52.** The average monthly income is $3794.   [7.4A]   **53.** The simple interest due is
$7200.   [6.3A]   **54.** The probability is $\frac{1}{3}$.   [7.5A]   **55.** China has 6.7% of the death count of the four
countries.   [7.1B]   **56.** The discount rate for the compact disc player is 28%.   [6.2D]   **57.** The weight of the box is
81 lb.   [8.2C]   **58.** The perimeter is approximately 28.56 in.   [12.2B]   **59.** The area of the composite figure is
approximately 16.86 cm².   [12.3B]   **60.** The number is 16.   [11.6A]

Glossary

absolute value of a number The distance between zero and the number on the number line. [10.1]

acute angle An angle whose measure is between 0° and 90°. [12.1]

acute triangle A triangle that has three acute angles. [12.2]

addend In addition, one of the numbers added. [1.2]

addition The process of finding the total of two numbers. [1.2]

Addition Property of Zero Zero added to a number does not change the number. [1.2]

adjacent angles Two angles that share a common side. [12.1]

alternate exterior angles Two nonadjacent angles that are on opposite sides of the transversal and outside the parallel lines. [12.1]

alternate interior angles Two nonadjacent angles that are on opposite sides of the transversal and between the parallel lines. [12.1]

angle An angle is formed when two rays start at the same point; it is measured in degrees. [12.1]

approximation An estimated value obtained by rounding an exact value. [1.1]

area A measure of the amount of surface in a region. [12.3]

Associative Property of Addition Numbers to be added can be grouped (with parentheses, for example) in any order; the sum will be the same. [1.2]

Associative Property of Multiplication Numbers to be multiplied can be grouped (with parentheses, for example) in any order; the product will be the same. [1.4]

average The sum of all the numbers divided by the number of those numbers. [1.5]

average value The sum of all values divided by the number of those values; also known as the mean value. [7.4]

balancing a checkbook Determining whether the checking account balance is accurate. [6.7]

bank statement A document showing all the transactions in a bank account during the month. [6.7]

bar graph A graph that represents data by the height of the bars. [7.2]

base of a triangle The side that the triangle rests on. [12.1]

basic percent equation Percent times base equals amount. [5.2]

borrowing In subtraction, taking a unit from the next larger place value in the minuend and adding it to the number in the given place value in order to make that number larger than the number to be subtracted from it. [1.3]

box-and-whiskers plot A graph that shows the smallest value in a set of numbers, the first quartile, the median, the third quartile, and the greatest value. [7.4]

British thermal unit A unit of energy. 1 British thermal unit = 778 foot-pounds. [8.5]

broken-line graph A graph that represents data by the position of the lines and shows trends and comparisons. [7.2]

Calorie A unit of energy in the metric system. [9.4]

capacity A measure of liquid substances. [8.3]

carrying In addition, transferring a number to another column. [1.2]

center of a circle The point from which all points on the circle are equidistant. [12.1]

center of a sphere The point from which all points on the surface of the sphere are equidistant. [12.1]

centi- The metric system prefix that means one-hundredth. [9.1]

check A printed form that, when filled out and signed, instructs a bank to pay a specified sum of money to the person named on it. [6.7]

checking account A bank account that enables you to withdraw money or make payments to other people, using checks. [6.7]

circle A plane figure in which all points are the same distance from point O, which is called the center of the circle. [12.1]

circle graph A graph that represents data by the size of the sectors. [7.1]

circumference The distance around a circle. [12.2]

class frequency The number of occurrences of data in a class interval on a histogram; represented by the height of each bar. [7.3]

class interval Range of numbers represented by the width of a bar on a histogram. [7.3]

class midpoint The center of a class interval in a frequency polygon. [7.3]

commission That part of the pay earned by a salesperson that is calculated as a percent of the salesperson's sales. [6.6]

common factor A number that is a factor of two or more numbers is a common factor of those numbers. [2.1]

common multiple A number that is a multiple of two or more numbers is a common multiple of those numbers. [2.1]

Commutative Property of Addition Two numbers can be added in either order; the sum will be the same. [1.2]

Commutative Property of Multiplication Two numbers can be multiplied in either order; the product will be the same. [1.4]

complementary angles Two angles whose sum is 90°. [12.1]

composite geometric figure A figure made from two or more geometric figures. [12.2]

composite geometric solid A solid made from two or more geometric solids. [12.4]

composite number A number that has whole-number factors besides 1 and itself. For instance, 18 is a composite number. [1.7]

compound interest Interest computed not only on the original principal but also on interest already earned. [6.3]

congruent objects Objects that have the same shape and the same size. [12.6]

congruent triangles Triangles that have the same shape and the same size. [12.6]

constant term A term that has no variables. [11.1]

conversion rate A relationship used to change one unit of measurement to another. [8.1]

corresponding angles Two angles that are on the same side of the transversal and are both acute angles or are both obtuse angles. [12.1]

cost The price that a business pays for a product. [6.2]

cross product In a proportion, the product of the numerator on the left side of the proportion times the denominator on the right, and the product of the denominator on the left side of the proportion times the numerator on the right. [4.3]

cube A rectangular solid in which all six faces are squares. [12.1]

cubic centimeter A unit of capacity equal to 1 milliliter. [9.3]

cup A U.S. Customary measure of capacity. 2 cups = 1 pint. [8.3]

cylinder A geometric solid in which the bases are circles and are perpendicular to the height. [12.1]

data Numerical information. [7.1]

day A unit of time. 24 hours = 1 day. [8.4]

decimal A number written in decimal notation. [3.1]

decimal notation Notation in which a number consists of a whole-number part, a decimal point, and a decimal part. [3.1]

decimal part In decimal notation, that part of the number that appears to the right of the decimal point. [3.1]

decimal point In decimal notation, the point that separates the whole-number part from the decimal part. [3.1]

degree Unit used to measure angles; one complete revolution is 360°. [12.1]

denominator The part of a fraction that appears below the fraction bar. [2.2]

deposit slip A form for depositing money in a checking account. [6.7]

diameter of a circle A line segment with endpoints on the circle and going through the center. [12.1]

diameter of a sphere A line segment with endpoints on the sphere and going through the center. [12.1]

difference In subtraction, the result of subtracting two numbers. [1.3]

discount The difference between the regular price and the sale price. [6.2]

discount rate The percent of a product's regular price that is represented by the discount. [6.2]

dividend In division, the number into which the divisor is divided to yield the quotient. [1.5]

division The process of finding the quotient of two numbers. [1.5]

divisor In division, the number that is divided into the dividend to yield the quotient. [1.5]

double-bar graph A graph used to display data for purposes of comparison. [7.2]

down payment The percent of a home's purchase price that the bank, when issuing a mortgage, requires the borrower to provide. [6.4]

empirical probability The ratio of the number of observations of an event to the total number of observations. [7.5]

energy The ability to do work. [8.5]

equation A statement of the equality of two mathematical expressions. [11.2]

equilateral triangle A triangle that has three sides of equal length; the three angles are also of equal measure. [12.2]

equivalent fractions Equal fractions with different denominators. [2.3]

evaluating a variable expression Replacing the variable or variables with numbers and then simplifying the resulting numerical expression. [11.1]

event One or more outcomes of an experiment. [7.5]

expanded form The number 46,208 can be written in expanded form as $40,000 + 6000 + 200 + 0 + 8$. [1.1]

experiment Any activity that has an observable outcome. [7.5]

exponent In exponential notation, the raised number that indicates how many times the number to which it is attached is taken as a factor. [1.6]

exponential notation The expression of a number to some power, indicated by an exponent. [1.6]

factors In multiplication, the numbers that are multiplied. [1.4]

factors of a number The whole-number factors of a number divide that number evenly. [1.7]

favorable outcomes The outcomes of an experiment that satisfy the requirements of a particular event. [7.5]

finance charges Interest charges on purchases made with a credit card. [6.3]

first quartile In a set of numbers, the number below which one-quarter of the data lie. [7.4]

fixed-rate mortgage A mortgage in which the monthly payment remains the same for the life of the loan. [6.4]

fluid ounce A U.S. Customary measure of capacity. 8 fluid ounces = 1 cup. [8.3]

foot A U.S. Customary unit of length. 3 feet = 1 yard. [8.1]

foot-pound A U.S. Customary unit of energy. One foot-pound is the amount of energy required to lift 1 pound a distance of 1 foot. [8.5]

foot-pounds per second A U.S. Customary unit of power. [8.5]

formula An equation that expresses a relationship among variables. [11.2]

fraction The notation used to represent the number of equal parts of a whole. [2.2]

fraction bar The bar that separates the numerator of a fraction from the denominator. [2.2]

frequency polygon A graph that displays information similarly to a histogram. A dot is placed above the center of each class interval at a height corresponding to that class's frequency. [7.3]

gallon A U.S. Customary measure of capacity. 1 gallon = 4 quarts. [8.3]

geometric solid A figure in space. [12.1]

gram The basic unit of mass in the metric system. [9.2]

graph A display that provides a pictorial representation of data. [7.1]

graph of a whole number A heavy dot placed directly above that number on the number line. [1.1]

greater than A number that appears to the right of a given number on the number line is greater than the given number. [1.1]

greatest common factor (GCF) The largest common factor of two or more numbers. [2.1]

height of a parallelogram The distance between parallel sides. [12.1]

height of a triangle A line segment perpendicular to the base from the opposite vertex. [12.1]

histogram A bar graph in which the width of each bar corresponds to a range of numbers called a class interval. [7.3]

horsepower The U.S. Customary unit of power. 1 horsepower = 550 foot-pounds per second. [8.5]

hourly wage Pay calculated on the basis of a certain amount for each hour worked. [6.6]

hypotenuse The side opposite the right angle in a right triangle. [12.1]

improper fraction A fraction greater than or equal to 1. [2.2]

inch A U.S. Customary unit of length. 12 inches = 1 foot. [8.1]

integers The numbers . . . , −3, −2, −1, 0, 1, 2, 3, ... [10.1]

interest Money paid for the privilege of using someone else's money. [6.3]

interest rate The percent used to determine the amount of interest. [6.3]

interquartile range The difference between the third quartile and the first quartile. [7.4]

intersecting lines Lines that cross at a point in the plane. [12.1]

inverting a fraction Interchanging the numerator and denominator. [2.7]

isosceles triangle A triangle that has two sides of equal length; the angles opposite the equal sides are of equal measure. [12.2]

kilo- The metric system prefix that means one thousand. [9.1]

kilowatt-hour A unit of electrical energy in the metric system equal to 1000-watt hours. [9.4]

least common denominator (LCD) The least common multiple of denominators. [2.4]

least common multiple (LCM) The smallest common multiple of two or more numbers. [2.1]

legs of a right triangle The two shortest sides of a right triangle. [12.1]

length A measure of distance. [8.1]

less than A number that appears to the left of a given number on the number line is less than the given number. [1.1]

license fees Fees charged for authorization to operate a vehicle. [6.5]

like terms Terms of a variable expression that have the same variable part. [11.1]

line A line extends indefinitely in two directions in a plane; it has no width. [12.1]

line segment Part of a line; it has two endpoints. [12.1]

liter The basic unit of capacity in the metric system. [9.3]

loan origination fee The fee a bank charges for processing mortgage papers. [6.4]

markup The difference between selling price and cost. [6.2]

markup rate The percent of a product's cost that is represented by the markup. [6.2]

mass The amount of material in an object. On the surface of Earth, mass is the same as weight. [9.2]

maturity value of a loan The principal of a loan plus the interest owed on it. [6.3]

mean The sum of all values divided by the number of those values; also known as the average value. [7.4]

measurement A measurement has both a number and a unit. Examples include 7 feet, 4 ounces, and 0.5 gallon. [8.1]

median The value that separates a list of values in such a way that there is the same number of values below the median as above it. [7.4]

meter The basic unit of length in the metric system. [9.1]

metric system A system of measurement based on the decimal system. [9.1]

mile A U.S. Customary unit of length. 5280 feet = 1 mile. [8.1]

milli- The metric system prefix that means one-thousandth. [9.1]

minuend In subtraction, the number from which another number (the subtrahend) is subtracted. [1.3]

minute A unit of time. 60 minutes = 1 hour. [8.4]

mixed number A number greater than 1 that has a whole-number part and a fractional part. [2.2]

mode In a set of numbers, the value that occurs most frequently. [7.4]

monthly mortgage payment One of 12 payments due each year to the lender of money to buy real estate. [6.4]

mortgage The amount borrowed to buy real estate. [6.4]

multiples of a number The products of that number and the numbers 1, 2, 3, ... [2.1]

multiplication The process of finding the product of two numbers. [1.4]

Multiplication Property of One The product of a number and one is the number. [1.4]

Multiplication Property of Zero The product of a number and zero is zero. [1.4]

negative integers The numbers . . . , −5, −4, −3, −2, −1. [10.1]

natural numbers The numbers 1, 2, 3, 4, 5, . . . ; also called the positive integers. [10.1]

negative numbers Numbers less than zero. [10.1]

number line A line on which a number can be graphed. [1.1]

numerator The part of a fraction that appears above the fraction bar. [2.2]

numerical coefficient The number part of a variable term. When the numerical coefficient is 1 or −1, the 1 is usually not written. [11.1]

obtuse angle An angle whose measure is between 90° and 180°. [12.1]

obtuse triangle A triangle that has one obtuse angle. [12.2]

opposite numbers Two numbers that are the same distance from zero on the number line, but on opposite sides. [10.1]

Order of Operations Agreement A set of rules that tells us in what order to perform the operations that occur in a numerical expression. [1.6]

ounce A U.S. Customary unit of weight. 16 ounces = 1 pound. [8.2]

parallel lines Lines that never meet; the distance between them is always the same. [12.1]

parallelogram A quadrilateral that has opposite sides equal and parallel. [12.1]

percent Parts per hundred. [5.1]

percent decrease A decrease of a quantity, expressed as a percent of its original value. [6.2]

percent increase An increase of a quantity, expressed as a percent of its original value. [6.2]

perfect square The product of a whole number and itself. [12.5]

perimeter The distance around a plane figure. [12.2]

period In a number written in standard form, each group of digits separated from other digits by a comma or commas. [1.1]

perpendicular lines Intersecting lines that form right angles. [12.1]

pictograph A graph that uses symbols to represent information. [7.1]

pint A U.S. Customary measure of capacity. 2 pints = 1 quart. [8.3]

place value The position of each digit in a number written in standard form determines that digit's place value. [1.1]

place-value chart A chart that indicates the place value of every digit in a number. [1.1]

plane A flat surface. [12.1]

plane figures Figures that lie totally in a plane. [12.1]

points A term banks use to mean percent of a mortgage; used to express the loan origination fee. [6.4]

polygon A closed figure determined by three or more line segments that lie in a plane. [12.2]

positive integers The numbers 1, 2, 3, 4, 5, . . . ; also called the natural numbers. [10.1]

positive numbers Numbers greater than zero. [10.1]

pound A U.S. Customary unit of weight. 1 pound = 16 ounces. [8.2]

power The rate at which work is done or energy is released. [8.5]

prime factorization The expression of a number as the product of its prime factors. [1.7]

prime number A number whose only whole-number factors are 1 and itself. For instance, 13 is a prime number. [1.7]

principal The amount of money originally deposited or borrowed. [6.3]

probability A number from 0 to 1 that tells us how likely it is that a certain outcome of an experiment will happen. [7.5]

product In multiplication, the result of multiplying two numbers. [1.4]

proper fraction A fraction less than 1. [2.2]

property tax A tax based on the value of real estate. [6.4]

proportion An expression of the equality of two ratios or rates. [4.3]

Pythagorean Theorem The square of the hypotenuse of a right triangle is equal to the sum of the squares of the two legs. [12.5]

quadrilateral A four-sided closed figure. [12.1]

quart A U.S. Customary measure of capacity. 4 quarts = 1 gallon. [8.3]

quotient In division, the result of dividing the divisor into the dividend. [1.5]

radius of a circle A line segment going from the center to a point on the circle. [12.1]

radius of a sphere A line segment going from the center to a point on the sphere. [12.1]

range In a set of numbers, the difference between the largest and smallest values. [7.4]

rate A comparison of two quantities that have different units. [4.2]

ratio A comparison of two quantities that have the same units. [4.1]

rational number A number that can be written as the ratio of two integers, where the denominator is not zero. [10.4]

ray A ray starts at a point and extends indefinitely in one direction. [12.1]

reciprocal of a fraction The fraction with the numerator and denominator interchanged. [2.7]

rectangle A parallelogram that has four right angles. [12.1]

rectangular solid A solid in which all six faces are rectangles. [12.1]

regular polygon A polygon in which each side has the same length and each angle has the same measure. [12.2]

remainder In division, the quantity left over when it is not possible to separate objects or numbers into a whole number of equal groups. [1.5]

repeating decimal A decimal in which a block of one or more digits repeats forever. [10.4]

right angle A 90° angle. [12.1]

right triangle A triangle that contains one right angle. [12.1]

rounding Giving an approximate value of an exact number. [1.1]

salary Pay based on a weekly, biweekly, monthly, or annual time schedule. [6.6]

sale price The reduced price. [6.2]

sales tax A tax levied by a state or municipality on purchases. [6.5]

sample space All the possible outcomes of an experiment. [7.5]

scalene triangle A triangle that has no sides of equal length; no two of its angles are of equal measure. [12.2]

scientific notation Notation in which a number is expressed as a product of two factors, one a number between 1 and 10 and the other a power of 10. [10.5]

second A unit of time. 60 seconds = 1 minute. [8.4]

sector of a circle One of the "pieces of the pie" in a circle graph. [7.1]

selling price The price for which a business sells a product to a customer. [6.2]

service charge A sum of money charged by a bank for handling a transaction. [6.7]

sides of a polygon The line segments that form the polygon. [12.2]

similar objects Objects that have the same shape but not necessarily the same size. [12.6]

similar triangles Triangles that have the same shape but not necessarily the same size. [12.6]

simple interest Interest computed on the original principal. [6.3]

simplest form of a fraction A fraction is in simplest form when there are no common factors in the numerator and denominator. [2.3]

simplest form of a rate A rate is in simplest form when the numbers that make up the rate have no common factor. [4.2]

simplest form of a ratio A ratio is in simplest form when the two numbers do not have a common factor. [4.1]

simplifying a variable expression Combining like terms by adding their numerical coefficients. [11.1]

solids Objects in space. [12.1]

solution of an equation A number that, when substituted for the variable, results in a true equation. [11.2]

solving an equation Finding a solution of the equation. [11.2]

sphere A solid in which all points are the same distance from point O, which is called the center of the sphere. [12.1]

square A rectangle that has four equal sides. [12.1]

square root A square root of a number is one of two identical factors of that number. [12.5]

standard form A whole number is in standard form when it is written using the digits 0, 1, 2, . . . , 9. An example is 46,208. [1.1]

statistics The branch of mathematics concerned with data, or numerical information. [7.1]

straight angle A 180° angle. [12.1]

subtraction The process of finding the difference between two numbers. [1.3]

subtrahend In subtraction, the number that is subtracted from another number (the minuend). [1.3]

sum In addition, the total of the numbers added. [1.2]

supplementary angles Two angles whose sum is 180°. [12.1]

terminating decimal A decimal that has a finite number of digits after the decimal point, which means that it comes to an end and does not go on forever. [10.4]

terms of a variable expression The addends of the expression. [11.1]

theoretical probability A fraction with the number of favorable outcomes of an experiment in the numerator and the total number of possible outcomes of the experiment in the denominator. [7.5]

third quartile In a set of numbers, the number above which one-quarter of the data lie. [7.4]

ton A U.S. Customary unit of weight. 1 ton = 2000 pounds. [8.2]

total cost The unit cost multiplied by the number of units purchased. [6.1]

transversal A line intersecting two other lines at two different points. [12.1]

triangle A three-sided closed figure. [12.1]

true proportion A proportion in which the fractions are equal. [4.3]

unit cost The cost of one item. [6.1]

unit rate A rate in which the number in the denominator is 1. [4.2]

variable A letter used to stand for a quantity that is unknown or that can change. [11.1]

variable expression An expression that contains one or more variables. [11.1]

variable part In a variable term, the variable or variables and their exponents. [11.1]

variable term A term composed of a numerical coefficient and a variable part. [11.1]

vertex The common endpoint of two rays that form an angle. [12.1]

vertical angles Two angles that are on opposite sides of the intersection of two lines. [12.1]

volume A measure of the amount of space inside a closed surface. [12.4]

watt-hour A unit of electrical energy in the metric system. [9.4]

week A unit of time. 7 days = 1 week. [8.4]

weight A measure of how strongly Earth is pulling on an object. [8.2]

whole numbers The whole numbers are 0, 1, 2, 3, ... [1.1]

whole-number part In decimal notation, that part of the number that appears to the left of the decimal point. [3.1]

yard A U.S. Customary unit of length. 36 inches = 1 yard. [8.1]

Index

Index of Applications

(Continued from inside front cover)

Student Registration and Enrollment Guide

Contents

What is Eduspace?

Overview

Welcome to the *Eduspace Registration and Enrollment Guide for Students*. This guide will tell you how to:

- Register with Eduspace.

- Enroll in your instructor's course.

- Access more information.

- Contact customer support.

Eduspace System Requirements

Minimum Requirements	Strongly Recommended Hardware/Software
• Microsoft Windows 2000 or Window XP **OR** Macintosh* OS 10.2 or 10.3	• Microsoft 2000 with Microsoft Internet Explorer 6.0 or Firefox 1.x **OR** Microsoft Windows XP with Internet Explorer 6.0 or Netscape Firefox 1.x **OR** Macintosh OS 10.3.9 with Safari 1.3 (or higher)
• Microsoft Internet Explorer 6.0 (or above) **OR** Firefox 1.x (for Windows XP or Macintosh OS 10.2 or 10.3) **OR** Safari 1.2 for Macintosh OS 10.2 or 10.3	
• Sun Java Run-time Environment (JRE) 1.5.x in your web browser (note use of Microsoft JVM is not supported)	• Sun Java Run-time Environment (JRE) 1.5.x in your web browser (note use of Microsoft JVM is not supported)
• Adobe Acrobat 6.0	• Adobe Acrobat 7.0 (or higher)
• Display with 256 colors and 800x600 resolution or higher	• Display with thousands of colors and 1024x768 resolution or higher
• 56K modem connection (A high speed connection is strongly recommended. If you are using a dial-up connection, your experience will not be optimal.)	• T1 line, cable modem, DSL, or company Internet LAN

*Macintosh users in Accounting, Chemistry and Math courses must use OS 10.3.9 with Safari 1.3 in order to view all homework content in those courses.

Depending on your course content, you may need one or more of the following plug-ins: Flash Player 7 or higher, QuickTime 5.0 (6 recommended), RealPlayer 9.0 (10.0 recommended), Shockwave 8.5.1. Note that when using any browser with Eduspace, cookies must be enabled.

What if I have Windows 98, Windows NT, or AOL?

Although Houghton Mifflin has not performed certification of Eduspace on AOL and therefore cannot say that we officially support those platforms, Houghton Mifflin is aware of users who are successfully using Eduspace in those environments. If you encounter problems once you are online with AOL, start an additional browser such as Microsoft Internet Explorer and access Eduspace using that browser.

Getting Help

If you encounter problems with using Eduspace or need help on using certain features, you can:

- Call Eduspace Technical Support at (800) 732-3223.

- Click the **Support** tab in Eduspace to view support information and answers to frequently asked questions and to electronically submit a question.

Getting Started

To begin using Eduspace, complete the following steps:

- Obtain a passkey from the inside back cover of this guide.

- Obtains a course code from your instructor.

- Register with Eduspace.

- Log in to Eduspace.

- Enroll in a course.

You only need to register once, but you must log in each time you want to use Eduspace.

Registering and Enrolling in a Course

1. Go to the Eduspace website **http://www.eduspace.com** and choose to **Register**.

   If you are already registered and have an Eduspace username, log into Eduspace and skip to step 4.

2. Follow the on-screen directions to fill in the required fields and then click **Create Account**.

3. Before you can enroll in a course, you must log in to Eduspace. Enter the username and password you just chose when registering in the field provided and click **Login**.

4. Click **Enroll In Your Course** in the **How Do I?** area on the My Eduspace tab. The course enrollment page opens.

5. Click on **Student** and then click **Continue**.

6. Enter the course code given to your by your instructor and click Submit.

7. Enter your passkey from the inside back cover of this guide and click Submit.

   Note: If you receive an error message that your passkey is not valid, you may have mistaken the capital letter O for the number zero (0) or the number one (1) for the capital letter I or the lowercase letter L. Substitute one character for another and try again.

8. Eduspace enrolls you in the course as a student. Close the enrollment window and click the Courses tab to see the course listed under "Courses in which you are enrolled".

9. Click the name of the course to enter the course.

Entering Your Course

When you have registered and enrolled in your course, you'll automatically be logged into Eduspace. To log into Eduspace and access your course in the future:

1. Go to the Eduspace website **http://www.eduspace.com** and choose to **Login**.

2. Enter the username and password you selected when you registered for Eduspace and login. You will be brought to the My Eduspace home page.

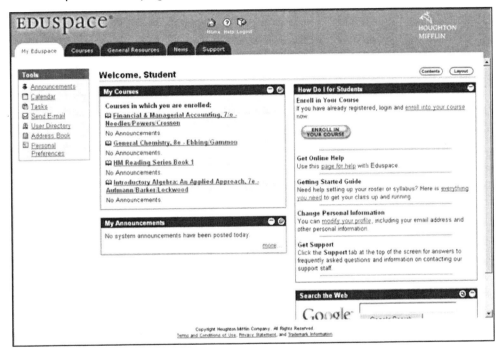

3. Look for the name of your course(s) in the **My Courses** area. Click the name of the course your wish to enter. You will be brought to your course's home page.

For More Information on Using Eduspace

Eduspace contains a wealth of functionality – for your online course, homework, and gradebook functions – beyond what is covered in this guide.

To learn more:

- Access our Online Guide to Getting Started with Eduspace after logging into Eduspace and from the My Eduspace tab clicking the guide link in the **How Do I?** area.

- Click the **Help** button at the top of any screen for comprehensive information on all Eduspace features.

- Get quick answers to using specific features of Eduspace or answers to questions you may have by contacting Eduspace Technical Support at (800) 732-3223.